SOIL PHYSICAL CONDITIONS
and
PLANT GROWTH

AGRONOMY

A SERIES OF MONOGRAPHS

PREPARED UNDER THE AUSPICES OF THE
AMERICAN SOCIETY OF AGRONOMY

Volume II

SOIL PHYSICAL CONDITIONS
and
PLANT GROWTH

Compiled by
The Joint Committee on Soil Tilth
American Society of Agronomy
American Society of Agricultural Engineers

BYRON T. SHAW, *Editor*

1952
ACADEMIC PRESS INC., PUBLISHERS
NEW YORK, N. Y.

56.4
J54 p
c. 3

CONTRIBUTORS

LYLE T. ALEXANDER, *Soil Scientist, Bureau of Plant Industry, Soils, and Agricultural Engineering, United States Department of Agriculture, Beltsville, Maryland*

R. M. HAGAN, *Assistant Irrigation Technologist, California Agricultural Experiment Station, Davis, California*

J. F. LUTZ, *Professor of Soils, North Carolina State College, Raleigh, North Carolina*

T. M. McCALLA, *Bacteriologist, Soil Conservation Service, United States Department of Agriculture, Lincoln, Nebraska*

H. E. MIDDLETON, *Assistant Chief of Research, Soil Conservation Service, United States Department of Agriculture, Washington, D.C.*

L. A. RICHARDS, *Soil Physicist, United States Regional Salinity and Roubidoux Laboratories, Riverside, California*

S. J. RICHARDS, *Associate Irrigation Engineer, University of California Agricultural Experiment Station, Riverside, California*

M. B. RUSSELL, *Head, Agronomy Department, University of Illinois, Urbana, Illinois*

BYRON T. SHAW, *Agricultural Research Administrator, United States Department of Agriculture, Washington, D.C.*

C. H. WADLEIGH, *Head, Division of Sugar Plant Investigations, United States Department of Agriculture, Beltsville, Maryland*

35082

v

PREFACE

This monograph has been prepared to meet a long-felt need among soil and plant scientists and agricultural engineers for a critical evaluation of the relation of soil physical conditions to plant growth. It has evolved from deliberations of a Joint Committee on Soil Tilth, established by the American Society of Agronomy and the American Society of Agricultural Engineers, for the purpose of establishing methods and procedures for measuring and evaluating "soil tilth."

The table of contents and the Introduction reveal what the monograph is about. It is necessary here to review developments that led finally to this selection and treatment of subject matter. The following extracts are from reports of the Joint Committee on Soil Tilth:

> 1943: No amount of empirical experimentation will tell us whether sub-surface tillage is superior to plowing, whether plowing is superior to disking, or what changes are desirable in the design of tillage machinery. Before we can make real progress we must know what soil physical state is desired for a given crop under specified climatic conditions. We must be able to measure the changes produced in soil tilth by our different management practices.

> 1944: The Committee has found that many research people desire to measure soil tilth, but no one seems to know how to do it. Unfortunately, the Committee cannot provide an exact yardstick.

> 1945: There has been considerable discussion of soil tilth over recent years. This Committee has reported annually that something ought to be done about it. Among other things we have suggested the establishment of a national tilth laboratory. Despite all that has been said and all that has been recommended, there has been very little done in the way of improving our situation with regard to measuring soil tilth and its effect on plant growth. We believe the reason for this is that there is very little enthusiasm among research workers for the present methods of approach to the tilth problem that we are now making. It seems that it is going to be necessary for us to make some new approaches.

It has been generally recognized that the soil characteristics influencing the biophysical condition of soil are those that affect air, water, and temperature relations. Since the nature and arrangement of aggregates in soils could be expected to have a profound influence on pore space, which in turn would govern air and water relations, wide use has been made of aggregate analyses to evaluate soil physical conditions. Experience has shown that it is difficult to interpret these analyses in terms of crop behavior on soils. Perhaps the chief difficulty arises from the fact that a given soil permeability, for example, can be obtained with an infinity of combinations of different sized aggregates.

The new approach the Committee had in mind was to break the problem down into manageable parts. Rather than study the influence of different tillage implements, soil management practices, or cropping systems on crop yields, it appeared preferable to begin by studying the influence of water on plant growth, this to be followed by or accompanied with studies of the influence of soil aggregation on water relations. Perhaps then the gap could be bridged from aggregation to plant growth. If so, and other studies showed the influence of management practices on soil aggregation, we might be able to understand the effect of a given management practice on plant behavior.

As a start, the Committee believed it might render a service in sponsoring a monograph that would make a comprehensive and critical study of the present state of our knowledge regarding the influence on plant growth of the four primary physical edaphic factors—soil water, soil air, soil temperature, and mechanical impedance to root penetration and seedling emergence. The American Society of Agronomy section of the Joint Committee assumed responsibility for preparation of the monograph. The members of the Agronomy section were J. F. LUTZ, E. N. FERGUS, T. M. McCALLA, M. B. RUSSELL, and B. T. SHAW. The members of the American Society of Agricultural Engineers section were M. L. NICHOLS, A. P. YERKES, F. A. KUMMER, R. M. MERRILL, and I. F. REED.

L. A. Richards and C. H. Wadleigh were invited to prepare the chapter Soil Water and Plant Growth. M. B. Russell, T. M. McCalla, and J. F. Lutz agreed to prepare the chapters on Soil Air, Soil Temperature, and Mechanical Impedance, respectively. It was decided initially to confine the discussions to the influence of the particular edaphic factors on plant growth and not treat, for example, soil water relations, soil characteristics affecting soil water relations, or ways in which soil water relations may be modified by management. After first drafts were reviewed by members of the Joint Committee, second drafts were prepared and sent to approximately twenty-five experts in the field for review and criticism. Many helpful suggestions were received. Aside from the suggestions and criticism on the specific subject matter treated, there was a general criticism running through all comments that the Committee's decision to confine the discussion to the influence of the particular edaphic factor on plant growth was unwise. A second general criticism was that it would be desirable to seek collaboration of plant physiologists on the chapters on soil temperature and soil air in much the same manner that had been used in the chapter on soil water.

In a meeting of all authors to consider necessary revisions it was decided to (1) modify each chapter to bring in a discussion of the edaphic factor *per se* and the soil characteristics affecting it, as well as the discussion of the influence of the edaphic factor on plant growth; (2) add an initial chapter as background for all others on "Soil as a Physical System," which would have two parts, the first treating the physical nature of soil and the second discussing the ways in which the physical characteristics of soil may be modified; and (3) invite additional authors to collaborate in the final preparation of the monograph. These decisions are reflected in the monograph. The reader should understand, however, that major attention is still directed at the influence of the four primary edaphic factors on plant growth.

The Joint Committee and the authors as a group have endeavored to guide the preparation of the monograph so that the several parts would fit into the theme adopted and serve the purpose intended. The authors of the separate chapters have been completely free to express their own opinions and they take full responsibility for their work.

The monograph is intended for all students of soil and plant science and engineering concerned with the effect of soil physical conditions on plant growth. It is particularly recommended to graduate students in soil physics and plant physiology in the hope that they might build on what is here set forth to bring about a better understanding of that abnormal plant behavior that is presently attributed to "poor soil physical conditions."

The Joint Committee on Soil Tilth gratefully acknowledges the splendid cooperation of the authors in the preparation of this monograph. The authors and the Committee extend their thanks to the following individuals for reviewing and offering comments on parts or all of the manuscript: D. B. ANDERSON; L. D. BAVER; G. B. BODMAN; F. L. DULEY; JOEL FLETCHER; WILLARD GARDNER; KARL HARRIS; M. L. JACKSON; V. C. JAMISON; O. J. KELLEY; C. E. KELLOGG; DON KIRKHAM; P. J. KRAMER; E. J. KRAUS; H. H. KRUSEKOPF; C. E. MARSHALL; C. E. MILLAR; A. E. MURNEEK; A. G. NORMAN; H. J. OOSTING; J. B. PAGE; R. Q. PARKS; C. B. TANNER; D. W. THORNE; C. H. VAN BAVEL; F. J. VEIHMEYER; C. C. WIGGANS.

We wish to make special acknowledgment of the help given by Dr. A. G. Norman, Chairman of the Committee on Monographs of the American Society of Agronomy. His advice has been most worthwhile and his patience has been greater than we had any reason to expect.

> BYRON T. SHAW, *Chairman*
> Joint Committee on Soil Tilth,
> American Society of Agronomy
> American Society of Agricultural Engineers

INTRODUCTION

There is widespread popular acceptance of the importance of the physical properties of soil to plant growth, but a large proportion of the statements commonly made on this subject are vague, qualitative, and frequently unsupported by factual evidence. It is the purpose of this monograph to provide students and professional agriculturists with a critical and authoritative evaluation of the present knowledge on this subject and to point out those areas in which additional data are needed.

The authors realize the difficulties involved in making an unambiguous separation of edaphic factors into classes such as physical, chemical, and biological. Not only are the factors themselves difficult to classify on the basis of their direct effects, but also most of the physical phenomena have important effects on chemical and biological soil properties and processes, which in turn influence plant growth. The soil as a physical system can be described in terms of such properties as grain size, apparent density, porosity, moisture content, temperature, and friability. This monograph is primarily a discussion of the direct effects of such physical attributes on plant growth. In addition, certain indirect effects of these parameters on such nonphysical edaphic factors, as nutrient supply and pH, are considered.

It is postulated that all physical attributes of the soil, such as apparent density, aggregation, pore-size distribution, friability, and others, influence plant growth through their effects on: (1) soil moisture, (2) soil air, (3) soil temperature, and (4) mechanical impedance to root development and shoot emergence. The first chapter of the monograph describes the soil as a physical system and considers methods by which the physical characteristics of the soil can be modified. The succeeding chapters deal with each of the four fundamental edaphic factors previously listed. In each chapter a description of the essential features of the phenomenon is first given. This is followed by a discussion of how the physical character of the soil affects the particular edaphic factor being discussed. An evaluation of the significance of that factor to plant growth follows. In the final part of the last chapter the interactions among the four fundamental factors are discussed in relation to other factors affecting plant growth.

CONTENTS

	Page
CONTRIBUTORS	v
PREFACE	vii
INTRODUCTION	xi

CHAPTER

1. Soil as a Physical System 1

BY LYLE T. ALEXANDER AND H. E. MIDDLETON

I. The Physical Nature of Soil	1
The Soil Profile	10
The Soil Skeleton	12
The Fine Materials	14
The Effect of Exchangeable Bases on Physical Properties of Soils	16
Organic Matter	17
Soil Structure	18
Classification of Natural Structural Units	19
Porosity	21
Claypans and Crusts	22
Hardpans	23
II. Modifying the Physical Properties of Soil	24
Modification of the Physical Properties of Virgin Soils in Preparing for Cultivation	24
Modification of the Physical Properties of Soil by Cultivation	25
Modification of the Physical Properties of Soil by Special Practices	34
Summary	38

2. Mechanical Impedance and Plant Growth 43

BY J. F. LUTZ

I. Surface Soil Characteristics	44
Texture	44
Structure	49
Depth of Topsoil	56
II. Subsoil or Substrata Characteristics	57
Texture, Structure, and Consistency	57
Bedrock	65
Consistency	67
Summary	67

3. Soil Water and Plant Growth 73

BY L. A. RICHARDS AND C. H. WADLEIGH

I. The Soil-Water System	74
II. Water Movement in Soils	76
Saturated Flow	77
Unsaturated Flow	78
Diffusion of Water Vapor through Soils	82
Soil-Water Movement in Relation to Plant-Root Extraction	83

III. Storage of Water in Soil.. 86

IV. Irrigation and Drainage.. 88
Irrigation 89
Drainage 89

V. The Physical Condition of Water in Soil........................... 91

VI. Methods of Measuring Soil-Moisture Tension...................... 93
Plates and Membranes for Tension Control...................... 93
Tensiometers 99
Moisture Meters for Use at High Tensions..................... 101

VII. Soil-Moisture Stress in Relation to Plant Growth................. 102
Experimental Conditions to Be Taken into Account.............. 106
Field Experiments with Fruits................................. 112
Field Experiments with other Crops........................... 119
Plant Experiments in Soil Containers......................... 136
Additional Studies Relating Soil-Moisture Stress to Turgescence and
Plant Growth... 145

VIII. Significance of the Wilting Percentage.......................... 151

IX. Entry of Water into Plants...................................... 157
The Plant Osmometer... 158
Mechanisms and Processes..................................... 166

X. Soil Moisture Effects on Plant Growth Not Related to the Energy
Status of the Moisture..................................... 187

XI. Soil Moisture and the Mineral Nutrition of Plants............... 189
Excess Moisture.. 189
Mineral Nutrition in the Moisture Range between Field Capacity
and the Wilting Percentage............................... 198

XII. Nutrient Accumulation in Plants in Relation to the Soil Moisture
Supply 203

XIII. Effect of Variations in Soil Moisture on Microbiological Activity.... 206

XIV. The Influence of Soil Moisture on Physiological Processes........... 207

XV. The Influence of Soil Moisture on the Various Phases of Plant Growth 214
Germination 214
Vegetative Growth.. 217
Maturation 220

XVI. Drought Tolerance.. 222

XVII. Efficiency of Water Use by Plants.............................. 225

4. Soil Aeration and Plant Growth.................................... 253
By M. B. RUSSELL
I. Characterization of the Soil Temperature........................ 254
II. Soil Processes and Properties Affected by Aeration.............. 261
III. Aeration and Plant Growth....................................... 265
IV. Aeration and Root Morphology.................................... 273
V. Aeration and Water Absorption by Roots.......................... 275
VI. The Effect of Aeration on Nutrient Absorption by Plants........... 278
VII. Soil Aeration and the Incidence of Plant Diseases................. 289
Summary 291

CONTENTS XV

Page

5. Soil Temperature and Plant Growth 303

By S. J. Richards, R. M. Hagan, and T. M. McCalla

Introduction 303

I. Soil Temperature 304
 Soil Temperature Measurements 304
 Factors Influencing Soil Temperatures 312
 Thermal Properties of Soils 319
 Cultural Practices Used to Influence Soil Temperature 328
 Soil Physical and Chemical Properties Affected by Soil Temperature 333

II. Temperature and Growth Processes 336
 Nature of Growth 336
 Growth Processes in Relation to Temperature 337
 Cardinal Temperatures 360
 Expressions for the Relation between Temperature and Growth.... 365

III. Soil Temperature and Plant Growth 367
 Germination and Seedling Emergence 367
 Sprouting of Bulbs, Tubers, and Similar Structures 378
 Growth of Roots and other Underground Organs 379
 Growth of Shoots 414
 Soil Temperature and Vegetative Growth 415
 Soil Temperature and Crop Quality 432
 Extreme Soil Temperature and Plant Injury 433
 Soil Temperature and Plant Disease 443

IV. Soil Temperature and Growth of Micro-organisms 447
 Distribution, Growth, and Numbers 447
 Decomposition of Organic Matter 449
 Ammonification and Nitrification 454
 Legume Bacteria (*Rhizobium sp.*) 456
 Soil Aggregation 457

V. Management and Soil Temperature 459
 Microbial Activity 459
 Crop Production 460

Epilogue 481

By Byron T. Shaw

Index 485

CHAPTER 1

SOIL AS A PHYSICAL SYSTEM

By Lyle T. Alexander and H. E. Middleton

I. THE PHYSICAL NATURE OF SOIL

By Lyle T. Alexander

TO SOME, soil is dirt; to others, it is any unconsolidated rock; to the farmer, it is a medium on which he expends his labor in a struggle for economic security; to all, it is the source of food and clothing. Although it seems hardly necessary to say, the soil may be defined as the natural medium for the growth of land plants. Since plants occupy the surface of the land mass almost continuously from pole to pole, soil likewise is found, in all degrees of development, where plants are established.

Soil furnishes the plant an anchor for its roots, water for its transpiration, minerals for its nutrition, and oxygen for its metabolism. On the other hand, the plant plays a vital part in determining the nature of the soil. Plant life, along with animal life, is one of the five genetic factors determining soil characteristics. The factors are living matter, climate, relief, parent rock, and time.

The effects of vegetation on soils are evident to all who have studied the soil. Muckenhirn *et al.* (1949) have summarized some of the specific differences brought about by a vegetation of grass or trees on similar parent soil material. Soils of quite different characteristics result. A striking effect of vegetation on soil properties is shown by the chemical composition of soil underneath and immediately adjacent to salt-tolerant or salt-loving vegetation in the Escalante Desert in southwestern Utah. Roberts (1950) noted striking differences between the pH, sodium content, and total salt content under some species of shrubs as contrasted with other species when referred to the corresponding values for bare ground between the plants. The greatest contrasts were noted between the soil under and away from the shrub greasewood (*Sarcobatus vermiculatus*). Plants such as greasewood and shadscale (*Atriplex confertifolia*) apparently take in enough salt from the soil to cause material changes in the salt content of the upper few feet of the soil profile immediately beneath the spread of the branches. Presumably the salt reaches the soil by leaching from the

1

live and fallen leaves.　　Table 1 gives some data that illustrate the point.
　　These data show that important changes in chemical and physical properties of soils can be brought about by the action of plants.　Although these soils were taken from well-established clumps of grease-

TABLE 1.—*Analyses of Antelope Springs silty clay loam at four sites, Beryl Enterprise area, Utah*[1]

Site	Depth	pH[2]	Exchangeable sodium content	Soluble sodium[3]	Permeability[4]
	Inches		*me/100 g.*	*Percent*	*cm./hr.*
No. 1—barren..............	0– 2	9.1	0.92	6.40	0.051
	2– 5	8.6	0.69	1.75	0.40
	5–10	8.6	0.58	1.50	9.2
	10–14	8.6	0.51	1.35	10.0
	14–28	8.7	0.82	1.65	18.0
	28–33	8.8	1.18	3.35	15.0
	33–48	9.0	1.28	5.85	6.1
No. 1G—9 feet from site No. 1, under greasewood	0– 2	10.1	8.15	31.12	0.60
	2– 6	10.3	12.19	38.75	
	6–13	10.3	17.07	36.25	0.005
	13–22	9.8	7.90	33.87	0.083
	22–30	9.5	5.62	40.62	0.30
	30–38	9.5	4.96	36.62	0.74
	38–44	9.5	5.35	32.50	0.58
	44–52	9.0	5.72	23.50	0.67
No. 2—barren.............	0– 2	8.7	0.48	3.05	0.38
	2– 8	8.8	0.53	1.85	2.2
	8–16	8.9	0.60	2.25	1.7
	16–21	9.2	1.15	3.15	4.2
	21–37	9.5	3.27	7.90	1.9
No. 2G—2⅓ feet from site No. 2, under greasewood	0– 2	10.0	10.92	52.75	0.11
	2– 8	10.0	10.29	22.20	0.022
	8–16	9.6	5.12	19.30	0.63
	16–21	9.3	3.34	14.20	5.0
	21–37	9.4	4.52	17.50	0.06

[1] Analyses by U. S. Regional Salinity Laboratory, using methods given in diagnosis and improvement of saline and alkali soils.　U. S. Salinity Lab. pub., 157 pp., illus.　1947 [Processed].

[2] 1 : 5 soil; water suspension.

[3] Sodium ion content of saturation extract.

[4] After a 6-inch irrigation or at end of 2 weeks, whichever was shorter.

wood, perhaps as much as 50 years old, distinct differences were found between the upper inch of soil of the barren area and of that under very small shadscale plants.　Soils developed under such a pattern of salt-accumulating vegetation and intervening bare spots present many difficulties from the standpoint of classification, amelioration, and use for agricultural purposes.

Root systems of plants have a profound effect on the physical characteristics of the several soil horizons. They penetrate, widen the cracks and crevices, and lower the water content. When the root decays it leaves a residue of soil organic matter and a channel for the movement of water until filled with material from above. Figure 1 shows a profile of Ruston sandy loam with a large root channel filled with sandy material from near the surface.

Animal life is also important in determining or altering the character of soils. Thorp (1949) has given estimates of the amount of material brought to the surface by burrowing animals at one location in Colorado. Enough coarse-textured material has been deposited in the upper horizon of the Rago soil to give it a loam texture in spite of the fact that the surface mantle consisted of 8 feet of wind-blown silt. Changing the texture of the soil is not the only effect of these rodents. Their abandoned burrows (Fig. 2) fill with material from higher in the profile and serve as channels through which downward penetrating water can move more rapidly than through the undisturbed soil. Although many soil areas have been altered by the action of such rodents, there are vast areas of loess-derived soils that are completely free from the coarse material found beneath the shallow mantle.

Microscopic life also plays an important part in soil formation, particularly in the formation of soil organic matter. This will be discussed in more detail in subsequent pages.

From the hot tropics to the frigid arctic zone, climate has its effect in determining soil characteristics. Moisture and heat are the direct effects of climate. Indirect effects of climate on plant and animal life are frequently more important than the direct ones. Climatic effects are usually of broad zonal character—the prairie, the tundra, the mountain meadows, the desert.

Table 2, condensed from Blumenstock and Thornthwaite by Muckenhirn *et al.* (1949), shows the general effects of climate on soils and vegetative distribution.

A small amount of water may make the difference between the desert and the grassland, and an additional amount, the margin between the short grass country and the tall grass prairie. Depending upon the sharpness in change of rainfall the gradation from fertile land suitable for intensive farming to sagebrush-covered desert land may be very gradual over long distances, as from Missouri to New Mexico, or it may be sharp when there is a mountain barrier or rapid change in elevation of the landscape. Vertical zonation is impressive because it

FIGURE 1.—Profile of Ruston sandy loam near Ruston, La. In lower left, note large root channel filled with sandy material from above.

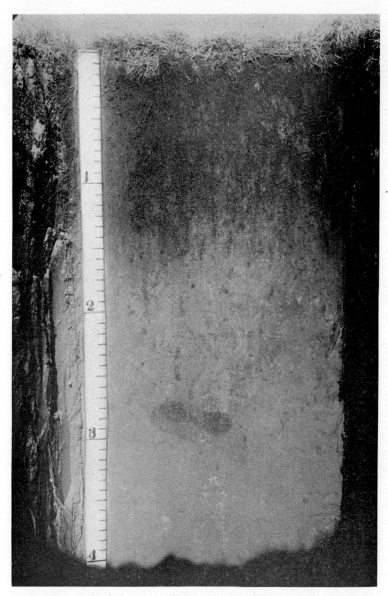

FIGURE 2.—Two animal burrows filled with material from the upper horizon. Water has penetrated to 3 feet through these channels and spread downward. (Rago silt loam, Colby, Kans.)

TABLE 2.—*Schematic representation of distribution of climatic types, vegetative formations, and major zonal soil groups on a hypothetical level continent*

Dry cold   Wet cold

Perpetual Snow and Ice				
Tundra				
Taiga				
Arid Desert grasses and shrubs	Semiarid Steppe	Subhumid Grassland	Humid Forests	Wet Rain forest

Climatic Types and Vegetative Formations label at left for upper rows; *Climatic Type Vegetative* label at left for bottom row.

Dry hot   Wet hot

A. Distribution of climatic types and vegetative formations

Dry cold   Wet cold

Perpetual Snow and Ice			
Tundra Soils			
Podzols			
Sierozems and Desert soils	Chestnut and Brown soils	Prairie soils and Cherno-zems	Podzols
			Gray-Brown Podzolic soils
			Red and Yellow Podzolic soils
			Lateritic soils

Dry hot   Wet hot

B. Distribution of major zonal soil groups on a climatic base

displays the range of climatic zones, with respect to both moisture and temperature, in a short distance. Most of the important agricultural areas of the world are found in relatively broad zones with respect to both rainfall and temperature.

The beneficial effect of larger amounts of water in promoting more vegetative growth is counterbalanced by the lowered fertility status of soils owing to leaching of plant nutrients out of the root zone by percolating water when rainfall is excessive. The productivity of the soil for native vegetation or for economic crops may be limited by lack of water or by lack of plant nutrients in a form available to the plants. Temperature effects on plant growth and on rate of chemical and mechanical weathering of soil-forming materials are important, but the changes are over greater distances than is the case with rainfall. Increasing temperature accelerates chemical weathering in accordance with well-known principles. The low fertility status of soils in and adjacent to the tropic regions that have moderate to high rainfall is a great limiting factor for plant growth except in areas having young rocks, such as recent volcanic ash.

The factor of relief directly influences the effectiveness of the water that falls on the soil. If the slope is steep, much of the water runs off; if the soil is level or at the foot of a slope, the water is more effective or else the soil may receive more than falls on it. The swamps and the hillsides have different kinds of soils because of the relief. The changes in nature of soils owing to differences in the relief factor take place over short distances in contrast to those caused by climate. A change in slope from nearly level to strongly rolling reduces effective rainfall by the amount of the runoff increase. The differences in water that actually gets into the soil are particularly great where the soil material is fine-textured and relatively impermeable. As a result of the lesser amount of rainfall passing into the soil, weathering proceeds less rapidly, less vegetation is produced, and consequently a shallower less differentiated soil profile develops. The runoff increases erosion, which also contributes to the shallowness of the soil. At the foot of such slopes, areas that receive much more water than the rain that falls may be excessively developed, or even swamps or peat bogs may be formed.

Direction and degree of slope also have important effects on soil temperature and water retention. It has been observed in Michigan that when north- and south-facing back slopes of highways are sodded alike with bluegrass sod from level areas, the north-facing slopes are soon all Kentucky bluegrass (*Poa pratensis*) and the south-facing ones are covered with Canada bluegrass (*Poa compressa*), which is more tolerant of drier situations.

Parent material differences usually cause local soil variations that are not due to relief. Basic intrusive igneous rocks in an area of leached sedimentary materials give rise to soils of contrasting physical and chemical properties. In the Triassic Basin of northern Virginia the Iredell soils are formed from basic intrusives in the red Pennsylvanian sandstones and shales. These soils have plastic intractable yellowish subsoils with nontronite as the principal clay mineral. The adjacent Penn or Bucks soils are friable and red and have little or no montmorillonite-type clay minerals in the fine fraction. The inherited red color of these soils is in sharp contrast with the yellow and grayish brown of the Iredell. Sometimes the line of demarcation between them is quite abrupt. The red color of the Penn soil is due to the hematite particles that were present in the sedimentary rock. Surface soil, subsoil, and parent material are all the same color. On the other hand, none of the color of the Iredell soil is inherited from parent rock; it is due to the color of the weathering products of the rock. Had the hematite not been present in the parent rock of the Penn soil, a characteristic color profile would have developed.

Sometimes a rock weathers so deeply and so characteristically that variations in topography do not have so great an effect on the color and degree of development of the profile. This is true of the deep red Davidson soils formed from greenstone in northern Virginia and in North Carolina and of the Aiken soils of northern California and adjacent Oregon. In contrast to this, many parent rock differences tend to be obliterated in the formation of the well-developed normal soils of humid regions. Even when soils inherit some outstanding characteristic, as the red color of the Penn series from the parent material, they may differ from the parent material in chemical and physical characteristics.

Time is an important factor in determining soil characteristics; this is evident to anyone who has observed the differences between alluvial soils of creek or small river bottoms and those of the adjacent upland. Soils that have been long in forming may remain youthful in point of development if the rate of removal of the geologic erosion is rapid relative to the rate of weathering of the minerals in the parent rocks. The soil should not be regarded as an isolated individual soil surrounded by other soils that are different from it. Rather, it should be considered as a dynamic three-dimensional piece of landscape that supports plants. It is an individual in a continuum. It is related in an ordinary manner to the individual soils that surround it. This can perhaps be best illustrated by Figure 3 (Riecken and Smith, 1949).

The age of a soil may be measured in years, but this is usually not possible because of the relatively long time that it takes a soil to develop a profile. Jenny (1941) has brought together data from a number of sources regarding the time required for soil formation. The evidence indicates that a well-developed Podzol in the Alps may form in 1,000 years; that a Rendzina 1 foot thick formed within 230 years in the Ukraine; that Hardy (1939) found 30 years after the deposition of volcanic ash in the British West Indies a soil had formed that contained 2.1 percent organic matter in the upper 6 inches. Chandler (1943)

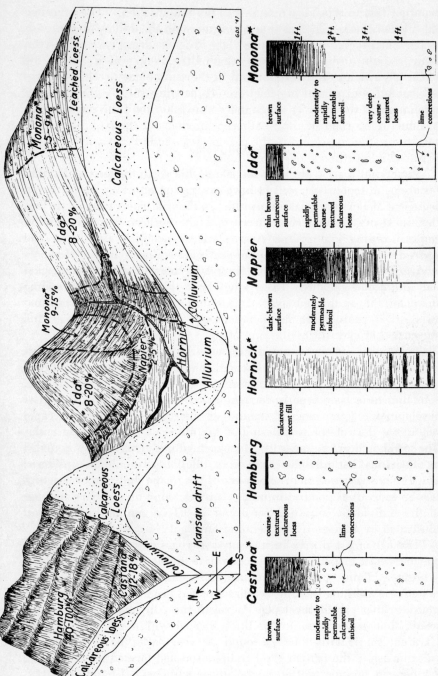

FIGURE 3.—Relation of major upland soils in MIH (Monoa-Ida-Hamburg) soil association area to parent material and slope. (Asterisks indicate tentative series.)

reported that in Alaska a true Podzol with an A_2 horizon 2 to 4 inches thick had developed in 1,000 years on morainic material.

Frequently the terms "young" or "old," when applied to soils, refer to degree of profile development rather than to chronological age. If a soil has reached equilibrium with its surroundings, its chronological age has little significance. Factors such as temperature, moisture, and vegetative growth may be much more significant than the mere passage of time.

The Soil Profile

A vertical section through the soil surface into the parent material exposes the various horizons comprising the soil profile. The kind and sequence of horizons making up the profile of a given soil are its most definite distinguishing characteristics. The degree of profile development in our agricultural soils varies from essentially none in the case of freshly deposited soil alluvium to several very strongly differentiated horizons in some soils that have been subjected to the chemical, physical, and biological forces for a long time. Here it should be pointed out again that time alone is not sufficient to bring about a differentiation of the soil profile into distinct horizons. If rainfall is limited, the formation of clay by weathering of the various minerals does not proceed rapidly. If the mineral nutrients in the profile are very low, vegetative growth is limited; hence, differentiation of horizons with respect to organic matter is retarded.

Unfortunately, there is no universally accepted system of horizon designation. For a normal upland soil most general usage designates the upper part of the profile as the A horizon or horizons; the middle part, the B horizon; and the unconsolidated material that has been affected very little by the plant roots, the C horizon. Subscripts such as 0, 1, 2, 3 are used to denote subdivisions of the A, B, and C horizons and zones of transition from one to the other. Since designations and definitions that are generally accepted cannot be given, it will suffice to reproduce a simple diagram that was given in the 1938 Yearbook of the United States Department of Agriculture (Fig. 4).

Soils of a given great soil group have similar kinds and sequences of horizons, although the degree of development or expression of a particular characteristic may vary greatly. At each lower category in the classification the range of variation with respect to a horizon criterion becomes less, until at the soil type level, the range is as small as is consistent with the detail of the survey that is made. As a practical matter, it is necessary to permit a considerable range, with respect to some of the horizon criteria, in all mapping units.

	Horizon	Description
Organic debris lodged on the soil; usually absent on soils developed by grasses.	A_{00}	Loose leaves and organic debris, largely decomposed.
	A_0	Organic debris partly decomposed or matted.
The solum (the true soil developed by soil-building processes).	A_1	Dark horizon containing a relatively high content of organic matter, but mixed with mineral matter.
	A_2	Light-colored horizon representing the region of maximum leaching.
	A_3	Transitional to B but more like A than B; sometimes absent.
	B_1	Transitional to B but more like B than A; sometimes absent.
	B_2	Usually a deeper colored horizon representing the region of maximum accumulation. In grassland soils this region has a definite structural character but does not have much if any accumulated materials and represents a transition between A and C.
	B_3	Transitional to C.
The weathered parent material. Occasionally absent, i.e., soil building may follow weathering so closely that no weathered material that is not included in the solum is found between B and D. May include zones of accumulation of calcium carbonate in grassland soils.	C	
Any stratum underneath the soil, such as hard rock or a layer of clay or sand, that is not parent material but that may affect the overlying soil.	D	Underlying stratum.

FIGURE 4.—Hypothetical soil having the principal horizons. No one soil would be expected to have all these horizons well developed, but every soil has some of them. The B horizon may or may not have an accumulation of clay.

Soils differ greatly with respect to their distinguishing horizon criteria. Many soils developed on the Coastal Plain of the Southeast have well-developed horizon differentiation with respect to color, texture, consistence, and organic-matter content but are without structure. On the other hand, some well-developed Chernozem, Chestnut, and Brown soils have horizons that are clearly different with respect to structure, consistence, color, and organic-matter content but have no textural differentiation. The various criteria are not of equal importance everywhere. The importance of the kind and sequence of horizons in determining the suitability of a soil for plant growth cannot be overemphasized. A single layer that is only slowly permeable to water limits the rate at which water can be taken into the horizons beneath—either by irrigation or from rainfall. A horizon impenetrable to roots because of cementation or compaction confines the plant to that part of the soil above it.

The Soil Skeleton

Although the soil horizons are fundamental units that have individual characteristics, they are in themselves heterogeneous systems. Soil horizons are made up of materials in three different states—solid, liquid, and gaseous. Proper proportions of these constituents are necessary for the soil to be a good medium for plant growth. The solid part of the soil consisting of both organic and inorganic matter forms the skeleton, or framework, and air and water fill the intervening space. The proportions of air and water vary from day to day, depending on the removal of moisture from the soil by transpiration, evaporation, or drainage and the addition of moisture by rainfall, irrigation, or capillary movement. The importance of air and water to plant growth is the subject to much of the text that follows.

The inorganic part of the soil is made up of particles ranging in size from that of fine clay to large rocks. Particle-size distribution is the principal characteristic determining the water-holding characteristics of mineral soils. Those having a large part of their discrete mineral particles falling within a narrow size range are not so favorable for plants as those having a wider range. This is generally true whether the dominant size falls in the coarse, medium, or fine fractions. Textural terms such as "loam," "sandy loam," and "clay loam" are of ancient origin and referred originally to the ease with which a soil could be cultivated. Soil texture, which as a first approximation is determined by particle-size distribution, received much attention in the early European literature because of the close correlation between it and tilth or structure. Later, when the study of soils was extended to other parts of the world, particularly to the large continents, it was found that structure was frequently more important than texture and that differences in clay content were overshadowed by differences in kind of clay or by the cations with which the clay was saturated.

Texture has been the field man's term for how a soil feels or how it behaves under cultivation. In this sense it is modified by organic

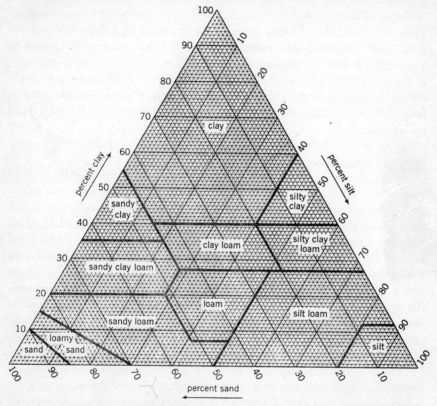

FIGURE 5.—Guide for textural classification used by the Bureau of Plant Industry, Soils, and Agricultural Engineering, United States Department of Agriculture.

matter, by kind of clay, and by the ions with which the clay is saturated. Organic matter tends to make a fine soil coarser in texture and a coarser one finer. Many of the silt loams of the Corn Belt of the United States owe their designation as such to the liberal supply of organic matter and to their granular structure that does not break down readily. A given percentage of the swelling clays of the montmorillonite type and the hydrous micas are more effective in giving a clayey feel and fine texture to soil than a similar amount of kaolinitic clay. When the clay fraction of soils is saturated with sodium the soil is stickier and appears to have a finer texture than when calcium or hydrogen is the dominant exchangeable ion in the clay.   One of the objections to the use of texture as a scientific term is that it cannot, as a field term, be defined precisely.

As stated previously, particle-size distribution can be used as a first approximation, or guide, to textural designation.   This is done in the Division of Soil Survey of the United States Department of Agriculture. Figure 5 shows the current usage of percentages of sand (2.0 to 0.050 mm.), silt (0.050 to 0.002 mm.), and clay (less than 0.002 mm.) as a guide in texture determination.

A breakdown is made within the sand, loamy sand, and sandy loam classes according to the prevailing proportions of sand particles of different sizes.   Thus a sandy loam, if a large portion of its sand falls within the limits of very fine sand (0.1 to 0.50 mm.), will be called very fine sandy loam.   The designations other than sandy are coarse, fine, and very fine.

The Fine Materials

Of particular importance is the fine fraction of the soil.   It determines, in most cases, the base- and anion-exchange characteristics.   It influences structure formation and water-retention properties and determines the ease with which the soil can be tilled.   Inorganic soils without appreciable percentages of clay are structureless and without much base-holding capacity.   When such soils are used for growing crops the nutrients have to be applied at frequent intervals.   Rains that come soon after fertilizer application may cause the loss of the added nutrients, particularly nitrogen.   Moisture relations are adversely affected.   On the other hand, too high a proportion of clay causes difficulty of tillage, of maintaining good structure, and of changing the base status of the soils owing to high exchange capacity.

In the soils that do not contain large amounts of organic matter the clay fraction determines, as a first approximation, the water-retentation characteristics.   In comparing fine-textured and coarse-textured soils the increased capacity caused by the higher clay content is not all in the range that is useful to plants.   Much of the water is so tightly held that it cannot be taken by plants.

The kind of clay is very important.   Kaolinitic clay, usually in conjunction with oxides of iron or aluminum, forms the fine fraction of most of the soils of the southeastern States.   This clay has a low base-exchange capacity.   It is not so sticky as other clays; neither does it swell or shrink to the extent they do.   The lattice structure of this clay mineral is of the 1 to 1 nonswelling type.[1] In contrast, montmorillonite has a high exchange capacity and is sticky, especially when saturated with sodium. Swelling and shrinking is an outstanding characteristic. The 2 to 1 crystal lattice expands as water wets the clay and shrinks when water is removed. Beidellite has characteristics very similar to montmorillonite. Illite, or hydrous mica, has properties that are, in general, intermediate between those of kaolin and of montmorillonite.

When it was established, by means of X-ray diffraction, that the fine fraction of soil was made up largely of crystalline clay minerals, the opinion was that all of the properties of the fine material were due to the crystalline clay minerals. As a first approximation, this may be true. However, there are a number of cases in which this is not true. The fine fractions of many soils from tropical regions are dominantly noncrystalline iron and aluminum oxides. The amount of water held at given moisture tensions is much higher than for most soils. This same condition seems to exist, to a much lesser extent, in the B horizons of Podzols. X-ray and differential thermal data indicate noncrystallinity for a considerable portion of the fine fraction of these soils.

Many heavy soils of the southeastern States have exchange capacities that are higher than can be accounted for on the basis of the amounts of clay minerals that have been determined. One possibility is that the kaolin in these soils has a higher exchange capacity than is usually assigned to it. Another is that the higher capacity is due to the presence of noncrystalline material. It may be, however, that the higher capacity is due to the presence of clay minerals as yet unidentified.

A number of instances have come to light where much of the exchange capacity of a soil is due to the fractions of coarser than clay size. Workers at the Macauley Institute (Mitchell and Muir, 1937) found that a soil derived from norite had an exchange capacity in excess of 100 milliequivalents per 100 grams in the sand-size fraction. Unpublished data of the Bureau of Plant Industry, Soils, and Agricultural Engineering indicate that the parent material of the Fauquier soil from northern Virginia has a high exchange capacity in the silt and sand fractions. Some soils of the Safford series from Tennessee have a high exchange capacity owing to weathered glauconite of silt

---

[1] For a treatment of the lattice structure of clay minerals, see Marshall, C. E., The Colloid Chemistry of the Silicate Minerals. Volume I of a series of monographs prepared under the auspices of The American Society of Agronomy, 195 pp., illus., 1949, Academic Press, New York.

size. It is not safe to assume that all the exchange capacity of a soil resides in the clay and organic fractions.

The Effect of Exchangeable Bases on Physical Properties of Soils

The ability of clay minerals to hold and exchange bases is their most outstanding characteristic. Not only is the clay mineral fraction of the soil responsible for the buffering action with respect to supplies of nutrient bases, but it is in itself profoundly affected by the kind of bases with which it is saturated and the degree of the saturation. A soil may be an impermeable dispersed mass or a well-granulated permeable medium for growth of plants, depending upon the kind and amount of positive ions with which it is saturated.

The calcium ion has long been considered the key to the maintenance of favorable structure in soil. Unfortunately, the direct effects of this ion on the physical properties of the clay fraction of soils have not been evaluated apart from the effect of calcium as a plant nutrient. When the physical condition of a soil is improved by liming, it is not possible to tell whether the increased granulation was caused by the calcium ion, or by the more vigorous root system resulting from an increased nutrient supply.

Russell (1938) reached the conclusion that there was a serious conflict between laboratory and field evidence on the effect of lime on soil structure. The laboratory evidence is rather conclusive that mere conversion of an acid clay to a calcium-saturated one does not improve its structure. Baver (1948) and Myers (1937) showed that acid washed clays have structures that are as stable as neutral ones. Peele (1936) showed that addition of calcium carbonate or calcium hydroxide to the subsurface horizons of soils having kaolinitic clay caused a deterioration of the structure.

It appears that soils having kaolinitic clays cannot be raised with safety to the pH values commonly considered desirable in those with hydrous mica and montmorillonite types. The well-known useful effect of gypsum and sulfur in the reclamation of alkali soils is due to a direct effect of a higher calcium ion concentration in the soil solution on the sodium in the exchange complex. This question will be discussed in more detail later in this chapter. Because of the low thermodynamic activity of calcium in the clay mineral complex, calcium-saturated clays have pH values from 7 to 8 that change very little on dilution.

The sodium ion contrasts sharply with calcium in its effect on soil structure. When sodium replaces calcium in a soil having structure, the soil becomes dispersed or deflocculated. When sodium ions comprise even a small fraction of the exchangeable bases in soils, the physical properties are adversely affected. Soils having more than one-half of their capacity saturated by sodium are usually intractable and relatively impenetrable to water. The sodium-saturated clay hydrolyzes readily on dilution with water of low salt content to give high pH values. The hydrolysis is suppressed in the presence of relatively high concentrations of neutral salts. Potassium and ammonium ions affect clay minerals in a similar manner but to a lesser degree than sodium; however, they are rarely found or applied in sufficient amounts to have a material effect on the physical condition of the soil.

The hydrogen ion, with help from the aluminum ion, fills the gap between exchangeable bases and the total exchange capacity. The most acid soils are the ones that are almost completely saturated by hydrogen owing to lack of the other cations. In a general way pH values of soils follow the degree of base saturation. It should be noted that pH values of soil suspensions or paste do not have the same connotation of concentration of hydrogen ions per unit of volume as in solutions. The hydrogen ion in soils is held to the surface of the clay particles in such a manner that the hydrogen electrode is not affected at an appreciable distance.

Organic Matter

Organic matter occurs in all size fractions but is usually concentrated in the fine portion. In many soils the organic-matter content of the clay fraction extracted from the soil is twice that of the soil as a whole. Organic matter contributes to the total exchange capacity of the soil a much greater amount than its total percentage would indicate. Many sandy soils owe their exchange capacity almost entirely to the organic matter they contain. On the other hand, some soils have been found by Anderson and Byers (1936) to increase in exchange capacity when treated with hydrogen peroxide to remove organic matter. This would indicate that exchange positions on the clay were blocked by the organic matter. It is also probable that, in such soils, there is chemical combination between the organic and inorganic fractions of the fine material.

Organic matter makes a material contribution to the stability of the granular structure of most arable soils. Organic matter of the soil should not be regarded as residues of plant material that have withstood decomposition by micro-organisms. While there are undoubtedly some undecomposed plants in all soils, recent evidence indicates that the true soil organic matter, or humus, dominantly is the product of microbiological decomposition of plant and animal residues. The composition and chemical behavior of the organic fraction of soil of a given series in a given location remains quite constant over a long period of time in spite of additions of large amounts of manure, green manures, or loss of organic matter in clean-cultivated areas. The reasonable explanation of such behavior is that the plant and animal residues merely serve as suppliers of the energy and mineral nutrient requirements of the micro-organisms and that their remains constitute the bulk of the soil organic matter.

Soil Structure

By structure of the soil we mean the arrangement or grouping of individual particles into units. The individual grains, or parts, making up a specific structural unit are more closely attached to or associated with each other than they are with corresponding grains not a part of this unit. Hence, a structural unit may be defined as one or more groups of soil particles held together in such a manner that the resultant physical properties differ from those exhibited by a corresponding mass of the individual particles. This definition would exclude the single-grain condition as a structural category and regard it as a complete lack of structure. On the other hand, massive, cloddy, or puddled conditions of soil materials might be regarded as naturally or artificially produced units of structure. Russell (1938), however, made no clear differentiations between natural and artificially produced structural units or clods. Much is to be said for the latter view, particularly when one is dealing with cultivated soil that had little structural development in the natural state. In such cases the structure produced by tillage may be essentially all that is present. Such structure usually has a very short life.

Soil structural units are much less mobile to the forces of wind and water than the individual constituents from which they are formed. Instead of the easily blown or washed dust formed by individual sand, silt, and clay particles, we may have a relatively stable surface even in the absence of a vegetative cover, provided the structural units are not too small. However, it will be apparent from subsequent discussion that the most important effect of structural units in the soil is to alter the water relationships. In general, the effect is one of increasing the larger pore spaces that are necessary for movement of water into and out of the soil and also needed for the rapid renewal of the soil's oxygen supply.

Structural units of the soil may be specified in terms of their size, shape and stability. Structural conditions that are reflected clearly in a soil property, such as permeability to water, may not be discernible under the conditions of moisture that prevail when the property is important. Reducing the moisture content usually accentuates the observable degree of aggregation or structural development. In fact, drying, either by evaporation or by plant transpiration, is one of the principal means of improving structure in soil. If observations of soil structural development are made when the moisture content is low, a false impression regarding the degree of development and firmness of the units may result. On the other hand, without drying the soil below the moisture content normally prevailing it may be impossible to make significant observations.

Classification of Natural Structural Units

In his book Baver (1948) has discussed a number of systems of classification of natural structural units of soil. Nikiforoff (1941) presented a detailed discussion of the morphological classification of soil structure that, with some modifications, has been adopted by the Division of Soil Survey of the United States Department of Agriculture.

Natural structural units of the soil may be classified with respect to type-shape, grade-distinctness, and class-size. Table 3 shows the types and classes of soil structure that are in current use in the Division of Soil Survey. The principal deviation of this table from the one given by Nikiforoff is the recognition of *columnar, nuciform,* and *crumb* as subdivisions of Nikiforoff's *prismatic, blocky,* and *granular,* respectively. This adds to the complexity of the system of classification. The use of a table such as this by survey personnel all over the United States adds materially to the morphological descriptions that are made by various workers.

The grade of structure refers to degree or distinctness of aggregation and expresses the differential between cohesion within the aggregates and the adhesion between aggregates. The following quotations are taken from the current definitions of grade of structure used in the Division of Soil Survey, Bureau of Plant Industry, Soils, and Agricultural Engineering.

0. *Structureless.*—That condition in which there is no observable aggregation or no definite orderly arrangement of natural lines of weakness. Massive if coherent; *single grain* if noncoherent.
1. *Weak.*—That degree of aggregation characterized by poorly formed indistinct aggregates that are barely observable in place. When disturbed, soil material that has this grade of structure breaks into a mixture of few entire aggregates, many broken aggregates, and much unaggregated material. If necessary for comparison, this grade may be subdivided into very weak and moderately weak.

TABLE 3.—*Types and classes of soil structure*

Type (Shape and arrangement of ped)

Class	Platelike with one dimension (the vertical) limited and greatly less than the other two; arranged around a horizontal plane; faces mostly horizontal	Prismlike with two dimensions (the horizontal) limited and considerably less than the vertical; arranged around a vertical line; vertical faces well defined; vertices angular		Blocklike, polyhedronlike, or spheroidal, with three dimensions of the same order of magnitude, arranged around a point			
				Blocklike; blocks or polyhedrons having plane or curved surfaces that are casts of the molds formed by the faces of the surrounding peds		Spheroids or polyhedrons having plane or curved surfaces which have slight or no accommodation to the faces of surrounding peds	
		Without rounded caps	With rounded caps	Faces flattened; most vertices sharply angular	Mixed rounded and flattened faces with many rounded vertices	Relatively non-porous peds	Porous peds
	Platy	Prismatic	Columnar	(Angular) blocky[1]	Subangular blocky[2]	Granular	Crumb
Very fine or very thin	Very thin platy; <1 mm.	Very fine prismatic; <10 mm.	Very fine columnar; <10 mm.	Very fine angular blocky; <5 mm.	Very fine subangular blocky; <5 mm.	Very fine granular; <1 mm.	Very fine crumb; <1 mm.
Fine or thin	Thin platy; 1 to 2 mm.	Fine prismatic; 10 to 20 mm.	Fine columnar; 10 to 20 mm.	Fine angular blocky; 5 to 10 mm.	Fine subangular blocky; 5 to 10 mm.	Fine granular; 1 to 2 mm.	Fine crumb; 1 to 2 mm.
Medium	Medium platy; 2 to 5 mm.	Medium prismatic; 20 to 50 mm.	Medium columnar; 20 to 50 mm.	Medium angular blocky; 10 to 20 mm.	Medium subangular blocky; 10 to 20 mm.	Medium granular; 2 to 5 mm.	Medium crumb; 2 to 5 mm.
Coarse or thick	Thick platy; 5 to 10 mm.	Coarse prismatic; 50 to 100 mm.	Coarse columnar; 50 to 100 mm.	Coarse angular blocky; 20 to 50 mm.	Coarse subangular blocky; 20 to 50 mm.	Coarse granular; 5 to 10 mm.	
Very coarse or very thick	Very thick platy; >10 mm.	Very coarse prismatic; >100 mm.	Very coarse columnar; >100 mm.	Very coarse angular blocky; >50 mm.	Very coarse subangular blocky; >50 mm.	Very coarse granular; >10 mm.	

[1] (a) Sometimes called *nut.* (b) The word "angular" in the name can ordinarily be omitted.
[2] Sometimes called *nuciform nut* or *subangular nut.* Since the size connotation of these terms is a source of great confusion to many, they are not recommended.

2. *Moderate.*—That grade of structure characterized by well-formed distinct aggregates that are moderately durable and evident but not distinct in undisturbed soil. Soil material of this grade, when disturbed, breaks down into a mixture of many distinct entire aggregates, some broken aggregates, and little unaggregated material. Examples are loamy A horizons of typical Chestnut soils in the granular type and clayey B horizons of such Red and Yellow Podzolic soils as the Boswell in the blocky type.

3. *Strong.*—That grade of structure characterized by durable aggregates that are quite evident in undisplaced soil, that adhere to one another weakly, and that withstand displacement and become separated when the soil is disturbed. When removed from the profile, soil material of this grade of structure is very largely of entire aggregates and includes few broken aggregates and no unaggregated material. If necessary for comparison the grade may be subdivided into moderately strong and very strong. Examples of strong grade of structure are the A horizons of the typical Chernozem in the granular type and the B horizon of typical Solonetz in the prismatic type.

Compound structure is common. The prismatic units of the Chestnut soils usually break into fine blocky structural units. Both the large prismatic units and the smaller blocky ones, of which the former are composed, are of importance in determining the water and oxygen relationship of the soil.

Structural units, or aggregates, in soils, whether produced naturally or by tillage operations, are subject to destruction by water and by cultivation. The A horizons of grassland soils have an excellent granular structure that is stable under cultivation for many years. However, this structure deteriorates with cultivation, particularly when used for clean-cultivated row crops or left fallow. As a first approximation, structure loss parallels organic matter loss.

Water brings about the decomposition of soil aggregates by slaking and by direct impact. Slaking destroys the relatively unstable aggregates that have been formed by physical forces such as drying, freezing and thawing, and tillage operations. More slowly formed aggregates that depend upon an organic matter-clay complex binding for their stability withstand slaking action much better. The direct impact of rain will destroy the most stable aggregates if continued for sufficient time. Each cultivation of the soil exposes a new group of soil aggregates to the action of raindrops if there is no vegetative cover.

Porosity

The total porosity, or pore space, of a soil is dependent upon both its size distribution and structure. Structure is particularly important in that it determines or affects the pore-size distribution. In terms of total porosity heavy clays are more porous than well-graded sands.

The pores are, however, so small that, in the absence of structural development or aggregation, there is essentially no movement of water or air into or through the soil. Thus pore-size distribution is particularly important in heavy soils. If a soil is too open and porous water moves through too freely and not enough is held in the range of water tension covered by plant growth. On the other hand, heavy clay soils may hold much water that is not available for plant growth.

Granular is perhaps the most desirable type of structure if the units are of adequate size to permit ready penetration of water and roots. An additional requirement is good porosity within the individual granules. This is what the farmer is striving for when he tries to improve the structure of his soil by good management practices.

Claypans and Crusts

We are particularly concerned with conditions that interfere with man's utilization of the soil for production of economic plants. Any soil horizon that interferes with the movement of air or water or that limits the penetration of roots is important in affecting plant growth. Usually the effects are detrimental. In a few cases impervious layers are beneficial.

Perhaps the most commonly occurring horizon that impedes the movement of water is the claypan. High clay content alone does not suffice to define this condition. Many of our best agricultural soils have high contents of clay in the B horizon. These good soils have well-developed structures with a good distribution of pore spaces in contrast to the very fine pores of clayey horizons without structure. Claypans occur at various depths in the soil and may be weakly, moderately, or strongly developed.

The claypan may have developed in place or it may be depositional. Higher content of clay in the B horizon of a soil has been generally regarded as evidence that clay has moved from the A horizon (eluviation) and deposited in the B horizon (illuviation). The extent to which this process occurs is not known. We do know that many soils dry out with resulting formations of cracks. When water falls on the soils the cracks are filled with material from on or near the surface. The material filling these fissures is not particularly high in clay. This process is most spectacularly demonstrated in the formations of the columns of the Solonetz. In a less striking manner the effects are seen in many kinds of soil.

Most frequently the increased clay content of B horizons is due to the weathering of minerals within the horizon itself. For this to happen moisture and minerals that can be weathered to give clay must be present and sufficient time must elapse to accomplish the necessary clay formation. Brown and Drosdoff (1940) have demonstrated this action in case of soils under desert conditions. There seems little doubt that the process goes more rapidly in soils that remain continually moist.

The presence of claypans is usually regarded as a measure of degree of profile development or of age. Although this is certainly true, the lack of a high clay content in the B horizon cannot be taken as proof of youth or lack of profile development. As pointed out previously, the presence of a granular structure in the A horizon and a well-developed blocky structure in the B horizon of a Chernozem is just as good evidence of horizon differentiation as the development of a clay layer in another soil. Soils that have a continual increase in clay content from surface horizon to parent rock may be just as mature as those with claypans. This is characteristic of many of our soils that are derived from hard limestone and basic igneous rocks. There seems little doubt that in these soils much clay is removed from the soil by decomposition and solution in the percolating water. Since these processes of clay destruction go on more rapidly at the surface than in the lower horizons, the result is a progressive decrease in clay content from parent material to the surface of the profile.

Hardpans

Hardpans are similar to claypans in that they obstruct the movement of water and the penetration of roots but differ in that they do not contain, as a rule, more clay than the other horizons of the profile. These pans are characteristically brittle. They have a positional hardness that is readily lost by brushing or wetting. Percolating water is usually stopped at the top of the pan. Frequently these brittle pans are dry and hard when there is a temporary water table above them. The cause of sealing off of water at the top of the pan has not been determined fully. Frequently, but not always, these pans form at or near the junction of two materials of different particle-size distribution. They are common in regions having a thin overlay of loess over clay, loess over sand, or loess over gravel. These pans are said to reform in a short time when disturbed mechanically. Usually the material above the pans is very high in silt. Frequently these soils are referred to as siltpans. Some workers have found a relationship between hardpan formations and the shape of the particles. The particles with one long axis and two short ones favor this condition.

II. MODIFYING THE PHYSICAL PROPERTIES OF SOIL

By H. E. Middleton

Modification of the Physical Properties of Virgin Soil in Preparing It for Cultivation

In their natural state, few, if any, soils are suitable for the production of cultivated crops without some treatment to modify their condition. This may consist of clearing woods or brush and removing stumps, breaking sod, burning undesirable vegetation too large or too inconvenient to plow under, draining to remove excess water, irrigating to overcome water deficiency, or a combination of treatments. The treatment to be used in a given case varies with the crop or crops to be grown on the soil. For example, the treatment may be quite different for tree crops like walnuts or peaches than for grain crops such as corn or rice.

After the preliminary treatment to prepare the soil for cropping, some conditioning is usually necessary. When the sod on the prairies of the Corn Belt was first broken it was not unusual to grow a crop of flax to occupy the soil while the sod was decomposing sufficiently so that a seedbed could be prepared for corn or small grain. The Rockdale rockland soils of Florida have to be scarified and pulverized so that the roots of crop plants can penetrate them. Peat and muck soils, when first brought under cultivation, usually require drainage, and desert soils require irrigation before cropping can begin.

When the soil is ready for cultivation it is often necessary to apply some amendment such as lime, fertilizer, manure, gypsum, or minor elements before crops can be grown satisfactorily. The natural vegetation may have required or tolerated a different soil reaction or smaller amounts of plant nutrients than the introduced crop. In some sandy soils it is necessary to apply practically all the nutrients the crop will use. It is obvious that it is necessary to apply amendments to overcome any deficiencies if the maximum crop production is to be attained.

Thus, it will be readily seen that many changes are made in the physical, chemical, and biological properties of a virgin soil before the crop is planted. In addition, removal of the native vegetation exposes the soil to the action of sun, wind, rain, and rapid changes in temperature. If the introduced crop provides more or less cover and protection than the original vegetation, further changes, either desirable or undesirable, are found to ensue from these agencies. Consequently, it is difficult, if not impossible, to ascribe the differences in physical properties between a virgin soil and a soil which has been prepared for the production of crops to any particular cause or set of causes.

The acreage of virgin soils that are suitable for intensive crop production remaining in this country is extremely limited. This makes it very difficult to study the changes brought about in preparing them for crop production. When comparisons are made between the properties of virgin soils and cultivated soils, the effect of this preparation should be borne in mind so that all of the changes noted are not necessarily ascribed to the cultivation process. Some of the differences which may be observed are changes in structure, in amount and character of the organic matter, and in the ease of working. In the potato-growing area of Maine, for example, the natural profile of the best potato soils is very thin, from 6 to 8 inches, as a rule. The first time the land is plowed the entire A and B horizons, and often some of the parent material, are mixed together. Many other examples might be cited, but perhaps this is enough to show the extent to which the physical properties of a virgin soil may be modified in preparing it for the production of crops.

Modification of the Physical Properties of Soil by Cultivation

As soon as cultivation of a soil begins, many changes in its physical properties may, and usually do, occur. The magnitude and character of the changes taking place depend largely on the crop and the soil management practices employed in its production. For our principal crops, such as corn, cotton, wheat, potatoes, and tobacco, which, with the exception of wheat, are grown in clean-cultivated rows, the principal changes taking place have been extensively studied.

These changes may be favorable or desirable, or unfavorable or undesirable. The exclusive cultivation of row crops usually brings about undesirable changes very rapidly, while with sod-forming crops the changes are slower but are more apt to be favorable. Figure 6 shows how the structure of a soil that has been in bluegrass sod differs from a sample of the same soil that has been intensively cultivated. The differences may be due to the actual physical manipulation of the soil by implements, to the effect of the plant or its byproducts, to change in organic-matter content, or to erosion, which may be just an acceleration of the other changes or cause additional changes such as the selective removal of soil particles, the intermixing of topsoil and subsoil, or the creation of rills and gullies. A symposium on the modification of soils caused by human activity was held by the Soil Science Society of America at the New Orleans meeting in 1939. Changes resulting from long use of land, Thorp (1939); erosion, Bennett (1939a); drainage, Roe (1939); and irrigation, Powers (1939) were discussed by specialists in the various fields.

Most of the changes in the physical properties of soils have been studied in their relation to soil structure. There is no simple way of measuring soil structure comparable to the determination of specific gravity or the moisture equivalent. Since the structure of the soil is determined by the arrangement of individual soil particles into aggregates, most indirect methods of determining it involve the measurement of the quantities of the individual soil particles, which are more or less

FIGURE 6.—Structure of a soil which has been in bluegrass sod (left) compared with that of the same soil which has been intensively cultivated (right). (Photograph by C. A. Van Doren, Soil Conservation Service.)

closely held together in aggregates of different sizes. Consequently, the usual procedure in determining the effect of disking, for example, on soil structure is to determine if there is any significant difference in aggregation of samples from plots or fields disked and not disked. This procedure may lead to erroneous conclusions if followed too rigorously because there may be no measurable difference in aggregation although there may still be important differences in the physical properties of the soil that affect the crop growth.

Effect of tillage implements

The implement that comes in contact with the soil, which pushes or pulls or shears it, has the first opportunity to bring about changes in soil structure. The effect of individual implements has not been

studied extensively in this country, more attention having been given
to combined effect of all implements used in a soil management system.
In Russia a number of workers have studied the effect of individual
implements. This work has been ably summarized by Russell (1938,
pp. 20–24) and will not be repeated here. The primary considerations in a study of the effect of implements on soil structure are the
type and weight of the implement and the moisture content of the soil.

FIGURE 7.—Effect of driving a truck across a field of silty clay loam soil while it was
very dry 3 years before picture was taken. (Photograph by Karl Harris, Soil
Conservation Service.)

If the soil is too wet or too dry when worked, its structure may be
permanently damaged. Figure 7 shows the lasting effect, 3 years later,
of driving a truck across a field while the soil was too dry. At the
most favorable or optimum moisture content the structure will usually
be improved or at least changed very little, since the aggregates which
are formed form the joining of individual particles will tend to counter-
balance those that are disrupted by the action of the implement. In
actual farming practice, the optimum moisture content is difficult to

determine. A field may contain varying types of soil, it will vary in topography, and its moisture content will change during the time required for the operation. The Russian work cited by Russell (1938) indicates that the optimum moisture content for tillage covers a very narrow range. It is therefore evident that it is practically impossible to till a field of any considerable size without having some of it below or above the most favorable condition for work.

One implement which has been studied quite intensively in this country is the subsoil plow, or chisel. In some soils it is beneficial to break up and shatter the subsoil to allow deeper root penetration and percolation of moisture. While many studies have been made, very few reports have been published, primarily because soils giving an increase in production equal to or greater than the cost of the operation seem to be rather limited in extent.

After reviewing the results of extensive experiments covering a wide range of crops, soils, and conditions in the Great Plains as well as experiments in Illinois, Pennsylvania, Mississippi, Texas, and southern Russia, Chilcott and Cole (1918) concluded that:

> Yields cannot be increased nor the effects of drought mitigated by tillage below depth of ordinary plowing. The quite general popular belief in the efficiency of deep tillage as a means of overcoming drought or of increasing yields has little foundation of fact, but is based on misconceptions and lack of knowledge of the form and extent of the root systems of plants and of the behavior and movement of water in the soil.

More recently, Volk (1947) has reviewed the work in several states having to do with subsoiling and the deep placement of fertilizers. He concluded that in those cases where the structure of the subsoil is improved by subsoiling some benefit can be expected from the deep placement of fertilizers.

Mechanized farming is believed to be having an important effect on soil structure. Machines are continually being made larger and heavier. Although the load per square foot of soil has not been materially increased, the number of square feet covered has increased enormously. The weight of the machinery and the speed of travel, together with the vibration caused by the power unit, would seem to tend toward general compaction of the soil, particularly where structure-deteriorating farming practices are being followed. The use of heavy farm machinery will have to be considered very carefully in order to avoid serious difficulty, particularly with soils which are easily compacted. Power machinery makes it possible to work larger areas of soil when it is at or near the optimum moisture content than would be possible with hand, or animal-operated equipment. It also makes it possible to work the soil when it is too wet or too dry, which is undesirable from the standpoint of developing and maintaining proper tilth.

Effect of crops

The structure of virgin soils depends to a large extent on the kind of natural vegetation growing on them. The character of the root system—the part of the plant in direct contact with the soil—is probably the most important factor. The above-ground part is important from the standpoint of the protection offered against the beating action of wind and rain, the trampling of animals, and the quantity and kind of plant residue returned to the soil. Crop plants are selected wholly on the basis of the economic value of the harvested portion without regard to their effect on the physical properties of the soil. Our most common cultivated crop plants vary tremendously in this regard. For example, a comparison of corn and cotton or of wheat and potatoes will show large differences in root systems, canopy protection produced, and residues returned to the soil. In addition, there is the difference in the weight of the harvested crops, which, although it has its most important effect on the fertility level, has an indirect effect on the physical properties of the soil as well.

Many studies have been made on the effect of various crops and cropping systems on soil structure, particularly as indicated by the effect on aggregation. Baver (1948, p. 181) shows a comparison of the aggregation of virgin forest, virgin prairie, and cultivated soils and points out that the degree of aggregation is much lower in the cultivated than in the virgin soils. In general, continuous intertilled row crops have been shown to deteriorate soil structure, while sod-forming crops and forest improve it. Alderfer and Merkle (1941) have summed up this idea as follows:

> When soils are brought under cultivation there is, in most instances, a significant structural breakdown. This degradation is greatest when intensively tilled row crops dominate the cropping system. It is possible, however, to retain a physical condition comparable with that of forest conditions if ample provision is made in the soil management program for the maintenance of biologically active soil organic matter by the frequent addition of manure or the use of fibrous rooted cover and green manure crops.

Land in bluegrass or other sod-producing grasses, if not subjected to compaction, may develop a degree of granulation equal to or better than that found in forested land.

Olmstead (1946), in a comprehensive study at Hays, Kans., has shown that soils used under all cropping systems that include continuous small grain, continuous row crops, and rotations including fallow have lost approximately 80 percent of their initial aggregation in the surface-tilled zone since they were broken from sod about 1902. The loss is based on the present aggregation of virgin buffalograss pasture. He shows that seeding to buffalograss approximately doubles the percentage of aggregation in 5 years.

Page and Willard (1946) in Ohio have shown the same trend for various cropping systems, not only in degree of aggregation but in pore space relationships as well. On the other hand Puhr and Olson (1937) in South Dakota show that cultivation has caused an average loss of 42 percent of the organic matter in their soils without marked change in structure. There was no significant difference in the distribution of aggregates in the virgin and the cultivated soils.

In a study of various cropping systems in Iowa, Johnston, *et al.* (1942) have shown that the size distribution of soil aggregates has been materially influenced by the cropping system, with the greatest number of larger sized aggregates in bluegrass, clover, oats, rotation corn, and continuous corn, respectively. Red clover in the rotation has maintained a loose granular structure, whereas continuous corn leaves the soil cloddy and difficult to work. Russell (1938, pp. 27–29) has reviewed the work in Russia on the effect of various crops on soil structure, which confirms the findings of this country to the effect that grasses and legumes tend to build up soil structure and annual crops tend to destroy it.

These conclusions indicate that the physical properties of the soil may be maintained and improved by selecting the crops in rotation so that the structure-deteriorating crops are offset by structure-improving crops. For example, a rotation of corn, wheat, and 2 years of meadow will maintain the soil structure and organic-matter content where conditions are such that erosion during the time the soil is planted to corn is not excessive.

Mack Gowder in Georgia (Martin, 1944) has demonstrated that the physical properties of steep erodible land can be maintained under cultivation and (as many others have shown) that much can be done toward reclaiming such land that has been abused and deteriorated.

Effect of organic matter

Lyon and Buckman (1943, p. 10) state that the difference between a fertile soil and a mere mass of rock fragments lies in the organic content. Puhr and Olson (1937, p. 21) state that organic matter affects the following physical properties of soils: "Weight, cohesion, structure, absorption, porosity, color, temperature, and tilth. Any change in the amounts of organic matter in the soil may affect one or all of the above physical properties." Organic matter also has very important effects on soil fertility, moisture relationships, and chemical activity, which will not be considered here.

The organic-matter content is an index to the physical condition of the soil in the same way that body temperature is an index to the condition of a patient. It does not tell the whole story but does indicate to a considerable degree whether physical conditions are improving or deteriorating. The relation of organic matter to soil structure and aggregation has been studied extensively. Ackerman and Myers (1943), Browning (1937), Hide and Metzger (1939), Kolodny and Neal (1941), Martin (1942), Myers (1937), Nijhawan and Dhingra (1947), Rost and Rowles (1940), Stauffer *et al.* (1940), Wilson and Browning (1945), Woodruff (1939), and others have reported that organic matter generally increases soil aggregation and improves soil structure. The effect of various crops on aggregation and structure is largely dependent upon their effect on the organic-matter content of the soil, although differences in root systems and cultivation processes also must be considered.

With few exceptions (Puhr and Olson, 1937, for example), it has been demonstrated that continuous cultivation of row crops destroys aggregation and deteriorates soil structure. With no known exceptions, such cultivation reduces the organic-matter content (Hopp and Slater, 1949a). However, cropping systems can be developed which will maintain or increase the organic-matter content of the soil as shown by Alderfer and Merkle (1941) quoted above, Stauffer (1936), Johnston *et al.* (1942), and others.

Simply mixing organic matter with the soil does not affect the aggregation of the soil particles. In order to be effective the organic matter must decompose, as shown by McHenry and Russell (1943). The organisms causing the decomposition and the decomposition products have been reported by Kroth and Page (1946), McCalla (1945), and Peele (1940) to be the active agents in binding the soil particles together.

Similarly, earthworms have been shown to have a favorable effect on soil structure by Hopp and Slater (1949b). As with bacteria and fungi, the worms must have an adequate supply of organic matter and moisture and favorable conditions for growth in order to have maximum effect in improving soil structure and aggregation.

Effect of fertilizers and soil amendments

There is no such unanimity of results on the effects of fertilizers and amendments in modifying the physical properties of the soil as there is in case of organic matter. Baver (1948, p. 192) has summed up the effect of fertilizers, manure, and lime on soil structure as benefiting primarily the sod crop in the rotation "to such an extent that outstanding increases in soil tilth will often occur." Elson (1943) found some increase in aggregation from line, manure, and fertilizer in Virginia. Bertramson and Rhoades (1938), however, reported no effect of manure on aggregation in Nebraska. Alderfer and Merkle (1943) found that fertilizers and various amendments had no effect on the structural stability of fallow soil in Pennsylvania. Peele (1936) has shown that lime has dispersing effect on the B horizon of Cecil soils in South Carolina. In general, however, the effect of fertilizers and amendments appears to be in promoting crop growth, which tends to increase the organic-matter content of the soil and thus, indirectly, affect the physical properties. It is not intended to overlook the fact that many amendments such as ashes, sand, sawdust, are added to the soil primarily to improve the physical condition rather than to stimulate crop production.

In arid regions, where irrigation is practiced, alkali conditions are very apt to develop unless extreme care and good soil management practices are followed. When alkali develops, the soil becomes saturated primarily with sodium ions, which cause dispersion of the soil aggregates and results in a soil that is easily puddled and very difficult to work. The alkali may develop to the point where the soil becomes too toxic for plant growth and the structure is completely destroyed, making the soil unfit for agricultural use. The reclamation of alkali soil involves providing adequate drainage and an ample supply of water with a low concentration of soluble salts so that the alkali salts may be leached from the soil and drained away (Kelley, 1937). In the case of black alkali, the process often may be speeded up by the application of gypsum or sulfur, which converts the alkali carbonates to less harmful sulfates and reduces the alkalinity. Powers (1939) suggests that it may be just as logical to apply sulfur periodically to reduce alkalinity in irrigated regions as it is to apply lime to reduce acidity in humid regions. However, the much greater cost of sulfur as compared with lime is a factor which must be considered and which may limit the application of sulfur to high-value-per-acre crops. A large literature has been built up on the use of amendments for the reclamation of alkali soils, but perhaps more from the standpoint of their toxic effect on plants rather than from the standpoint of their effects on the physical properties of the soil, although both are important.

Effect of erosion

Erosion has been defined (Anonymous, 1938, p. 1167) as "the wearing away of the land surface by running water, wind, or other geological agents, including geological creep." When a seedbed is prepared for a cultivated crop the soil is laid bare to the destructive action of wind and water. As the seedling begins to grow some protection is offered to the soil surrounding it. The leaves and stem of plant break the force of the wind and rain. If the area around the plant is cultivated to remove weeds and reduce competition, loose soil is still available to be picked up by gusts of wind or runoff water. Where the soil is completely covered, as in the case of sod-forming grasses, there is little or no opportunity for it to be carried away. With annual crops,

FIGURE 8.—Entire plow layer blown away in one storm. (Photograph by the Soil Conservation Service.)

however, such as corn, cotton, and potatoes, the soil is vulnerable to the erosion processes for a large part of the year unless cultural practices are followed which afford maximum protection. The effect of erosion on the physical properties of the soil varies from zero under complete cover, such as grass and forest, to complete destruction where the entire plow layer is washed or blown away in a single storm, as shown in Figure 8. With cultivated row crops it is impossible to separate the effect of erosion from the other effects which have been discussed as shown by Stauffer *et al.* (1940). It is practically impossible to produce intertilled crops in the humid area without some water erosion. If the weight of soil lost by erosion does not exceed the weight of the harvested crop, the practical minimum to which erosion can be reduced has probably been attained, except under the most favorable conditions.

The effects of erosion on the physical properties of the soil include reduction in organic-matter content, decrease in aggregation, deterioration of soil structure, as in the cultivation processes which have been discussed, and, in addition, changes in texture and topography, including the production of rills and gullies. Practices which have been developed to control erosion generally result in improved soil structure and increased crop production. Subsurface tillage, by which plant residues are kept on the surface of the soil to protect it from wind and rain, improves soil moisture relationships and promotes biological activity favorable to improved aggregation and other physical responses. Reduction in erosion makes it easier to maintain or build up the organic-matter content of the soil, which in turn helps to make it more resistant to erosion.

Bennett (1939b, pt. 1), Baver (1948, ch. 10), and Lyon and Buckman (1943, ch. 9) have produced texts recently which discuss the subject of soil erosion and its effects, to which the reader is referred for more detailed information.

Modification of the Physical Properties of Soil by Special Practices

Many of the operations which are performed on the soil in order to promote the growth of crops have a direct or indirect effect on its physical properties. Some of the operations which are performed for a particular purpose may have desirable effects or very undesirable effects unless special precautions are observed. Operations, such as drainage and irrigation, and some soil conservation practices, such as mulching, terracing, contour furrowing, basin listing, and pitting, have been employed to modify the physical properties of the soil.

Drainage

The primary purpose of drainage is to remove excess water. The excess water may be seasonal or perennial. Where it is seasonal, it often happens that there is an excess at one season and a deficiency at another. The removal of excess water and lowering of the water table allows roots and air to penetrate to greater depths, which, with the accompanying biological activity and oxidation processes, results in improved soil structure. The alternate wetting and drying of the soil following a continuous wet condition tends to promote more stable aggregation. Roe (1939) has presented evidence on the increase in permeability of the soil resulting from drainage, which bears out the general observations of many others.

When drainage is followed by poor soil management practices that reduce the organic-matter content, soil structure deteriorates and the drainage system becomes inadequate. This has been especially true in northwestern Ohio, as demonstrated by Baver and Farnsworth (1940) and Page and Willard (1946).

Owing to their method of formation, highly organic soils such as peat and muck require drainage before they can be cultivated. When these soils first dry out, a very large shrinkage takes place, which is irreversible. This shrinkage causes a lowering of the ground surface, which is called subsidence. After cultivation begins further subsidence takes place owing to the oxidation and compaction of the organic matter, according to Clayton *et al.* (1942) and Roe (1939). Figure 9

FIGURE 9.—Subsidence of nearly 6 feet in Everglades peat between 1914 and 1943. (Photograph by R. V. Allison, Everglades Experiment Station.)

shows the subsidence in Everglades peat after 30 years of cultivation. Subsidence cannot be prevented if these soils are cultivated, but the rate may be retarded considerably by controlling the water table and not allowing the soil to dry out any more than absolutely necessary. A further hazard in the drainage of organic soils is that they are susceptible to burning and complete destruction if they become too dry and, owing to the light weight of the organic material, they are particularly susceptible to wind erosion.

Irrigation

Formerly, irrigation was practiced only in arid regions, where it was necessary to apply water to the soil artificially in order to meet practically the entire requirement of the crop. There are few places where rainfall is adequate or sufficiently well distributed to insure maximum crop production. Consequently, irrigation is becoming common in the semiarid and humid regions in order to supplement natural rainfall and prevent soil moisture deficiency. The effect of irrigation on the physical properties of the soil is somewhat different under these two conditions and will be discussed separately.

Irrigation in arid regions.—In the arid regions the soils are inherently different from those in regions of higher rainfall. The surface soil is usually deep and can be planed to a uniform slope by land leveling so that the water may be applied uniformly by gravity flow. Owing to the lack of leaching, the heavier textured soils, particularly, have a higher content of soluble materials, and alkali conditions can rapidly develop when water is applied to them unless extreme caution is observed. This condition is not apt to be as serious with the sandier soils. Once this condition has developed, drainage, flooding, and leaching, and the use of amendments such as gypsum and sulfur are necessary to ameliorate it. Care must also be exercised in the application of water on sloping land to prevent excessive erosion. In addition, the water used for irrigation in these regions generally contains considerable quantities of soluble salts and sediment. Powers (1939) reports that soil on the Yuma Mesa in 10 years has been changed to plow depth from a loamy sand to a clay loam by sediment contained in the irrigation water.

Irrigation in semiarid and humid regions.—Where the quantity of rainfall is nearly adequate for production of crops or where the quantity is adequate but the distribution of it is unfavorable, the soils are more leached and the danger of alkali formation is not so great as in the arid regions. The surface waters normally do not contain as large quantities of soluble salts and underground waters are nearer the surface and more available. Under these circumstances the effect of irrigation on the physical properties of the soil is not great if the water is not applied fast enough to cause erosion and if good management practices are followed. Owing to the nature of the soils, it is not generally possible to level them, so the water is more often applied by sprinklers, either fixed or portable.

Where fixed sprinklers are used there is a tendency to intensify cultivation of the area served by them. This generally results in a deterioration of the soil structure and decrease in organic-matter content. The large investment in equipment to apply the water tends to discourage use of soil management practices and crop rotations which will maintain or improve the physical characteristics of the soil under intensive cultivation. Where portable sprinklers are used there is less tendency to concentrate on particular areas, and better farming practices can be followed.

Soil conservation practices

The growing realization of the importance of preventing the unnecessary destruction of the soil by erosion has resulted in intensified studies of methods of tilling the soil and producing crops with minimum danger of the soil body being carried away by wind or water. Some of the methods which have been developed and are being adapted and used by farmers over increasingly wide areas have important effects in modifying the physical properties of the soil. One of the most effective methods of preventing erosion with intertilled crops is to keep the bare soil surface between plants covered with a mulch, which absorbs the kinetic energy of the rain and impedes overland flow of wind or water. The mulch may consist of applied material such as straw, sawdust, leaves, or the stubble and plant residues from the previous crop which have been handled so as to keep them on the surface of the soil rather than being burned, buried, or mixed with soil as in ordinary farming practices.

Mulching tends to increase the moisture content of the soil by increasing infiltration and decreasing evaporation. Musgrave and Nichols (1942) have reviewed the data available on the effect of mulches on increasing infiltration, and many studies have shown the effect of mulches in decreasing erosion. The work of Borst and Woodburn (1942) is an example. Mulching also tends to lower the soil temperature and slow down biological activity. This may be disadvantageous in some cases or advantageous in others, from the standpoint of maximum crop production. Havis (1943) has shown that mulches are even more effective than sod in promoting aggregation under orchard conditions in Ohio. Alderfer and Merkle (1943), however, report no fundamental structural change from mulch in 4 years in Pennsylvania. Van Doren and Stauffer (1943) have described the effect of mulches in preventing compaction of the surface soil and in improving aggregation. In addition to their effectiveness in preventing erosion, the evidence by Stauffer (1936) tends to show that mulches are effective in maintaining or improving the physical conditions in the soil.

Soil conservation practices such as contour furrowing, basin listing, and pitting involve manipulation of the surface soil with the primary objective of increasing infiltration and have little direct effect on the physical properties of the soil. They have an indirect effect insofar as they conserve moisture and reduce erosion. Terracing involves considerable movement of surface soil and, where the soil is thin, may result in exposed subsoil in the terrace channel and a concentration of surface soil in the terrace ridge. Where the physical properties of the surface soil and subsoil are very different, this results in an undesirable condition from the standpoint of moisture relationships, time of working, fertilizer practice, and crop production. Terraces are effective in conserving moisture and preventing gullies and support and reinforce other agronomic and tillage practices which have been developed to control erosion.

SUMMARY

From the foregoing, it can readily be seen that any number of agents, either singly or in combination and varying in character from a fungus to a 75-horsepower tractor, can modify the physical properties of soil. Some processes improve the physical characteristics and some impair them. In any soil management system it is important that the improving agents and processes equal or overcome the impairing ones.

The United States is in the intermediate zone between an abundance and a scarcity of good land. In order to postpone the day when productive land is scarce in this country, it will be necessary to make the most efficient use of the land available. As long as the physical properties of the soil are improving, crop production will be improving, erosion will be controlled, and agriculture will be stabilized.

Literature Cited

PART I

ANDERSON, M. S., and BYERS, H. G. 1936. Neutralization curves of the colloids of soils representative of the great soil groups. *U. S. Dept. Agr. Tech. Bull.* **542.**

BAVER, L. D. 1948. Soil physics. Ed. 2, 398 pp., New York.

BROWN, I. C., and DROSDOFF, M. 1940. Chemical and physical properties of soils and of their colloids developed from granitic materials in the Mojave desert. *J. Agr. Research* **61:** No. 5.

CHANDLER, R. F., Jr. 1943. The time required for podzol profile formation as evidenced by the mendenhall glacial deposits near Juneau, Alaska. *Soil Sci. Soc. Am. Proc.* (1942) **7:** 454–459.

HARDY, F. 1939. Soil erosion in St. Vincent, B. W. I. *Trop. Agr. Trinidad* **16:** 58–65.

JENNY, HANS. 1941. Factors of soil formation. McGraw-Hill Book Co., New York.

MITCHELL, R. L., and MUIR, A. 1937. Base exchange capacity and clay content of soils. *Nature* **139:** 552.

MUCKENHIRN, R. J., *et al.* 1949. Soil classification and the genetic factors of soil formation. *Soil Sci.* **67:** No. 2, 93–105.

MYERS, H. E. 1937. Physio–chemical reactions between organic and inorganic soil colloids as related to aggregate formation. *Soil Sci.* **44:** 331–359.

NIKIFOROFF, C. C. 1941. Morphological classification of soil structure. *Soil Sci.* **52:** No. 3.

PEELE, T. C. 1936. The effect of calcium on the erodibility of soil. *Soil Sci. Soc. Am. Proc.* **1:** 47–58.

RIECKEN, F. F., and SMITH, G. D. 1949. Lower categories of soil classification: family, series, type, phase. *Soil Sci.* **67:** No. 2, 107–115.

ROBERTS, R. C. 1950. *Trans. Intern. Congr. Soil Sci. 4th Congr., Amsterdam.*

RUSSELL, E. W. 1938. Soil structure. *Imp. Bur. Soil. Sci. Tech. Commun.* No. 37.

THORP, JAMES. 1949. Effects of certain animals that live in soils. *Scientific Monthly* **68:** No. 3.

PART II

ANONYMOUS. 1938. A glossary of special terms. *In* Yearbook of Agriculture. 1938, 1232 pp., illus.

ACKERMAN, F. G., and MYERS, H. E. 1943. Some factors influencing aggregation of claypan soils. *Soil Sci.* **55:** 405–413.

ALDERFER, R. B., and MERKLE, F. G. 1941. Structural stability and permeability of native forest soils compared with cultivated areas of the same soil type. *Soil Sci. Soc. Am. Proc.* **6:** 98–103.

ALDERFER, R. B., and MERKLE, F. G. 1943. The comparative effects of surface applications vs. incorporation of various mulching materials on structure, permeability, runoff, and other soil properties. *Soil Sci. Soc. Am. Proc.* **8:** 79–86.

BAVER, L. D., and FARNSWORTH, R. B. 1940. Soil structure effects in the growth of sugar beets. *Soil Sci. Soc. Am. Proc.* **5:** 45–48.

BAVER, L. D. 1948. Soil Physics. Ed. 2., 398 pp., New York.

BENNETT, H. H. 1939a. Soil changes due to erosion. *Soil Sci. Soc. Am. Proc.* **4:** 399–401.

BENNETT, H. H. 1939b. Soil conservation. 993 pp. New York.

BERTRAMSON, B. R., and RHOADES, H. F. 1938. The effects of cropping and manure applications on some physical properties of a heavy soil in eastern Nebraska. *Soil Sci. Soc. Am. Proc.* **3:** 32–36.

BORST, H. L., and WOODBURN, R. 1942. Effect of mulches and surface conditions on the water relations and erosion of muskingum soils. *U. S. Dept. Agr. Tech. Bull.* **825:** 16 pp.

BROWNING, G. M. 1937. Changes in the erodibility of soils brought about by the application of organic matter. *Soil Sci. Soc. Am. Proc.* **2:** 85–96.

CHILCOTT, E. C., and COLE, J. S. 1918. Subsoiling, deep tilling and soil dynamiting in the Great Plains. *Agr. Research* **14:** 481–521.

CLAYTON, B. S., NELLER, J. R., and ALLISON, R. V. 1942. Water control in the peat and muck soils of the Florida Everglades. *Fla. Agr. Expt. Sta. Bull.* **378:** 74 pp.

ELSON, J. 1943. A 4-year study of the effects of crop, lime, manure, and fertilizer on macroaggregation of dunmore silt loam. *Soil Sci. Soc. Am. Proc.* **8:** 87–90.

HAVIS, L. 1943. Aggregation of an orchard and a vegetable soil under different cultural treatments. *Ohio Agr. Expt. Sta. Bull.* **640:** 28 pp.

HIDE, J. C., and METZGER, W. H. 1939. Soil aggregation as affected by certain crops and organic materials and some chemical properties associated with aggregation. *Soil Sci. Soc. Am. Proc.* **4:** 19–22.

HOPP, H., and SLATER, C. S. 1949a. A principle for maintaining structure in clean-cultivated soils. *J. Agr. Research* **78:** 347–352.

HOPP, H., and SLATER, C. S. 1949b. The effect of earthworms on the productivity of agricultural soil. *J. Agr. Research* **78**: 325–339.

JOHNSTON, J. R., BROWNING, G. M., and RUSSELL, M. B. 1942. The effect of cropping practices on aggregation, organic matter content, and loss of soil and water in marshall silt loam. *Soil Sci. Soc. Am. Proc.* **7**: 105–107.

KELLEY, W. P. 1937. The reclamation of alkali soils. *Calif. Agr. Expt. Sta. Bull.* **617**.

KOLODNY, L., and NEAL, O. R. 1941. The use of micro–aggregation or dispersion measurements for following changes in soil structure. *Soil Sci. Soc. Am. Proc.* **6**: 91–95.

KROTH, E. M., and PAGE, J. B. 1946. Aggregate formation in soils with special reference to cementing substances. *Soil Sci. Soc. Am. Proc.* **11**: 27–34.

LYON, T. L., and BUCKMAN, H. O. 1943. The nature and properties of soils. Ed. 4, 499 pp. New York.

McCALLA, T. M. 1945. Influence of microorganisms and some organic substances on soil structure. *Soil Sci.* **59**: 287–297.

McHENRY, J. R., and RUSSELL, M. B. 1943. Elementary mechanics of aggregation of puddled materials. *Soil Sci. Soc. Am. Proc.* **8**: 71–78.

MARTIN, H. 1944. Man with a bull-tongue scooter. *The Land* **3**: 281–286.

MARTIN, J. P. 1942. The effect of composts and compost materials upon the aggregation of the silt and clay particles of collington sandy loam. *Soil Sci. Soc. Am. Proc.* **7**: 218–222.

MUSGRAVE, G. W., and NICHOLS, M. L. 1942. Organic matter in relation to land use. *Soil Sci. Soc. Am. Proc.* **7**: 22–28.

MYERS, H. E. 1937. Physio–chemical reactions between organic and inorganic soil colloids as related to aggregate formation. *Soil Sci.* **44**: 331–359.

NIJHAWAN, S. D., and DHINGRA, L. R. 1947. Some characteristics of soil aggregates in cultivated soils of Punjab, India. *Soil Sci. Soc. Am. Proc.* **12**: 39–43.

OLMSTEAD, L. B. 1946. The effect of long-time cropping systems and tillage practices upon soil aggregation at Hays, Kansas. *Soil Sci. Soc. Am. Proc.* **11**: 89–92.

PAGE, J. B., and WILLARD, C. J. 1946. Cropping systems and soil properties. *Soil Sci. Soc. Am. Proc.* **11**: 81–88.

PEELE, T. C. 1936. The effect of calcium on the erodibility of soils. *Soil Sci. Soc. Am. Proc.* **1**: 47–58.

PEELE, T. C. 1940. Microbial activity in relation to soil aggregation. *J. Am. Soc. Agron.* **32**: 204–212.

POWERS, W. L. 1939. Soil changes due to irrigation and related treatments. *Soil Sci. Soc. Am. Proc.* **4**: 410–414.

PUHR, L. F., and OLSON, O. A. 1937. A preliminary study of the effect of cultivation on certain chemical and physical properties of some South Dakota soils. *S. Dakota Agr. Expt. Sta. Bull.* **314**.

ROE, H. B. 1939. Some soil changes resulting from drainage. *Soil Sci. Soc. Am. Proc.* **4**: 402–409.

ROST, C. O., and ROWLES, C. A. 1940. A study of factors affecting stability of soil aggregates. *Soil Sci. Soc. Am. Proc.* **5**: 421–433.

RUSSELL, E. W. 1938. Soil structure. *Imp Bur. Soil. Sci. Tech. Commun.* No. **37**, 40 pp.

STAUFFER, R. S. 1936. Influence of soil management on some physical properties of a soil. *J. Am. Soc. Agron.* **28**: 900–906.

STAUFFER, R. S., MUCKENHIRN, R. J., and ODELL, R. T. 1940. Organic carbon, pH, and aggregation of the soil of the morrow plots as affected by type of cropping and manurial addition. *J. Am. Soc. Agron.* **32:** 819–932.

THORP, JAMES. 1939. Soil changes resulting from long use of land in China. *Soil Sci. Soc. Am. Proc.* **4:** 393–398.

VAN DOREN, C. A., and STAUFFER, R. S. 1943. Effect of crop and surface mulches on runoff, soil losses, and soil aggregation. *Soil Sci. Soc. Am. Proc.* **8:** 97–101.

VOLK, N. J. 1947. Problems connected with subsoil placement of fertilizers. Proceedings Twenty-Third Annual Meeting of the National Joint Committee on Fertilizer Application, pp. 78–86.

WILSON, H. A., and BROWNING, G. M. 1945. Soil aggregation, yields, runoff and erosion as affected by cropping systems. *Soil Sci. Soc. Am. Proc.* **10:** 51–57.

WOODRUFF, C. M. 1939. Variations in the state and stability of aggregation as a result of different methods of cropping. *Soil Sci. Soc. Am. Proc.* **4:** 13–18.

CHAPTER 2

MECHANICAL IMPEDANCE AND PLANT GROWTH

By J. F. Lutz

THE PHYSICAL properties of soils in general are dealt with in Chapter 1; and Chapters 3, 4, and 5, respectively, deal specifically with soil water, soil air, and soil temperature as they affect plant growth. This chapter treats the remaining soil physical properties that affect plant growth or seedling emergence, or which result in mechanical damage to plants during tillage. It does not consider the various pedological factors involved in the formation of soil characteristics such as hardpans, claypans, and surface crusts. The chapter deals only briefly with the various forms of these; it is confined primarily to their direct effects on plants. The indirect effect of these impedances to plants are mainly on soil water, air, and temperature and are discussed in the chapters dealing with those subjects.

The importance of mechanical soil factors is widely recognized. Farmers all over the world have spent much time, effort and money removing stones, breaking surface crusts, crushing clods, subsoiling, and doing other similar things to make conditions more suitable for plant growth. Even though many of the benefits from such practices were indirect, through improved moisture and air relations, the motivating force behind most of them undoubtedly was to eliminate or correct a direct mechanical impedance to plant growth. Likewise, agricultural scientists, particularly the agronomists and agricultural engineers, have spent much time, effort and money developing and using machinery to eliminate or ameliorate the mechanical interference to plant growth caused by surface crusts, claypans, clods, and the like.

Although tangible results have been received from these efforts, only very few data are available on the *direct* mechanical benefits; it is difficult, and in most instances impossible, to separate them from the *indirect* effects. However, an attempt is made to present in this chapter what is known about mechanical impedance to root development and shoot emergence by such soil characteristics as stones, sand and gravel strata, clods and granules, sod mats, surface crusts, compact soils, claypans and hardpans, plastic sticky soils, and bedrock. For convenience the discussion is divided into two parts: (1) The surface soil, and (2) the subsoil or substrata characteristics.

I. SURFACE SOIL CHARACTERISTICS

Texture

For convenience in discussion three textural groups are recognized; namely, stones, sands, and clays. The mechanical effects of stones are more clearly defined than are those of sands and clays, both of which are modified by structural properties.

Stones

Rock fragments on and in the topsoil interfere with practically all tillage operations. Frequently there are enough to make it practically impossible to keep tillage implements in the ground. Under such conditions it is very difficult to prepare a satisfactory seedbed. Clods smaller than the stones are not crushed because the implements do not come in contact with them. Other tillage operations such as planting and cultivating are difficult and inefficient or ineffective. In fact, cultivation undoubtedly is detrimental in many instances; the seedlings are destroyed by the stones pushed or rolled over them. If the land is stony it is almost impossible to destroy by cultivation such pests as Bermuda grass in row crops without destroying the crop.

If a large percentage of the surface is covered with stones, many seeds will be covered with them at planting and the chances of seedling emergence are reduced accordingly. The seedlings of most of the common cultivated plants die if the seed germinates under a stone as much as 2 or 3 inches in diameter. Poor stands and reduced yields result.

Usually the larger the particles the less the total pore space in a soil mass. When particles of different sizes are mixed the smaller ones occupy some of the space between the larger ones and thus reduce total pore space. The minimum space exists when there are just enough small particles to occupy the pores between the large ones. Thus, a mixture of stones and of vastly smaller particles, say very fine sand (apparent volume equal to the pore space among the stones), will have an approximate total porosity of only 6 or 7 percent. Adding successively smaller particles continues to reduce slightly the calculated space. However, aggregation of the finer material will prevent the actual values from going as low as the calculated. The volume of space for roots to grow in is therefore much less when rocks are present than when fine particles occur alone.

Lutz and Chandler (1946) reported that reasonable amounts of rock in clay soils were favorable to tree growth but that rocks in sandy soils were detrimental to plant growth. Larsen (1930) and Pearson and Marsh (1935) found that ponderosa pine grew better when the soil contained some rocks. Larsen (1930) attributed this to the higher summer temperature of the rocky soil. When the rocks occupied more than 20 percent by volume of the soil, they had a detrimental effect because root space and water relations were unfavorable.

A reduced volume of pores means a corresponding reduction in water and air capacity. A mass of stones has a low water-holding capacity because of the small volume of fine pores; a mixture of coarse and fine particles has a low capacity because of a low total volume of pores. Lutz and Chandler (1946) cited numerous references to the effect that rocks tend to make fine textured soil "more porous," thus facilitating the movement of water and air, and that rocks in and on the surface reduce evaporation. Lamb and Chapman (1943) found that removing surface stones larger than 2 inches doubled water runoff. They stated that, "A 65 percent stone cover compared to the normal 18 percent . . . reduced the loss by evaporation, increased water absorption, decreased soil loss, and maintained a relatively high water-holding capacity." Apparently, then, two effects are rather definite: (1) Stones in and on heavy soils increase water absorption, and (2) they reduce evaporation. The net result of these effects is a higher *soil-moisture content*, which apparently is what Lamb and Chapman interpreted as a higher *water-holding capacity*.

Another important effect of stones is on soil temperature. They exert the effects in two ways: (1) Their thermal conductivity is greater than that of clay soil, and (2) they affect the specific heat of the soil mass because of their effect on soil water. This is illustrated by the following values for heat conductivity (k) and heat capacity (c) for several stones and other substances; some values are from Baver (1948); others from Lange (1946); and still others from Patten (1909).

Substance:	Heat conductivity (k)[1]	Heat capacity (c)[2]
Air (zero degrees centigrade)	0.0000557	0.2399
Water	0.00136	1.000
Clay (dry)	0.0022	0.22
Kaolin		0.233
Sand (dry)	0.0093	0.194
Quartz (flint)	0.0024	0.188
Granite	0.00817	0.192
Basalt	0.0052	0.20

[1] Calories per square centimeter per second for a temperature gradient of 1 degree per centimeter.
[2] Calories per gram.

According to Patten (1909) heat will pass from soil to water 150 times easier than from soil to air. An air-dry soil has a low heat conductivity because of the poor contact between soil particles. Even though water has a lower conductivity than the solid mineral material, increasing the water content of soils increases the heat conductivity by giving better contact between particles and by replacing the air, which has a much lower conductivity than water. Thus, increasing the amount of water until all air is replaced increases the heat conductivity.

However, the increased conductivity probably will not be accompanied by a corresponding increase in temperature, for the heat capacity of water is greater—approximately five times greater—than that of soil particles or stones. The exact effect of stones on soil temperature depends on two factors, of opposite effect: (1) The extent to which the water-holding capacity is reduced, and (2) the extent to which evaporation is reduced. Stony soils usually have a lower total porosity and therefore a lower water-storage capacity than similar soils without stones. With sufficient water to give good contact between particles, stony soils have a higher heat *diffusivity* (i.e. heat conductivity/heat capacity). Their temperature fluctuates more readily with changes in atmospheric temperature. This is a particularly important factor in areas where a rapid spring warm-up is desirable. Stones reduce the nutrient-adsorbing capacity by reducing the internal surface area of the soil mass. As shown in Table 4, adding 25 percent stones and keeping the original ratio of sand, silt, and clay reduces the surface area approximately 24 percent.

TABLE 4.—*Internal surface area in soil with and without stones*[1]

| Separate | Soil without stones | | Soil with stones | | Percentage reduction of surface area due to adding stones |
	Percentage of separate	Internal surface area	Percentage of separate	Internal surface area	
		Acres		*Acres*	
Clay (0.002 mm.)	33.3	82,500	25	62,500	
Silt (0.05 mm.)	33.3	3,330	25	2,500	
Sand (0.5 mm.)	33.3	416	25	315	
Stones (3 in.)	0.0	0	25	1	
Totals..........	....	86,246	..	65,316	24

[1] Calculations based on 2 million pounds per acre, the density of quartz (2.65), and spherical particles. Absolute values of surface area recognized as low because particles are known to be not spherical; however, relative values are valid.

Sands

There are large areas of sands in the United States and throughout the world on which plant growth is very limited. Some of the principal areas in the United States are along the Atlantic and Gulf Coasts, including the sand hills of North Carolina, South Carolina, and Georgia; in the Great Plains, including the sand hills of central and western Nebraska, with smaller areas in the Dakotas and in Colorado; in the arid western intermountain region; and along the Pacific coast, especially in Washington and Oregon. Other smaller areas occur in Indiana, in Michigan, and elsewhere.

In arid regions, or on dry dunes in humid regions, plant growth on sands is affected several ways. The moisture relations are so poor that only certain species survive under natural conditions. The water-plant relations are discussed in the chapter on Soil Water and Plant Growth. Dry sands are easily moved by wind, and the movement is detrimental to plants in several ways. The sand grains, when driven by a strong wind, have sufficient abrasive force to shear plants off at the soil surface. This is one of the main reasons why natural vegetation never gets established in sandy areas. The effect is not limited, however, to natural vegetation; many acres of cultivated crops are destroyed or damaged each year in this way. The greatest damage usually occurs if strong winds prevail when the plants are young and tender, but considerable injury might occur at any stage of growth and to any type of plant from prostrate forms to tall trees (Braun-Blanquet, 1932, pp. 146–153).

Many plants are covered while others are uprooted by the shifting sands (Braun-Blanquet, 1932, p. 151; United States Department of Agriculture, 1938, p. 1136; Throckmorton and Compton, 1937; Rule, 1939; Dale, 1947). Both may occur within small areas at the same time, the sand moved from around the roots of plants in one area being deposited on nearby plants. The volume of sand moved might vary from 1 or 2 surface inches to 10 or more feet. Even a few inches is enough to uproot or to cover small young cultivated plants. Large dunes frequently cover or severely damage full-grown fruit trees or other large plants. Many acres of various crops are destroyed in this way each year in the United States. Many other acres are left denuded by the removal of sand or are covered with sand so that they are practically worthless for crop production.

Sands have a very low nutrient-holding capacity. The low specific surface, together with a very small number of surface-adsorption points (negative), gives them a low cation-adsorption capacity. This, together with the low water-holding capacity and the consequent great and rapid percolation, results in rapid losses of cations and anions by leaching. In many sandy areas split applications of fertilizers or top dressing are used to replenish that lost by leaching.

Clays

Although sands frequently occur without appreciable amounts of silt and clay, clays usually do not occur without considerable silt and/or sand (see Fig. 5, Chapter 1). This applies particularly to surface soils, since subsoils usually do contain a higher percentage of clay. However, there are many areas where the surface layer is high in clay. Some of these result from clay deposition by water; others by erosion of the topsoil, leaving the clay subsoil exposed; and others have a high clay content throughout the entire profile as a result of the type of parent material.

The physical properties of clays, as related to plant growth, are quite different from those of sands. They have a great specific surface; a high water-holding capacity, which may result in large volume changes upon wetting and drying; and they can be formed into a variety of structural conditions, some of which are beneficial and others detrimental to plant growth. Work at the erosion experiment stations showed that crop yields on exposed subsoils declined 77 percent below those on adjacent plots still retaining a good topsoil (Bennett, 1939, pp. 213–225). Even when fertilized the exposed subsoils gave lower yields than the unfertilized topsoils, thus indicating that the physical condition was the limiting factor. The greatest decline was, in general, on soils that have a heavy clay subsoil, particularly those with dense, plastic, sticky clays. The decline in yield was not so great on the Cecil, which has a brittle subsoil. In fact, the fertilized subsoil produced more cotton than the unfertilized topsoil.

Root crops usually produce low yields of poor quality on clay soils. This is illustrated by the data of Baver and Farnsworth (1940) with sugarbeets grown on the Paulding clay in northwestern Ohio. Yields were approximately 1.5 tons per acre where no cover crops were used. Improving the physical condition of the clay by turning under barnyard manure or soybeans as green manure increased the yields to approximately 6 or 7 tons per acre.

The increased yields were due primarily to better soil tilth which permitted a higher survival of beets at the end of the growing season. . . . It is extremely doubtful if the nitrogen from the soybeans or from the manure was the contributing factor in light of the small effect of the side dressing of 200 pounds of $(NH_4)_2SO_4$ in the fertility experiments. Not only was the yield increased, but also the sugar content of the beets.   Similar results were obtained in greenhouse studies by Smith and Cook (1946).

Structure

A general discussion and a classification of soil structure appears in Chapter 1; therefore, this section will be limited to the effects on plant growth of such structural properties as clods and granules, surface crusts, compact soils, and sod mats.

Clods and granules

Clods differ from stones in being permeable to air, water, and roots; also, they can be crushed to a certain extent with ordinary farm ma-

TABLE 5.—*Relation of cotton stand and yield to the pulverization modulus of the soil* (*Yoder, 1937*)

Pulverization modulus	Percentage of complete stand			Yield of seed cotton (grams per plot)			
	Ten days after planting	Twenty days after planting	At maturity	First picking	Fourth picking	Total yield
CLOD MIXTURES						
0.00	14	86	82	77	. . .	316
.66	29	86	86	81	. . .	378
1.43	72	100	93	172	. . .	498
2.29	21	100	93	150	. . .	456
3.18	0	93	93	61	28	472
4.06	0	93	89	59	19	463
5.03	0	100	66	26	29	445
6.03	0	79	54	19	38	267
CLOD SEPARATES						
2.00	36	100	89	159	24	724
3.00	0	93	75	163	14	663
4.00	0	86	72	42	29	455
5.00	0	79	75	6	55	430
6.00	0	64	54	. . .	44	279
7.00	0	57	50	. . .	106	233

chinery.   However, they have some of the same effects as stones on plant growth.   They prevent preparation of a good seedbed, reduce seedling emergence, and cause injury to the plants at cultivation.   All of these factors will reduce crop yields.   Yoder (1937) separated various sizes of clods from a Cecil clay and grew cotton in the individual separates and in mixtures of them. He expressed the coarseness of the mixtures by the "pulverization modulus" which is the cumulative summation of the percentages of the various sizes, beginning with the largest, divided by 100. That is, the greater the percentage of large aggregates the larger the value of the modulus (Table 5).

TABLE 6.—*Effect of particle size on growth and yield of millet and wheat (Krause, 1931)*

Millet	Size of particles in millimeters				
	60% 0–1 & 40% 2–3	30% 0–1 & 70% 2–3	15% 0–1 & 85% 2–3	100% 2–3	100% 5–7
Pot experiment:					
Days to maturity	99	98	96	95	94
Height (average centimeters)	47.6	50.2	53.2	57.9	54.6
Grain yield (grams)	5.07	6.32	7.26	12.86	9.48
Straw and chaff yields (grams)	7.10	8.11	9.04	13.22	10.50
Roots (grams)	2.67	2.73	2.79	3.57	3.01
Percentage grain	34.2	35.7	38.0	43.3	41.2
Field experiment:					
Days to maturity	99	97	95	93	91
Height (average centimeters)	46.3	51.1	53.0	64.6	57.2
Grain yield (grams)	5.01	7.50	9.35	14.65	11.86
Straw and chaff (grams)	8.99	10.90	12.05	15.56	13.64
Roots (grams)	2.27	2.79	3.18	4.09	3.79
Percentage grain	20.8	35.2	38.6	42.4	40.5

Wheat	Size of particles in millimeters				
	100% <0.05	60% 0–0.5	30% 0–0.5	100% 1–2	100% 2–3
Height (centimeters)	47	57	57	67	60
Relative total yield (grain plus straw)	33.3	53.4	61.8	100	93.7
Relative grain yield	23.6	51.9	62.7	100	95.2
Relative transpiration coefficient	129	112.5	114.3	100	103.5

Krause (1931) cited a similar experiment by Kwasnikow who grew wheat and millet in the field and millet in pots, all with known sizes of soil particles (mostly secondary). The results are given in Table 6.

It is obvious from the work of Yoder (1937) and Kwasnikow (cited by Krause, 1931) that maximum growth and yield cannot be produced with all large or all small particles. If all the particles are large a poor seedbed results. Many seeds fall into the large spaces and do not germinate and live. The volume of soil in which the roots can grow without growing into large open spaces is limited. Many plants, such as cotton and alfalfa, require a firm soil for the seedling roots to get established, and this cannot be produced in an extremely coarse soil.

With transplanted crops such as tomatoes, sweetpotatoes, and tobacco, a cloddy soil results in injury to the plants at planting time. Many plants are killed and others are stunted or delayed in growth so that reduced yields result.

Surface crusts

Soil crusts are those hard layers that form on the surface as a result, apparently, of the beating effect of raindrops and the subsequent drying of the compacted layer of oriented particles. Crusts form on soils of almost any texture except coarse sands with an extremely low silt and clay content. Some of the hardest crusts seem to occur on sandy loams. A higher clay content apparently causes sufficient shrinking and cracking on drying to prevent large pieces of hard crusts. A mixture of sand, silt and clay, in just the right proportions for the successively smaller particles to occupy the pores between the larger ones, seems to be the condition under which the hardest crusts form (Duley, 1939). Hilgard (1910) stated that clay loams (as given by him 17 to 19 percent clay) with a high percentage of medium to fine sands are more apt to form crusts. Data by Baver (1948) and Duley (1939) show that if the beating effect of the rain is reduced or eliminated, artifically or by vegetation, the crusts do not form.

Perhaps the most important effect of crusts is the prevention of seedling emergence. Crusts frequently are too hard for seedlings to penetrate. This is especially true of, but not limited to, plants that germinate slowly and plants from small seeds; the latter usually have tender seedlings. A loose soil beneath the crust makes it even more unlikely that the seedling will emerge. Carnes (1934) stated that one of the greatest problems in cotton production is obtaining good stands and that soil crusts are one of the major reasons for poor stands. He used the modulus of rupture ($R = ae^{bx}$) to evaluate crusts. In this formula R equals modulus of rupture; x equals amount of rain in inches; and a and b are constants. Thus, it is seen that crusting increases exponentially with rainfall.

When the crusts are hard it is practically impossible to cultivate small plants without injuring or killing them; the plants are either broken or uprooted by the crust.

Surface crusts reduce infiltration of water and the rate of air renewal. Duley (1939) studied the effects of surface covers on the formation of crusts by sprinkling and the effects of the crusts on infiltration of water. As long as the surface was covered, either with burlap or vegetative matter, infiltration was rapid and about constant. However, when the cover was removed infiltration decreased rapidly. Baver (1948) gave data on the effects of vegetation on rainfall interception and runoff which indicate that a good vegetative cover would prevent crusting and reduce runoff. In many soils increasing infiltration increases the supply of available water. Since surface crusts have low porosities, and since air diffusion is determined by the effective porosity, it follows that the crusts reduce the rate of air renewal.

As indicated, crusting can be prevented or materially reduced by keeping the land covered. This, however, is not possible with many of the cultivated crops. In such cases additions to the soil of organic residues are very beneficial. If crusting does occur, then cultivation is usually necessary after each hard rain.

Compact soils

Some soils become compact naturally as a result of their textural composition and the moisture changes, particularly drying; others are compacted by tillage operations. Hilgard (1910) stated that the granular (coarse) sediments themselves, in the absence of clay, may, because of their angular shape, form a very closely packed mass far from suitable for vegetative growth. Likewise, clays may become very compact if not aggregated, but normal surface soils usually do not contain sufficient clay to be considered separately. Mixtures of different sizes of particles give a greater apparent density than does a single separate. The maximum compaction possible will depend upon the sizes, shapes, and quantities of particles present. A single separate of spherical particles (closely approached in many Coastal Plain sands) of diameter "d" and with tetrahedral packing will have approximately 74 percent solids and 26 percent pore space. Adding one smaller separate, with particles of sufficient size (0.232d) to fit the spaces among the larger ones, will increase the solids less than 1 percent. However, if the added separate consists of particles vastly smaller than "d," it can occupy approximately 74 percent of the space, giving a mixture with more than 93 percent solids. Such a compact condition frequently is sought and obtained in engineering work. The sand-clay roads common in many sections of the country are good examples. Adding sand to clay, as is commonly done in small yards, gardens, and so on, very likely will give the same result—a much more compact condition than originally existed in the clay. Maximum apparent density results when there are just enough successively smaller particles to occupy the spaces among the large ones. Thus, with several sizes present and with maximum compaction, the pore space might be reduced to only 4 or 5 percent.

Compaction not only decreases the total pore space but also reduces the size of the pores. Veihmeyer and Hendrickson (1946) grew sunflowers in the laboratory and grapevines in the field and found that the roots penetrated Bale gravelly loam to the depth at which the apparent density was 1.8. They stated that apparent density alone was not the limiting factor, but the size of the pores. From this it would be concluded that clays with lower apparent densities would be more difficult to penetrate than sands of higher apparent densities. In a later paper (1948) they showed this to be true. They found that no roots penetrated any soil with an apparent density of 1.9 or above. In some soils 1.7 to 1.8 were the limiting values, while in clays 1.6 to 1.7 were the critical points. In Aiken clay there was no root penetration above an apparent density of 1.46. They attribute the failure of roots to penetrate soil above the critical apparent density to the size of the pores and not to the lack of oxygen; roots penetrated saturated noncompacted soils.

Townsend (1918) found that a hard layer near the surface, which was not successfully broken up, made the growing of beets for sugar impossible. The beets were pushed out of the ground as they grew, and they were short, giving a low yield with a low sugar content.

Baver and Farnsworth (1940) reported losses in stands of sugarbeets of nearly 50 percent on soils in which the noncapillary porosity was less than 2 percent. The beets on such soils were short and stubby with many auxiliary roots and a low sugar content as compared to those grown on soils with 7 to 10 percent noncapillary porosity. Smith and Cook (1946) obtained similar results on compacted soils in greenhouse studies with sugarbeets.

Parker and Jenny (1945) found that resistance values (foot-pounds needed to drive a core sampler 1 inch) increased exponentially with increases in core weight. The soil was a Ramona loam at Riverside, Calif. The values give an indirect estimation of the relative amounts of work done by roots in penetrating tight soils. Taubenhaus, Ezekial, and Rea (1931) in Texas found that compact soils prevented or seriously affected root penetration (Fig. 10). They reported similar results in Arkansas and Mississippi.

Compaction of loose soil to a certain apparent density is desirable to give good water relations and a good seedbed. As shown by Veihmeyer and Hendrickson (1948), the *critical* apparent density varies with texture.   It would be expected that the *optimum* apparent density would also vary with texture and with other factors such as granulation and humus content.   Optimum compactness is that apparent density at which the particular soil has the pore-size distribution that will give the water and air capacity and movement best suited for plant growth. Such soils always should be easily tilled when the moisture content is suitable.   Excessive packing to a high apparent density reduces water

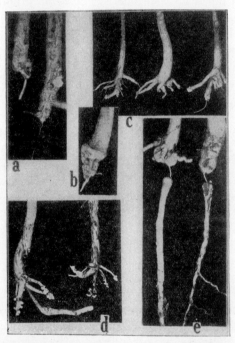

FIGURE 10.—Constriction of cotton roots caused by a compact layer in the soil: *a*, *b*, *c*, and *d* show parts of taproots above the compact layer.   Note the needlelike tips (*a*, *b*, and *c*) and the beadlike calluses (*d*).   Excavation of entire roots (*e*) showed the constricted connection between upper and lower parts caused by the compact layer.   (Taubenhaus, Ezekial, and Rea, 1931.   Picture furnished by A. A. Dunlap of Texas A. and M. College.)

and air capacity and movement; thus, it adversely affects root growth and makes tillage and good seedbed preparation difficult.   Soils with low apparent densities usually are well aerated, easily tilled, and easily penetrated by roots; nevertheless they may have low available water-holding capacities, depending on the pore-size distribution.

Parker and Jenny (1945) found that water infiltration decreased as core weights increased.   These results were observed after fertilization was started in an orange grove on Ramona loam at Riverside, Calif.   They were found to be caused partly by driving a tractor over the land and by disking. Elimination of cultivation for 8 years and the growing of cover crops partly restored a good physical condition.

Lutz *et al.* (1946) found that turning under winter cover crops gave significant or highly significant increases in the percentage of large pores (those drained at 10 and at 60 centimeters water tension) and in total porosity. The increase in total porosity was directly proportional to the increase in large pores. Penetrometer measurements were made on the vetch and no-cover-crop plots. The vetch produced significant or highly significant increases in the depth of penteration on the various plots. The depth of penetration and the porosity data for the same date gave the following relations:

	r values	Regression coefficient
Penetration and porosity at 10 centimeters tension	0.78[1]	2.09
Penetration and porosity at 60 centimeters tension	0.88[1]	4.57
Penetration and total porosity	0.73[2]	5.25

[1] Significant at the 1-percent level.
[2] Significant at the 5-percent level.

In fine-textured soils with the 2:1 (montmorillonitic) type of clay, excessive packing apparently reduces the pore size to radii smaller than the thickness of the water films on the particles. Thus, practically all of the pores are filled with water, which is held with forces of pF 4.5 or greater. There is, therefore, no water or air available to the plant roots.

Compact soils usually offer considerable resistance to tillage implements. There are, however, so many factors involved in resistance that no definite relation to compactness has been established. Clays are considered heavy soils in the sense that they offer much resistance, but sandy loams and especially silt loams frequently offer as much or more resistance than some clays. In fact, some clays are quite brittle when dry and very friable when moist. This is particularly true of soils in which the clay is predominantly of the 1:1 type.

The methods of measuring resistance to penetration—dynamometers and penetrometers—are subject to wide variation with soil-moisture changes. They vary also with humus content, with structure, and with texture. Because of these variations it is difficult to establish resistance values that are satisfactory for comparing soils from different areas. They do give valuable information about any particular area when the measurements are made under uniform conditions. For example, the values given by Keen and Haines (1925) give valuable information about the Rothamsted fields.

None of the measures of resistance to machines give the desired information concerning the forces exerted by roots in penetrating soils.

Even the relative resistance values found on different soils with machines might not apply to plant roots because of the one major point of difference: The root tips of plants are moist. The plants can even transfer moisture from one layer of soil to another in sufficient quantity to allow slight growth. Hunter and Kelley (1946) grew corn for 30 days in tar-paraffin pots filled with moist soil surrounded with dry soil. Roots penetrated the dry soil and actually increased its moisture content, but not up to the wilting percentage. However, the plants failed to absorb phosphorus (radioactive), which was added to the dry soil.

Sod mats

Some plants form very thick fibrous root systems. Included in this group are many of the common grasses and legumes. Plowing under cover crops such as vetch or Italian ryegrass often leaves a poor seedbed and makes it difficult to prepare a good one until the roots decay. Frequently it is not feasible to wait that long. If winter cover crops are left late enough in the spring to make good growth, the succeeding summer crop must be planted soon after turning. Under these conditions the root mats are usually detrimental to the following crop, especially a clean-cultivated row crop. One of the most noticeable effects is the interference of the sod mats in transplanting crops such as sweetpotatoes, tomatoes, and tobacco. Many plants are injured during transplanting and die, and the result is a poor stand. Many of those that survive have poor root-soil contact and make only limited growth. The sod mats frequently make good cultivation impossible. Not only do they clog up the cultivator, but they are dragged by it and pull up the young plants.

Not all of the effects of sod mats are undesirable. They make the beating effects of raindrops less detrimental and they undoubtedly are beneficial in reducing runoff and erosion. The reduced runoff might or might not increase the supply of water available to plants, depending on the depth to which the water penetrates and the pore-size distribution in the root zone. If the tillage operations are such that sod is left on the surface, it serves as a mulch and probably reduces evaporation.

Depth of Topsoils

In soils of otherwise good physical condition, usually the deeper the topsoil the better the soil. The harder and the more impermeable the substrata the more important the depth of the topsoil becomes. Though each species has a characteristic root system, some more deep-rooted than others, it is well known that various soil strata modify them considerably as shown by Taubenhaus, Ezekial, and Rea (1931). Any stratum which limits root growth reduces top growth accordingly, since for most species of plants, a rather definite relation exists between root and top growth (Weaver, 1926). Coile (1948) found that the site index for both loblolly and shortleaf pine increased logarithmically with an increase in the depth of the A horizon. In addition to the direct root-volume limitations imposed by shallow soils, the water and air volumes are also limited. Since the total pore volume is limited, shallow soils are droughty in dry weather and easily saturated in wet periods. There is, therefore, in most climatic areas only short inter-mittant intervals of favorable moisture conditions. Because of the wide fluctuation in moisture, the temperature will change rapidly and widely.

II. SUBSOIL OR SUBSTRATA CHARACTERISTICS

Texture, Structure, and Consistency

The physical properties of soil profiles are discussed in Chapter 1. Some of the properties or conditions there mentioned are favorable to plant growth and need no further discussion, but other conditions of texture, structure, and/or consistency physically impede plant growth. The impedance may be exhibited directly as a mechanical barrier to root penetration, or indirectly as an unfavorable moisture condition (see Chapter 3).

Sand and gravel strata

Strata of sand and gravel affect plants mainly by affecting the air, water, and nutrient supply and the soil temperature. Coarse-textured materials have low water-holding capacities and, unless the rainfall is plentiful and well 'distributed, are apt to be droughty. Exceptions, of course, are those with a water table near the root zone. Since many sand and gravel strata are water-deposited, many of them are still near water level. Aeration usually is good unless the water table is too near the surface. If the coarse substratum is deep, rapid and excessive percolation of water and a low cation-absorption capacity make leaching losses heavy.

Claypans

A claypan is a dense layer with very high clay content and poor structural development; it is plastic, sticky, and relatively impermeable to water and air when wet. Under normal conditions in humid climates, with the rainfall distributed throughout the year, they never dry to a low moisture content. This is especially true of the 2:1 types of clays. Frequently claypans are dense enough to serve as mechanical barriers to roots. The pores are so small that the larger roots do not penetrate them, as shown by Veihmeyer and Hendrickson (1948).

Clay soils have high water-holding capacities. The water may or may not be available, depending upon the magnitude of the force with which it is held. It is possible for clays to be almost 100 percent saturated at the wilting point, except for the cracks caused by lateral shrinkage. Such soils contain very little available water; roots do not grow into them, partly because of their failure to supply water. Woodruff (1940) found that two soils with which he worked held from 30 to 50 percent water (by weight) at pF 5. Assuming a density of 2.7, then 1 gram occupies 0.37 cubic centimeters. This adsorbs from 0.3 to 0.5 cubic centimeters of water, or considerably more than the pore space before swelling. Lutz (1934) found that the colloids from the Iredell and Putnam soils adsorbed more water than needed to fill the pores; Lutz and Leamer (1939) calculated, from the amount of clay present, that the water held by the clay in Iredell subsoil is more than enough to fill all the pores without swelling. Such soils usually contain practically no available water or free pore space, and root growth into them is very limited. Carlson (1925) grew two varieties of alfalfa on (1) clay loam with a compact clay subsoil, (2) a sandy loam, (3) a gravelly loam, and (4) a stony loam and studied the root systems at various stages of growth. Deep taproots developed in the sandy loam, but only stubby taproots with many laterals developed in the clay loam.

Fitzpatrick and Rose (1936) studied the distribution of wheat and Buffalo grass roots in nonclaypan, semiclaypan, and claypan soils in Oklahoma. They found an increase in root concentration in the claypan but a marked decrease in the poorly drained gray layer immediately above the claypan. The roots had penetrated the dense claypan rather than having gone around the outside of claypan columns. However, the total depth of root penetration was less on the claypan soils.

Sweet (1935) found a very close relation between depth of rooting of apple trees and yields in New York. One of the factors causing shallow rooting and low yields was compact clay subsoils. Other bulletins from the New York Station (Batjer and Oskamp, 1935) supplement and confirm the earlier work. Storie (1938) found that dense clay subsoil reduced apple production in Santa Cruz County, Calif. Soils of uniform texture to a considerable depth and without a dense subsoil produced an average of 1,088 boxes (40 pounds each) per acre. Older soils on the terraces with moderately dense subsoil produced only 379 boxes per acre; the old terrace soils with very dense subsoil had poor stands of shallow-rooted stunted trees and produced only 215 boxes per acre.

Turner (1936), in a study of soil factors affecting forest types, reported that the poorest pine sites were on the shallow soils with hard or impervious and plastic subsoils. Coile (1948) showed that the site index for loblolly and shortleaf pine decreased as the imbibitional water values of the B horizons increased. High imbibitional water values were associated with dense, plastic, sticky, impermeable clay subsoils.

It seems to be generally believed that impermeable substrata increase runoff and erosion (Whitson, 1936). However, this probably is not true except when the tight layer is very near the surface or during prolonged wet periods. The condition of the surface is more important than that of the subsoil as shown by Duley (1939). When the topsoil is deep enough, a reasonably heavy subsoil is frequently beneficial. It reduces percolation losses of both water and dissolved nutrients.

Hardpans

In this paper a hardpan is defined as either an indurated or a cemented layer. If cemented, the cementing materials may be organic or inorganic, or both, and the cemented materials may be sands, silts or clays, but frequently with only small amounts of clay. The degree of cementation may vary from practically none (indurated, Daytona Beach type sand) to a true ortstein (a hard, rocklike layer). Usually hardpans are found at the junction of two distinctly different layers where penetration of water and/or the dissolved or suspended materials is retarded or stopped by clay layers, water tables, or other factors.

According to Robinson (1936), material in true solution or in colloidal suspension may be irreversibly precipitated in certain horizons, thus cementing the constituents of those horizons. He considered two principal types: (1) Those formed by the deposition of hydrated ferric oxide, which, according to him, are formed under almost any climatic condition; and, (2) calcareous or gypseous pans which occur only under semiarid to arid conditions. His grouping does not include the hardpans in humid regions which are cemented with material other than iron oxide, or those which are not cemented.

Winters (1942) reported that many soils in Tennessee and related areas have hardpans which restrict root and water penetration. He suggested that they form as a result of precipitation and dehydration of silica. Hilgard (1910) stated that granular (coarse) sediments themselves, in the absence of clay, may because of their angular shape, form a very closely packed mass far from suitable for vegetative growth. He described what "would be called a very sandy loam" which at depths varying from 18 to 36 inches had a hardpan impervious to water and to roots. It contained no cementing material and when taken out was easily crushed between the fingers. Its imperviousness was due almost solely to the close packing. He stated that the compact arrangement developed rapidly again after being broken up by sub-soiling or blasting. Mechanical analyses of the hardpan without cementing material (Hilgard, 1910, p. 103) were as follows:

	Diameter in millimeters	Percent
Sand	0.50	10.93
	0.30	21.23
	0.16	7.58
	0.12	7.27
Silt	.072	9.63
	.047	12.00
	.036	7.19
	.025	1.25
	.016	14.20
Clay	(?)	8.64

This author has observed the same condition in many sections of the Coastal Plain of North Carolina. In Martin County a farmer digging a ditch for tile drainage could not spade the layer of hard white sand and had to use an ax to chop it. When taken out it was brittle. Porosity measurements showed only about 30 percent total porosity, and an apparent density of approximately 1.85. Pore-size distribution was determined, but the data are not valid because the samples were found to be shattered when removed from the cylinders. Mechanical analysis by the Bouyoucos method (1928) showed a clay content too low to read on the hydrometer. The Daytona Beach sand apparently represents a similar condition. There is just enough of the right size small particles to occupy the spaces among the large ones. The size (diameter) of small spheres which would just fit between larger ones of uniform size with close (tetrahedral) packing is shown as follows:

Diameter (d) of large particles in millimeters	Maximum diameter (d_1),[1] in millimeters, of small particles that could be placed in spaces among the larger ones
2.00	0.464
1.00	0.232
0.50	0.116
0.25	0.058
0.10	0.0232
0.05	0.0116

[1] $d_1 = 0.232d$.

So far the discussion on hardpans has dealt primarily with the kinds and some of their properties, with very little relation to plants. They have considerable influence on the growth of plants. It is well known that hardpans impede root growth (Hilgard 1910; Krusekopf 1942; Veihmeyer and Hendrickson 1948; Woodruff 1940). If the hardpan is completely impermeable to roots, then it has essentially the same effect on plants as bedrock. One difference might be the greater permeability to water of some hardpans (compact sands) as compared to most rocks. The data of Veihmeyer and Hendrickson (1948) show that as the apparent density of soil increases above certain values, varying with the soil type, the soil becomes more impermeable to roots until a critical value is reached beyond which roots do not penetrate it. Figure 10 shows what happened to cotton roots when they encountered a hard layer.

In many instances the hardpan is rather impermeable to water and to air. In wet periods the soil above the hardpan becomes too wet, and therefore too poorly aerated for good plant growth. During the wet periods, in addition to limiting the oxygen supply to the roots, conditions are conducive to reduction, and as a result toxic substances are produced. These might be either incompletely oxidized organic decomposition products or inorganic compounds, especially reduced iron. In dry periods the top layer dries beyond the wilting point. Even in soils like many along the Atlantic Coast (Leon, St. Johns) with the water table immediately below the hardpan only limited savanna-type vegetation exists.

Treatment of hardpans and claypans

Several methods may be used to study the relation of hardpans and claypans to plant growth and yield. First, compact layers can be prepared in pots or other containers and the root distribution and plant growth determined. This approach has been used by Veihmeyer and Hendrickson (1948), by Lawton (1945), and by Smith and Cook (1946). The method most commonly used is to treat the tight layer and measure the results in terms of crop growth. The treatments used may be physical, chemical, or biological, or combinations of them.

Biological treatments: Treatments, principally deep-rooted crops, have been used in many attempts to improve the physical condition of tight subsoils. As early as 1910 Hartley stated that impermeable subsoils are best made permeable by growing deep-rooted plants such as clover and alfalfa. According to him the channels left by the decaying roots enhanced percolation and made those soils tillable sooner following rains than adjacent ones which had no deep-rooted crop.

Such conclusions apply only to those subsoils which can be penetrated by the roots; some layers are too hard for root penetration. Where the subsoil is penetrated, there can be little doubt that the results are beneficial, but carefully collected experimental data on the exact physical effects are lacking. It is therefore difficult to determine how much of the increase in crop yields was due to physical and how much to chemical changes (nitrogen added, and so on).

Chemical treatments: Chemicals are used for one or more of three major purposes: (1) To produce flocculation and/or dehydration of the soil colloids; (2) to dissolve the cementing agents; and (3) to add plant nutrients which will encourage root growth into the dense or hard layer. Some of the sodium-saturated soils in arid regions are improved physically and made more productive by replacing the sodium ions on the colloidal particles with calcium or by converting the alkali carbonates to the less harmful sulfates. Calcium sulfate and sulfur are the two materials most frequently used, even though iron sulfate and alum are sometimes applied. The calcium sulfate decreases the pH and replaces some of the sodium ions on the clay complex with calcium ions. Sulfur is readily oxidized, forming sulfuric acid, which converts the alkali carbonates to the sulfates; also, some sodium may be replaced by hydrogen ions. Replacement of the sodium ions on the clay with calcium or hydrogen results in a less hydrated and a less dispersed system with a better physical condition. Some saline soils, unproductive because of their high salt content, can be made productive by leaching out the soluble salts; others, however, become so hard, dry, and impermeable that they are as unproductive as before. According to McGeorge et al. (1926) they become "puddled" or "freeze up" and will not "take water." They stated that the condition is caused by the precipitation of colloidal aluminum hydroxide as a viscous solidlike material. Botkin (1933) used a number of materials—manure, superphosphate, $Al_2(SO_4)3$, $FeSO_4$, S, and $(NH_4)_2SO_4$—in an attempt to alter this hard, dry, impermeable condition and to make the soil productive. None of the treatments increased the permeability of the soil or the yield of cotton.

On compact deflocculated clay subsoils chemicals which produce flocculation or dehydration might be expected to be beneficial. However, it should be remembered that flocculation is not granulation, even though it is very probably the first step to granulation. The author is not aware of any appreciable direct physical benefits to subsoils which have resulted from chemical treatments alone. However, if accompanied by physical and/or biological treatments, benefits may accrue, as shown by Woodruff and Smith (1946). They plowed Putnam soil to depths of 10 to 12 inches with an ordinary riding plow and followed that with a heavy-beamed 12-inch walking plow which attained a total depth of 16 to 20 inches.   In some plots 2 tons of lime and 200 pounds per acre of 8–20–10 fertilizer were applied and mixed with the subsoil. Subsoil plowing alone had little effect on the growth of oats and sweet-clover; it depressed the yields of barley and increased the yields of corn. Sweetclover produced shallow taproots with many laterals on the un-shattered subsoil and also on the shattered but unlimed subsoil.   When lime was applied to the shattered subsoil, deep taproots with few laterals were formed.   They stated that this was the most significant result.

Physical treatments: Subsoiling, especially, is a physical treatment that as been used extensively to meliorate claypan and hardpan soils. There are considerable data dealing with the effects of subsoiling on plant growth, as measured by yields and a few data on certain physical properties of the soils.   The main benefits usually attributed to sub-soiling are increased water absorption, higher water content, less runoff and erosion, better aeration, and therefore better crop growth.   Some of these are not supported by experimental data.

King (1914) conducted a very limited experiment for a short period of time and, unfortunately, his conclusions have had a profound in-fluence on tillage practices for many years.   Because of their tre-mendous influence his conclusions are quoted.   He said:

> The results which have been given in the last section illustrate.
> (1) Subsoiling increases the percentage capacity of the soil stirred for moisture.
> (2) Subsoiling decreases the capillary conducting power of the soil stirred.
> (3) Subsoiling increases percolation through the soil stirred or its gravitational conducting capacity.

Following the publication of the first edition of King's book, consid-erable subsoiling was practiced throughout this country and, according to Rotmistrov (1913), also in Russia.   Cates (1917) gave farmer opinion on the benefits of subsoiling to both cotton and corn.   For both crops a large majority were in favor of subsoiling, even though no data were given.   Rotmistrov (1913) quoted Kostichew as follows: ". . . for the protection of plants against drought it is necessary to bring the soil into such a condition that it is able to preserve better and hold more water out of a usual quantity of rain."   One of the measures recom-mended, especially by Shiskin (cited by Rotmistrov, 1913) was "deep mellowing."   About this Rotmistrov (1913) said:

> Deep mellowing of the soil which all the writers on this subject regard as a matter of great importance with regard to fighting against drought, has also very little real significance. . . . The argument in favor of deep ploughing, that deeply mellowed soil imbibes more atmospheric residue, falls through. . . .

Ratcliffe (1934) found that subsoiling 2-year and 4-year rotation plots in *February* reduced root rot of cotton one-third, compared to adjacent similarly treated unsubsoiled plots.   On plots subsoiled in the *summer,* 9 months before planting cotton, the average loss on the subsoil plots was only slightly less than on the unsubsoiled ones.   The data were 21-year averages.

Cardon (1915) summarized the results of deep tillage for winter wheat in Utah as follows:

The results of 5 years show that there was no advantage in deep plowing or subsoiling over shallow plowing so far as moisture conservation is concerned.   There was no material differences in the yields obtained from plots plowed at different depths, varying from 5 to 18 inches.   The highest average yield was obtained from plots plowed 10 inches deep, and the lowest average yield was from plots subsoiled 18 inches deep, while the 5-inch plowing yielded higher than the 15-inch subsoiling.

Subsoiling a silt loam underlain by a tight clay in Illinois, (Mosier and Gustafson, 1915) gave an 8-year average *decrease* in corn yield of 2.7 bushels per acre.   Experiments in Pennsylvania (Noll, 1912–13) on the Hagerstown soil compared deep with regular plowing.   The results showed that the two kinds of plowing gave practically the same yields for all crops grown—corn, oats, barley, wheat, and alfalfa.   Subsoiling a Houston clay in Mississippi gave no increase in corn yields as shown below (Ricks, 1915):

	Bushels yield in 1913	Bushels yield in 1914
Treatment:		
Not subsoiled (plowed 7 inches deep)	31.8	30.0
Subsoiled with plow (March 13, 1913)	25.5	27.2
Subsoiled with dynamite (March 13, 1913)	27.7	29.1

From experiments on subsoiling at San Antonio, Tex., Hastings and Letteer (1913) drew the following conclusions:

[1] The yields of corn, cotton and oats for hay and for grain have been either slightly increased or slightly decreased on subsoiled land.   In no instance has the difference been significant.   [2] In the soil-moisture studies so far made at San Antonio it has been found that subsoiling has not increased the moisture content of the soil.

Chilcott and Cole (1918) reported results of subsoiling at 12 stations in the Great Plains from North Dakota to Texas.   From four to seven crops were grown at each station each year, and extensive soil moisture studies were made.   They concluded that: (1) for the Great Plains as a whole, no increases in yields could be expected from subsoiling, deep-tilling, or dynamiting; (2) there was no marked difference between crops; and (3) subsoiling was of no value in overcoming drought, but on the contrary reduced yields even lower in unfavorable seasons (dry years). They stated that:

Roots do not penetrate dry soil—and, where shallowness of soil restricts root development to a depth less than normal, the plants may attain complete development, provided the water content of the zone occupied by the root is maintained above the limit of availability.

Bennett (1939) stated that in the southeastern United States soils with brittle subsoils, such as the Cecil, are benefited by subsoiling, but that those with plastic subsoils are not. However, he cited no actual experimental data.

Since none of the treatments used to alter the subsoil characteristics have resulted in any appreciable economic benefits, one is forced to conclude that: (1) the subsoil conditions studied were not limiting factors in plant growth, or (2) the methods of treatments used were not satisfactory.

Cole and Mathews (1939) gave soil-moisture data from a number of the Great Plains stations already mentioned. The data were obtained over a long period of years by taking soil samples with a King tube and oven drying them. The samples were taken at 1-foot intervals of depth to well below the root zone. The data show that, except at one or two locations and for a very few wet years, ". . . the entire annual cycle of charge and discharge is confined to only a portion of the zone where roots can develop freely, and no water reaches the underlying subsoil." Since the subsoil was below the depth of available water and below the root zone, the negative results reported for subsoiling, dynamiting, and deep tilling would be expected. This does not explain the negative results obtained in more humid areas of Illinois, Pennsylvania, Texas, and Mississippi.

Bedrock

Solid bedrock serves as a mechanical barrier to roots. The extent to which this is detrimental depends on the depth to bedrock as compared with the normal root depth of the species. Conditions like that shown in Figure 11 are very harmful. The red oak shown is about 2.5 feet in diameter at the base and has about 2 feet of soil (soil material) above the solid granitic gneiss. Evidence of branching is obvious, and just above the portion shown are numerous branches. The tree has no economic value except for fuel.

If the rock is weathered, roots penetrate it and further aid in its decomposition. If it is stratified, with the strata in a vertical or approaching vertical position, roots will grow between the strata. The volume available for roots might still be a limiting factor. Batjer and Oskamp (1935) classified soils as submarginal for fruit trees if they supported shallow-rooted trees with low yield. They found that two of the main factors affecting depth of rooting were (1) bedrock, slate, or shale near the surface, and (2) unweathered compact gravelly till substrata.

Rock strata near the surface limit the root zone of plants. The small amount of water and nutrients held by the shallow soil layer is

FIGURE 11.—A red oak growing in shallow soil material over solid bedrock. A field of several acres just to the right of the picture has been abandoned, and many pines to the left of the picture have died because of shallow depth to bedrock.

sufficient to support only a few plants of certain species. A thin layer of soil over bedrock dries more completely during dry periods than one in contact with moist soil below.

With certain types of rock strata it is possible to grow crops satisfactorily, especially with heavy fertilization and with irrigation when needed. The Rockdale rocklands of southern Florida are being used rather extensively for various fruit trees and, to a limited extent, for vegetables (Jones, 1948). The rock is mainly Miami oolite. It is a cross-bedded and/or stratified limestone having numerous solution holes and sufficient permeability to yield water to shallow wells.

Consistency

Even though no data can be cited on the effects of consistency on plant growth a few general statements are in order. According to Russel *et al.* (1929):

> [Consistency is a term used] to designate the manifestations of the physical forces of cohesion and adhesion acting within the soil at various moisture contents. These manifestations include (a) the behavior toward gravity, pressure, thrust and pull, (b) the tendency of the soil mass to adhere to foreign bodies or substances, and (c) the sensations which are evidenced as feel by the fingers of the observer.

It is obvious, therefore, that consistency is those properties which we commonly know as stickiness, plasticity, or their opposite, friability. Soils which are plastic and sticky when wet are likely to be hard and cloddy when dry. If cultivated at moisture contents above optimum they adhere in large masses to the tillage implement and pull many plants, especially young ones, out of the soil. If cultivated when the moisture content is below optimum, the large clodlike masses push or pull many plants out of the ground or damage them so that stunted growth results. In many plastic soils the optimum moisture range for cultivation is very narrow.

Another characterstic of plastic soils is the large change in volume with change in moisture content. Frequently large cracks result from drying. Roots growing across the plane of cracking are broken or sheared off. Others grow into the vapor-saturated cracks and later die. As a general rule, soils capable of becoming highly plastic are apt to have poor water and air relations for plant growth. This applies particularly to subsoils.

SUMMARY

It is recognized that such soil physical factors as stones, bedrock, hardpans, claypans, sand and gravel strata, surface crusts, clods, sod mats, and perhaps others, have definite, usually harmful, effects on the growth of plants. Some of the effects are known to be indirect through their influence on soil water, soil air, soil temperature, nutrient supply, or otherwise; others are direct mechanical barriers to the growth of plants. The above-ground or below-ground parts of plants may be affected. There is no sharp line of demarcation between the direct and indirect effects; usually if an undesirable soil property—for example a surface crust—is present, it exerts both effects. However, it has been the principal purpose of this chapter to discuss the direct effects.

There is a large volume of general information regarding the physical soil properties considered. In fact, many of them are paramount factors in soil classification. Major as well as minor separations are based on them. Almost all of the soil survey reports contain verification of this.

Unfortunately, this general information is not well substantiated with experimental data definitely relating physical soil properties directly to plant growth. A "good" physical condition of the soil for plant growth is easily recognized, but as yet it has not been satisfactorily defined in mathematical or physical terms. There is no single value or group of values to express the optimum conditions desirable. This is true of the whole field of soil physics in general and of the factors considered in this chapter particularly. Perhaps the nearest approach to relating a physical soil property to plant growth is in the studies of soil water; the availability of water to plants as a function of the force with which it is held is reasonably well established. Other physical soil properties, as related to plant growth, are usually expressed in relative terms such as "good," or "poor." Since the desired limits of the various physical factors are not known, it is difficult to know how to proceed in preparing soils for plants. Too frequently it is a hit-or-miss proposition. Tillage operations which give a good seedbed on one field might give a poor one on another, or under different conditions. Excessive disking followed by heavy rains frequently causes a very hard compact soil. Without the *hard* rains a good seedbed might result.

One of the limiting factors in evaluating physical soil properties in relation to plant growth has been adequate methods. Many properties are inadequately measured; others are impossible to measure with present techniques. Soil structure, for example, is ill-defined in terms of pore-size distribution or of aggregate analysis, yet these are the only methods available. There are no methods for measuring the amount of work done by seedlings in breaking through a surface crust, or by roots in penetrating a hard subsoil.

Three major tasks therefore loom before us. First, is that of developing techniques for accurately and specifically evaluating soil properties, both in absolute physical terms, and as related to plant growth. Second, experiments must be sufficiently comprehensive and so designed as to make possible accurate evaluation of all factors; only when all factors are properly measured and evaluated in relation to each other can data from one set of conditions—soil, climate, crop or otherwise—be interpreted and applied to any other set of conditions. Third, the direct physical factors (implied immediately above) must be separated from the indirect or associated factors, with all factors being properly evaluated. By proper evaluation is meant, not only a measure of the magnitude of a factor but also an understanding of *why* it is so and *how* it got that way.

Literature Cited

BATJER, L. P., and OSKAMP, J. 1935. Soils in relation to fruit growing in New York. Part VII. Tree behavior on important soil profiles in the Kinderhook, Germantown, and Red Hook areas in Columbia and Dutchess Counties. *N. Y. (Cornell) Agr. Expt. Sta. Bull.* **627.**

BAVER, L. D., and FARNSWORTH, R. B. 1940. Soil structure effects in the growth of sugar beets. *Soil. Sci. Soc. Am. Proc.* **5:** 45–48.

BAVER, L. D. 1948. Soil Physics. Ed. 2. John Wiley and Sons, Inc., New York.

BENNETT, H. H. 1939. Soil conservation. McGraw–Hill Book Co., New York.

BOTKIN, C. W. 1933. The effects of acidifying amendments and impermeable soils. *N. Mex. Agr. Expt. Sta. Tech. Bull.* **210.**

BOUYOUCOS, G. J. 1928. The hydrometer method for making a very detailed mechanical analysis of soils. *Soil Sci.* **26:** 233–238.

BRAUN–BLANQUET, J. 1932. Plant Sociology. McGraw-Hill Book Co., New York.

CARDON, P. V. 1915. Tillage and rotation experiments at Nephi, Utah. *U. S. Dept. Agr. Bull.* **157.**

CARLSON, F. A. 1925. The effect of soil structure on the character of alfalfa root systems. *J. Am. Soc. Agron.* **17:** 336–345.

CARNES, A. 1934. Soil crusts. Methods of study, their strength, and a method of overcoming their injury to cotton stand. Proceedings of the 35th Annual Convention of the Association of Southern Agricultural Workers.

CATES, H. R. 1917. Farm practices in the cultivation of cotton. *U. S. Dept. Agr. Bull.* **511.**

CHILCOTT, E. C., and COLE, J. S. 1918. Subsoiling, deep tilling, and soil dynamiting in the Great Plains. *J. Agr. Research* **14:** 481–521.

COILE, T. S. 1948. Relation of soil characteristics to site index of loblolly and shortleaf pines in the lower piedmont region of North Carolina. *Duke Univ. School of Forestry Bull.* **13.**

COLE, J. S., and MATHEWS, O. R. 1939. Subsoil moisture under semiarid conditions. *U. S. Dept. Agr. Tech. Bull.* **637.**

DALE, T. 1947. When drought returns to the Great Plains. *U. S. Dept. Agr. Farmer's Bull.* **1982.**

DULEY, F. L. 1939. Surface factors affecting the rate of intake of water by soils. *Soil. Sci. Soc. Am. Proc.* **4:** 60–64.

FITZPATRICK, E. C., and ROSE, L. E. 1936. A study of root distribution in prairie claypan and associated friable soils. *Am. Soil Survey Assoc. Bull.* **XVII:** 136–145.

HARTLEY, C. P. 1910. Corn cultivation. *U. S. Dept. Agr. Farmer's Bull.* **414.**

HASTINGS, S. H., and LETTEER, C. R. 1913. Experiments in subsoiling at San Antonio. *U. S. Dept. Agr., Bur. Plant Ind. Circ.* **114.**

HILGARD, E. W. 1910. Soils. The Macmillan Co., New York.

HUNTER, A. S., and KELLEY, O. J. 1946. The extension of roots into dry soil. *Plant Physiol.* **21:** 445–451.

JONES, L. A. 1948. Soils, geology, and water control in the Everglades region. *Univ. Fla. Agr. Expt. Sta. Bull.* **442.**

KEEN, B. A., and HAINES, W. B. 1925. Studies in soil cultivation. *J. Agr. Sci.* **15:** 375–406.

KING, F. H. 1914. A Textbook of the Physics of Agriculture. Ed. 6, Pub. by Mrs. F. H. King, Madison, Wis.

KRAUSE, M. 1931. Russische forschungen auf dem gebiete der Bodenstruktur. *Landw. Jahrb.* **73:** 603–690.

KRUSEKOPF, H. H. 1942. The hardpan soils of the Ozark region. *Soil Sci. Soc. Am. Proc.* **7:** 434–436.

LAMB, J., JR., and CHAPMAN, J. E. 1943. Effect of surface stones on erosion, evaporation, and temperature, and soil moisture. *J. Am. Soc. Agron.* **35:** 567–578.

LANGE, N. A. 1946. Handbook of Chemistry. Ed. 6. Handbook Publishers, Inc., Sandusky, Ohio.

LARSEN, J. A. 1930. Forest types of the northern Rocky mountains and their climatic controls. *Ecology* **11:** 631–672.

LAWTON, K. 1945. The influence of soil aeration on the growth and absorption of nutrients by corn plants. *Soil Sci. Soc. Am. Proc.* **10:** 263–368.

LUTZ, H. J., and CHANDLER, R. F., JR. 1946. Forest soils. John Wiley and Sons, Inc., New York.

LUTZ, J. F. 1934. The physico–chemical properties of soils affecting soil erosion. *Mo. Agr. Expt. Sta. Research Bull.* **212.**

LUTZ, J. F., and LEAMER, R. W. 1939. Pore-size distribution as related to the permeability of soils. *Soil Sci. Soc. Am. Proc.* **4:** 28–31.

LUTZ, J. F., NELSON, W. L., BRADY, N. C., and SCARSBROOK, C. E. 1946. Effects of cover crops on pore-size distribution in a coastal plain soil. *Soil Sci. Soc. Am. Proc.* **11:** 43–46.

McGEORGE, W. T., BREAZEALE, J. F., and BURGESS, P. S. 1926. Aluminum hydroxide in alkali soils and its effect upon permeability. *Ariz. Agr. Expt. Sta. Tech. Bull.* **12.**

MOSIER, J. G., and GUSTAFSON, A. F. 1915. Soil moisture and tillage for corn. *Ill. Agr. Expt. Sta. Bull.* **181.**

NOLL, C. F. 1912–13. Deep versus ordinary plowing. *Pa. Agr. Expt. Sta. Ann. Rpt.*

PARKER, E. R., and JENNY, H. 1945. Water infiltration and related soil properties as affected by cultivation and organic fertilization. *Soil Sci.* **60:** 353–376.

PATTEN, H. E. 1909. Heat transference in soils. *U. S. Dept. Agr., Bur. of Soils Bull.* **59.**

PEARSON, G. A., and MARSH, R. E. 1935. Timber growing and logging practice in the Southwest and in the Black Hills region. *U. S. Dept. Agr. Tech. Bull.* **480.**

RATLIFFE, G. T. 1934. Cotton root rot as affected by crop rotation and tillage at San Antonio, Texas. *U. S. Dept. Agr. Tech. Bull.* **436.**

RICKS, J. R. 1915. Corn results from Central Station. *Miss. Agr. Expt. Sta. Bull.* **170.**

ROBINSON, G. W. 1936. Soils, their Origin, Constitution, and Classification. Thomas Murby and Co., London.

ROTMISTROV, V. G. 1913. The nature of drought according to the evidence of the Odessa experiment field. I. Skalsky, Kolontaevsk Street, Odessa [Transl. from Russian].

RULE, G. K. 1939. Crops against the wind on the southern Great Plains. *U. S. Dept. Agr. Farmer's Bull.* **1833.**

RUSSELL, J. C., OLMSTEAD, L. B., and HENDRICKSON, B. H. 1929. Forms of soil structure. *Am. Soil Survey Assoc. Bull.* **IX:** 120–133.

SMITH, F. W., and COOK, R. L. 1946. The effect of soil aeration, moisture, and compaction on nitrification and oxidation and the growth of sugar beets following corn and legumes in pot cultures. *Soil Sci. Soc. Am. Proc.* **11:** 402–406.

STORIE, R. E. 1938. Effect of claypan on the growth and production of apples in California. *Soil Sci. Soc. Am. Proc.* **3:** 317–322.

SWEET, A. T. 1935. The soil factor in commercial apple production in the Hudson Valley of New York. *Soil Survey Assoc. Bull.* **XVI:** 46–48.

TAUBENHAUS, J. J., EZEKIAL, W. N., and REA, H. E. 1931. Strangulation of cotton roots. *Plant Physiol.* **6:** 161–166.

THROCKMORTON, R. I., and COMPTON, L. L. 1937. Soil erosion by wind. *Kans. State Bd. Agr. Rpt.* No. 224–A, v. **LVI.**

TOWNSEND, C. O. 1918. The beet sugar industry in the United States. *U. S. Dept. Agr. Bull.* **721.**

TURNER, L. M. 1936. Some soil characters influencing the distribution of forest types and rate of growth of trees in Arkansas. *Soil Sci. Soc. Am. Proc.* **1:** 345.

UNITED STATES DEPARTMENT OF AGRICULTURE. 1938. Soils and men. U. S. Dept. of Agriculture Yearbook. 1938, 1232 pp.

VEIHMEYER, F. J., and HENDRICKSON, A. H. 1946. Soil density as a factor in determining the permanent wilting percentage. *Soil Sci.* **62:** 451–456.

VEIHMEYER, F. J., and HENDRICKSON, A. H. 1948. Soil density and root penetration. *Soil Sci.* **65:** 487–493.

WEAVER, J. E. 1926. Root Development of Field Crops. McGraw-Hill Book Co., Inc., New York.

WHITSON, A. R. 1936. Some soil conditions and associated factors likely to influence future land use. *Amer. Soil. Survey Assoc. Bull.* **XVII:** 57–62.

WINTERS, E. 1942. Silica hardpan development in the red and yellow podsolic soil region. *Soil Sci. Soc. Am. Proc.* **7:** 437–440.

WOODRUFF, C. M. 1940. Soil moisture and plant growth in relation to pF. *Soil Sci. Soc. Am. Proc.* **5:** 36–41.

WOODRUFF C. M., and SMITH, D. D. 1946. Subsoil shattering and subsoil liming for crop production on claypan soils. *Soil Sci. Soc. Am. Proc.* **11:** 539–542.

YODER, R. E. 1937. The significance of soil structure in relation to the tilth problem. *Soil Sci. Soc. Am. Proc.* **2:** 21–33.

CHAPTER 3

SOIL WATER AND PLANT GROWTH

By L. A. Richards and C. H. Wadleigh

OIL MOISTURE is related to plant growth in many ways, directly and indirectly. Direct effects pertain to the adequacy of the moisture supply or the readiness with which the moisture in the vicinity of the root can enter the plant through the root surface. Indirectly, soil moisture influences plant growth through its effect on properties of soil, which in turn condition plant growth.

Mechanical properties of soil such as bearing strength, shearing strength, friability, penetrability, plasticity, and cohesion are greatly altered by the amount of moisture present. Attempts to measure the physical condition of soil with penetrometers have been complicated considerably by the large effect of soil moisture on the readings. Allyn and Work (1941) have proposed a method for estimating the available water present in soil by measuring the soil resistance to a standard deformation.

The work required for tillage operations is critically dependent on the soil moisture content, as is also the effect of these operations on the structure and physical properties of the soil. Working the soil when too wet may cause breakdown of structure and puddling, and if worked too dry some soils become cloddy and difficult to reduce to a good seedbed.

Shrinking and swelling accompany moisture changes in most soils and in some soils are of paramount importance in determining management practices. Beneficial physical changes of soils, perhaps related to shrinkage, often accompany dehydration. For example, Reitemeier et al. (1948) found that thorough drying was as effective as any of several reclamation treatments that were tried for improving water penetration in an alkali soil.

Gaseous diffusion in soils depends critically on the moisture content, as has been redemonstrated with methods recently developed by Taylor (1949) and Raney (1949). Moisture content thus affects all physical, chemical, and biological processes that are related to aeration in soil.

Thermal properties of soil, such as thermal conductivity, thermal capacity, and thermal diffusivity, as well as absorptivity and emissivity,

73

are materially affected by soil-moisture content and hence definitely influence soil temperature.

Plant growth in relation to the mechanical nature, aeration, and temperature of soils, including the effect of water on these properties, is dealt with in other sections of this monograph. The following section will be concerned primarily with the more direct relations between soil water and plant growth.

I. THE SOIL—WATER SYSTEM

The size and mechanical nature of the soil particles and the structural elements composed of groups of particles have already been described. Pore space is present in all soils and may be more or less occupied by water. The idealized cube shown in Figure 12 can be

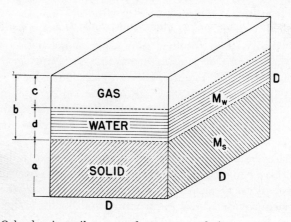

FIGURE 12.—Cube showing soil-water and pore space relations:

D = length of the edge of the cube d = depth of the water
a = depth of the soil Ms = mass of the soil
b = depth of the water plus gas Mw = mass of the water
c = depth of the gas

used to clarify some of the relations among the solid, the gaseous, and the water phases in the soil. In the present discussion both the liquid water, if any, and the films of water adhering to the soil surface are included in the water phase.

In addition to symbols shown on Figure 12 the following will be used:

ρw = density of water in bulk
ρP = density of the soil particles
ρB = bulk density of the soil, i.e., the mass of soil per unit of soil volume

Direct water content determinations are made by observing the loss in weight (M_W) of a sample of soil after drying to a constant weight (M_S) at a standard temperature, usually 105°C. Often a sampling device is used which gives a more or less undisturbed core of known volume. In the above symbols this volume is presented by D^3. As pointed out by Bodman (1942), it is permissible for many agronomic and engineering purposes to make certain simplifying assumptions. We shall here overlook the complications that arise from the difference in density between film and liquid water, the difficulty of obtaining a true particle density measurement, and the volume changes that occur in some soils when the moisture content is changed. Table 7 summarizes the symbols, the defining equations, and the equations for calculating some useful soil-moisture quantities.

TABLE 7.—*Definitions of quantities related to soil moisture*

Name	Symbol	Definition	Experimental evaluation
Moisture percentage...............	P_W	$100\dfrac{M_W}{M_S}$	$100\dfrac{M_W}{M_S}$
Water ratio.......................	R	$\dfrac{dD^2}{D^3} = \dfrac{d}{D}$	$\dfrac{M_W}{\rho_W D^3}$
Total porosity....................	E	$\dfrac{bD^2}{D^3} = \dfrac{b}{D}$	$1 - \dfrac{M_S}{\rho_P D^3}$
Unfilled porosity.................	E'	$\dfrac{cD^2}{D^3} = \dfrac{c}{D}$	$1 - \dfrac{1}{D^3}\left(\dfrac{M_W}{\rho_W} + \dfrac{M_S}{\rho_P}\right)$
Saturation percentage.............	P_S	$100\dfrac{dD^2}{bD^2} = \dfrac{100d}{b}$	$\dfrac{100\rho_P M_W}{\rho_W(\rho_P D^3 - M_S)}$

Soil-moisture percentage $(P_W = 100M_W/M_S)$ is the grams of water per 100 grams of soil. This is probably the most commonly used index for moisture content of soil.

The water-depth ratio $(R = d/D)$ expresses the moisture content of soil in terms of the equivalent depth of free water per unit depth of soil. Since $R = dD^2/D^3 = d/D$, it is seen that R is equal also to the volume of water per unit volume of soil. The depth ratio R is well adapted for use in irrigation engineering work.

Obviously it is relevant to consider pore space in relation to soil water. Total porosity $(E = bD^2/D^3 = b/D)$ is the fraction of the soil space occupied jointly by water and the gaseous phase. The porosity unfilled by water $(E' = cD^2/D^3 = c/D)$ is the fraction of the soil space occupied by the gaseous phase alone. The quantities E and E' can be calculated by drying soil cores of known volume and known particle density or can be more directly measured by air pycnometers as recently described by Kummer and Cooper (1945) and by Page (1947). Torstensen and Erickson (1936) and Russell (1949) have demonstrated the use of air pycnometers for measuring the unfilled pore space, and from this measurement have calculated the moisture content of soil.

The percentage of the total volume of pore space that is occupied by water ($P_s = 100dD^2/bD^2 = 100d/b$) is frequently a very useful index of soil moisture. When the soil pore space is filled with water, $P_s = 100$, $R = E$, and $P_w = 100E\,\rho_w/(1-E)\,\rho_P$. This condition is approached below the water table, and in fine-textured soils the pore system may be substantially saturated for a considerable distance above the water table, in the region sometimes referred to as the capillary fringe.

II. WATER MOVEMENT IN SOILS

Permeability to water is an essential characteristic of soils that are suitable for producing plants. The supply of water in the soil near the roots must be replenished from time to time, and rainfall is the principal natural source. The process of the downward entry of water into soil, either rain or irrigation, is referred to as infiltration. This process has been extensively studied, as evidenced by the considerable bibliography compiled by Davidson (1940).

For any given condition of soil there exists a maximum entry, or infiltration, rate. When the rainfall rate exceeds the infiltration rate, runoff or impounding occurs. The infiltration rate of a given soil is dependent upon many factors, such as plant cover, cultural history, tillage practices, surface organic litter, and the moisture content of the profile. Good soil management often involves the objective of keeping the infiltration rate of the soil as high as possible so as to facilitate moisture recharge of the root zone and to minimize erosion of the surface by runoff.

When the permeability of the surface layer of soil is low, or where the soil permeability increases with depth, water moves downward through the soil under appreciable tension, that is, by unsaturated flow. This condition is commonly met in the field and is illustrated by the records obtained by Richards and Huberty (1941). Conversely, when the permeability decreases with depth, perched water tables may develop during rainfall and irrigation. Hardpans, plow soles, or other soil layers having low permeability cause the formation of temporary water tables such as have been observed by Richards and Lamb (1937).

The movement of water in soils is a complicated process in which several different mechanisms are involved. For purposes of discussion we may distinguish several special cases.

Saturated Flow

It seems to be well established that in saturated soils, particularly of coarse texture, the Darcy flow law holds. Darcy (1856) reported that the rate of flow water through sand filter beds may be described by the equation

$$Q = \frac{ks(H + e)}{e}$$

This equation, referred to in the following discussion as equation No. 1, was applied to the case where the pressure "under the filter is equal to the weight of the atmosphere" and where Q represents the volume of water passed in unit time; s is the area of the bed; e, the thickness of the bed; H, the height of the water on the filter; and k, "a coefficient depending on the nature of the sand." The equation was thus applied to steady linear flow through saturated sand. Two driving forces are involved. Gravity, of course, acts with a force of 980 dynes per gram in the downward direction. A pressure gradient within a liquid water system also supplies a water-moving force in the direction of the greatest rate of decrease in pressure. The use of hydraulic gradient by the engineers as a convenient method for representing the vector sum of these two forces in soil-water systems has been reviewed by Richards (1940).

Thus, from equation No. 1 we may define the hydraulic gradient $i = (e + H)/e$ and the transmission velocity $v = Q/s$. Substituting these new symbols in equation No. 1 gives equation No. 2 as follows: $v = ki$. Equation No. 2 is a vector equation applying to three-dimensional flow in isotropic media and may be taken as the general form of the Darcy flow law. It is seen that k is equal to the transmission velocity when the hydraulic gradient is unity; that is, when the driving force is equal in magnitude to the force of gravity, or 980 dynes per gram. Muskat (1937) has reviewed the conditions under which the law is valid and has given a summary of methods and examples for application of the law to practical flow problems in saturated soils. Definitions and methods for measuring permeability are based directly on the Darcy law. Numerous permeability units have been considered and discussed by Muskat (1937), Richards (1940), and others. The simple Darcy coefficient, k, is most commonly used in agricultural soils work. Methods for measuring the permeability of soil samples having disturbed (Fireman, 1944) and undisturbed (Van Doren and Klingebiel, 1949; Bower and Petersen, 1950) structure have been described. Methods have also been developed by Luthin and Kirkham (1949) for measuring the permeability of soil below a water table in the field.

Numerous workers have contributed to the theory and the experimental technics for the application of the Darcy flow law to the solution of ground-water problems in the field.   The papers by Christiansen (1943) and Reeve and Jensen (1949) are examples of the use of piezometers for measuring the hydraulic head of ground water for the purpose of obtaining ground-water flow patterns and for measuring subsurface permeability.   Our knowledge of the movement of water in saturated soils is approaching a quantitative stage.   In unsaturated soils, however, the case is not so clear-cut.

Unsaturated Flow

As the moisture content of soil decreases from the maximum value at 100-percent saturation of the pore space, the air phase invades the larger pores.   It is in these larger pores that the water moves most readily; consequently, a transition from saturated to unsaturated flow is accompanied by a marked decrease in the rate at which water is transmitted by soils.   Richards (1931) has proposed that we assume as a working hypothesis that the Darcy-flow equation holds for the unsaturated as well as the saturated flow cases for soils under isothermal conditions.   For the case of unsaturated flow, the permeability becomes a function of the moisture content of the soil and is referred to as the unsaturated permeability.   The hydraulic head of water in unsaturated soil is defined in the same way as for saturated soil; namely, it is the elevation at which water stands in a riser or piezometer connected to the point in question.   The relation of hydraulic head to gravitational head and tension head may be clarified by reference to the porous cup-manometer units illustrated in Figure 13.

In Figure 13 the porous cups designated by the letters a, b, c, and d are connected through vertical tubes to the mercury manometers above the soil surface.   The units are vacuum tight and are completely filled with water.   Units of this type have been used by soil scientists throughout the world for measuring the equivalent negative pressure of water in soil and are often called tensiometers.   The literature on this subject has recently been reviewed by Richards (1949b). Water manometers are sketched in Figure 13 at the lower right to illustrate and clarify the definition of terms.   The manometer pattern illustrates conditions that exist in a fallow soil some time after a rain. Assume for this example that there is no horizontal variation in the soil moisture.   The pressure in the water in the porous cups is less than atmospheric pressure and may be read from the mercury manometers above ground.   This pressure is referred to as pressure deficiency or soil-moisture tension and can be expressed in terms of a water column of length equal to the vertical distance from the porous cup down to the surface of the water in the equivalent water manometer at the right. Soil-moisture tension is defined as the negative pressure that must be applied to the water in the porous cup in order to have hydraulic equilibrium through the porous cup wall with the water in the soil. It is not inferred that the water in the soil has the same hydrostatic pressure as the water in the porous cup, but surface-force actions arising at the water interface boundaries in the soil combine to produce a certain attraction for the soil moisture, which is measured by the negative pressure that must be applied to the water in the cup in order

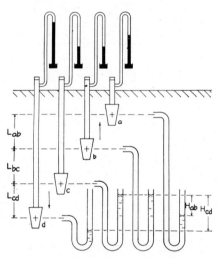

FIGURE 13.—Tensiometers for measuring hydraulic head of water in the field. Mercury manometers shown above ground; equivalent water manometers shown at the right.

to attain zero transfer between the cup water and the soil water. The hydraulic head of the water in the soil is the elevation at which water stands in a riser or manometer connected to the point in question in the soil.

When water-flow relations are under consideration, it is proper to refer to the vertical distance from the porous cup down to the open surface in the water manometer as the tension head of the water in the soil at the cup. Algebraically this is a negative quantity and is opposite in sign to pressure head. Some attention should be given to consistency in the use of terms. Engineers may prefer to use tension head instead of soil-moisture tension for all soil-moisture work. However, the practice of using a length of liquid in a manometer for expressing a pressure difference is very old in physics and will be followed in this paper because soil-moisture tension (i.e., negative pressure) is more appropriate than tension head in thermodynamical considerations. Expressing tensiometer readings in terms of centimeters of water is preferred because of ease in converting to tension head when water flow is to be considered.

As the flow problem is illustrated in Figure 13, we may define the gravitational head of the water in soil at a given point as being equal to the elevation of the point with respect to an arbitrary datum. The hydraulic head of water in soil is the algebraic sum of the gravitational and tension (or pressure) heads. Consideration of examples in the figure will show that this sum is simply the elevation at which water stands in a riser or manometer connected to the point in question. If the point lies below a water table, a vertical piezometer tube may be used. If the soil is not saturated, a porous cup must be used to make connection to the water in the soil. In Figure 13 the hydraulic head of the water at the various cups is equal to the elevation of the meniscus in the appropriate water manometer. It is apparent that the hydraulic head of the water at cup b is higher than the hydraulic head of the water at cup a. The difference in hydraulic head between these two cups is H_{ab}. The hydraulic gradient in the vertical soil interval ab is equal to the difference in hydraulic head divided by the vertical distance between cups, i.e., $i_{ab} = H_{ab}/L_{ab}$. According to our hypothesis, moisture flows in the direction of the greatest rate of decrease of the hydraulic head or in the direction of the hydraulic gradient; consequently, moisture movement in the soil interval ab is upward as indicated by the arrow.

In the example it is noted that the hydraulic head at cup b is the same as at cup c. The average hydraulic gradient in this interval is therefore zero, and the net soil-moisture movement in this interval is zero. The soil-moisture tension in this interval increases in the upward direction, and the upward force arising from the tension gradient is just equal to the downward force of gravity. This is the condition that is satisfied when soil water is at rest under gravity.

The hydraulic head at cup c is shown in Figure 13 to be greater than at cup d, so $i_{cd} = H_{cd}/L_{cd}$ is downward, and moisture movement is downward in this soil interval. Richards, Neal, and Russell (1939) and Richards and Huberty (1941) have published observations on the direction and magnitude of the hydraulic gradient in unsaturated soils in the field. Experiments have been conducted by Bodman and Colman (1943), Colman and Bodman (1944), and Marshall and Stirk (1949) to clarify water-moving force and gradient relations during the downward entry of water into soils. The relation of potential gradient to hydraulic gradient has been illustrated and discussed by Richards (1940).

Figure 14 summarizes and presents unsaturated permeability measurements made by a number of different workers. These data, for a variety of soils, are shown plotted to a linear scale.

The saturated permeability of soils that may be regarded as relatively normal with respect to their moisture properties may vary from

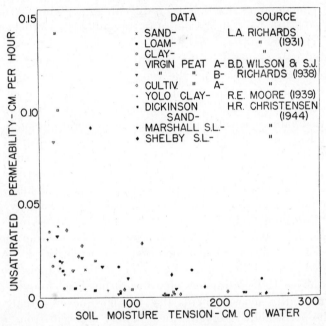

FIGURE 14.—Representation of unsaturated permeability on a linear scale to show the rapid decrease to low values at tensions above 150 centimeters of water.

approximately 0.2 to 20 centimeters per hour. It is seen from Figure 14 that as the soil-moisture tension increases up to about 25 centimeters of water, the unsaturated permeability drops very rapidly. The soil-moisture tension for most of the soils represented in the figure has been reduced to a relatively low value by the time the tension reaches 100 centimeters of water.

Previously, unsaturated permeability data have been represented on semilogarithmic graphs, and the significance of the very rapid decrease of the unsaturated permeability to low values at tensions of the order of 100 centimeters of water or less has been neglected or overlooked. The shape of this unsaturated permeability curve is related directly to the moisture properties of soils in the field. The ordinary definition for field capacity, which is applied for deep well-drained soils, may be paraphrased as follows: Field capacity is the moisture content of soil 2 or 3 days after a heavy rain or irrigation when *downward drainage has reduced the moisture content of the soil and the thickness of the moisture films to such an extent that the unsaturated permeability is not longer appreciable* and further downward drainage of water is negligible.

The data in Figure 14 provide a simple explanation for another soil-moisture phenomenon that has been difficult to explain. After water has been added to dry soil, the moisture content of the wetted zone soon becomes relatively uniform and near field capacity, and there is usually a steep moisture gradient in the transition zone between wet and dry soil. The tension gradient in the wetting front is large and supplies the water-moving force from wet to dry soil. When the addition of water to the soil is stopped, the moisture content in the wetted zone drops to that value where the unsaturated permeability is small, and the boundary between wet and dry soil remains reasonably distinct because the unsaturated permeability at the dry edge is extremely small.

It appeared to L. A. Richards (1936) and L. A. Richards and Wilson (1936) that when the moisture content is decreased sufficiently in the l-atmosphere tension range the unsaturated permeability becomes zero. Wilson and S. J. Richards (1938), however, working with the same apparatus, later identified certain moisture losses from the system and showed that the previous conclusion was not justified. Although unsaturated permeability attains low values as the soil-moisture tension increases above 150 centimeters of water, it has been found for all recent permeability measurements that the flow never actually ceases, and so the permeability remains measureably different from zero. In other words, the absorbed moisture films on the soil particles do transmit water, even though the soil-moisture tension may be very high. This appears to be conclusively demonstrated by the work of Richards and Weaver (1944) where they found that for a sample of soil on the pressure membrane and after attainment of equilibrium with the membrane, each pressure increment produced a water outflow increment, even at pressures corresponding to soil-moisture tensions in the range from 20 to 100 atmospheres.

Diffusion of Water Vapor through Soils

On the basis of experiments by Lewis (1937), it is inferred that in the plant-growth moisture range and in the absence of temperature gradients, the movement of water in soils takes place primarily in the liquid phase through the pore channels or in the adsorbed film phase over the surface of the soil particles, and that compared with these processes, the movement of water in the vapor phase is negligible. This is reasonable, for the whole plant-growth moisture range corresponds to a relative humidity range of less than 2 percent, and therefore vapor-pressure gradients would always be small under isothermal conditions.

If there is an appreciable temperature gradient, however, vapor transfer of water through field soils may be more important than film flow, particularly at moisture contents near the wilting percentage. However, little quantitative data on this point appear to be available. Field measurements in central California by Edlefsen and Bodman (1941) indicate that an upward movement of water takes place during the winter, apparently in response to the temperature gradient. Their measurements did not distinguish between vapor and film transfer, but it seems likely that vapor transfer was significant. Hilgeman (1948) measured the moisture content of a bare soil in Arizona to a depth of 8 feet during a period of 22 months. The total loss of water was 9.8 inches, or 47 percent of the water available for plant growth. The most rapid losses occurred in summer. In this case also, it appears likely that vapor transfer under the action of temperature gradients played an important part in moisture loss from the subsurface soil.

Soil-water Movement in Relation to Plant-root Extraction

The effect of plant roots on the flow and distribution of water in soil is a matter of practical interest. The cases for a newly developing root system and for an old established root system are distinctly different.

Consider a newly planted hill of corn after a soaking rain. When the rain stops, the moisture moves gradually out of the larger pores in the downward direction. This water movement takes place primarily under the influence of gravitational force because when the whole profile is very wet, gradients in soil-moisture tension are small.

Concomitant with the recession of water in the larger pores, air is drawn into these pores. As the soil approaches field capacity there is a reasonably continuous gaseous phase throughout the soil, but the moisture films covering the soil particles become so thin that additional moisture movement in these films is considerably restricted. It should be kept in mind that the condition of field capacity can exist only in well-drained soils. When soil horizons having low permeability are present in the profile, or when a nearby ground water table exists, then the root zone may remain excessively wet for long periods.

Thus, several days after the rain has stopped the soil-moisture tension may rise into the range of 0.05 to 0.15 atmospheres (50 to 150 centimeters of water), and moisture movement in the profile becomes considerably restricted.   Water-vapor loss will occur from the surface few inches of soil, owing to air circulation and the elevated temperature of the surface soil, but vapor loss from soil layers a few inches below the surface is usually slow.   When the corn seeds germinate, the rootlets remove moisture from the immediately adjacent soil and can build up soil-moisture tensions of the order of 10 to 20 atmospheres.   The high tension in the soil moisture in the vicinity of the root sets up a tension gradient and thereby a force action in the soil-water system that tends to move water toward the root.   This tendency of water to move toward plant roots in response to tension gradients is of considerable importance for perennial plants with large developed root systems because a small distance of movement over a considerable combined length of root system would account for an appreciable volume of water, even at the slow rates at which water moves through dry soil.   However, for young plants with a newly developing root system this movement is so slow that sufficient water for normal growth would not be supplied unless the plant roots are able to extend themselves outward into a fresh soil-moisture supply.   Therefore, as has been described by Davis (1940), when a new corn plant is developing, the available moisture is extracted in the vicinity of the base of the plant and the soil approaches the wilting percentage, whereas just a few inches farther away from the plant the soil may be at or near field capacity.   The roots of the newly developing plant must extend themselves outward in order to maintain a continuous supply of available water.   When the roots of the plant have permeated the soil region in which they can grow well, the soil-moisture content throughout the soil region occupied by roots will be reduced into the wilting range.   Unless additional moisture is supplied by rain or irrigation, vegetative growth will cease and the plant will wilt.

This pattern of moisture extraction by corn has been followed by Russell, Davis, and Bair (1940) using tensiometers in the field.   They state:

Corn roots first absorbed moisture at a shallow depth directly beneath the corn hills.   The zone of absorption extended laterally until most of the available moisture at that depth was depleted.   The lateral expansion of the moisture absorption zone occurred at successively lower depths as the growing season progressed.

Conrad and Veihmeyer (1929) measured soil moisture and root density under grain-sorghum plants.   They concluded that the moisture is absorbed from progressively expanding zones if there is no material addition of moisture during the growing season.

In irrigated areas the pattern of moisture extraction for mature perennial tree crops has been extensively studied by Hendrickson and Veihmeyer (1929, 1934, 1942a). Starting with a deep permeable soil when the whole profile was wet, they found that moisture is continuously extracted at all depths down to 6 or 8 feet or deeper, depending on the soil and the species of tree. The surface 2 or 3 feet may approach the permanent-wilting percentage at about the same rate. Often, however, the rate of extraction is greater near the tree and near the soil surface, so that available water is first depleted from the surface layers of soil.

Veihmeyer and Hendrickson (1938) have used the pattern of moisture extraction as an indication of the probable root distribution, and state:

> The fact that soil samples taken at any place within the experimental plots in mature peach, prune, and walnut orchards which have had an even application of water, agree at comparable depths, shows that these trees, under conditions existing at Davis, have a uniform distribution of roots.

Such observers assume that moisture depletion from a soil region is evidence that active roots traverse that region of soil. The effective distance through which water in the available range can move toward the root is certainly of the order of inches and not feet. The pattern of moisture extraction in soils is therefore largely a matter of the active root distribution. Root distribution, as recently discussed by Kramer (1949), is mainly determined by the genetic character of the plant but is modified by plant spacing as well as by soil and climatic factors.

For most soils from which the available moisture has been depleted, the re-entry of water is extremely slow unless the moisture content of the soil at the wetting front is maintained near or above field capacity. Shaw (1927), Hendrickson and Veihmeyer (1933, 1941a), Veihmeyer (1939), Kirkham and Feng (1949), and others have shown that when a limited amount of water is applied to dry soil, the water spreads relatively rapidly until the moisture content of the wetted portion is reduced approximately to the field capacity. The moisture distribution thereafter in many soils changes only slowly with time. This characteristic of the soil-wetting process was pointed out by Shantz (1925) many years ago, and an understanding of this normal mode of wetting of soils is of paramount importance in experimental work on the relation of soil moisture to plant growth.

Experiments by Hendrickson and Veihmeyer (1931b, 1941a) and Richards and Loomis (1942) indicate that, because of the low unsaturated permeability of soils, it is not possible to maintain a constant percentage of moisture in soil at or near the surface of active roots. It appears that the only feasible method for effecting a degree of moisture

control, in the available range during plant growth, is to space irrigations so as to limit the degree of drying of the soil.   The water applied
with each irrigation should be sufficient to bring the soil in the whole
root zone to the field capacity.

III. STORAGE OF WATER IN SOIL

Soil particles are wetted by water and have considerable attraction
for water; consequently, soils exhibit a capacity to take up and retain
water.   This water is distributed through the pore system of the soil
and over the surface of the soil particles.

The capacity of soils to absorb and retain moisture provides a
reservoir which enables plants to absorb water and to grow during
periods when soil moisture is not frequently replenished.   The mois-
ture-retaining properties of soils, therefore, have been intensively
studied, and various soil-moisture constants have been defined and
used as an index of moisture retention by soils.   Among those which
might be mentioned, for example, are: Gravity water, capillary water,
and hygroscopic water as classified by Briggs (1897); the moisture-
holding capacity of Hilgard (1906); lento-capillary moisture as defined
by Widtsoe and McLaughlin (1912); the normal moisture capacity of
Shaw (1927); the pendular and funicular stages of water in granular
media as represented by Haines (1930); field capacity as defined by
Israelsen and West (1922) and Veihmeyer and Hendrickson (1927a);
moisture equivalent of Briggs and McLane (1907); wilting coefficient
of Briggs and Shantz (1912a); permanent-wilting percentage of Hendrickson and Veihmeyer (1945); first permanent-wilting percentage of
Furr and Reeve (1945); ultimate-wilting percentage of Taylor *et al.*
(1934); and the hygroscopic coefficient as used by Alway (1913).

Most of these terms are concerned with hypothetical concepts or
with measurements made in accordance with standardized procedures
and are not readily identified with the physical properties of the soil
or water.   There has emerged from a wealth of observational experience the very useful concepts of "available water" and the "range of
available water" that can be stored in soil and be available for growing
crops.   Soil-moisture constants associated with the upper and lower
limits of available water in the field therefore take on a special and
practical significance.

Field capacity is usually defined as the upper limit of available
water.   Moisture above field capacity is most readily available, but it is
of little use to plants because in well-drained soils it is present but a
short time.   Field capacity is the moisture percentage that is retained
in soil 2 to 3 days after the soil profile is thoroughly wetted by rain or

irrigation water. The term applies mainly for deep well-drained soils and requires special interpretation if there is restricted drainage. Although the term "field capacity" is not capable of precise and general definition for all cases, the concept is based on the observed fact that 2 to 3 days after wetting there is for many soils a marked decrease in the rate of loss of water by drainage. After that time, especially in the presence of moisture extraction by plant roots, loss of water from the soil by drainage or by surface evaporation at depths below 6 or 8 inches is often negligible for practical purposes.

Field capacity is usually equal to or slightly less than the moisture equivalent for soils having medium to fine texture; that is, for moisture-equivalent values above 20. For coarse-textured soils, however, there appears to be no generally satisfactory laboratory method for estimating field capacity. The explanation of field capacity from the standpoint of the hydraulics of soil moisture has not been fully demonstrated. As already indicated, however, the phenomenon appears to depend directly on the rapid decrease in the unsaturated permeability as the moisture content of soil is decreased.

"Field capacity" is a useful concept for practical purposes, but for scientific work individual cases should be scrutinized. There are soils for which there is no sharp break in the drainage curve and for which it is difficult to pick a time after which downward movement can be neglected. This possibility is indicated by the data in Figure 14, where it is seen that the unsaturated permeability of some soils decreases much more slowly than others as the soil-moisture tension is increased.

The field-moisture study made by Edlefsen and Bodman (1941) illustrates the drainage characteristics of a deep permeable soil after thorough wetting. They found that after 2 or 3 days the rate of loss of water caused by drainage from the surface 3 feet of soil dropped to less than $\frac{1}{10}$ of the initial rate, and after 5 days the rate dropped to $\frac{1}{100}$ of the initial rate. For the surface 9 feet of this soil the moisture equivalent ranged from 20 to 26 percent, with occasional layers going up to 33 percent. The soil was fallow and protected from evaporation, and approximately 28 days were required for the surface 3 feet of soil to reach a moisture content approximating the moisture equivalent. At the end of 842 days after the initial wetting, the moisture content of the surface 3 feet of soil ranged from 60 to 70 percent of the moisture equivalent.

The dry end of the range of soil-moisture values that will permit the growth of plants is commonly referred to as the wilting coefficient or the permanent-wilting percentage and is a somewhat more definite limit than the field capacity. Veihmeyer and Hendrickson (1948a) have recently discussed "The permanent-wilting percentage as a reference for the measurement for soil moisture." They cite references and present data to show that under plants in regions of rainless summers the permanent-wilting percentage is reached year after year in the soil below the surface layer that is affected by surface evaporation. Curves showing soil-moisture content plotted against time slope downward during the early part of the summer until the permanent-wilting percentage is reached. Then the curves continue nearly horizontally. The soil moisture is slowly reduced to a minimum which is slightly below the permanent-wilting percentage. In consequence, the permanent-wilting percentage is a satisfactory reference point from which can be calculated the amount of water available for plant use, and also the amount needed to raise the soil to its field capacity. Nomographs prepared by Bodman (1942) greatly facilitate this type of calculation.

Hendrickson and Veihmeyer (1945) and Veihmeyer and Hendrickson (1949) have recently reviewed their procedure for determining the permanent-wilting percentage. With training and skill, the permanent-wilting percentage is a single-valued moisture constant that can be repeatedly reproduced if the standardized procedures are carefully followed. The soil-moisture value obtained will depend upon the condition of the plants and the degree of severity of wilting symptoms that are taken as the end point of the determination.

IV. IRRIGATION AND DRAINAGE

The importance of soil-water in relation to plant growth and crop production is generally recognized. The agriculture of the world is located in regions where rainfall is suitable or where the soil-moisture supply can be augmented by summer fallowing or irrigation. It is interesting to see from the writings of the early agricultural scientists in this country how little the views on this subject have changed in the last half century. F. H. King (1914) in his book on soil management stated:

In the semiarid and arid sections of Canada, as in those corresponding in the United States, the duty, conservation and availability of soil moisture are of vital industrial interest, but scarcely more so than they should be in almost every agricultural district on the globe; for it is doubtful if there are agricultural soils to be found anywhere, under existing climatic conditions where, in the majority of seasons, deficiency of available moisture must not become a marked limiting factor of yield. In stating this general conclusion to which my own research work and that of others have led me, it is always to be understood that sound seed of high vigor, good physical and climatic conditions, abundance of available plant food and good management coexist, and that when they do almost without exception, deficiency of available soil moisture must come to be the limiting factor of yield where supplemental irrigation is not practiced.

The widespread and continuing installation of supplemental irrigation facilities in the so-called humid regions of this and other countries substantiates the view expressed in the foregoing statement. Also, O. R. Mathews recent unpublished summary of data supplied by the State agricultural experiment stations indicates that the total area of cultivated land on which summer fallowing is practiced in the western United States is approximately 20,000,000 acres. This is substantially equal to the area of irrigated land in the United States.

Irrigation

The practice of artificially applying water to soil for promoting plant growth is an age-old art. Higher yields are generally obtained on irrigated land, because under irrigation soil moisture can be maintained more readily available for plant use. An appreciable fraction of the world's population today is supported by irrigation agriculture. Much has been written on the subject of irrigation. Thorne and Peterson (1949) have recently published a book on the fertility and management of irrigated soils. Engineering phases of irrigation are dealt with in standard texts such as that by Israelsen (1950). The problems of how to irrigate and when to irrigate involve a whole series of physical variables such as climate, soil, crop, and irrigation water, as well as economic and social considerations. Underlying all of this, of course, is the beneficial effect of irrigation on the yield and quality of the crop. The relation of soil-moisture status to plant growth has particular application to irrigation agriculture, because under irrigation the soil-moisture status is subject to a certain amount of control. The problem of adapting farm management to include irrigation is complicated by other factors which must be coordinated and controlled, such as soil structure, salinity, drainage, weeds, and mechanical operations such as tilling, fertilizing, spraying, and harvesting. Nevertheless a knowledge of the relation of crop response to the soil-moisture status is a primary consideration in establishing the most economical over-all management plan.

Drainage

Artificial land drainage is another form of soil-moisture control. Whenever a water table occurs in the soil sufficiently near the surface to be harmful to the development of the roots of crop plants, artificial drainage should be considered. The condition may arise from excess rainfall or irrigation or may be caused primarily by low moisture transmission rates in subsurface layers. Many millions of acres of land in the United States have been artificially drained, both in humid and arid regions, and land drainage is an established branch of engineering. New principles and technics are being applied to the design of drainage systems. As with irrigation, many variables are involved and simple general rules pertaining to drainage operations are difficult to formulate.

Salinity control is a definite feature of drainage in arid regions where the salt content of the soil and the ground water tend to increase. It seems to be firmly established that for a permanent irrigation agriculture, subsurface drainage must be adequate to permit some leaching or deep percolation through the root zone of the soil. Otherwise, salts applied to the soil in the irrigation water will accumulate and ultimately impair crop growth. Subirrigation is sometimes practiced, but salinity must be carefully watched and controlled. In arid regions, shallow ground water is usually saline and the upward movement of salt into the root zone and the surface soil is a continuing hazard. Except when subirrigation is practiced, it is generally considered desirable to keep the ground water table lower than 6 feet below the soil surface. If the soil texture is coarse, a water table nearer the soil surface can be tolerated.

In humid climates where precipitation appreciably exceeds transpiration and surface evaporation, a shallow, controlled water table can be used to advantage to ameliorate short-time drought effects on crops without the attendant salinity hazards that exist in arid regions. Shallow water tables are carefully controlled in extensive areas in the Low Countries of Western Europe for this purpose and contribute greatly to the productivity of the land, especially for shallow-rooted crops.

Strangely enough, a fluctuating shallow water table in humid and subhumid regions may produce drought effects. Roots of most crop plants require aeration and do not extend below the water table. During periods of low rainfall or when the water table recedes, the limited moisture available in the shallow soil zone occupied by the roots is quickly depleted.

Data have been presented by Richards (1941a) on the uptake and retention of water by soil as determined by distance to a water table. At static equilibrium the soil-moisture tension head will be equal to the distance to the water table, so that moisture-retention curves like those shown in Figure 17, page 97 show the distribution of moisture with height, if equilibrium is attained by downward drainage to the water table.

In the absence of moisture extraction by plant roots, appreciable amounts of moisture may continue to flow to the soil surface from a water table at a depth of 6 or 8 feet. In arid regions this is evidenced by the accumulation of salt on the surface of abandoned farms underlain with shallow ground water. This upward movement is not sufficiently rapid to support vigorous crop growth, however, unless the ground water is within 2 or 3 feet of the soil surface, and even then there is a tendency for the root extraction to get ahead of the moisture supply and dry out the topsoil. Richards and Loomis (1942) found that when this drying occurs the soil will not wet up again, even if soil water at comparatively low tension is nearby.

The question is sometimes raised as to whether it is possible to overdrain irrigated soils. The best answer to this question seems to be No, except in those rare situations where subirrigation is feasible.

V. THE PHYSICAL CONDITION OF WATER IN SOIL

It is becoming increasingly clear that certain definite advantages accrue when the relation of soil moisture to plant growth is considered in terms of the work required to remove water from soil. This point of view was first presented by Buckingham (1907) and has been further advanced by Gardner (1920), Richards (1928), Schofield (1935), Edlefsen and Anderson (1943), Russell (1939), Bodman and Day (1943), Wadleigh (1946), Kohnke (1946), and others. Various terms, such as "capillary potential," "thermodynamic potential," "free energy," "pF" "total potential," "moisture potential," and "soil-moisture stress" have been used for expressing the physical condition of moisture in soil. Definitions and nomenclature have not been fully clarified, so there is some confusion in the literature regarding the use of these terms.

The free-energy function from thermodynamics is well suited to express the physical condition of moisture in soils and plants, and the nature and use of this function in this connection have been presented recently by Edlefsen and Anderson (1943) and Broyer (1947a). Since a general guiding theory for the condition and distribution of water in soils and plants is available, immediate scientific progress in this field appears to rest on critical observations and crucial measurements to check and apply the theory. It is anticipated that in the future these experimental facts will be increasingly correlated and interpreted in terms of dynamical and thermodynamical relations.

In this review of the relation of soil moisture to plant growth no particular attempt will be made to harmonize the nomenclature and the views presented in various papers on the subject of the physical condition of water in soil. The terms used and the definitions given by the writers will be chosen mainly as aids in reviewing and understanding the contributions of various workers.   In the discussion that follows immediately, the physical condition of moisture in soil will be described in terms of the "soil-moisture tension," the "osmotic pressure" of the soil solution, and the sum of these two, which has been termed the "total soil-moisture stress."   Other pertinent terms and functions will be introduced and used further on in the course of the discussion.

We shall assume that in soil the attraction for water arising from surface-force action at the interface boundaries in the soil-moisture system may be expressed in terms of soil-moisture tension.   This quantity is the negative pressure of the water in a porous tensiometer cup when moisture transfer to or from the soil ceases.   Defined in this way, soil-moisture tension is dimensionally a stress, as the term is used in physics; that is, force per unit area.   In other words, soil-moisture tension is the pressure difference that must be maintained across the wall of a porous cup in order to attain zero transfer rate between water in the soil, which is subject to surface-force action, and water in the cup, which is not subject to surface-force action.   The equilibrium in question is hydraulic in nature and relates to the streaming of water through the porous wall.   In the establishment of this equilibrium osmotic pressure is not operative, because no semipermeable wall is involved.   Soil-moisture tension is thus a stress that is equivalent to surface-force action in producing a certain energy status of water.

The osmotic pressure of a solution can also be expressed in terms of an equivalent stress.   Without change in the conventional meaning of the term, osmotic pressure of a solution may be defined as the negative pressure to which water must be subjected in order to be at equilibrium with the solution through a semipermeable membrane.   If the solution in question is contained in soil and is subjected to surface-force action, then the water in a measuring cell or osmometer must be subjected to an additional negative stress equal to the soil-moisture tension before the water-transfer rates across the semipermeable membrane are balanced.   Thus, we may express the state, or condition, of soil moisture in terms of the negative stress on the water, which in an idealized osmometer, is equivalent in its effect on the physical condition of water to the combination of surface-force action and osmotic-force action in the soil. It often may be permissible in speaking of total soil-moisture stress to omit the word "equivalent," but "equivalent" must be understood to be included in the definition of total soil-moisture stress.   Otherwise, it is questionable whether the word "stress" could properly be used in this connection, because the density of water in thin adsorbed films corresponds actually to a positive stress.   Also, in the absence of semipermeable membranes, pressure differences arising from osmotic pressure do not occur.

Soil-moisture tension and osmotic pressure both reduce the freezing point and the vapor pressure of water in soil. Presumably, both of these physical properties can be used for appraising soil-moisture stress.

Richards and Campbell (1948a, 1948b) have recently adapted inexpensive resistance thermometers for measuring the freezing point of solutions and have devised procedures so that freezing-point measurements can now be quickly made on soil cores having undisturbed structure. Freezing-point measurements are readily obtainable over the whole soil-moisture range that will permit plant growth for most soils, and formulas for calculating free energy have been proposed and developed by Schofield (1935) and Day (1947). Before it is possible to evaluate accurately free energy or total stress in soil by this method, it is necessary to make a correction on the observed freezing point that is related to the amount of ice formed during freezing, and also a correction arising from the fact that the formulas, which have been developed from thermodynamic theory, relate freezing point to the free energy at $0°$ C., whereas the free-energy value at the root-growth temperature is wanted. The magnitude of these corrections has not yet been accurately evaluated.

Unfortunately, also, vapor-pressure measurements in the range of soil moisture that plants can grow in cannot yet be made with acceptable ease and precision. The vapor-pressure range that is of interest in this case extends only from about 98 to 100 percent relative humidity. New methods have been proposed by Edlefsen (1934) and Davidson and Schofield (1942), but additional improvements appear desirable.

In nonsaline soils the osmotic pressure of the soil solution is negligible, so the total equivalent soil-moisture stress is substantially equal to the soil-moisture tension. While direct methods of measuring soil-moisture tension over the plant-growth moisture range are not yet available, indirect methods can be used.

VI. METHODS OF MEASURING SOIL-MOISTURE TENSION

Plates and Membranes for Tension Control

Porous ceramic plates and permeable membranes are the most convenient means for measuring the relation between soil-moisture tension and moisture content in the plant-growth moisture range. Centrifugation methods employing a controlled-outflow boundary condition have been successfully used for this purpose by Gardner (1937), Russell and Richards (1938), and by Russell et al. (1940), but the method is not well suited to routine use. Cryoscopic methods have been used and, with recent improvement, promise to be very useful. The details of the procedure for calculating soil-moisture tension or free energy from the observed freezing-point depression have not at yet been worked out, but the method has satisfactory reproducibility and sensitivity for many purposes.

Curves showing the relation between moisture content and soil-moisture tension have been referred to as sorption curves by Russell *et al.* (1940), characteristic curves by Childs (1940), and retention curves by Richards (1941a). Schofield (1935) proposed a logarithmic scale, which he called the *pF*, and which has been considerably used. Moisture relations during removal of moisture from soil are of chief interest from practical agricultural considerations because in the field infiltration processes are usually of shorter duration than moisture-removal processes. Haines (1930) studied and described hysteresis effects for porous media, and this phenomenon has been observed and measured in soils by L. A. Richards (1931, 1941a), L. A. Richards and Weaver (1943a), S. J. Richards (1938), and Scofield (1945b). In view of the hysteresis effect, perhaps the expression selected for designating the curves should indicate the direction of the measuring process; that is, sorption versus desorption; uptake versus retention. Retention may overstress the static idea. Perhaps uptake and release would make a better combination, retention being reserved as a neutral term for covering both processes. The term "sorption" has been misused in connection with soil-moisture curves because the work is derived from the latin *sorbere*, meaning to suck in, whereas *sorption* has been more often applied to moisture-release data, for which it would have been better to use the term *desorption*. The terms "*moisture characteristic*" or "*characteristic curve*" are good, and absence of a directional feature may be considered both as an advantage and as a disadvantage.

The relation between soil-moisture content and soil-moisture tension can be obtained by the placement of a porous-cup-manometer combination in a vessel of soil that can be weighed from time to time during moisture depletion to get moisture-content data. This method has been successfully used by Scofield (1945b) and others. An alternate method is to take moisture samples adjacent to a tensiometer in the field as has been done by Russell *et al.* (1940) and Veihmeyer, Edlefsen, and Hendrickson (1943). Far the most common method for obtaining moisture-retention data is that of controlling the soil-moisture tension and allowing the soil-moisture content to come to a steady value by transfer through a porous wall. Porous ceramic cells and plates are suited for measurements in the 1-atmosphere tension range.

The relation of moisture uptake and release processes to pore-size distribution and structure in soils has directed considerable attention to measurements in the low tension range. For this purpose, suction units making use of filter paper, blotting paper, and sintered glass funnels have been used. Such measurements give very useful information on soil structure and pore-size distribution as shown by Donat (1937), Bradfield and Jamison (1939), Leamer and Shaw (1941), and Lutz et al. (1946).

Suction apparatus is necessarily limited to moisture-tension values of less than 1 atmosphere. Schofield (1935) mentioned the possibility of using air pressure to attain higher tension values. S. J. Richards (1938) used specially cast ceramic pressure cells for this purpose. The pressure-plate apparatus described by Richards and Fireman (1943) has, over a period of years, proved to be very satisfactory for measuring moisture uptake and release by soils. The gasket seal for the porous plate has been trouble-free, as has also been the water-tower pressure-control system they described. If the desired measurements extend over a considerable period, some precaution must be taken to prevent evaporation from the buret. No apparatus correction is necessary, because over the 1-atmosphere range the water release by the porous plate and mounting is negligible. Porous-plate apparatus suitable for making measurements on large numbers of sample has been described by Richards (1948, 1949a, 1949b) along with a mercury tower for air-pressure control.

During the last few years many thousands of single moisture-retention values have been made by the Bureau of Reclamation (1948) to appraise field capacity, which becomes a critical factor in the classification of sandy soils. This work was conducted at the Yuma Land Classification Laboratory under the direction of M. N. Langely and is unique in its completeness of data on the chemical and physical properties of soils under consideration for irrigation, especially with respect to moisture characteristics as represented by moisture-release curves.

To obtain moisture-tension control beyond the limit of ceramic plates, Woodruff (1940) and Richards (1941b) independently used pressure-membrane apparatus somewhat similar in construction to ultrafiltration equipment. Improvements in the construction of pressure-membrane apparatus, along with suggestions on pressure controls, have recently been published by Richards (1947, 1949b). Pressure-membrane apparatus is now commercially available and is in use in a number of soil research laboratories.

The curves shown in Figures 15, 16 and 17 are reproduced from the paper by Richards (1949b). Figure 15 shows a moisture release curve

for Chino clay, an agricultural soil from Orange County, Calif.   Data
for the 1-atmosphere range were obtained with pressure-plate apparatus; those from 1 to 15 atmospheres, with the 12-inch pressure membrane units; and those at a higher pressure, in a specially constructed
4-inch cell.   Visking sausage casing was used as the membrane.   This
material has proved, over a period of years, to be of uniform high
quality and well suited to this special use and has been employed at
membrane pressures up to 175 atmospheres.   Extensive work at high
pressures has not been done, but results this far seem to indicate that

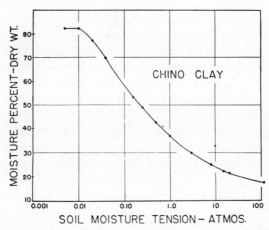

FIGURE 15.—Moisture-release curve for Chino clay obtained by use of porous
    membranes.

leaks through the membrane often develop at pressures above 110
atmospheres.   The independent variable, which for this case was soil-
moisture tension, has been plotted on the horizontal axis.   The logarithmic scale is used to compress the range.   This may or may not be
desirable.   For some purposes, especially when moisture availability to
plants is considered, it seems preferable to use the linear scale for
plotting.

Figure 16 gives moisture-release curves for five soils over the entire
moisture-tension range that will permit growth of crops.   Even for the
finer textured soils, the major part of the available water has been removed when a tension of 3 to 5 atmospheres is attained.   This fact is
illustrated in another way by the method of plotting used for the same
data in Figure 17.   The data are shown on a linear scale to 0.85
atmosphere, after which the scale is broken and a straight line is drawn
sloping down to the 15-atmosphere percentage.

The moisture-release data for the curves in Figures 15, 16, and 17

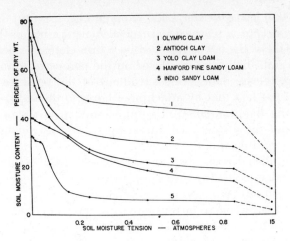

FIGURE 16.—Relation of moisture content to soil-moisture tension over the tension range from 0 to 20 atmospheres. The data from 0 to 1 atmosphere tension are the same as those shown in Figure 17.

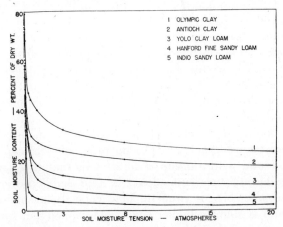

FIGURE 17.—Relation of moisture content to soil-moisture tension for five soils. Soils were air-dried and passed through a 2 millimeter sieve; determinations were made on a porous ceramic plate.

were obtained on samples that had been air-dried and passed through a 2-millimeter sieve. The samples were then placed on the porous plate or membrane, were thoroughly wetted, and were brought successively to the indicated tensions. The data thus relate to moisture conditions in cultivated soil. The curves would be appreciably different in the low-tension range if the measurements had been made on samples having undisturbed field structure. Such samples can be conveniently obtained with the Lutz sampler (Lutz *et al.*, 1946), with which the soil core is retained in a metal moisture box. When ready for test, the lid of the box is replaced by a thin cloth retainer, and after wetting the soil, the boxes are placed on the porous plate for obtaining the moisture-release data. One advantage of the pressure-type apparatus lies in the fact that by attaching a buret to the outflow, information regarding the attainment of equilibrium can be obtained conveniently without the disturbance caused by successive weighings during approach to equilibrium.

Pore-size distribution data, as calculated from moisture-release curves on undisturbed structure samples, can be obtained on samples 5 centimeters or more in height in reasonable time because ½ atmosphere or, at most, 1 atmosphere of tension covers the range of principal interest. At higher tensions with the pressure-membrane apparatus, it has been found expedient for equilibrium studies to restrict the sample height to 1 centimeter or less. Occasional soils have been found for which several days have been required to attain equilibrium at 15 atmospheres with a sample height of only 2 millimeters.

Richards and Weaver (1944) defined the ⅓-atmosphere percentage as the percentage of moisture in a sample of soil subjected to the following treatment: (1) Air-drying, (2) passage through a 2-millimeter round-hole sieve, (3) wetting for at least 6 hours with an excess of water on a porous plate, and (4) bringing to equilibrium at ⅓-atmosphere tension. Care is required to make sure replicate subsamples are similar in texture and represent the main sample. The ⅓-atmosphere percentage was found to correlate closely with the moisture equivalent, which has been considerably used as an index of field capacity. Colman (1947) found with a group of forest soils that the ⅓-atmosphere percentage (like moisture equivalent) is appreciably lower than field capacity in coarse soils, is equal to field capacity at moisture values around 20, and is slightly higher than field capacity in finer textured soils. In some sandy soils the 100-centimeter moisture-retention value as determined on a porous plate agrees very well with the field-capacity value.

From the experimental fact that the ⅓-atmosphere percentage is substantially equal to the moisture equivalent, one might expect, at least for medium- and fine-textured soils, that tensiometer readings would be near 345 centimeters of water as field capacity. In the West, however, results with tensiometers used in a variety of soils in the field over a number of years indicate that, under conditions ordinarily designated as field capacity, tensiometer readings usually lie in the range from 30 to 150 centimeters of water. Smith and Browning (1947), working in the Midwest, have reported a slightly lower range of 25 to 125 centimeters of water.

The reasons for this discrepancy are not definitely known. Structure may be a factor, because moisture-release curves for sieved and field-structure samples usually differ appreciably. Hysteresis and the degree of wetting may also play a part. The screened sample on the porous plate is very likely more thoroughly saturated with water than is soil in the field. The observations of Smith and Browning (1947) support this view.

Tensiometers

The contributions of various workers to the development and use of tensiometers have recently been reviewed by Richards (1949b). Several different types have been used, depending on the materials available and the conditions under which measurements were to be made. Improvements will continue to be made as new materials become available. Some skill is required in the use of these instruments, but the design and construction have been brought to the stage where the units are fairly widely used for routine moisture measurements, and conventional types are commercially available.

For experimental work, the mercury-manometer types are generally to be preferred because of the precision afforded. Units employing Bourdon vacuum gages are not suitable for long-time outdoor use unless the gage case is hermetically sealed, as is now done for gages used on commercial tensiometers. The precision afforded by Bourdon vacuum gages is ordinarily about ±2 percent of full range and is satisfactory for irrigation control work and some other applications.

Tensiometer readings are unreliable unless it is known that the unit is substantially filled with water. Otherwise the volume of water that must be displaced through the cup wall to attain equilibrium with the soil will be excessive. For this reason, it is desirable for most installations to mount a transparent air trap above ground and to make a connection to the cup in such a manner that any air entering the system becomes visible in the air trap. Where necessary, tensiometer cups have been mounted at considerable distances from the vacuum gage by using small-bore tubing for making the connection. Provisions must be made, however, for complete filling of the system with water and for checking to insure that the unit remains substantially air-free.

The form, size, and arrangement of tensiometers parts can be varied considerably to suit individual requirements. Essential elements consist of a porous cup, a vacuum gage, and means for filling with water and removing air.

The walls of the porous cup should be as permeable as possible and still have an air-entry value greater than 1 atmosphere.   That is, when the walls of the porous cup are saturated with water, the cup should withstand an air-pressure difference of more than 15 pounds per square inch without leaking air.   Suitable cups can be made from ceramic clay by the drain-casting process, as described in books on ceramics such as that by Binns (1922), or cups can be purchased.   The size most commonly used for field work was originally chosen so the cup could be inserted in the 1⅛-inch hole made by the standard Viehmeyer (1929) soil-sampling tube.   Synthetic material such as Koroseal and Neoprene are superior to rubber on tensiometer systems because they are less permeable to gases and less subject to change with age and exposure to light.   Rubber tubing should not be used directly on copper, because the formation of copper sulfide soon destroys the seal.

Tensiometers have been used for measuring soil moisture under field, greenhouse, and laboratory conditions.   The tension range covered by tensiometers extends from 0 to about 850 centimeters of water, or about 0.85 atmosphere.   This is only a small fraction of the tension range over which soil moisture is available for plant growth, since the permanent-wilting percentage corresponds approximately to the 15-atmosphere percentage.   When the soil-moisture tension at the porous cup exceeds 0.85 atmosphere, water is extracted from the tensiometer and the gage reading becomes unreliable.

The limitation of the useful range of tensiometers appears less severe when stated in terms of the available moisture-content range of the soil.   Insufficient data are at hand for any broad generalization, but experience tends to confirm the earlier tentative conclusion of Richards and Weaver (1944) that in the finest textured soils the tension range of 0 to 0.85 atmosphere covers about half of the moisture-content range between field capacity and the wilting percentage.   For the coarser sandy soils the tensiometer may cover more than 90 percent of this range.   Stoeckeler and Aamodt (1940), for example, found that "when the mercury depression exceed 35 centimeters, the moisture content for the loamy sand soils is at or within a few percent of the wilting coefficient; watering will thus be necessary soon after this pull is attained."   Similar conditions were found by Kelley et al. (1946) for Coachella loamy sand.

The curves shown in Figure 18 are derived from the curves in Figure 16 and show the percentage of available water remaining in the various soils at different soil-moisture tensions.   The curves were calculated on the assumption that the available moisture range extends from the 0.15-atmosphere percentage to the 15-atmosphere percentage.   Experimental points are shown on the curve at the 1-atmosphere value; at this value it can be seen that the sandy soil at 1 atmosphere of tension retains only about 15 percent of the available water, as compared with 45 percent for the clay soil.

Tensiometers have a unique advantage over other moisture-measuring devices now available in that they measure a property of soil water directly related to the work plants must do against surface-force action

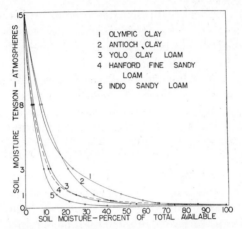

FIGURE 18.—Percentage of the total amount of available water remaining in the soils at various moisture tensions. Curves were obtained from data presented in Figure 16 by assuming that the available moisture range extends between the tension values of 0.15 and 15 atmospheres.

to extract water from the soil. Consequently, for many purposes, the calibration of tensiometer readings against soil-moisture content is unnecessary.

Moisture Meters for Use at High Tensions

Several different types of instruments have been proposed, which with proper calibration are suitable for measuring soil-moisture tension over the whole plant-growth range; some of these have been extensively used in field work. Electrothermal units such as those proposed by Shaw and Baver (1939) and gravimetric sorption blocks like those proposed by Davis and Slater (1942), Davidson and Schofield (1942), and Richards and Weaver (1943a) should be usable if a sensitive element with a satisfactory pore-size distribution is used.

A measurement of the electrical resistance or capacitance of a porous absorption unit buried in soil has been found to have a reproducible relation to the soil-moisture tension. Gypsum blocks proposed by

Bouyoucos and Mick (1947) are widely used.   There is some variation in the calibration of different units, and these blocks are not very sensitive to changes in wet soils.   Toward the dry end of the available range, however, gypsum blocks are very responsive to moisture change.   More recently Bouyoucos and Mick (1948) have described a Nylon-nickel resistance unit, and Colman and Hendrix (1949) have developed a Fiberglas-Monel resistance unit.   Data from field tests on the newer units are not yet available.

Soil units of the electrical-resistance type are subject to disturbance from salts in the soil water.   This should cause no trouble in leached soils, but the effect should be kept in mind if fertilizers are applied to the soil or if the units are used in saline soils.

Kelley *et al.* (1946) have given a comparison of measurements and characteristics for several types of moisture meters.   They also have given an excellent discussion of conditions that are encountered in the field in any attempt to measure and control soil moisture.

VII. SOIL-MOISTURE STRESS IN RELATION TO PLANT GROWTH

Soil moisture has long been known to be an important environmental factor affecting plant growth.   Direct and indirect evidence from various sources bear on this point.   King (1907) has shown that in humid climates large increases in yields can be obtained with numerous crops by supplemental irrigation.   In subhumid climates soil-moisture supply is the most critical factor in crop production.   For example, Cole (1938) has summarized data for 387 crop years at 19 field stations in the Great Plains relating the yield of spring wheat to the annual precipitation for the year ended July 31.   He found that coefficients of correlation between yield and average precipitation at the several stations ranged from 0.61 to 0.90 and averaged 0.76.   Reviews by Kramer (1944, 1949) give useful information and an introduction to the extensive literature on plant-water and soil-water relations.

The wide range in texture and in specific surface of soils precludes any close relation between plant response and the moisture content of the soil.   A plant may grow vigorously in a sandy soil at a moisture content of 5 percent, yet the growth of the same species may be stopped completely by moisture deficit in a clay soil containing 30 percent water on a dry-soil basis.   Reference of the moisture content of soil to the moisture range between field capacity and the permanent-wilting percentage makes it possible to relate moisture content to availability of the moisture for plant growth, but there seems to be a more direct approach to this problem.   Over the years, the idea has evolved that the tenacity with which water is held by soil, or the work required to remove water from soil, may be a particularly useful index for expressing the condition of soil moisture in relation to plant response. Richards (1928) supported this view and stated:

> The problem of the availability of soil moisture to plants becomes very much simplified when considered in terms of the potentials. The term "availability" involves two notions, namely, (a) the ability of the plant root to absorb and use the water with which it is in contact and (b) the readiness or velocity with which the soil water moves in to replace that which has been used by the plant.

Soil-moisture stress and unsaturated permeability appear to be directly related to moisture availability. Not much progress has been made in separating these two aspects of water availability because of the difficulty of determining moisture gradients in the immediate vicinity of small roots. Livingstone and Koketsu (1920) proposed the use of porous porcelain cones for measuring what they called the moisture-supplying power of the soil. With this method the uptake of moisture by an absorption unit during a certain time of contact with the soil is measured. Livingstone and Norem (1937) measured the moisture-supplying power of soils and obtained reasonably consistent results for soils at the permanent-wilting percentage. The procedure is direct but has not been widely used, perhaps owing to difficulty in the standardization of the absorbers. No attempt has been made to specify the action of the absorbers in terms of water-moving force or energy gradients.

Measurements and observations by Veihmeyer and Hendrickson (1927b, 1938); Aldrich, Work, and Lewis (1935); and others have shown reasonably conclusively that moisture will not move from root-free soil at a moisture content below field capacity at a rate adequate to supply roots in adjacent soil at distances of the order of a number of centimeters away. Nevertheless, the fact that a wet sample of soil 1 centimeter deep can be brought in 24 hours to equilibrium with a membrane supporting a pressure difference of 15 atmospheres indicates that unsaturated permeability is not negligible in the moisture range above the wilting percentage. This fact further indicates that in a root zone where the maximum distance of soil from roots is less than 1 centimeter, soil-moisture tension gradients may largely disappear during the overnight period when transpiration is lessened. Thus, moisture-stress measurements averaged over an appreciable soil region, as obtained with a tensiometer, or a freezing-point measurement on a soil core, may satisfactorily represent soil-moisture conditions at the root for at least part of each day.

Calculations made by Edlefsen (1941) indicate that of the total change in free energy of water between the soil and the aerial environment of the leaves of plants, only a small fraction of this change occurs between the soil and plant root. The total soil-moisture-stress range from saturated soil to the wilting percentage is of the order of 20 atmospheres or less, whereas an over-all stress difference of the order of 1,000 atmospheres may be operative during transpiration. In a fluid transmission system, large energy changes in the fluid occur where resistance is high, and conversely, small energy changes occur where resistance is low. From this it might be inferred that soil-moisture stress is not significantly related to plant growth, because it represents such a negligible fraction of the total stress difference. Yet, as Gradmann (1928) and Van den Honert (1948) point out, most of this total differential in stress occurs over the intercellular spaces of the leaf parenchyma, the stomata, and an air layer over the leaf surface. That is, the diffusion pressure deficit in the parenchyma cells of leaves rarely exceed 50 atmospheres. The living tissues of the plant actually incur relatively little resistance in the fluid transmission system from soil to free air in comparison to the relatively high resistance presented by the gaseous phase extending from the internal air spaces of the leaf outward through a thin air "film" over the surface of the leaf. Consequently the range of moisture stress observed in soils is of the same order of magnitude as the diffusion pressure deficit range found in plants.

Direct support for the basic hypothesis that plant growth is simply related to soil-moisture stress appears to come from water-culture experiments. Hayward and Spurr (1944a), for example, using potometers attached to the roots of corn plants immersed in solutions of various salts and sugars, found that the rate of entry of water was inversely proportional to the osmotic pressure of the solution, and for tests of short duration, was independent of the kinds of solutes used. Studies by Long (1943) and Eaton (1941) have shown that when roots of plants are distributed into zones of solution differing in osmotic pressure, nearly all of the water is absorbed by that portion of the root system at the lower stress, even though the difference in stress is only 4 atmospheres. Magistad et al. (1943), Hayward and Spurr (1944b), and Gauch and Wadleigh (1945) have shown that the growth and yield of some plants is definitely retarded by a few atmospheres of osmotic stress in the water-culture medium. In these experiments it should be noted that the second aspect of water availability mentioned above—that is "the readiness, or velocity, with which soil water moves in to replace that which has been used by the plant"—is not present. A complicating factor in soils comes from the fact that solutes carried to the root surface by moisture movement but not absorbed by the plant will accumulate near the roots and will not be dissipated during overnight adjustment when soil-moisture tension gradients tend to disappear.

The importance of this factor cannot be evaluated at the present time because pertinent data are lacking.

There is little direct information bearing on the relation of plant growth to soil-moisture stress, for except by irrigating to limit the maximum stress value attained, there is no known method of controlling soil-moisture stress during plant growth. Also, satisfactory methods for measuring soil-moisture stress have not been available. Nonetheless, recent information of both direct and indirect nature indicates that the vegetative growth of some plants decreases significantly as the soil-moisture stress increases in the 1-atmosphere range and becomes zero before a soil-moisture stress of 15 atmospheres is attained. This is out of harmony with the commonly held view that soil moisture in the so-called available range is equally available for plant growth. Obviously, this subject is of considerable importance to agriculture.

Veihmeyer and Hendrickson (1927b, 1933, 1936) have made extensive field tests to determine the most efficient methods for irrigating in California; on the basis of their observations on perennial fruit crops, they have reported that moisture is equally available over the range from field capacity to near the permanent-wilting percentage. They state (1933) that their studies with grapevines, peaches, prunes, apricots, apples, and pears in field plots and containers and with sunflowers in containers show there is no single percentage of moisture above the permanent-wilting percentage at which plants grow better than at another percentage and which therefore could be considered optimum for plant growth. Their experiments show that favorable conditions of soil moisture extend from the field capacity to about the permanent-wilting percentage.

This view has been widely adopted and has had an important influence on irrigation engineering practices. The irrigation procedures recommended by Veihmeyer and Hendrickson are based on field tests in the area studied and are well founded, but their conclusions regarding the relation of growth rate to soil-moisture conditions in the available range are not in harmony with the observation of other workers, particularly with respect to plants grown in pots and containers. As far as field-irrigation practices are concerned, this discrepancy in some cases may be more apparent than real. It appears that the main objective of the irrigation experiments made by Veihmeyer and Hendrickson was that of developing irrigation practices for farmers where net cash income was the prime consideration. Thus, such matters as cost of applying the water, water losses from evaporation, water and nutrient losses from deep percolation, effect of moisture regime in soil structure, and effect of soil moisture on the quality of the marketable product and on the longevity and susceptibility to disease of perennial crops must be taken into account. Often the quantity of irrigation water available is less than could be used to advantage, and also the very life of certain irrigation projects depends on not developing a ground-water and drainage problem through overirrigation. Therefore many factors influence toward a sparing use of irrigation water, which would naturally be taken into account in recommending irrigation procedures. The present discussion, however, is concerned with the physiological response of plants to soil moisture, economic aspects not being considered.

It is essential that the evidence be closely examined in relation to whether or not growth response is affected by variations in soil-moisture content within the available range. To evaluate the evidence provided by a given experiment involving variation in soil moisture supply, it is essential that consideration be given to (1) the nature of the soil involved; (2) the type of experimental plant studied, including the criterion of growth response; and (3) climatic factors.

Experimental Conditions to Be Taken into Account

Soil factors

The texture, structure, and depth of the soil in the root zone determine the capacity of the soil for storing the water available for plant growth and, in addition, are very important in determining the change in soil-moisture stress taking place with time and change in moisture content as the plant withdraws the water from the soil. For irrigation purposes, the capacity of a soil for storing available water can be expressed conveniently in terms of the maximum-available-water ratio (R_{AM}). Following the nomenclature of Figure 12, this ratio is expressed in terms of the difference between field capacity (FC) and the wilting point (W) as follows:

$$R_{AM} = \frac{(FC - WP)}{100} \times \frac{\rho_B}{\rho_W}$$

This ratio usually lies in the range from 0.1 to 0.2. In other words, the maximum depth of available water in soil varies from 10 to 20 percent of the soil depth, with the fine-textured soils often but not always having the higher values. The total available water-storage capacity for the root zone is obtained by adding R_{AM} values for each depth interval. Doneen and MacGillivray (1946) give data for a soil where the available water capacity is 22.1 inches for a root-zone depth of 12 feet. A deep-rooted crop with low water requirement would not be expected to show much response to irrigation on this soil. Shallow sandy soils may have a very low storage capacity for available water.

The intensity aspect of available water is indicated by moisture-release curves such as those shown in Figures 16 and 18. It is apparent that with Indio sandy loam 85 percent of the available water is released before the soil-moisture tension exceeds 1 atmosphere. Evidently it would be difficult to use this soil for studying the effect of moisture stress on plant growth, for more than 90 percent of the moisture-stress range occurs in 15 percent of the available water range. Conversely, response to irrigation in the available range would be difficult to observe unless the soil moisture in the root zone were reduced nearly to the wilting percentage. On the other hand, a soil like Olympic clay (Fig. 18), where less than 55 percent of the available water is released at tensions below 1 atmosphere, would be more likely to show growth response to soil-moisture additions in the available range. The Meyer clay adobe studied by Aldrich *et al.* (1940) appears to be such a soil. Hunter and Kelley (1946c) found contrasting moisture characteristics for two soils on which they conducted irrigation experiments with guayule. They reported that more than two-thirds of the available water was released from Delano sandy loam at tensions below 1 atmosphere, but only about one-fourth of the available water was released from Sorrente silty clay loam at tensions below 1 atmosphere. The differences in the quality of growth of guayule in relation to the moisture treatments on these two soils was thought to be due to this difference in moisture-release characteristics.

The mechanical impedance of soil to root permeation can markedly affect root distribution and under unfavorable circumstances can greatly complicate soil-moisture studies. Veihmeyer and Hendrickson (1948b) found that the bulk density of soil is sometimes high enough under field conditions to preclude root penetration. This factor was studied with artifically compacted soils, and these workers found that densities greater than 1.75 grams per cubic centimeter for sands and 1.46 to 1.65 grams per cubic centimeter for clays prevented the intrusion of sunflower roots.

Soil stratification and depth have an important bearing on the response of plants to soil moisture. Deep permeable soils thoroughly permeated with roots provide good water-transfer contact between the soil and the plant. In such soils the roots of crops may extend into soil zones well supplied with moisture so that depletion of moisture from the top several feet of soil would have little effect on the plant. On the other hand, claypans, plow soles, sand layers, or bedrock may severely restrict the root zone and make the plant much more susceptible to drought effects. High planting density may restrict the volume of the root zone per plant as effectively as subsurface barriers to root growth.

A fluctuating water table may also contribute to the tendency toward droughtiness by restricting live roots of perennial crops to shallow soil layers. On the other hand, a deep relatively stable ground water table may serve as the main moisture supply for deep-rooted crops and thus make the plants unresponsive to moisture changes in the surface soil. Likewise, the depth and method of irrigation will affect the apparent susceptibility of plants to moisture depletion. If only a limited amount of water is supplied, as by rain or by sprinkler irrigation, the depth of penetration is small and root activity will be limited to a restricted soil layer.

Plant Factors

The specific characteristics of the experimental plant must be taken into account in considering its response to soil-moisture conditions. The nature of the root system is especially pertinent. Kramer (1949) has given well-merited emphasis to the characteristics of root systems in his recent text on water relationships in plants. The extensive studies of Weaver (1926) and Weaver and Bruner (1927) show that the roots of various crop plants differ widely in their inherent capacity to penetrate deeply into the soil. Asparagus and alfalfa roots grow to depths of 12 to 15 feet or more, if the nature of the soil is favorable. Under such crops, soil-moisture studies confined to the surface foot or even the surface 3 feet might well be meaningless. On the other hand, soil-moisture investigations under such shallow-rooted crops as onions and potatoes would need to be largely concerned with the surface 2 feet of soil, for few roots of these crops extend beyond this depth. Differences among varieties of a given species may actually be involved in this consideration. Kiesselbach and Weihing (1935) noted that upon hybridization, the depth of penetration and combined length of all main roots of corn increased materially in the first generation. This observation is probably related to the superior yields obtained with hybrid corn.

In addition to the extent of root penetration, consideration must also be given to root proliferation or the spacial density of root distribution. Owing to the slow rate of unsaturated flow in soils, the exhaustion of soil moisture by plants is very dependent on thorough permeation of the soil mass by fine rootlets. Onions and celery characteristically have root systems exhibiting poor proliferation and permeation. Successful celery culture is largely dependent upon supplemental irrigation, even in humid climates. On the other hand, many of the grasses thoroughly permeate the soil with their fine roots. In consequence, grasses not only efficiently remove available moisture from the fine interstices of the soil but also are especially effective in generating good structural characteristics in the soil. It appears that these two effects are to some extent related.

The character of top growth may need to be taken into account in evaluating soil-moisture conditions in relation to optimum crop production. Grapevines are especially noteworthy in their ability to withstand long periods of drought. This capacity is not solely due to the deeply penetrating root system of grapes. Hendrickson and Veihmeyer (1931a) report an experiment with Thompson Seedless grapes on a Fresno sandy loam wherein infrequent irrigation was compared with irrigations sufficiently frequent to maintain the soil moisture continuously above the permanent-wilting percentage. Under the infrequent irrigation, the soil moisture was reduced to or below the permanent-wilting percentage in the surface 3 feet for extended periods of time. Correspondingly, the vines infrequently irrigated were wilted on numerous occasions and made consistently poorer growth than the frequently irrigated vines. Hendrickson and Veihmeyer comment that it was surprising that the vines subjected to drought made as good growth as they did, since the soil-moisture deficits were severe. Surprisingly enough, these vines produced grapes nearly as large as those from the frequently irrigated vines.

As a marked contrast to the performance of grapevines, Clements and Kubota (1942, 1943) found that maximum production by sugarcane is closely related to the maintenance of the moisture content of the tissues at or above a given level. They found that the soil-moisture regime should be so adjusted that the moisture content of the leaf sheaths does not crop below 85 percent of the green weight during the first 12 months of growth. Clements (1948) states that in order to maintain this water content in the plant tissues, the soil moisture should be prevented from approaching the permanent-wilting percentage and that the soil should be irrigated when the soil-moisture tension is only 0.25 to 0.3 atmosphere.

Egyptian cotton provides a good example of the extent to which the character of the top growth must be considered in studying plant response to soil-moisture conditions. Hope, King, and Parker (1936), working in the Salt River Valley of Arizona, observed that when Pima Egyptian cotton plants were irrigated after being subjected to moisture stress, the plants developed a proliferous vegetative growth that was relatively nonfruitful. This condition, designated as "crazy top," could be largely prevented on Pima cotton by adjusting the irrigation schedule so as to limit the degree and duration of the moisture stress on the plant.

When ascertaining the response of a crop to a given set of experimental conditions, the results may well be conditioned by the criterion of growth response adopted. This is illustrated by the investigations of Adams, Veihmeyer, and Brown (1942). Cotton was subjected to three different irrigation regimes. These investigators found marked differences in vegetative growth, depending on the adequacy of the soil-moisture supply; but there was no significant differences among the three treatments when measured in terms of yield of seed cotton.

Hendrickson and Veihmeyer (1929, 1934, 1936, 1941b, 1942a, 1942b) have made extensive use of the enlargement in fruit size as a primary criterion for measuring growth response of fruit trees under various soil-moisture conditions. This standard of judging growth was especially valid in their studies in view of their ultimate interest in the economic value of the crop. It should be recognized, however, that measurement of growth in terms of fruit enlargement may not entirely corroborate growth data based on various phases of vegetative development.

Bartholomew (1923, 1926) found, with recording auxanometers, that the fruits lost water to the vegetative part when internal moisture deficits were induced in a lemon tree. Haas and Klotz (1935) also noted this effect and found that the osmotic pressure of the extracted sap of the fruits was appreciably lower than that of the leaves. These observations on lemons were further substantiated by the work of Furr and Taylor (1939), who found the size of lemon fruits to be the most sensitive index of any part of the plant to deficiency in the soil-moisture supply. On the other hand, Hendrickson and Veihmeyer (1931a) found that the size of grape berries was surprisingly unaffected by even extreme degrees of soil-moisture stress. Doneen et al. (1939) report that the size of watermelon fruits was not greatly reduced on unirrigated plots, even though the soil-moisture content was depleted to permanent-wilting percentage in much of the root zone. It is of interest to note that Briggs and Shantz (1914) observed during the course of their extensive studies on water requirement that on the basis of production of fruit, the watermelon proved to be exceptionally efficient. The water requirement of the fruits of watermelon was found to be only 46 percent on a fresh-weight basis.

In evaluating crop response to soil moisture there are instances when economic aspects require that emphasis be placed on quality in addition to the quantity of fruit or vegetative growth produced. Hendrickson and Veihmeyer (1929) observed the maximum vegetative growth of peach trees on plots that had the most abundant water supply. However, the quantity of fruit produced on these trees was not superior to those irrigated less frequently, and the keeping quality of the fruit from the frequently irrigated trees was quite inferior.   Hunter and Kelley (1946c) and Wadleigh *et al.* (1946) found that guayule made poorer vegetative growth if the soil was allowed to become drier before irrigating, but production of rubber in the plants was accentuated by a moderate level of moisture stress.

Weather factors

Although this section of the monograph is concerned primarily with the influence of the water content in soil upon plant growth, it is self evident that the desiccating power of the atmosphere has an important modifying effect on the use of soil moisture by the plant.   Air temperature, sunshine, humidity, and wind movement condition the efficiency with which the water in the soil reservoir will be used in plant growth. The classic investigations of Briggs and Shantz (1913a, 1913b, 1914, 1916a, 1916b, 1917) thoroughly demonstrated these relationships.   By way of illustration, these authors (1917) present the water requirement data given in Table 8.

TABLE 8.—*Water requirement of alfalfa* (*Briggs and Shantz, 1914*)

Location	Experimental period	Water requirement			
		Water used	Dry matter produced	Shallow-pan evaporation for period	Ratio of water requirement to evaporation
		Grams	*Grams*	*Inches*	
Williston, N. Dakota	7/29 to 9/16	518	±12	7.5	33
Newell, S. Dakota	8/9 to 9/24	630	± 8	8.6	34
Akron, Colorado	7/26 to 9/6	853	±13	9.5	38
Dalhart, Texas	7/26 to 8/31	1,005	± 8	11.0	34

The transpiration values in this table are indices of the integrated effect of the aerial environment upon evaporation.   More specifically, Briggs and Shantz (1916b) determined the correlation coefficients between the various physical factors of the environment and the transpiration of crops considered as one population.   Their correlation coefficients for the 1914 season at Akron, Colo., were stated as follows:

Transportation with radiation, 0.50 ± 0.01; with temperature, 0.64 ± 0.01; with wet-bulb depression, 0.79 ± 0.01; with evaporation (shallow tank), 0.72 ± 0.01; with evaporation (deep tank), 0.63 ± 0.01; and with wind velocity, 0.22.

Observations on water requirements of plants will be considered in detail in later sections, but the foregoing comment suffices to indicate the

marked influences of weather and climatic conditions on the efficiency
with which a plant utilizes the water present in the soil. The importance of this consideration is illustrated by the irrigation experiments of
Hendrickson and Veihmeyer (1942a) on pears and apples. Yolo clay
loam in an unirrigated Bartlett pear orchard located near the coast of
Monterey Bay, Calif., was not dried to the wilting percentage during the
entire growing season, even though practically no rainfall occurred during this time. The climate in this area is characterized by moderate
temperatures and frequent morning fogs. By contrast, Zamora clay
loam in a comparable Bartlett pear orchard at Concord, Calif., had dried
to the permanent-wilting percentage in the first 5 feet on the unirrigated
plot by June 7. The summer temperatures at Concord are appreciably
higher than along the coast, and morning fogs are less frequent and less
persistent. It is pertinent to note that Hendrickson and Veihmeyer observed a growth response to irrigation in the experiment at Concord, but
not in the one near the coast of Monterey Bay.

Field Experiments with Fruits

In order to study the response of peaches to irrigation in the San
Joaquin Valley of California, Hendrickson and Veihmeyer (1929) set
up an experiment on Oakley fine sand at Delhi. Four primary treatments were established as follows:

W–1: Irrigated with sufficient frequency to maintain soil moisture continuously
above permanent-wilting percentage (treatments A and F).

W–2: Irrigated as in W–1 until fruit began to turn slightly yellow, but with
virtually no further irrigation until after harvest about August 1 (treatment
D).

W–3: Irrigated according to general practice, with the result that moisture in
the upper 3 feet of soil was reduced, often for rather prolonged periods, to
the permanent-wilting percentage or below (treatment B).

W–4: Irrigated at infrequent intervals so that trees received much less water
than would be considered practical commercially, with the result that the
trees remained in a permanently wilted condition for long periods during
the growing season (treatments C, G, and E).

Within a few years after the initiation of this experiment, the trees
most frequently irrigated (treatment A) had developed the largest
trunks, and their evident superiority in this measurement of tree size
continued to increase with time. There were few consistent differences
in the measurements for trunk size among the other three treatments;
but, at the end of the experiment, those subjected to drought for long
periods of time (treatments C, G, and E) were the smallest, and those
irrigated according to commercial practice (treatment B) the next smallest. The experiment showed that maximum growth of peach trees could

not be attained on this soil if the moisture content was allowed to reach the permanent-wilting percentage in the upper 3 feet of soil at any time during the growing season.

The data on vegetative growth of these trees tended to be reflected by the yield of peaches. After the initial fruiting year, the production of trees on treatments A and F (frequently irrigated) significantly exceeded that of trees on B treatment, the second most productive. After the second year of fruiting, yield of trees having treatments C, G, and E (extended drought) was definitely inferior to the production under the other treatments. Thus, continuous maximum yields were not obtained on this soil unless the trees were irrigated with sufficient frequency to maintain the surface 3 feet of soil above the permanent-wilting percentage. An extended drought during the growing season appeared to be relatively more deleterious to fruiting than to vegetative growth.

Hendrickson and Veihmeyer (1929) present data on the cumulative size of peaches produced by the various treatments during the season of 1928. By the latter part of June, when the young fruits had a volume of about 40 cubic centimeters, those on treatment A (frequently irrigated) had become definitely the largest; and the size differential was maintained or increased over the fruits on less frequently irrigated trees. Fruits on the prolonged drought treatment C enlarged as rapidly as those under treatment A during the first 5 or 6 weeks of development but were quite inferior in size by the end of the season. The data show that the development of fruit size by peaches on this sandy soil may be definitely inhibited if the soil-moisture content drops to the permanent-wilting percentage during the latter part of the fruit-development period.

An irrigation experiment on prune trees at Davis, Calif., provided Hendrickson and Veihmeyer (1934) with data similar to those obtained for peaches at Delhi. The experiment was carried out on a Yolo loam, and the treatments used were as follows:

W–1: Frequently irrigated so that soil moisture content was never reduced to permanent-wilting percentage during growing season (treatment A).
W–2: Irrigated before but not after July 1 (treatment B).
W–3: Not irrigated until after July 1 (treatment C).
W–4: No irrigation during the growing season (treatment D).

For the first 4 years of this study there were found to be no significant differences in the sizes of the trunks of the trees on the various treatments. By the fifth year, trees on treatment A definitely had the largest trunks, and their superiority in this respect tended to increase over the 8 additional years of the experiment. By the seventh year, the trees on treatment D (prolonged drought) gave evidence of being the smallest, and their inferiority became much more pronounced during the next 6 years. There was never any significant difference between the trunk sizes of trees on treatments B and C. Thus, as with the peach trees on the sandy soil, prune trees made maximum growth over the course of the experiment when the moisture content of the surface 3 feet of soil was maintained above the wilting percentage. Lack of irrigation had an especially serious effect on older trees. It appears that when recharged by winter rain, the moisture-reservoir capacity of this soil is sufficiently large to supply small sparsely planted trees adequate water without irrigation.

During the early years of fruiting there were few significant differences in yields among the experimental treatments, possibly because of the situation just stated. During 1930, all trees under experimental treatment bore their heaviest crops. The yields that year were definitely the best on trees under which the soil was maintained continuously moist, and were quite inferior on the unirrigated trees. It is evident from the data that irrigation treatments had little effect on yields during years of general low production; but that during years of high general yields the irrigation regime usually had a marked effect on production.

The growth of the prunes was determined over the season of 1932 for the fruits produced on trees under the four irrigation treatments. The largest fruits were produced by treatment A (continuously moist); whereas the smallest were found on treatments D (prolonged drought) and C (unirrigated until July 1). That is, an irrigation regime permitting the soil to reach the permanent-wilting percentage in the surface 6 feet of this Yolo loam was associated with a decrease in the size of prunes.

Hendrickson and Veihmeyer (1942a) carried out irrigation experiments with pears and apples at various locations in California. Their data well illustrate the marked effect of prevailing weather conditions upon the need for and response to irrigation. One study on Bartlett pears located on a Yolo clay loam in the Hollister area showed no effect from irrigation in terms of fruit enlargement, which was the criterion of growth response used. The climate in this area is rather mild, with morning fogs frequently persisting to 9 or 10 o'clock. The annual rainfall there is 20 to 25 inches and is probably adequate to replenish the relatively large moisture reservoir in this fine-textured soil. In fact, the moisture content of the second foot of soil never approached the permanent-wilting percentage during the course of the season.

In contrast to the foregoing observation, irrigation had a marked effect upon enlargement of fruits in a Bartlett pear orchard on Zamora clay loam in Contra Costa County. The rainfall is less than observed at Hollister, and the summer temperatures are higher. In the year studied the soil-moisture reservoir was depleted by early June in the unirrigated plot so that the moisture content of the root zone was at the permanent-wilting percentage during much of the fruiting period. As noted in previous fruit-tree experiments, when the moisture content in the soil under pear trees drops to the permanent-wilting percentage, the size of the developing fruit is definitely depressed. It is of interest to note that of the irrigation experiments on apples reported by Hendrickson and Veihmeyer (1942a), no difference in size of fruit as related to irrigation regime was found in two of the experiments; and that in the third, the larger fruits were produced on the unirrigated plot. The latter experiment was carried out in an orchard west of Sebastapol, Calif., on Gold Ridge sandy loam. This area has heavy winter rainfall, comparatively cool conditions during the growing season, and early morning fogs. Even on the unirrigated plot, the moisture content never reached the permanent-wilting percentage below 2 feet of soil. Irrigation in this orchard was useless when the soil-moisture reservoir was not depleted.

Numerous other investigators (Aldrich et al., 1940; Bartholomew, 1926; Boynton, 1937; Cullinan and Weinberger, 1932; Furr and Taylor, 1939; Hurley and Masure, 1938; and Magness et al., 1935) in addition to Hendrickson and Veihmeyer have observed fruit growth to be a good index of water deficiency in fruit trees. The enlargement of fruits under ideal conditions is characterized by a sigmoid curve, and correspondingly, the rate of change in size of fruit with time is parabolic. Under natural conditions, environmental factors are continuously varying, and the net effect upon plant response may likewise vary extensively over a day's time, or even during a given hour. This continuing succession of changes in the environment is reflected by deviations from the ideal locus of the growth curves. Auxographic records on developing pear (Hendrickson and Veihmeyer, 1941b), apple (Harley and Masure, 1938), and lemon (Bartholomew, 1926) fruits show that the diurnal tendency for enlargement is most rapid at night. During the day, the fruits may enlarge slowly, cease growth for a few hours, or actually contract, depending upon the conflux of soil-moisture supply and atmospheric conditions.

Daily measurements on rate of fruit growth, expressed in terms of the increase in volume per unit of time, may show wide fluctuations. Hendrickson and Veihmeyer (1941b) observed that pear trees irrigated by sprinkling or sprayed for pest control showed a large increase in rate immediately following such treatment and a comparable drop back to normal the next day. The unirrigated pear trees showed the greatest change in growth rate during and immediately after a spray application.

The extensive data of Aldrich, Lewis, and Work (1940) on pear fruit growth show that trees subjected to moisture stress early in the fruiting season have abnormally low rates of enlargement; and even though these rates approached the ideal, or maximum, following an irrigation, the loss in cumulative size was never regained. Boynton (1937) and Magness, Degman, and Furr (1935) obtained comparable data on the growth of apples in relation to soil-moisture supply. The latter investigators noted that reductions in rate of fruit enlargement owing to soil moisture depletion usually occurred sometime during the season, even in years of abnormally high rainfall. They found that under ideal conditions the rate of increase in the volume of fruit is linear with time over a period from 6 to 8 weeks after blooming to near harvest. The rate of growth decreased if a substantial fraction of the root zone approached the wilting percentage, but was resumed at the normal rate when moisture became available, providing serious defoliation had not occurred. The size of fruit at the end of the season was reduced in proportion to the duration of the drought.

Boynton (1937) found a definite decrease in growth of apples on a shallow soil in New York, if the soil-moisture content of the surface 2 feet decreased to the wilting percentage. That is, the moisture reservoir for these shallow-rooted apple trees was nearly exhausted under the stated condition. The evidence suggests that apple trees are efficient in removing available soil moisture without significantly affecting fruit growth. Harley and Masure (1932) state as a result of their irrigation experiments on a sandy soil in Wenatchee, Wash., that:

> With a given leaf area, Delicious apples continued to increase in volume in the 'dry' plots at about an equal rate with those on trees growing in soil maintained at approximately field capacity. After the wilting percentage was reached, however, the fruit growth rate decreased rapidly until water was applied.

Experiments with Jonathan applies on a heavy, deep, clay loam led these investigators to the same conclusion. Magness *et al.* (1935) and Harley and Masure (1932) regarded their observations on fruit enlargement with respect to soil moisture conditions as in general agreement with the conclusions of Hendrickson and Veihmeyer (1929, 1934). However, Boynton and Savage (1938) compared the growth rates of apples at numerous locations in New York State during 1936 and 1937, the latter being a higher rainfall year. In all of the reported cases the rate of fruit growth were higher in the wet year, even though the soil moisture seldom was depleted to the wilting percentage in any of the soil plots in either year.

Aldrich, Lewis, and Work (1940) studied the response of Anjou pear trees to irrigation on Meyer clay adobe soil in Oregon and found:

That with the heavy soil and the climatic conditions at the Medford Station, whenever a reasonably large number of fruits are set, larger fruits will be produced by maintaining soil moisture high in the available range throughout the season, and particularly late in the season.

Their experimental treatments were as follows:

W–1: Frequently irrigated throughout the season; i.e., irrigated when about 50 percent of available water was removed in the first 3 feet of soil.

W–2: Permitted to become relatively dry before irrigation; i.e., when 80 to 90 percent of available water was removed, but in no case was the average moisture content allowed to reach the permanent-wilting percentage in the first 3 feet.

W–3: Same as W–2 during early part of season, and W–1 during latter part.

W–4: Same as W–1 during early part of season, and W–2 during latter part.

Over the 6-year duration of this experiment, the pears produced by treatment W–1 were consistently the largest, and those produced by treatment W–2 the smallest. The size of fruits on treatment W–2 averaged 26 percent smaller than fruits from treatment W–1, and the yield per tree averaged 33 percent less than for W–1. The fruit produced under treatments W–3 and W–4 was intermediate as to size and yield, but neither of these treatments was consistently better than the other. It is rather significant to note that the data of Aldrich *et al.* (1940) show that the diminished rate of fruit growth per day under the "dry" treatment was the result not only of a diminished rate of water accumulation per fruit per day but also of a diminished rate in accumulation of dry matter. Reduced rates of fruit growth were thus observed when the average moisture content of the upper 3 feet of soil was reduced below about 50 percent of the available capacity. This observation is in harmony with other publications from the same station. For example, Work and Lewis (1936) state:

As a result of irrigation requirements of pear trees, Aldrich and Work (1932) and Lewis, Work, and Aldrich (1934) found that differential amounts of soil moisture within the available range exert a profound influence upon pear fruit size and consequent yield.

Work and Lewis (1936) also found that "during periods of relatively uniform weather conditions moisture is lost from all soil depths at a decreasing rate as the moisture content decreases, beginning ordinarily when from 50 to 60 percent of the available soil moisture is still present." These workers recognized that their findings were out of harmony with the view that soil moisture is equally available down to the permanent-wilting percentage. Nonuniform root distribution and slow moisture movement in the clay adobe soil were mentioned as possible explanations for the observed effects.

Under some conditions, because of variability of soil and root distribution, it is difficult to appraise from soil-moisture-content measurements the response fruit trees make to soil-moisture availability. This point is well emphasized by the observations of Furr and Taylor (1939). In line with previously mentioned investigators, they used the apparent growth rate of lemon fruits to evaluate soil-moisture conditions; their experiments showed this criterion to be an excellent index of relative water deficit in lemon trees. They found from fruit volume studies that under decreasing soil moisture a turgor deficit in the tree is evident before the first visible sign of wilting appears or before there is a decrease in transpiration rate, and that this deficit is accentuated as the soil dries out until the tree is completely wilted. Their observations are partially summarized as follows:

In all lemon orchards where investigations were conducted, root concentration and extraction of soil moisture varied greatly. As time from irrigation increased, the moisture content of regions of highest root concentration was reduced to the wilting range before a water deficit was evident from fruit measurements. As the moisture content of increasing proportions of the root zone reached the wilting range, a gradual increase in water deficit became apparent. Before the moisture content of all the soil of any easily delineated zone, such as the top foot, was within the wilting range, appreciable parts of the soil had remained in the wilting range for long periods and high water deficits had developed in the trees. At the times when apparent fruit growth first showed that water deficit had developed, it was usually possible to find soil-moisture contents varying from within the wilting range to near field capacity. Even in locations where root distribution and soil-moisture extraction were most uniform, variations in soil-misture content were so great that the use of averages of soil-moisture percentages proved unreliable as a measure of the water supply of the trees.

The publications by Hendrickson and Veihmeyer (1929, 1934, 1942a, 1942b) on the irrigation of fruit trees contain such statements as:

The term *readily available moisture* is applied to the range of moisture between the field capacity and about the permanent wilting percentage since previous investigations by the authors have shown no difference in the rate of soil-moisture extraction in this range. . . . Work at this station has indicated that the soil moisture above the permanent wilting percentage is readily available for use by plants. . . . apparently, with the plants and soils studied, no one moisture content (within the available range) could be considered as *optimum* for plant growth.

The soil-moisture extraction data presented by these workers appear to be linear down to near the permanent-wilting percentage, but this may not necessarily indicate that over the linear extraction range the soil moisture is equally available for the maintenance of plant turgor and growth. Much of their work emphasizes the adverse effects brought about by soil moisture being reduced to the permanent-wilting percentage in a major fraction of the root zone. Their irrigation experiments usually involved comparisons between one treatment in which the moisture was maintained in the available range and other treatments in which the soil moisture was depleted to the permanent-wilting percentage for various periods of time. Their high-moisture treatments invariably produced the largest trees and the highest yields of the largest fruits, but treatments providing a comparison between various degrees of moisture depletion in the available range were not emphasized.

Field Experiments with other Crops

Factors related to the effect of soil moisture on plant growth to be taken into account in field studies have been discussed by MacGillivray and Doneen (1942), and irrigation experiments with truck crops have been reported by Doneen and MacGillivray (1946). Starting with deep alluvial soil with the soil moisture at field capacity, responses to various irrigation treatments were observed. They state: "Little difference in growth or yield is noted on a deep-rooted crop, such as Connecticut field pumpkins. Plot A (non-irrigated) produced 22½ tons per acre; plot B (irrigated), 26½ tons." Watermelons also showed little response to irrigation, the volume of fruits being increased only about 10 percent by irrigation. An unirrigated plot of tomatoes, which were classed as a deep-rooted crop, yielded about 50 percent when compared to the irrigated plots. In this plot all of the available water was used down to a depth of 6 feet by about August 20, and down to 11 feet by October 10. These workers also found that "shallow-rooted crops, such as sweet corn (Oregon Evergreen), show marked reduction in size of plant and yield on the non-irrigated plot A as compared with the irrigated plot B. There was some rolling of the leaves on the dry plot." In 1940 the height of irrigated Golden Bantam corn was approximately double the height of the nonirrigated corn. Tests were conducted with snap beans, using irrigated and nonirrigated plots. "Beans were obtained on both plots, but the yield was greatly reduced under the dry treatment (though without wilting). Both plots were grown on clay loam soil at Davis." These authors also state:

Onions are very shallow-rooted. With this crop it is necessary to maintain available water in the surface 6 to 10 inches for maximum yields. Potatoes, lettuce, and corn develop poor root systems. A few roots penetrate deeply, but they are not numerous enough to permeate the soil thoroughly at greater depths. It is necessary to keep available water in the surface foot of soil, especially for the first part of the growing season.

For the above tests the degree of soil-moisture depletion was not reported except for the unirrigated tomato plot.

Irrigation experiments on sweet corn have been reported by Mac-Gillivray (1949). Two varieties, Golden Bantam and Oregon Evergreen, were grown during 1940 and 1941 under four different irrigation treatments at Davis, Calif., on soil initially filled with available water to a depth of 6 feet. Treatments were as follows:

W–1: No irrigation water.   W–3: 3 irrigations.
W–2: 6 to 8 irrigations.   W–4: 2 irrigations.

During 1940, each irrigation averaged about 3 inches of water, but irrigations of 5 to 6 inches were used in 1941. The status of soil moisture under the various treatments was not reported. The markedly

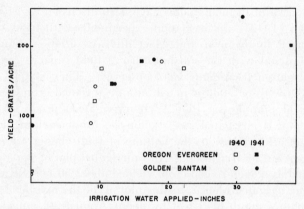

FIGURE 19.—Yield of sweet corn at Davis, Calif., as related to the depth of irrigation water applied (MacGillivray, 1949).

positive relationship between yield of sweet corn and the amount of irrigation water applied is shown in Figure 19. The response to irrigation water in terms of vegetative growth was just as pronounced. MacGillivray states:

Most vegetable plants grown in the field do not exhibit wilting under conditions of low soil moisture. As the moisture supply declines, a reduction in growth takes place first, and finally a cessation of growth. Usually a plant is able to absorb sufficient moisture from soil below the major root regions to remain turgid. Sweet corn plants growing under such conditions, however, exhibited several degrees of wilting. The plants on the dry plots showed the greatest rolling of leaves, but wilting was also noticeable in the plants on the wet plots a day or so after irrigating. . . . Rapidly growing corn plants may transpire so fast that the roots are unable to obtain a sufficient volume of water to keep the leaves turgid. A somewhat similar condition has been noted on Irish potatoes—another crop with a shallow and limited root system.

These results are in line with the observations of Thut and Loomis (1944) on the growth of field corn.

Excellent experimental work on the irrigation of Acala cotton was conducted during the years 1927 to 1930 inclusive at Shafter, Calif., by Beckett and Dunshee (1932). The moisture-equivalent values reported indicate that the Delano sandy loam, on which the tests were made, were unusually uniform to a depth of 5 feet, with an average moisture equivalent of 10.1 and a permanent-wilting percentage of 3.5. The following irrigation treatments were followed for the 4-year period:

W–1: Irrigated when the average moisture content of the top 5 feet of soil reached approximately 7 percent. This is about half way between field capacity and the permanent-wilting percentage.

W–2: Irrigated when the plants wilted at 4 p.m. Midafternoon wilt shows a lack of available moisture in the soil; a change in color of foliage from a light green to a dark bluish green indicated that the plants are approaching wilting.

W–3: Irrigated when the plants wilted at 9 a.m. Early morning wilt was considered to indicate definite distress in the plant resulting from a lack of soil moisture.

W–4: Irrigated as in treatment W–1 until midseason (about July 20), after which water was not applied until the plants wilted at 9 a.m. It was anticipated that in this treatment an abundance of soil moisture would be available during the first half of the season, with a definite deficiency during the last half.

W–5: Irrigated during the first half of the season (until about July 20) when the plants wilted at 9 a.m., as in treatment W–3, after which irrigation was as in treatment W–1. Treatment W–5 thus provided for a deficiency in available moisture during the first half of the season and no deficiency during the second half.

The plots were 16 by 90 feet; there were nine replications for treatments W–1 and W–2, eight for W–3, and five for W–4 and W–5. Water was measured onto the plots and the soil moisture was brought to field capacity to a depth of at least 5 feet with each irrigation. A soil-sampling pattern was established, and approximately 3,000 soil-moisture determinations were made each year. Treatments W–1, W–2, and W–3 were duplicated in outdoor tanks holding 20 cubic feet of soil each. Compared with the plants in the field plots, the plants in the tanks were smaller, the yield per plant was 45 percent higher, and the plants used 47.5 percent more water. The field plots averaged 2,120 pounds of water per pound of seed cotton; in the tanks the average was 2,090 pounds. Summary data for the field-plots experiment are given in Table 9.

TABLE 9.—*Water use and yield of Acala Cotton at Shafter, Calif., 1927–30, for various irrigation treatments (Beckett and Dunshee, 1932)*

Item	Treatment[1]				
	W–1	W–2	W–3	W–4	W–5
Irrigation:					
Number of irrigations	7	4	3	5	5
Acre-inches per acre of water applied	38.6	24.8	22.6	28.0	26.2
Relative percentages for water applied[2]	171	110	100	124	116
Growth:					
Height of plants in inches	48.0	39.3	35.6	41.2	48.1
Number of bolls per plant	18.9	15.6	12.6	14.7	18.0
Yield:					
Pounds seed cotton per plot	55.8	41.4	32.6	37.6	34.0
Estimated pounds seed cotton per acre[3]	3,100	2,300	1,810	2,090	1,890
Estimated bales lint per acre[4]	2.06	1.53	1.20	1.39	1.26
Relative percentages for yield obtained[2]	171	127	100	116	105
Pounds seed cotton per acre-inch of water	80.0	93.0	80.0	75.0	72.0

[1] See accompanying text.
[2] Treatment W–3 used as base for relative percentages in treatments, W–1, W–2, W–4, and W–5.
[3] Based on 10,000 plants per acre.
[4] Based on 35 percent lint and a 500-pound bale.

Moisture-percentage measurements given by Beckett and Dunshee indicate that the soil moisture in the wet treatment (W–1) was in the upper part of the available moisture range at all times. In the W–2 treatments before irrigations, the moisture was depleted nearly to the permanent-wilting percentage in the surface 3 feet early in the summer, and in the surface 5 feet later in the summer. In treatment W–3 the available soil moisture was almost exhausted from the surface 5 feet of soil before each irrigation. Detailed records were kept of the size and stage of growth of the plants, and the authors state:

> Continuously available moisture, as under treatment W–1, produced the largest number of flowers per plant, the lowest percentage of shedding, the largest number of bolls per plant, the highest percentage of five-lock bolls, the longest staple, the highest lint index, and the largest yields. Treatment W–3 (9 a.m. wilt) consistently produced the least number of flowers, the highest percentage of shedding, the least number of bolls, the lowest percentage of five-lock bolls, and the lowest yields. The results obtained under treatment W–2 (4 p.m. wilt) were consistently between those obtained under treatments W–1 and W–3.

From the table it is seen that relative to treatment W–3, a 71 percent increase in water applied gave a 71 percent increase in yield of seed cotton. The last line of the table shows the efficiency of water use by the plants, expressed as pounds of seed cotton per acre-inch of water.

Similar irrigation experiments on Acala cotton were continued by Adams, Veihmeyer, and Brown (1942) in other sections of the San Joaquin Valley of California during 1931–35.   During 1931, preliminary field observations were made on six farms with respect to use of water, growth and yield, soil cracking, and root development.

During 1932 and 1933 comprehensive experiments were carried out on a Panoche adobe soil on the west side of Fresno County.   The moisture equivalent was found to be 30 to 35 percent, and the permanent-wilting percentage ranged from 16 to 18 percent.   There were 75 plots in the experiment, and the principal irrigation treatments involved 9 replications. The primary treatments in 1932 were set up to be as follows:

W–1: Irrigated when soil moisture in upper 6 feet of soil had been reduced to about midpoint between moisture equivalent and permanent-wilting percentage.

W–2: Irrigated when cotton plants showed indication of wilt.

W–3: Usual practice of neighboring growers.   Irrigated on June 29, July 23, August 20, and September 16, 1932.

W–4: No irrigation.

W–5: First irrigation applied on July 22, with three later irrigations.

In evaluating the soil-moisture conditions on the various treatments, it is important to note that no water was applied to treatment W–2 during the season, implying that the plants did not wilt on this soil even when unirrigated.   Soil-moisture records on treatment W–2 indicate that the permanent-wilting percentage was reached in the upper 2 feet by August 31.   Soil-moisture content approached but did not reach this value in the lower strata.   The moisture conditions were approximately the same under treatment W–4.

Under treatments W–1, W–3, and W–5, each of which received four irrigations, soil-moisture levels were quite comparable, with the possible exception that the soil under W–5 became somewhat drier during mid-July.   In each case the soil moisture in the first foot reached the permanent-wilting percentage on one or two occasions just before an irrigation, and approached this value in the second foot.   At lower strata the moisture content was maintained in the upper two-thirds of the available range.   Plant growth and yields of seed cotton are given in Table 10.

Data in Table 10 show that irrigations on the Panoche adobe soil doubled the yield of cotton in addition to inducing significant increases in vegetative growth.   Since treatment W–2 was to be irrigated when the cotton showed symptoms of moisture stress, the absence of any irrigation suggests that these symptoms did not develop.   Even though

TABLE 10.—*Responses of cotton plants to irrigation in 1932 (Adams, Veihmeyer, and Brown, 1942)*

Treatment	Total depth of water applied exclusive of preirrigation	Average plant height at end of growing season	Average yield of seed cotton per plant
	Inches	*Inches*	*Pounds*
W–1	19.2	24.0 ± 0.36	0.19 ± 0.004
W–2	0	17.5 ± .28	0.09 ± .009
W–3	20.8	28.5 ± .44	0.21 ± .006
W–4	0	18.0 ± .27	0.11 ± .006
W–5	15.9	25.0 ± .32	0.23 ± .009

symptoms of moisture stress, as characterized by wilting, were apparently not observed in cotton plants on this soil without irrigation, the yield of cotton was doubled by irrigation.

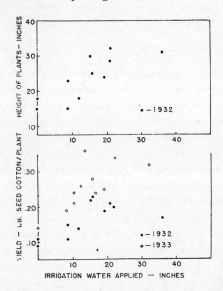

FIGURE 20.—Scatter diagrams showing positive relation between height and yield of Acala cotton and depth of irrigation water applied in tests during 1932 and 1933 in the San Joaquin Valley, Calif. (Adams *et al.* 1942).

The five major treatments used in the tests on Panoche adobe soil in 1932 were repeated on the same soil in 1933. In addition six supplemental irrigation treatments were employed in both 1932 and 1933. All of the height and yield data for these treatments, as given in Table 20 of the bulletin by Adams *et al.* (1942), are shown in Figure 20 and are plotted against the total irrigation water applied in each treatment during the period between planting and harvest. Except for the highest moisture treatment, there is a marked positive relationship between the amount of water applied and both the vegetative growth and yield of seed cotton per plant. This treatment, which called for weekly irrigations, amounted to 36.1 inches of irrigation water in 1932 and 32.2 inches in 1933. These amounts were apparently excessive for the fine-textured adobe soil and produced conditions less favorable to growth.

The investigations during 1934 were located on Panoche clay loam in the same general area of the experiment set-up in 1932–33. There were three irrigation treatments, with 11 replications of each of the treatments, given as follows:

W–1: Irrigate when any single soil-moisture determination below a depth of 0.5 foot showed a moisture-percentage drop equivalent to the upper third of the available range.

W–2: Irrigate when the soil moisture closely approached the permanent-wilting percentage but did not reach it in more than one soil sample for any foot depth from any plot.

W–3: Allow the cotton plants to show severe distress in at least two-thirds of the plots of the treatment before irrigation.

In treatment W–1, receiving seven irrigations, the soil-moisture content did as follows: (1) dropped to within 2 percent of the permanent-wilting percentage before an irrigation; (2) maintained itself in the upper third of the available range within the second and third foot; and (3) remained near the moisture equivalent in the fourth and fifth foot. In treatment W–2, receiving three irrigations, the soil-moisture content (1) dropped to within 2 percent of the permanent-wilting percentage on two occasions prior to irrigation; (2) maintained itself in the upper two-thirds of the available range in the second foot, and in the upper third of the third foot; and (3) remained near the moisture equivalent in the fourth and fifth foot. Under treatment W–3, receiving one irrigation at a time when a majority of the plants showed severe moisture stress, the soil moisture-content (1) dropped to the permanent-wilting percentage in the upper 3 feet several days before the irrigation was applied, but (2) was maintained in the upper half of the available range in the fourth foot, and in the upper third of the fifth foot. Cotton plant responses to irrigation are summarized in Table 11.

The soil-moisture content was maintained in the available range in both treatments W–1 and W–2, though it was generally somewhat higher in W–1 than in W–2. Nevertheless, the vegetative growth under treatment W–1 was significantly higher than under W–2. That is, a significant difference in growth response was effected within the available range of soil moisture, with the greater growth on the treatment inducing the lesser soil-moisture stress. Treatment W–3, inducing the greatest moisture stress, produced the poorest vegetative growth. The weights of the plants actually showed much greater differentials in vegetative vigor than are apparent from the data for height.

TABLE 11.—*Responses of cotton plants to irrigation in 1934 (After Adams, Veihmeyer, and Brown, 1942)*

Treatment	Irrigation water applied	Average height of plants	Average yield of seed cotton per plant
	Inches	*Inches*	*Pounds*
W–1	42.8	32.5 ± 0.26	0.28 ± 0.0064
W–2	25.5	29.5 ± .26	0.28 ± .0064
W–3	13.5	23.6 ± .28	0.26 ± .0076

There were no significant differences in yields of seed cotton per plant among the treatments in 1934. It should be pointed out, however, that cotton may readily become highly vegetative, with an accompanying impairment in fruiting. It is well recognized in the San Joaquin Valley that excessive vegetative vigor may be detrimental to yields. These data emphasize the divergence in conclusions that may be arrived at, depending on the criterion of growth adopted.

Adams *et al.* (1942) set up their experiment in 1935 on Hesperia fine sandy loam in Kern County. Three irrigation treatments were established, with 12 to 14 replications of each treatment. These were as follows:

W–1: Soil moisture not to be allowed to drop below the upper third of the available range.

W–2: Soil moisture to be allowed to approach closely to the permanent-wilting percentage, but not to reach it in more than one sample.

W–3: Cotton plants to be allowed to show severe distress in at least two-thirds of the plots of the treatment before irrigating.

Soil moisture records show that the treatment aims were only partially attained. In treatment W–1, receiving seven irrigations, the soil moisture in the first and second foot was maintained most of the time in the upper third of the available range, but on a few occasions dropped to the lower third; in the third, fourth, and fifth foot the soil moisture was maintained in the upper quarter of the available range. In treatment W–2, receiving four irrigations, the moisture content was maintained in the upper three-fourths of the available range in the first foot; in the upper half in the second foot; and near the moisture equivalent in the lower horizons. Under treatment W–3, receiving only two irrigations, the moisture content reached the permanent-wilting percentage in the upper foot; barely reached that value in the second foot; and was maintained in the upper third of the available range within the third, fourth, and fifth foot. Although the plants under treatment W–3 were not to be irrigated until they evinced moisture stress by wilting, it was not mentioned whether or not they ever did wilt. The soil-moisture records suggest that plants in all three treatments were continuously supplied with water in the available range, but that they differ in the degree of depletion of moisture within this range. Table 12 shows the cotton plant responses observed.

TABLE 12.—*Responses of cotton plants to irrigation in 1934 (After Adams, Veihmeyer, and Brown, 1942)*

Treatment	Irrigation water applied	Average height of plants	Average yield of seed cotton per plant
	Inches	*Inches*	*Pounds*
W–1	33.0	59.4 ± 0.50	0.25 ± 0.011
W–2	24.3	50.2 ± .67	.27 ± .008
W–3	20.3	43.0 ± .73	.29 ± .026

As in the previous study on a fine-textured soil, there were highly significant differences in vegetative growth of plants on the various treatments, even though soil moisture was maintained within the available range, but with different degrees of exhaustion. As in the results of the study during the previous year, differences in vegetative vigor under the three treatments were not accompanied by significant differences in yield of seed cotton per plant.

In general, the investigations of Beckett and Dunshee (1932) and of Adams, Veihmeyer, and Brown (1942) show that the vegetative growth of the cotton plant is sensitive to variations in level of soil moisture within the available range, and that in some instances the productiveness of the plant shows the same response, but not in all cases, since vegetative vigor in cotton is frequently not associated with a comparable degree of productivity.

The relation between yield of cotton in the San Joaquin Valley and total irrigation water applied, as illustrated in Figure 20, is in harmony with duty-of-water measurements made on cotton prior to 1920 in Arizona. Figure 21 shows the yield of cotton lint in pounds per acre for 14 farms at different locations in the Salt River Valley as reported by Marr (1927). All of the farms were on Maricopa sandy loam, and the depth of water applied as shown in the figure, includes the irrigation prior to seeding. Marr states:

The water requirements as they are understood in this Valley after 11 or more years of experimenting are as follows: An abundance of water is applied to the soil just prior to planting. After this initial irrigation, water is withheld until signs of suffering are noticeable. When cotton foliage turns to a dark green color, water should be applied. A light green color denotes a rapid and luxuriant growth. This practice of withholding water is continued until just before the formation of squares. From this stage on throughout the fruiting period, cotton should not be allowed to suffer for moisture.

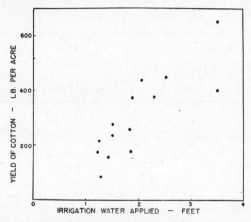

FIGURE 21.—Yields of cotton in the Salt River Valley, Ariz., from fields receiving different depths of irrigation water (Marr, 1927).

The marked positive relation between yield and water applied strongly suggests that on the farms on which the measurements were made water was a prime factor limiting yields.

The effect of soil-moisture stress on the amount and character of growth of nursery-grown guayule was studied by Kelley, Hunter, and Hobbs (1945), on Chualar loam soil at Salinas, Calif. They established five moisture treatments as follows:

W–1: Between field capacity and 850 centimeters of water at the 6-inch depth.
W–2: Between field capacity and 850 centimeters of water at the 12-inch depth.
W–3: Between field capacity and the wilting point at the 6-inch depth.
W–4: Between field capacity and the wilting point at the 12-inch depth.
W–5: No irrigation after the plants became established.

Treatments were randomized with eight replications at each of two fertility levels. The seeds were planted June 3, with the soil profile

wet to a depth of 6 feet, and the differential moisture treatments were
started July 13. At the October 19 sampling the average mean
weights per plant for the respective treatments were 272.6, 253.5,
236.3, 230.9, and 111.9 grams. Statistically, these differences were
highly significant. Root studies indicated there was little difference in the depth of root penetration for the five moisture treatments.

Another study of the effect of moisture stress on the growth and
rubber content of guayule was conducted in field plots by Hunter
and Kelley (1946c). Plots were located on Sorrento clay at Crows
Landing and on Delano sandy loam near Shafter, Calif. The moisture characteristics of these soils were mentioned in a preceding
section. The field plots were 8 rows wide by 100 feet long and
comprised 2.5 acres at each site. There were eight randomized
replications of five moisture treatments at two fertility levels. The
plants were transplated from the nursery early in 1943 and were
uniformly irrigated until the spring of 1944, when the differential
treatments were applied. The five irrigation treatments were as
follows:

W–1: Soil moisture maintained at or above field capacity at all times.
W–2: Irrigated when 25 percent of the available water at the 12-inch depth was
  used by the plants.
W–3: Irrigated when 66 percent of the available water at the 12-inch depth
  was used.
W–4: Heavy initial irrigation in April.
W–5: No irrigation.

Irrigations were guided by intensive soil-moisture content
samplings, and treatments W–1, W–2, and W–3 were approximated
when the irrigation intervals in days were 6 to 7, 9 to 10, and 14
to 15, respectively, through June; and 5 to 6, 10 to 12, and 20 to 22,
after June. The differential moisture treatments produced significant or highly significant shrub-growth differences by the time of
the November 15, 1944, sampling; and except between W–1 and
W–2, these differences were maintained through the winter under
normal rainfall and without irrigation. The effect of moisture
stress on plant characteristics other than vegetative growth will
be referred to in a later section.

Experiments have been conducted on the irrigation requirements
of sugarbeets, with somewhat variable results being obtained by different workers. Doneen (1942) observed the effects of moisture treatments on growth and nitrogen nutrition. The tests were conducted on
Yolo loam soil for which, in the surface 5 feet, the moisture equivalent

ranged from 23.2 to 19.8 percent and the permanent-wilting percentage ranged from 12.6 to 10.9 percent. Nine randomized replications were used for the following treatments:

W–1: Plots in which soil-moisture content was maintained at a relatively high level so the plant always had a large amount of readily available moisture throughout the growing season. Eleven irrigations were applied.

W–2: In the "medium treatment" readily available soil moisture was reduced to a lower level than in the "wet treatment," but soil moisture was not allowed to reach the permanent-wilting percentage. Six irrigations were applied.

W–3: The third series of plots was not irrigated until soil moisture was reduced to the permanent-wilting percentage in the top 3 feet of soil. Several times slight wilting occurred before water was applied. This series was termed the "dry treatment" and received five irrigations.

There is indication from the soil-moisture data presented that poor moisture penetration may have interfered with attainment of the proposed moisture treatment. The available moisture for the wet treatment was about 95 percent depleted from the surface 2 feet of soil on two occasions during June and July. Subsequent irrigation applied to this treatment did not raise the moisture content in the 2- to 3-foot soil interval above the halfway point on the available range except for a period during the first half of September. Depths of water applied were not given. Moisture conditions below the 3-foot depth were substantially the same on all treatments. The dry treatment differed from the medium treatment by one irrigation. Periodic measurements were taken on the nitrogen content of the soil, the growth and sugar content of the beet roots, the dry and fresh weight of the leaves, and the nitrogen content of the leaves and roots. No consistent differences among the treatments were found for these quantities. Concerning growth, Doneen stated: "The growth of sugar beets is independent of soil moisture as long as readily available water is present in the soil; or the mass of soil in contact with the roots is maintained above the permanent wilting percentage."

The effects of soil moisture, spacing, and fertility on sugarbeet production in Utah were studied by Haddock and Kelley (1948) in an experiment using factorial design. The four moisture treatments were:

W–1: Continuously moist below 750 centimeters water tension at 8-inch depth (6 irrigations).

W–2: Continuously moist until August 5; no irrigation thereafter (3 irrigations).

W–3: After July 15 the soil was allowed to reach wilting at 18-inch depth (3 irrigations).

W–4: After July 15 the soil was allowed to reach wilting at 30-inch depth (3 irrigations).

Highest yields of beets and sugar were obtained with the high moisture treatment, W–1, when plant density and fertility were high. This work clearly indicates the need for testing a range of the pertinent variables in combination, because in these tests response to the high fertilized applications was not significant except at the high moisture levels.

Alfalfa is an important crop in irrigated areas, and considerable attention has been given to the water requirements of this crop. Early

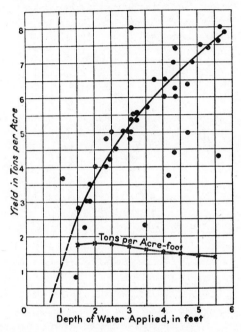

FIGURE 22.—Duty-of-water measurements on alfalfa on 42 farms in the Salt River Valley, Ariz. (Marr, 1927).

investigations were often concerned with the duty of water or the total depth of water applied to the land during crop production. For example, Figure 22 shows duty-of-water measurements made by Marr (1927) during 1913, 1914, and 1915 on 42 farms in the Salt River Valley of Arizona. The farms were mostly in the same township and all but four were on Maricopa sandy loam. The stands were 3 to 15 years old and in localities where the water table was 10 to 15 feet below the surface. In view of the multitude of factors that can influence yield, the scatter diagram in Figure 22 indicates rather definitely that water is one of the principal variables and that in general, within the limits shown, the more water applied the higher is the yield.

Similar results are reported from replicated field-plot experiments with alfalfa on Maricopa loam, as shown in Figure 23, reproduced in part from the bulletin by Marr (1927). In addition, measurements reported by Bark (1916) in Idaho and Beckett and Robertson (1917) in California are also shown in the figure. The ascending parts of the curves are roughly parallel, but are separated more than is accounted for by rainfall differences. Climate, fertility, and other soil factors are

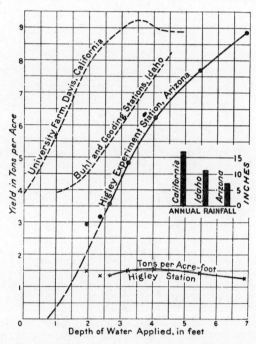

FIGURE 23.—Comparative graphs of duty-of-water on alfalfa at Higley, Ariz.; Buhl and Gooding, Idaho; and Davis, Calif. (Marr, 1927).

undoubtedly involved in these differences. Growth will become invariant with respect to water applications whenever any other factor becomes definitely limiting. This effect is seen in the California data.

The data in Figures 22 and 23 have only indirect bearing on the relation of the vegetative growth rate to soil-moisture stress. The growth rate becomes zero as the available water in the root zone approaches exhaustion. Larger yields can be attained only by maintaining a higher average growing rate. Larger total water applications may mean a greater wetted root zone, but depending on frequency of irrigation and depth of water per irrigation, not necessarily a lower average soil-moisture stress. For the Arizona data in Figure 23, the time of irrigation was the same for all plots, but the depth of water applied per irrigation depended on the irrigation treatment.

The effect of moisture stress on the growth of alfalfa has been studied in field plot studies at Hermiston, Oreg. Leamer, Olsen, Larson, and Domingo (1949) in a preliminary unpublished report of their work compared two irrigation treatments along with sulfur, phosphorus, and boron applications. The statistically segregated effect of moisture level on yield is shown in Table 13 and was greater than the effect of the other treatments on yield.

TABLE 13.—*Effect of two irrigation treatments on quality and yield of alfalfa at Hermiston, Ore., in 1948 (Leamer et al.)*

Item	Treatment	
	W-1	W-2
Irrigations, number	17	11
Average depth of water per irrigation, inches	4.0	4.2
Total depth of water applied, inches	67.3	46.3
Tension at 12-inch depth before irrigation, atmospheres	0.4[1]	4.0[2]
Nitrogen content of crop, %	2.45	2.37
Yield, tons per acre	7.64	6.27

[1] Tension measured by tensiometer.
[2] Tension measured by gypsum block.

The relation of sugarcane growth to soil moisture has been intensively studied in Hawaii. Wadsworth (1934) has presented graphical data indicating decreased growth when the average moisture content of the soil drops below a fairly definite level which he identified with the wilting percentage in the surface 30 inches of soil. Other growth curves for sugarcane given by Wadsworth (1936) are similar to growth curves given by Wadleigh and Gauch (1948) for cotton in that the growth rate decreases continuously following irrigation and before the change in transpiration rate that is ordinarily associated with the attainment of the permanent-wilting percentage in the soil.

Heck (1934) reported that the rate of growth of the cane plants in the field is definitely retarded if the soil-moisture tension at the 12-inch depth exceeds 250 to 375 centimeters of water. This conclusion has more recently been confirmed by Clements (1948) who, after many years of observation of cane plant characteristics, developed what he refers to as the "crop log." The "moisture index"—one element in the crop log and based on the moisture content of a leaf sheath

—gives a reliable indication of the moisture status of the cane plant. Clements states: "Unfortunately, the moisture index cannot be used to determine when the next round of irrigation should be applied. The reason for this is that when there is a drop in the moisture index, we are too late for the irrigation." In discussing soil moisture content determination as a method for irrigation control, he says:

It is only fair to state that were the method applied as defined by the original investigators it would not work for sugar cane. I refer, of course, to the statement that plants are able to withdraw soil water with equal facility down to the wilting point. Our studies at Waipio over a five-year period show this simply not to be true. Thus, the field capacity of the soil I worked with ranged from 35–37 percent. Its wilting point as determined by the sunflower test was between 24–25 percent [;] yet, whenever the soil moisture dropped below 28 percent, there was a check in growth and a drop in the moisture index. Thus, if this method is followed, irrigations are called for considerably before the wilting point is reached.

Clements found that as the moisture percentage of the Waipio soil approaches 28, which from his figures corresponds to a 65 or 70 percent depletion of the available water, the soil-moisture tension rises into the range of 250 to 300 centimeters of water (0.25 to 0.30 atmosphere). These results tend to indicate that the soil-moisture stress range for the most rapid growth of sugarcane may be well below 1 atmosphere. It should be emphasized that the maximum rate of vegetative growth may not be directly associated with maximum rate of sugar production. Swezey and Wadsworth (1940) investigated this question under field conditions and reported that sugar production cost could be cut by extending the interval between irrigations. This extension of interval inhibited cane growth but did not decrease sugar production.

The effect of different soil-moisture levels in the available range on commercial head lettuce production during the winter season in the Salt River Valley of Arizona has been reported by Schwalen and Wharton (1930). Preliminary work was done during 1925–26 by Wharton, and best yields were obtained with the treatment where the soil moisture was maintained at the highest level. Lettuce irrigation studies were continued in 1926–27 by Wharton and Armstrong and they stated their conclusions as follows:

From these results, again it appears that a relatively high and uniform moisture supply is conducive to the production of large heads. Plats of treatment I (irrigated every 2 weeks) both cultivated and non-cultivated are consistently higher in weight than any of the other plats.

During the winter growing seasons 1927–28 and 1928–29, Schwalen and Wharton continued the lettuce studies, using four replicate field plots of each of the following irrigation treatments:

W–1: Soil kept uniformly moist at approximately the field water-holding capacity from thinning to harvest.

W–2: Water applied at such intervals that the soil moisture will not fall below a point midway between the field water-holding capacity and the wilting point.

W–3: Water applied only when soil moisture has been reduced to approximately the wilting point.

W–4: Water applied only when soil moisture has been reduced to approximately the wilting point until heading starts, then by frequent irrigations to keep the soil moisture as near the field water-holding capacity as possible to harvest.

W–5: Soil kept uniformly moist at approximately the field water-holding capacity until heading starts and then irrigated only when the soil moisture has been reduced to approximately the wilting point.

The experiments were conducted on Laveen clay loam soil, which had uniform texture in the top 4 feet, and for which the average moisture equivalent was 19.6 percent and the calculated wilting coefficient was 10.6 percent. Extensive moisture samplings were made, and the average moisture content in the surface 3 feet was kept above 11 percent in all treatments at all times. Winter rains interfered with the complete attainment of the proposed moisture treatments, and, as would be expected, growth differentials created by differential moisture treatments were obscured during the time when temperature was the principal factor limiting growth rate. During the fall and spring, when temperature was more favorable, growth differences caused by differential moisture treatments were significant. Schwalen and Wharton (1930) present extensive data on the weight of heads, percentage of total heads that were of commercial quality, percentage of burst and slimed heads, and percentage of wrapper leaves. These workers concluded:

Harvest data have shown that the maintenance of a high uniform soil moisture content at or above the field water-holding capacity is favorable for production of heavy lettuce heads, however, a soil moisture content slightly below this does not materially reduce the head weight. . . . An abundance of soil moisture at or near the field water-holding capacity of the soil produces the maximum number of plants heading. Irrigation at maturity immediately following a definite soil moisture deficiency results in a low rate of heading. Abundant soil moisture during the growth period with soil moisture reduction during harvest is favorable for a high rate of heading. . . . The percentage of bursted heads is found to be the lowest under conditions of uniformly high soil moisture conditions throughout the season. Any definite soil moisture deficiency during the growing season is favorable to a high rate of bursted heads. This is especially true when the deficiency occurs just previous to harvest and is followed by an irrigation under temperature conditions favorable for rapid growth. . . . The production of heads affected by slime increased in proportion to the amount of irrigation water applied. The withholding of irrigation water previous to and during harvest does not decrease this tendency.

The maximum percentage of slimed heads for all treatments was 2 percent, so this factor was less important than burst heads, the percentage for which varied between 7 and 27.   Schwalen and Wharton also state that "solidity or compactness of the lettuce head is directly affected by irrigation treatment with the maximum solidity resulting from a uniformly high soil moisture content throughout growth."

Veihmeyer and Holland (1949) have reported eight field-plot experiments on the irrigation of lettuce during 1938–1940 in the Monterey Bay region of California.   The results are somewhat similar to those reported by Schwalen and Wharton (1930) in that best production was obtained when soil moisture was maintained high in the available range.   Soil-moisture samplings were made, and in no treatment for any of the experiments did the moisture percentage approach the wilting percentages, even in the 0- to 6-inch soil layer. The different soil-moisture treatments were obtained by varying the amount of irrigation water applied and the time of its application.   In five of the eight experiments the highest moisture treatment gave the greatest weight of marketable lettuce per acre, calculated on the basis of 20,000 plants per acre.   Maximum yields for the other three experiments were obtained on the next to the highest moisture treatment; but since the soil was maintained relatively wet in all treatments, yield differences among the highest yielding moisture treatments were not always significant.

In view of the many factors that enter into field experiments, some controllable and some not, it is difficult to obtain reliable information from field tests concerning the relation of soil-moisture stress to the growth rate of plants.   Also, the authors realize that the extensive literature related to this subject has been inadequately covered in the foregoing review; they will appreciate having significant additional papers called to their attention.

Plant Experiments in Soil Containers

Large outdoor tanks were used by Veihmeyer (1927) to study the water use and growth of young French prune trees.   Yolo clay loam soil was used in tanks 23 to 27 inches in diameter and 48 to 72 inches deep.   This was an historic experiment in that it involved definite recognition of the fact that uniform soil moisture in the available range in an active root zone can be controlled in plant experiments only if the degree of moisture depletion is limited by applying sufficient water to bring the whole root zone to field capacity.   Data from the tank experiment, along with the irrigation treatments used, are given in Table 14.

TABLE 14.—*Water use and growth from March 1 to November 4, 1922, of French prune trees on myrobalan roots under controlled soil-moisture conditions (Veihmeyer, 1927)*

[Trees planted on April 14, 1921, in large containers in Yolo clay loam soil]

Irrigation treatment[1] and tree number	Minimum soil moisture	Container size— diameter and depth	Length of growth	Leaves per tree	Water used	Leaf-water loss	Growth-water ratio[2]
	Percent	*Inches*	*Inches*	*Number*	*Lb. per tree*	*Lb. per sq. in. leaf surface*	
W–1:							
12.............	(^{3})	26 by 48	214	239	316	0.254	0.678
W–2:							
16.............	16	27 by 72	365	510	572	0.215	.638
19.............	16	27 by 72	491	627	712	.218	.690
20.............	16	27 by 72	698	828	1,020	.237	.683
Average.........................			518	655	768	.223	.670
W–3:							
4.............	12	23.5 by 48	536	756	782	0.198	.685
13.............	12	26 by 48	363	474	544	.220	.666
21.............	12	27 by 72	351	398	508	.245	.690
Average.........................			417	543	611	.221	.680
W–4:							
5.............	16–12	26 by 48	348	394	499	0.237	0.698
7.............	16–12	26 by 48	404	346	626	.347	.644
Average.........................			376	370	563	.292	.671
W–5:							
15.............	16–12	27 by 72	333	316	427	0.259	0.778
17.............	16–12	27 by 72	372	451	587	.250	.634
18.............	16–12	27 by 72	185	154	261	.325	.709
Average.........................			297	307	392	.278	.707

[1] For details concerning irrigation treatments, see text.
[2] Efficiency of water use measured by length of shoot in inches per pound of water used.
[3] Water table.

The following moisture treatments were used:

W–1: Water table was continuously maintained 2.5 feet below the soil surface.

W–2: The average moisture content of the soil in the container was brought to 22 percent (moisture equivalent) by irrigation each time the average moisture content was reduced to 16 percent by root extraction.

W–3: The average moisture content of the soil in the container was raised to the moisture equivalent when the moisture content fell to about the wilting coefficient, 11 to 12 percent.   ..

W–4: Soil kept above 16 percent moisture until about the middle of August, when the soil moisture content was allowed to fall to about the wilting coefficient.

W–5: Same as W–4, except after the middle of August these trees were allowed to wilt several times.

In his interpretation of the data in Table 15, Veihmeyer stressed the efficiency and rate of use of water in the various moisture treatments.   He states:

The coefficient of correlation between water loss and leaf area is 0.97 ± 0.11. The coefficient of correlation between water loss and length growth is 0.995 ± 0.002. Coefficients of correlations with such high values as these, and so much greater than their probable errors, may be considered to be decidedly significant. It may, then, be safely said that the use of water by these young prune trees grown in clay loam soil in tanks, under the conditions prevalent at Mountain View, has not been materially influenced by the differences in amounts of water available for growth, and that optimum moisture conditions for growth cover a range of soil moisture from the maximum field or capillary capacity to about the wilting coefficient.

Data presented on the rate of loss of water from the tanks indicates that this rate depended on the leaf area and on the evaporative conditions of the aerial environment but was not influenced by variation in the soil-moisture content in the range from moisture equivalent to the wilting coefficient.   It is seen from columns in Table 14 that the rate of water loss from the leaves, expressed as pounds of water per square inch of leaf surface, and the efficiency of water use, as measured by the length of shoot growth per pound of water used, was substantially independent of the moisture treatments.

In the summary, Veihmeyer states:

Studies of young prune trees grown in tanks under controlled conditions indicate that the use of water by these young trees was not influenced by the amount of water in the soil above the wilting coefficient. Under comparable atmospheric conditions the rate of extraction of moisture by the roots of the trees was the same whether the moisture content of the soil above the wilting coefficient was high or low. Apparently the roots of these trees were able to obtain water as readily when the soil moisture had been reduced almost to the wilting coefficient as when the soil was filled with water to its maximum field capacity.

The foregoing statements on the rate and efficiency of water use are supported by the data. However, he went on to state:

> The results obtained from the controlled studies made with prune trees in tanks indicate that not only the use of water but the trees themselves were not affected by variations in amounts of soil moisture above the wilting coefficient. While these results apply only to these young prune trees, it appears that many of the current views regarding soil-moisture relations of other plants may also be questioned.

The foregoing statement relating the moisture treatments to growth is quite a different matter and justifies a reexamination of the data. Two columns of data in Table 14 show the total length of shoot growth and the number of leaves for each tree. Under treatment W–1 it was found that tree 12, with a water table at 30 inches in the clay loam soil, gave the smallest growth of any of the treatments. Treatment W–2, in which soil moisture varied from 100 percent down to 60 percent of the available range, produced an average of 518 inches of shoot growth and 655 leaves per tree; whereas in treatment W–3, where the soil moisture varied from 100 percent down to 0 percent of the available range, an average of 417 inches of shoot growth and 543 leaves per tree were obtained. It might be expected that the growth of trees in treatment W–4 would have been intermediate between W–2 and W–3. Marked growth depression was caused for W–5 trees by the wilting treatments to which they were subjected and which were illustrated by photographs.

The correlation coefficients calculated above and the other data from this experiment indicate that water over the soil-moisture range from moisture equivalent to near the wilting percentage may be substantially equally available for evaporation, but the difference in the treatment-means for treatments W–2 and W–3 indicate that soil moisture near the wilting percentage is not so readily available for producing vegetative growth of young prune trees as soil moisture near the moisture equivalent. At the time, Veihmeyer may have thought this trend in the data was not statistically significant. Controlled experiments with various plants by subsequent investigators, however, invariably support the hypothesis that the rate of vegetative growth is reduced as soil-moisture stress is increased in the moisture-content range from field capacity to near the wilting percentage.

Kenworthy (1948, 1949) made a greenhouse study of the effect of soil moisture on the growth of young apple trees. He used tensiometers to indicate soil-moisture condition and spaced irrigations so that in four treatments the trees used 20, 40, 60, and 80 percent of the available water before irrigation. In the fifth treatment the trees were irrigated when observable wilting symptoms appeared. Averages of his data for 2 years are shown in Table 15. Six trees per treatment with a 3-month growing period were used the first year, and nine trees per treatment with a 4-month growing period for the second year. The average trunk diameter was about 1 centi-meter at the start, and 1 cubic foot of soil was used per tree. It is possible that the soil moisture corresponding to 60 centimeters of

TABLE 15.—*Growth and chlorophyll content of young apple trees as influenced by the percentage of available soil water used before irrigation (Kenworthy, 1948)*

Item	\multicolumn{5}{c} Percentage available moisture used before irrigation					Mean difference for significance at —	
	20	40	60	80	100	5%	1%
Soil-moisture tension before irrigation, cm. H_2O	60	97	243	570	[1]		
Shoot growth, cm.	193	208	194	142	92	59	99
Chlorophyll, mg. per tree	253	272	243	169	95	59	98
Increase in trunk diameter, cm.	0.36	0.36	0.34	0.18	0.10	0.8	0.13
Total leaf area, dm.^{2}	28	28	26	18	11	6.8	11.8
Increase in dry weight, gm.	83	93	83	49	26	21	35

[1] Wilted.

water tension was somewhat above a true field capacity for this soil because the moisture content of the wettest treatment was evidently too high for maximum growth, and aeration became a factor in the experiment. Significant growth decreases occurred, however, with the less frequent irrigations corresponding to the lower moisture levels in the available range.

Scofield (1945a) grew alfalfa in cans containing 87 kilograms of soil. The soil depth was approximately 2 feet, and three different irrigation regimes were followed:

(a) Cans 5 to 8 were surface-irrigated infrequently, i.e., when the plants had used approximately all of the available water and began to wilt; (b) cans 1 to 4 were surface-irrigated frequently, i.e., when the plants had used approximately half the available water; and (c) cans 9 to 12 were sub-irrigated by maintaining through a drainage tube, a continuously available supply of water in the ground so that soil at the bottom of the can was always saturated.

The relative yields for the three treatments were as follows: (a) 100, (b) 147, and (c) 206. These figures represent the dry weight of tops for seven successive cuttings.

The growth and yield of beans in drums containing soil in the greenhouse were found by Ayers, Wadleigh, and Magistad (1943) to depend on the fraction of the available water present in the soil. Yields of 81, 60, and 33 grams of dry beans were obtained when the average soil moisture, as determined from weighings of the soil drums, was depleted to the point where there was respectively 64, 35, and 10 percent of the available water remaining at the time of irrigation.

Davis (1942) grew nutgrass (*Cyperus rotundus L.*) in gallon pots in the greenhouse. A group of 45 pots was divided into five groups, and individual pots in each group were watered when the minimum average moisture content of the soil, as determined from weighings, was within 1 percent of the levels 18, 15, 12, 9, and 6 percent, respectively. The moisture equivalent of the soil was 16.9 percent, and the determined wilting percentage for corn was 8.2 percent. The pots were watered by standing in pans for 24 hours or until the soil surface was wet, at which time the average moisture content was approximately 22 percent. He found significant growth reductions for each successive minimum level of moisture extraction. For the minimum moisture levels of 18, 15, 12, 9, and 6 percent the average fresh weight of tops for the groups was 33.7, 24.9, 16.5, 9.5, and 4.1 grams, respectively; the fresh weight of tubers was 129.7, 116.5, 79.6, 50.4, and 26.3 grams, respectively. Haynes (1948), working in the greenhouse, studied the effect of moisture availability on the vegetative growth of corn plants. He grew single plants in an artificially aerated loam soil in containers having 4 liters capacity, and employed three moisture treatments. The maximum soil-moisture tensions before irrigation were 0.01, 0.7, and 12.0 atmospheres, and the corresponding vegetative growths, as expressed in grams of dry weight per plant, were, respectively, 33.9, 24.0, and 11.8.

The effect of variation in available water on the yield and quality of potatoes grown in greenhouse pots was studied by Cykler (1946). The galvanized iron containers used were 12 inches in diameter by 30 inches deep and held 105 pounds of sandy loam soil. The field capacity of the soil was 23.87, and the wilting point was 10.8 percent. Seven replicates of three moisture treatments were employed. The pots were weighed twice a day, and sufficient irrigation water was added to bring the moisture content of the soil to field capacity when a predetermined fraction of the available water had been used by the plants. The moisture contents at irrigation for the three treatments were:

W–1: 18.1 percent, corresponding to 52 percent of the available range used.
W–2: 15.2 percent, corresponding to 64 percent used.
W–3: 12.4 percent, corresponding to 88 percent used.

Bliss Triumph seed potatoes were cut in thirds, with one piece going to a replicate in each moisture treatment. A greenhouse temperature of approximately 72° F. was maintained. The potatoes were planted March 18, 1942, and were harvested June 3. The data for the experiment are summarized in Table 16.

TABLE 16.—*Yield and quality of Bliss Triumph potatoes as related to soil moisture (Cykler, 1946)*

| Item | Moisture treatment[1] | | |
	W–1	W–2	W–3
Percentage soil moisture at time of irrigation	18.1	15.2	12.4
Percentage of available water used	52	64	88
Average yield in pounds per pot	13	11.75	10.4
Relative percentage for yield obtained[2]	125	113	100
Number of tubers larger than 1 inch	158	132	125
Number of tubers smaller than 1 inch	246	219	182
Total pounds of water applied	125	121.4	106.4
Probable error of the mean	4.82	3.04	4.82
Slope of moisture-extraction curve in degrees	68.5	68	65.3
Pounds irrigation water applied per pound of tubers obtained	9.62	10.32	10.22

[1] See accompanying text for explanation of treatment.
[2] Treatment W–3 used as base for relative percentages in treatments W–1 and W–2.

Analyses of data showed that the difference in yields was significant at the 5-percent level, but the variation in tuber size with moisture treatment was not. The rate of soil-moisture extraction with time was substantially independent of the moisture treatment. Tests by other workers indicate that moisture depletion by as much as 50 percent of the available range may cause a significant depression in the yield of potatoes.

The effect of soil moisture on the rate of growth of sunflowers in cans was studied by Furr and Reeve (1945). They found, as shown by their data, which are reproduced in Figure 24, that the rate of elongation decreases continuously with time as the soil moisture is reduced below the moisture equivalent. They found that growth ceases at the soil-moisture condition which they designated as the first-permanent-wilting percentage.

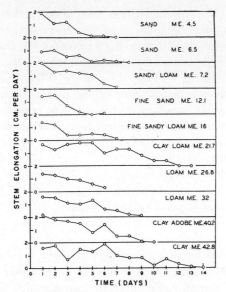

FIGURE 24.—Daily rate of stem elongation of sunflower plants in different soils that accompanies decrease in soil moisture from field capacity (when growth measurements were begun) to first permanent-wilting point (when last measurements were taken). Moisture equivalents (M.E.) given.

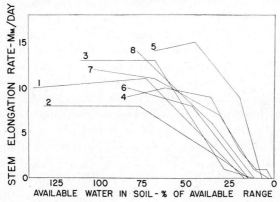

FIGURE 25.—Daily rate of stem elongation of sunflower plants as related to the soil-moisture content expressed as percentage of the total available water remaining in soil (Hesperia loamy fine sand).

Blair, Richards, and Campbell (1950) also measured the rate of elongation of sunflower plants in relation to moisture depletion and obtained the data shown in Figure 25. The elongation rates for the central stem of the plants are shown plotted against the percentage of the available moisture remaining in the soil. The value of 100 represents the field capacity, which was based on field measurements, and 0 represents the permanent-wilting percentage. Each curve is the average of four closely agreeing replicates for the respective foot-depth intervals represented by the numbers on the curves for Hesperia loamy fine sand. These data show there is a definite falling off in the growth rate before half of the available water is used and that growth ceased some time before the permanent-wilting percentage was reached. This decreasing growth rate of sunflowers with soil-moisture depletion was observed in every instance where measurements were made.

Post and Seeley (1947) have shown that for roses grown in greenhouse beds the highest production of marketable flowers is obtained if the soil-moisture tension is kept below 200 centimeters of water. It seems fairly certain that other factors such as light, temperature, and fertility must be maintained at very favorable levels to obtain growth response to water applications at these low tensions. Shanks and Laurie (1949) also grew rose bushes in containers of soil and used Fiberglas wicks to maintain different soil-moisture levels by varying the distance between the water level and the soil. The condition of the soil moisture was indicated by means of tensiometers. Soil-moisture tension levels of 0, 180 to 280, and greater than 850 centimeters of water were reported for the three treatments. Much the best growth was observed at 180 to 280 centimeters of tension; those maintained at greater than 850 centimeters made no top growth, and those at 0 tension were yellowish and made poor growth. The use of porous wick structures to maintain a predetermined level of moisture in soil in which a plant is growing has been shown to be ineffective under certain conditions (Richards and Loomis, 1942).

· From the irrigation and soil-moisture experiments mentioned in the foregoing sections it is apparent that there is considerable evidence that significant differences in growth rates occur along with varying degrees of moisture depletion within the so-called available soil-moisture range. In the interpretation of the statement that soil moisture is equally available until moisture is depleted *about* to the *wilting percentage*, several factors should be kept in mind. Both from the standpoint of supporting evidence and applications, use of the term "available" in this connection should be restricted in its meaning to the rates of soil-moisture extraction and water use by plants. Various experimenters have found that during an irrigation cycle the rate at which an established root system removes water from a soil root zone is approximately uniform down to *about* the *wilting percentage*. In this statement the interpretation of "about" and "wilting percentage" is somewhat variable. If by "about" is meant 2 or 3 percent of soil moisture, then in many cases this moisture-content range covers the major part of the soil-moisture tension range over which plants can grow. In the rest of the moisture range above and below field capacity, soil-moisture tension changes only slowly with soil-moisture content because of the hyperbolic nature of the soil-moisture-release curve. Also, the wilting condition of plants, both temporary and permanent, corresponds to an appreciable range in soil-moisture content. In the field, on successive days temporary wilting occurs during an increasing fraction of the diurnal cycle and merges indistinguishably into a range of permanent-wilting stages as has been pointed out by several investigators. Throughout the moisture-depletion process the soil-moisture stress increases continuously, and much experimental evidence supports the hypothesis that the growth rate of various plants decreases markedly in the available soil-moisture range and that vegetative growth is completely inhibited by the time the soil moisture is depleted to the permanent-wilting range.

Additional Studies Relating Soil-Moisture Stress to Turgescence and Plant Growth

There is an accumulating body of evidence to support the theory that growth rate is related to turgidity. Thut and Loomis (1944) in studying the relation of light to the growth of corn state:

All measurements, both axes and leaves, showed a tendency for size increases to follow the temperature curve and thus, other factors being equal, to be increased by sunlight. Growth, however was checked by water deficits within the plant. Such deficits are generally inversely proportional to light intensity, temperature and air movement. The plants investigated made a greater growth in the daytime when temperature was a limiting factor and a greater growth at night when moisture was limiting. Very commonly, the interaction of these two factors produced a double peak of early morning and early evening growth.

When appreciable quantities of soluble salts are present in the soil, the osmotic pressure of the soil solution must also be considered as a component of the soil-moisture stress that influences directly the rate of entry of water into roots. Certain plants have specific toxic reaction to excesses of certain ions, but with or without such reactions, rate of moisture entry and growth are always affected by the osmotic pressure of the soil solution. The moisture stress of water in soil in which plants are growing is continuously changing as a result of the wetting and drying processes. In leached soils of humid regions, the range of variation in stress is minor unless the soil dries to near the wilting percentage. This fact is illustrated by the curves in Figure 17, which show the tension-moisture relations for the whole plant-growth range. It is clear that even for the fine-textured soils a major fraction of the available water must be depleted before a tension of 2 or 3 atmospheres is attained. In a saline soil there is a large change in moisture stress accompanying a change of moisture content because a decrease in the amount of soil-water present is also accompanied by a proportionate increase in the solute concentration and the osmotic pressure of the soil solution.

Salt distribution in a saline soil or in a heavily fertilized soil of a humid region is usually exceedingly variable within the root zone. As shown by the measurements of Wadleigh, Gauch, and Strong (1947) and Wadleigh and Fireman (1948), although a large quantity of water may be present in the soil volume occupied by the plant roots, a major part of this water might be available to the plant only under high stress because of solute content; whereas the water at the same moisture content in another part of the root zone might be available at low stress because of low content of solute.

A growing plant is influenced by and makes adjustments to soil-moisture stress along with all other prevailing influences. In order to study the effect of soil-moisture stress on plant growth, a technic was developed by Wadleigh (1946) to relate the total water content of drums of salinized soil to the equivalent stress of the soil moisture. To do this, the general relation of moisture content and salt content to soil-moisture stress was determined for the particular soil. Observations were made on the distribution of salt and moisture in the soil. By using the foregoing information, it was possible, by a method of integration, to relate soil-moisture stress, which at any given time was assumed to be uniform throughout the moisture-absorbing root zone, to the total moisture content of the soil. From daily weighings of the drums it then became possible to plot the soil-moisture stress as a function of time between irrigations and to calculate the average integrated stress over an irrigation interval.

Figure 26 shows the observed variations in moisture content of a large container of nonsaline soil on which guayule was growing, as reported by Wadleigh, Gauch, and Magistad (1946). The concurrent variations in moisture stress, which were derived by the method of integration just described, are also shown. These curves represent conditions in a nonsaline soil; the trend of the moisture-stress curve reflects largely the trend of the moisture characteristic of the soil. That is, after irrigation a considerable decrease in moisture content causes only a minor increase in moisture stress; but when a substantial fraction of the available moisture has been used, then a small additional loss of

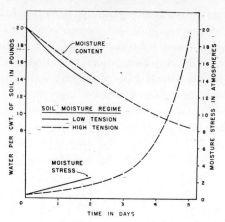

FIGURE 26.—Variation with time in the average moisture content and the total soil-moisture stress for two drums of nonsaline soil containing guayule. Two different irrigation intervals were used.

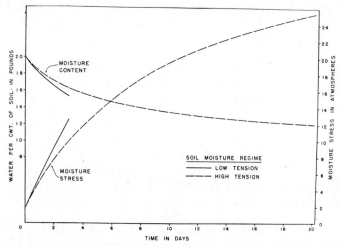

FIGURE 27.—Variation with time of the average moisture content and the total soil-moisture stress for two drums of moderately saline soil containing guayule. Two different irrigation intervals were used.

moisture from the soil causes a large increase in the moisture stress. This general relation is illustrated by the curves in Figure 26 and helps to explain the relatively sudden wilting of plants in gradually drying soil, for when this rapid increase in stress takes place the compensating physiological changes within the plant cannot take place rapidly enough to prevent the loss of turgor.

Figure 27 shows findings concerning rate of change in moisture

stress with change in moisture content in a slightly saline soil in
which depletion of the soil moisture brings about increases in the osmotic pressure of the soil solution in addition to the effect of soil-
moisture tension.   The resulting effect was that moisture stress was
found to have a nearly linear rate of change with time, in contrast to
the curvilinear effect noted for the nonsaline soil.

    When more highly saline soil was studied it was found, as shown in
Figure 28, that the curve for rate of change in moisture stress with time
was concave downward, indicating that plants on saline soil, after reaching high stress, remain for a long period of time with comparatively

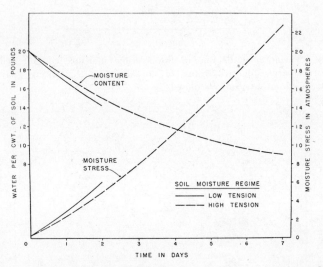

FIGURE 28.—Variation with time in the average moisture content and the total
    soil-moisture stress for two drums of strongly saline soil containing guayule.
    Two different irrigation intervals were used.

little change in that stress.   It is frequently observed that plants on
saline soils make virtually no growth for weeks at a time, and yet they
do not wilt, even though the stress is sufficiently high to induce wilting
in plants on nonsaline soil.   The explanation probably lies in the fact
that the rate of change in stress is sufficiently low that the plant is
capable of making compensating internal adjustments.   On integration
of the areas under these time-stress curves, it is possible to derive a
value for the average stress over the irrigation interval.

    The effect of variation of soil-moisture stress under different treat-
ments in the experiment on guayule is shown in Figure 29, where the
green weight of the plants is shown plotted against the average soil-
moisture stress for the duration of the experiment.   The letters by the

data points designate the treatments, which are explained in the legend for the figure. The average curve is closely similar to that observed in an earlier experiment with beans by Wadleigh and Ayers (1945). It is noteworthy, in view of the inherent errors in the methodology, that the growth responses correspond so closely with the average values of the soil-moisture stress.

The data presented in Figure 29 represent the effect of soil-moisture stress on plants over a growth season and involve the average

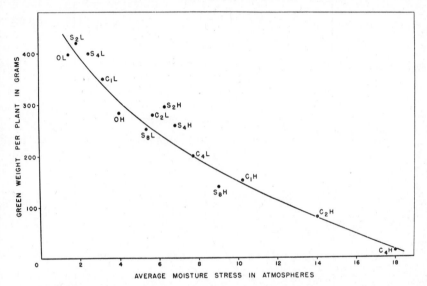

FIGURE 29.—Relation of the green weight of guayule plants to the average soil-moisture stress over the experimental period. $L =$ low tension (frequent irrigation); $H =$ high tension (infrequent irrigation); O denotes no salt added; C_1, C_2, and C_4 denote, respectively, 0.1, 0.2, and 0.4 percent added NaCl; S_2, S_4, and S_8 denote, respectively, 0.2, 0.4, and 0.8 percent added Na_2SO_4, all on dry-soil basis.

for many irrigation cycles. The immediate day-to-day effect of moisture stress on the rate of elongation of cotton leaves has been studied by Wadleigh and Gauch (1948). Typical curves showing the length of leaves of a cotton plant as a function of time during several irrigation cycles are given in Figure 30. The times of irrigations are indicated by arrows; it is clear that the elongation of leaves ceased before an irrigation when the soil-moisture stress was allowed to approach the wilting condition but that growth was resumed after irrigation.

By the previously mentioned method of analysis (Wadleigh, 1946), it was possible in this experiment to obtain the curves for the length of leaves as a function of stress. The curves were parabolic in shape, and best-fit equations were obtained by the method of least squares. From these equations the expression for the rate of change in leaf length with respect to stress was obtained and is shown plotted against stress in Figure 31.

The rate of change in leaf length with respect to time is called growth. We have no common name for the derivative, dL/dS, which

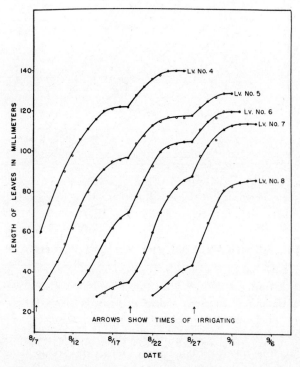

FIGURE 30.—Length of cotton plant leaves in relation to time in days. Arrows indicate irrigations.

is the rate of change of leaf length with respect to stress. The lines in Figure 31 are straight because the leaf length-stress curves were assumed to be parabolic. Physically, $dL/dS = O$ when the stress is so high that the leaf length has become invariant with respect to stress. The narrow range in stress values at which growth ceases, as shown in Figure 31 is rather remarkable, and is especially significant because the results were obtained by an analytical method in which personal bias was not involved in determining the time or the stress at which growth ceased.

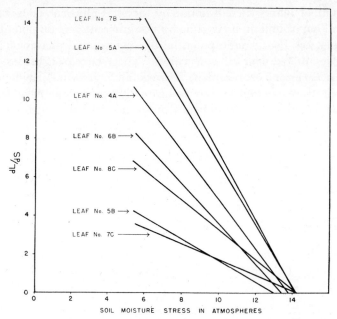

FIGURE 31.—Rate of change in length of cotton plant leaves as related to soil-moisture stress. The intercept indicates the stress which corresponds to the cessation of growth.

VIII. SIGNIFICANCE OF THE WILTING PERCENTAGE

The moisture balance in plants and the state of turgescence depends on a delicate balance between the rate of uptake and the rate of loss of moisture. Wilting of leaves is one indication of moisture deficit of the tissues. The classical work of Briggs and Shantz (1911, 1912a, 1912b, 1912c) contributed greatly to an understanding of the relation of soil moisture to moisture deficits in plants and the wilting of leaves. Plants growing under apparently optimum water-culture conditions, when subjected to a sudden increase in the evaporating power of the aerial environment, may show severe wilting symptoms. In this case, the water-absorbing and perhaps also the water-transmitting properties of the roots and stems are inadequate to supply the moisture losses. Within certain limits, plants can make adjustments to attain moisture balance, either by cutting down the transpiration rate or by increasing the moisture intake rate, or both. The closing of stomata and the increase in the osmotic pressure of tissue fluids during soil-moisture depletion are examples of such adjustments. A good discussion of the factors affecting the soil-moisture content at which plants wilt is presented by Miller (1938).

Growth of plants is conditioned by the total physical, chemical, and biological environment, as well as by the inherent genetic potentialities of the plant. The genetic potentialities delimit the phases of growth and represent an over-all constraint. Turgescence of tissues apparently is a necessary requirement for vegetative growth. Evidence presented in the foregoing pages indicate that some plants experience limitation of growth rate unless soil-moisture tension in at least part of the root zone is considerably less than 1 atmosphere. Turgescence, or something related to it, may influence the phase of growth, because moisture stress in some plants is known to stimulate the reproductive phase. The present discussion is concerned primarily with the relation of vegetative growth to limitations in the soil-moisture supply.

As previously noted, Bartholomew (1926) and Furr and Taylor (1939) found the apparent rate of increase in volume of lemon fruits to be a sensitive index of turgor in vegetative tissues of the tree. The latter stated: "With decreasing soil moisture, a turgor deficit arises before the first visible sign of wilting appears, or before there is a decrease in transpiration rate, and increases progressively, as the soil dries out, until the plant is completely wilted."

Published photographs by Hendrickson and Veihmeyer (1945) and Veihmeyer and Hendrickson (1949) show that wilting symptoms in the lower leaves of sunflowers develop considerably in advance of the symptomatic stage they have designated as permanent wilt. The range and progressive nature of wilting also has been illustrated in the literature with photographs by Furr and Reeve (1945). Wadleigh and Gauch (1948) found that during the increase in soil-moisture stress, the growth of older leaves of cotton plants stops before the rate of growth of young leaves is appreciably slowed. Furr and Reeve (1945) have defined the first-permanent-wilting percentage as:

That percentage of soil moisture at which the forces acting on the water in the soil are at approximate equilibrium with the forces acting on the water in the plant which is at that stage of turgor at which vegetative growth practically ceases. At moisture percentages above the first permanent wilting point, temporary wilting or even death of much of the leaf surface, may result from prolonged exposure to conditions that produce intense transpiration. As long, however, as the moisture content of the soil is above the first permanent wilting point, vegetative growth of the plant may be resumed if transpiration is reduced to a negligible rate and other conditions are kept favorable for growth.

They found that there is a considerable moisture-content range between what they called the first-permanent-wilting percentage, which is indicated by the dropping of the lower leaves of sunflower plants, and an ultimate-wilting percentage, which corresponds to the wilting of the growing tip. These author's show that between these two wilting points lies a moisture-content range of nearly 10 percent for some soils and that generally this wilting range amounts to between 15 and 30 percent of the available moisture range.

Shull (1916) was the first investigator to make a quantitative estimate of the surface-force action in soil at the permanent wilting percentage. He determined the amount of moisture that air-dry seeds of *Xanthium pensylvanicum* would imbibe during 48 hours when placed in salt solutions varying in concentration to provide a wide range in osmotic pressure. He also determined the amount of moisture these seeds would imbibe during 48 hours from a given soil adjusted at various moisture contents near the wilting percentage. Assuming osmotic pressure of solutions and surface-force action in soils, expressed in atmospheres, to be equally effective in controlling moisture absorption by the test seeds, he constructed a curve showing the relation between surface-force action in soil and the soil-moisture content of soil. By interpolation on this curve he estimated that the surface force in soils at the wilting percentage acting to withhold water from the root hairs of plants was no greater than 3 or 4 atmospheres.

The data available at present tend to indicate that permanent wilt is but one somewhat arbitrarily defined and designated stage in a series of stages. Assuming all other factors favorable and with constant evaporative conditions in the aerial environment, there is indication that low soil-moisture stress values produce mild symptoms of wilting and growth retardation, and that wilting increases and the growth rate decreases progressively as the soil-moisture stress increases. Furr and Reeve (1945) found that the central stem of the sunflower stops growing at about the first-permanent-wilting percentage and that the top leaves wilt at the ultimate-wilting percentage. Richards and Weaver (1944) estimated that total soil-moisture stress ranges from 7.5 to 16 atmospheres at the first-permanent-wilting percentage and from 18 to 60 atmospheres for the ultimate-wilting percentage.

Freezing-point measurements have been used to evaluate the condition of soil moisture at the wilting point. For most of this work, an experimental curve for the relation of freezing point to moisture content has been plotted, and the freezing point corresponding to the wilting percentage has been obtained from the curve for a given soil by interpolation. Schofield and daCosta (1935), from freezing-point measurements on seven soils, found that pF ranged from 4.0 to nearly 4.34. Converting to equivalent negative pressure or soil-moisture stress, this corresponds to a range from 10 to approximately 21.2 atmospheres. Bodman and Day (1943) likewise obtained the freezing-point depression for seven soils at the wilting percentage and calculated moisture-potential values ranging from -10.3 to -22.0×10^6 ergs per gram. This corresponds to a stress range from 10.2 to 21.7 atmospheres.

Robertson and Kohnke (1946) obtained freezing-point depression values on 20 samples of Indiana soils at the wilting percentage and calculated pF values ranging from 4.0 to 4.28. This corresponds to a stress of from 10 to 19 atmospheres. Veihmeyer and Hendrickson (1949) gave freezing-point curves from which the interpolated freezing points at the permanent-wilting percentage for 5 of the soils ranged from -0.7 to $-1.8°$ C. This corresponds to a stress range from 8.4 to 21.7 atmospheres. Richards, Campbell, and Healton (1949) have shown that freezing points can be readily measured on cores of soil in which plants have wilted. They found, as would be expected from the shape of the curves in Figure 16, that small variations in the determined wilting percentages correspond to large variations in the equivalent soil moisture-stress values, which were obtained by multiplying the observed freezing point by 12. For four wilting replicates of one soil, for example, they found that a soil-moisture wilting range of 5.9 to 6.3, representing a difference of 0.4 percent of moisture, corresponded to a measured soil-moisture stress range of 14 atmospheres. The average rate of change in stress with moisture content in the interval for this soil was therefore 35 atmospheres for 1 percent in the moisture content of the soil. Confirming earlier indirect observations, they found in their experiment with sunflowers that permanent wilting occurred over a stress range from 7 to 43 atmospheres, depending on the severity of wilting symptoms.

Richards and Campbell made freezing-point measurements on subsurface samples of soil at the United States Salinity Laboratory in November 1949. Plant cover consisted mainly of annual weeds. Rains during the preceding winter totaled only 7 inches so that the moisture status of the profile corresponded to two summers of extraction by plant roots since the whole profile had been wet.

Starting down the profile, the first sample that could be frozen by the technic used was at the 3-foot depth, and it gave a stress value of 69 atmospheres. Stress values decreased consistently to 42 atmospheres at the 5.5 foot depth, which was the deepest sample taken. How much of the moisture depletion was due to vapor transfer through the soil is not known, but the observed stress-distribution might well have been caused by plant-root action, and might still have been in the wilting range for the soil.

Furr and Reeve (1945) state:

The soil moisture within the wilting range provides the plant with an emergency reservoir that enables many species of plants to survive periods of prolonged drought or to mature seed after vegetative growth has ceased as a result of water shortage. With the reduction in the rate of absorption, which occurs near the first permanent wilting point, and the severe water shortage that follows, the various mechanisms by which transpiration is greatly reduced, such as stomatal closure and abscission of leaves, are set in motion; but after these changes are in progress there still remains the available water of the wilting range, which may be slowly absorbed over a relatively long period. Since the magnitude of the wilting range of different soils, even though they may be of similar texture, varies widely, it seems likely that this characteristic of a soil may be of some importance among those factors that effect the survival of plants during periods of drought.

From a biological standpoint, the permanent-wilting percentage represents one arbitrary point within a relatively wide soil-moisture range within which turgor deficits occur. Permanent wilt is a definite stage of wilting that has been carefully described, but there is an appreciable range of soil-moisture content, soil-moisture stress, and degree of flaccidity of plant tissues on either side of the permanent wilt. The permanent wilt symptoms as now chosen and described for sunflower plants appear to correspond approximately to the lower limit of soil moisture that will permit vegetative growth. Experience and skill are required to recognize precisely the symptoms corresponding to permanent wilt, and the experimental reproducibility of the permanent-wilting percentage depends largely on the nature of the hyperbolic relation between soil-moisture content and stress. The physiological status of the plant at the time of the wilting test and the degree of permeation of the soil by the roots appear to be conditioning factors. The appraisal of the growth-rate reduction that accompanies the approach of a certain fraction of the root zone to the permanent-wilting percentage is difficult to determine under field conditions and apparently will depend on the fertility, root activity, and moisture stress in the remaining fraction of the root zone.

Koketsu (1928) concluded from his studies on the amount of water in wilting leaves that leaf-water contents at the critical wilting point of different plants differed widely, as did also the ratio of the critical water content to the content at full turgidity. This ratio appeared, moreover, to have a characteristic value for a given plant and to indicate the resistance of the plant to wilting. This ratio, therefore, presumably might be used as an index for comparing the degree of xerophytism of plants. These observations and conclusions certainly merit further study.

The significance of the permanent-wilting percentage in relation

TABLE 17.—*Regression equations showing the relation of various wilting points to the 15-atmosphere percentage*
[*UWP* = ultimate-wilting percentage; *FPWP* = first-permanent-wilting percentage; *PWP* = permanent-wilting percentage; *FAP* = 15-atmosphere percentage]

Regression equation	No. of samples	Standard error of estimate	Standard error of the regression coefficient	Wilting data by—	FAP data by—	Soils
$UWP = 0.36 + 0.863 \times FAP$	71	0.67	0.013	Furr and Reeve (1945)	Richards and Weaver (1944)	Southern California
$FPWP = 1.50 + 1.022 \times FAP$	71	1.26	0.025	Furr and Reeve (1945)	Richards and Weaver (1944)	Southern California
$PWP = 1.15 + 0.930 \times FAP$	67	0.51	0.047	Veihmeyer	Richards and Weaver (1943b)	Washington
$PWP = 0.69 + 0.993 \times FAP$	51	0.85	0.035	Veihmeyer	Richards and Weaver (1943b)	California
$PWP = 0.99 + 0.97 \times FAP$	21			Peele, Beale, and Lesense (1948)		South Carolina
$PWP = 0.22 + 0.993 \times FAP$	8	0.45	0.119	Thorne (1949)		Hawaii
$PWP = 0.66 + 0.943 \times FAP$	52	0.27	0.019	Blair, Richards, and Campbell (1950)		Central Valley, Calif.

to the lower limit of available water is generally emphasized in irrigation engineering work. For practical engineering purposes, the 15-atmosphere percentage may serve equally well. Richards and Weaver (1943b) determined 15-atmosphere percentage on a group of soils on which F. J. Veihmeyer determined the permanent-wilting percentage and found a close relation between these two measurements. Regression equations relating to the 15-atmosphere percentage to the permanent percentage, as determined by various workers on diverse soils, are given in Table 17. The equation for the ultimate-wilting percentage and the first permanent wilting percentage of Furr and Reeve (1945) are also included for comparison.

The equation relating permanent-wilting percentage to the 15-atmosphere percentage, based on the weighted values for the 199 soils represented in Table 17, is $PWP = 0.85 + 0.96FAP$.

It is evident from the first two equations in the table that the soil-moisture content at permanent wilting depends on the degree of severity of the wilting symptoms. In other words, the regression line for the percentage which corresponds to a mild wilting symptom lies above all of the regression lines for the permanent-wilting percentage. Also, the regression line for the ultimate-wilting percentage, which corresponds to a severe stage of wilting, lies below all of the regression lines for the permanent-wilting percentage. Since it is difficult to give a critical definition of the degree of wilting at *permanent wilt* it is possible that the cessation of vegetative growth would be a better biological criterion for designating lower limit of soil moisture having agricultural significance.

It is evident that additional work must be done to clarify the physics and physiology of wilting phenomena. While the correspondence of a moisture-retention value, such as the 15-atmosphere percentage, to the permanent-wilting percentage indicates rather definitely that the energy of retention of water by soil is an important factor, it is not as yet clear to what extent the specific moisture-transmitting properties of the soil (unsaturated permeability), length of root-soil contact, and other characteristics of the plant are involved.

IX. ENTRY OF WATER INTO PLANTS

Use of the free-energy function for analyzing and expressing the energy status and driving forces of water in soils and plants has been proposed by Edlefsen (1941) and Edlefsen and Anderson (1943) and has been more recently extended by Broyer (1947a, 1947b). Efforts toward applying the uniform terminology of thermodynamics to the soil-plant-water system are laudable, since the system is complicated by a variety of physical and chemical processes and at present is plagued with a multiplicity of terms and nomenclatures.

Broyer's analysis of the problem employed a thermodynamic approach, but the various components were discussed as volumed specific free energies expressed in atmospheres. Free energy is a thermodynamic function involving energy relations of molecules. It is ordinarily expressed in terms of a quantity of energy associated with a definite quantity of matter, such as calories per gram molecular weight, or ergs per gram. Energy per unit volume is dimensionally the same as pressure, i.e., force per unit area. Broyer multiplied molal free energy by −1 and divided by molal volume to obtain what he called *osmotic free energy* or *specific free energy* and which he expressed in atmospheres. Thus, Broyer's usage of the term "specific free energy" differs from the more conventional usage which is followed by Edlefsen and Anderson (1943). Broyer (1947a) also used the term "action capacity" as synonymous with "osmotic specific free energy"; but he later recognized (Broyer, 1950) that there are certain disadvantages connected with the use of the term "action capacity."

The thermodynamic approach to the problem is not yet widely used and is hampered by lack of direct methods for measuring free energy with satisfactory convenience and precision. It is more common at present to express water relations in plants and soils in terms of equivalent pressures instead of the free-energy units. In the earlier parts of this review the condition of water in soil was discussed in terms of *soil-moisture tension, osmotic pressure*, and the sum of these two, *soil-moisture stress*. These quantities appear in the current soils literature and are susceptible to reasonably precise definition. The nomenclature for describing the condition and transfer of water in plants is still in a state of flux, but pressure units related to diffision processes as summarized by Meyer (1945) are predominantly used by plant physiologists in this country. Much attention has been given to water relations in living plants, and in the following pages current theory on this subject will be reviewed. Applications of the theory will be made to the problem of the entry of water from the soil into the plant and the relation of soil-moisture stress to turgescence and plant growth.

The Plant Osmometer

In the classical discussion of water relations in plants, it is customary to consider the case of an isolated cell with a perfectly semipermeable membrane. Meyer and Anderson (1939) and more recently, Crafts, Currier, and Stocking (1949), have given extensive discussions of this case, and only a brief review will here be given.

Several quantities entering into the discussion are here briefly defined.

Osmotic pressure (OP): The pressure difference that must be exerted across a semipermeable membrane to effect zero net transfer between pure water and a solution is termed "osmotic pressure." The term is used here as an index of solution concentration and will not imply the actual presence of such a pressure in the solution.

Turgor pressure (TP): The hydrostatic pressure in the liquid system within the plant or plant cell is termed "turgor pressure." This pressure may or may not have its origin in diffusion processes such as osmosis. Atmospheric pressure is normally taken as the zero reference pressure. Turgor pressure may be greater or less than zero, i.e., positive or negative.

Wall pressure (WP): Wall pressure is equal to and synonymous with turgor pressure for an isolated cell under equilibrium conditions. Some authors emphasize the relation of the forces in the cell wall in relation to the pressure in the cell fluids and speak of wall pressure as being equal and opposite to turgor pressure. However, hydrostatic pressure is a scalor quantity and has no direction aspect in space.

Diffusion-pressure deficit (DPD): In biological systems, diffusion-pressure deficit is the differential between the diffusion pressure of molecules of pure water under reference conditions and that of water molecules in a given system i.e., modified by presence of solute, imbibant, and pressure. It is an equivalent pressure directly related to the direction of transfer of water through the plant systems. Under suitable conditions diffusion-pressure deficit may become an actual pressure, and for a vacuolated plant cell it is defined by the relation $DPD = OP - TP$. Water in the plant system moves in the direction of the increase in diffusion-pressure deficit; and the diffusion-pressure-deficit difference $(DPDD)$, is a measure of the driving force. Although soil physicists do not now use the term "diffusion-pressure deficit," continuity of thought with reference to movement of water from soil into plant will be aided by keeping in mind that soil-moisture stress is identical in concept and dimensions with the diffusion-pressure deficit of the water in a soil.

By way of illustration, consider a plant cell which is at incipient plasmolysis but which has a vacuolar sap with an osmotic pressure of 20 atmospheres. This osmotic pressure may be represented on the vertical pressure scale in Figure 32, which is a diagram adapted from the work of Thoday (1918), Hofler (1920), and Broyer (1947a). If the cell is placed in pure water, osmotic diffusion causes the water to move into the cell with several concurrent actions that are shown qualitatively by lines in the figure. It is convenient to represent the cell volume in relation to the volume at incipient plasmolysis. Relative cell volume is therefore represented on the horizontal axis. As the cell volume increases, the osmotic pressure of the cell contents decreases in accordance with the equation, $PV = $ constant. This process is represented on the diagram by the hyperbolic segment CB. At incipient

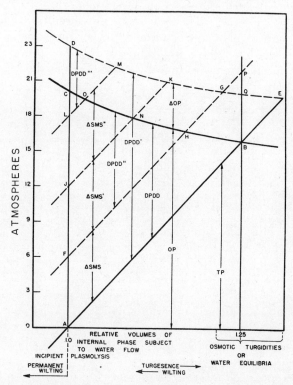

FIGURE 32.—Diagram illustrating the interaction of factors that determine the movement of water in plants. Principal symbols: OP, osmotic pressure; TP, turgor pressure; SMS, soil-moisture stress; $DPDD$, diffusion-pressure deficit difference.

plasmolysis the tension forces in the cell wall and the turgor pressure in the cell contents approach zero, as represented by the point A on the diagram, where the relative volume has the value of 1. As the cell enlarges, the hydrostatic pressure of the cell contents increases because of the elastic constraint of the cell wall. This increase in hydrostatic pressure with enlargement is represented by the line AE on the diagram. At any given cell volume, the vertical distance to the line AE represents the turgor pressure as read on the pressure scale, and is indicated by the vertical line, TP. Likewise, by definition, at any given cell volume the diffusion-pressure deficit of the cell contents is represented by the vertical distance between lines *CB* and *AE*. This distance, in the present example, also represents the diffusion-pressure-deficit difference, *DPDD*, across the cell wall, since the cell is surrounded by pure water for which diffusion-pressure deficit equals zero.

In the diagram at a relative volume of 1.25 it is seen that curves *CB* and *AE* intersect at *B*, where diffusion-pressure-deficit differences becomes zero and water entry stops. At this point, osmotic pressure equals 16, and turgor pressure equals 16 atmospheres. The transfer of water to the solution within the cell results in a decrease in the free energy or activity of the water molecules, i.e., the tendency for the water molecules to diffuse is decreased by the presence of solute. The decrease in the free energy of water molecules on entering a solution is directly measured by the hydrostatic pressure necessary to stop net inflow into the cell. In other words, the hydrostatic pressure supplied by the cell wall at point *B* on the diagram equalizes the free energy of water molecules inside and outside of the cell. For the preceding example the solute content of the cell was assumed to be constant along the line *CB*. If during the course of time there should be an increase, ΔOP, in the osmotic pressure of the cellular fluid owing to intake of inorganic solute or from accumulation of organic solute from metabolism, the relation between osmotic pressure and relative cell volume may be shifted to that of curve *DE*. In effect then, the locus of curve *CB* is shifted upward by an increase in solute in the cell, and downward by a decrease in solute. It is also evident that for a given relative volume the shift of ΔOP from *CB* to *DE* increases the diffusion-pressure-deficit differences as represented by the vertical line *DPDD'*. The new equilibrium will tend toward *E*, where *DPDD'* equals zero. The high osmotic pressure of the tissue fluids of halophytes specifically illustrates the pertinence of this consideration.

Figure 32 has been constructed so that it can also be used to illustrate water relations in plants during water entry from soils. For example, let us start with a root cell that is in contact with soil moisture for which the soil-moisture stress (*SMS*) is 6 atmospheres. At incipient plasmolysis, assume the diffusion-pressure deficit of the cell contents to be 20 atmospheres. This is the generalized osmotic pressure which includes all possible metabolic and nonmetabolic actions, such as osmosis and imbibition, which induce movement of water into the cell. This action again may be represented by the hyperbolic segment *CB* and the vertical line *OP* at various cell volumes. Actions inducing an outward movement of water from the cell will now include not only the turgor pressure, which again may be represented by the line *AE*, but also 6 atmospheres of soil-moisture stress. The sum of these two at various cell volumes is represented by the line FP. The resulting diffusion-pressure-deficit difference is seen to be represented on the diagram by the line $DPDD''$. At incipient plasmolysis, turgor pressure equals zero, so diffusion-pressure-deficit difference equals osmotic pressure minus soil-moisture stress, or $20 - 6 = 14$ atmospheres. Consequently, water inflow and cell enlargement occur until equilibrium is attained at the point H, where $DPDD''$ equals zero. Increase in the turgor could be effected by increase in the osmotic pressure of the cellular fluid, ΔOP, so that OP is at the locus DE and the cell volume could conceivably increase to the intercept at G. That is, increase in the solute content of cells increases the ability of the plant to maintain turgescence with increasing soil-moisture stress.

If the soil-moisture stress is further increased by $\Delta SMS'$ or $\Delta SMS''$, there is a concomitant decrease in the theoretical maximum in the expanded volume of the cells at a given level of osmotic pressure as indicated by intercepts N and O in curves JK and LM. An increase in osmotic pressure of ΔOP will tend to mitigate this effect. Nevertheless, the resultant driving force for net inward diffusion, $DPDD''$, $DPDD'''$, and so on, would probably be inadequate to effect sufficient water entry for transpiration, so that the condition of the cells would move nearer to incipient plasmolysis and the plant would approach a wilted condition.

It should be emphasized that soil-moisture stress (SMS) is seldom constant under field conditions. Thus, immediately after a rain, the soil-moisture stress will probably be only about 0.10 atmosphere, and the plant will tend to be at full turgor as at intercept B. As the soil dries out there will be a slow but gradual increase in soil-moisture stress, but because of the hyperbolic relation between soil-moisture stress and the moisture content of the soil, soil-moisture stress will not become sufficiently large to affect seriously the net inward diffusion until much of the available water in the soil has been removed. As the wilting percentage of the soil moisture is approached, the rapid increase in soil-moisture stress induces a concomitant rapid decrease in the net inward driving force (diffusion-pressure-deficit difference) that causes water to enter the plant, and thus results in loss of turgidity, reduction in the rate of growth, and finally permanent wilting of the plant. It is evident that if the soil-moisture stress is maintained at an appreciable level by solute, as in the saline soils of the West or the heavily fertilized sandy soils of the Atlantic seaboard, the relative volume of the internal phase will be maintained below theoretical maximum and the plant will take on a stunted appearance.

Transpiration can be taken into account in the application of the diagram in Figure 32. Evaporation of water from the plant shoot produces a decrease in the volume of the internal phase and an associated increase in diffusion-pressure-deficit difference. The extent to which transpiration will adversely affect the cell volume will depend upon the magnitude of the diffusion-pressure-deficit difference necessary to effect intake of water fast enough to compensate for transpiration loss. As pointed out by Thut and Loomis (1944), water deficits produced by transpiration may limit the expansion of cells and tissues.

In discussing Figure 32, an inverse interdependence between turgor pressure and cell volume was implied, i.e., extension of the cell is conditioned by internal hydrostatic pressure. The observation of Ursprung and Blum (1924) that turgor pressure was relatively low in the growing root cells of *Vicia faba* in the region of maximum growth, has frequently been referred to as evidence that internal hydrostatic pressure was not a major factor in cellular enlargement. It is possible that the low turgor pressure observed in the cells of rapidly growing tissues might be due to easy extensibility and hence low constraining action of newly formed wall material. Consideration of all of the present evidence inclines the writers to the view that internal hydrostatic or turgor pressure is an important factor effecting cellular enlargement.

Burström (1948) has recently presented a concept of turgor pressure that is at variance with earlier definitions of the term. He states that "this turgor pressure is not caused by a net diffusion of water, nor by an increase in volume and a hydrostatic pressure as in an osmometer, but only by the diffusion pressure of the water molecules." Thus, Burström's definition and diagrammatic representation of turgor indicates that it is synonymous with the diffusion-pressure-deficit difference in the terminology of Meyer (1945). Broyer (1950) has pointed out that Burström's concept deviates from the usual viewpoint. It is possible that Burström's unusual deduction may be partially explained by the fact that he did not take into account time involved in shifts in osmotic equilibria. The writers concur with Broyer that "under practical conditions, rigidity change, involving finite time, is usually conceived as associated with a net movement of water and corresponding change in volume of the inner phase."

Experimental data supporting the pertinence of the diagrammatic scheme in the figure to actual plant response has been provided by Hayward and his associates (1941, 1943a, 1943b, 1944a, 1944b). Rate of entry of water into corn roots immersed in substrates varying in osmotic pressure was measured potometrically (Hayward and Spurr, 1943b and 1944a).   At a given stage of anatomical development of the root, the rate of water entry was inversely related to osmotic pressure of the culture medium.   Typical data are presented in Figure 33.   In addition to the marked inverse effect of osmotic pressure on the rate of entry, it was found that the rate at a given level of osmotic pressure was practically independent of the solute used.   These data are directly interpretable in Figure 32.   An increase in osmotic pressure of the water-culture solution corresponds to ΔSMS in Figure 32.   The decreased diffusion-pressure-deficit difference ($DPDD$), which corresponds to the

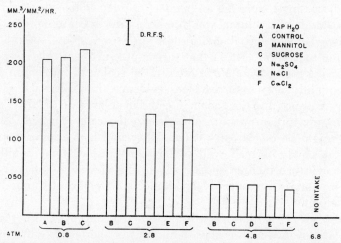

FIGURE 33.—Comparison of average rates of entry of water for individual roots in organic and inorganic solutions at isosmotic pressures.   Difference required for significance (DRFS), as derived from pooled error variance, equals 0.033 at the 5-percent level.   (Hayward and Spurr, 1944a.)

decreased driving force causing water entry, seems to explain satisfactorily the reduced rates that were observed.

It may be implied directly from Figure 32 that plants grown at higher levels of osmotic pressure in the culture solution should be characterized by relatively smaller cell volumes.   This relationship has been observed on tomato plants by Hayward and Long (1941, 1943a) and on flax by Hayward and Spurr (1944b).   Figure 34 shows: (1) A transection of a median internode of the main stem of a flax plant grown in a control nutrient solution at 0.5 atmosphere osmotic pressure; and (2), the analagous section from a comparable plant grown in a culture solution having an osmotic pressure of 4.5 atmospheres.   At the higher concentration of the water culture solution the cambium was less active, the secondary xylem cells smaller, and the phloem fibers fewer and smaller in diameter.

The foregoing observation on decreased cambial activity accompanying decreased physiological availability of water is a key consideration in evaluating the effect of soil-moisture availability on plant growth. Growth takes place through cell division and enlargement. Turgescence conditions both of these phases of growth, but principally that of enlargement. Factors affecting cell volume will be reflected in the growth of the plant. For example, Bachman (1922) constructed a

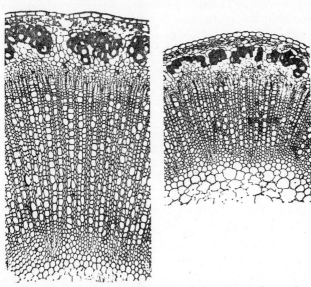

FIGURE 34.—At left, transection of a median internode of the main stem of flax from a control plant (grown in solution culture at 0.5 atmospheres osmotic concentration), showing development of phloem fibers and amount of secondary thickening of the axis. At right, transection of a corresponding internode from a plant grown in the NaCl solution culture at 4.5 atmospheres osmotic concentration. The formation of wood fibers in the xylem region is shown. Comparison of two transections indicates the inhibitive effect of high concentration of salt on cambial activity and size of cells. (Photomicrographs at same magnification originally published as Figure 5, p. 294, Hayward and Spurr, 1944b.)

sensitive "Hebelpachymeter" which enabled him to measure the thickness of leaves with an accuracy of 1.35 to 1.9 microns. Thickness of the leaves reflected the turgor of the cells, and detectable changes in thickness took place even under small fluctuations in the moisture deficit of the atmosphere. If a decrease in atmospheric humidity were accompanied by a decrease in soil moisture, the turgor of the leaf, as reflected by thickness, was still further reduced. There are indications that the cells of a growing plant are seldom at full turgor during the daytime, but it is not possible at present to state what degrees of turgor deficit can be tolerated in cells without affecting growth, or what degrees of turgor deficit correspond to a serious inhibition of growth.

Mechanisms and Processes

In the apt words of Preston (1948), "the entry of water into, and passage through the root system involves mechanisms upon the nature of which there is no settled opinion." A review of the literature makes it clear that this subject cannot be discussed with precision and finality. There are within the plant four distinguishable but more or less arbitrary categories of forces which may be involved in the entry of water: (1) Imbibitional, (2) osmotic, (3) metabolic, and (4) tensive, or transpirational pull. These forces are all components of the specific free energy as employed in Edlefsen's (1941) terminology, or in terms of more general usage, each may contribute to the diffusion-pressure deficit (*DPD*) within the plant. The relative contribution of these various components to the diffusion-pressure deficit will depend upon the species considered and the prevailing conditions under which it is growing. The first three groups of forces are effective within the roots and may be present in the top; the fourth arises from activity within the shoot. Renner (1912) early recognized that those forces arising in the roots induced the development of positive pressures in the conductive tissues resulting in guttation from leaves and exudation from cut stems; whereas the forces arising from activity within the top induced negative pressures in the conductive tissues. Renner used the term "active" absorption to characterize the former groups of forces and "passive" absorption for the latter. These terms have been widely adopted. Crafts *et al.* (1949) and Kramer (1945, 1949) have presented good reviews and discussions of the literature on this subject.

Imbibition

Imbibitional properties of hydrophilic colloids play an important role in the movement of water into plant cells under certain conditions (MacDougal, 1920; Rosa, 1921; Schull, 1916, 1924). Imbibition of water by the seed coat is the first step in the germination of seeds, followed by imbibition of water by the embryo and endosperm. Schull (1916) found that the imbibition effects in *Xanthium pensylvanicum* seeds are sufficient to cause a small amount of water to enter the seeds from a salt solution having an osmotic pressure of 375 atmospheres. In other words, the energy of hydration by biocolloids may be a major component of the action effecting entry of water into plants. MacDougal (1920) observed that hydrophilic colloids are important in the water economy of many desert species. He concluded that the process of growth was dependent on the degree of hydration of the protoplasmic colloids. Environmental conditions that limit the possible degree of hydration in the protoplasm correspondingly limit growth. The role of imbibition in the entry of water from soil is directly interpretable in Figure 32 on the basis of its varying effect on the total diffusion-pressure deficit (*DPD*). Although the effect of imbibition on net *DPD* is analogous to that of osmotic pressure, the potential effects of these two forces may not be directly additive, since the quality and quantity of the solute will condition the imbibitional capacity of biocolloids.

Much has been written on the water "bound" by the hydrophilic colloids, with reference to its role in the tolerance of plants to environmental stresses (cf. Gortner, 1932). Water so held on colloidal surfaces is characterized by a decrease in activity and loss in colligative properties and solvent action. Briggs (1931) measured the activity of water contained in casein by an isotensoscope method and offered evidence that the water-binding capacity of a protein is the *sum* of the water-binding capacity of the isoelectric protein and the water-binding capacity of ionized atoms which are bound to the protein when the salts are formed. The sodium-caseinates were found to be nearly 100 percent ionized, as compared to calcium-caseinates, which were about 20 percent ionized. Hence, the antagonistic effect of these two cations becomes apparent in their influence on the degree of hydration of colloids. Briggs (1932) pointed out that "bound" water is not a fixed quantity of water associated with the colloid but will vary with the activity of water in the system in a manner consistent with the vapor-pressure isotherm of the colloid.

Nevertheless, Grollman (1931) and Chandler (1941) have emphasized the view that water of hydration is of little consequence in a complex system such as plant sap. Chandler (1941) points out that water in biological tissues referred to as "bound" is probably two kinds: (1) The small amount intimately associated with the colloid and having special thermo-dynamic properties (cf. Briggs, 1931 and 1932), and (2) a hypothetical amount estimated to account for aberrations in the colligative properties of water in complex solutions as compared to a simple solution. The latter category includes the "bound" water estimated by Newton and his associates (1922, 1924, 1926) in their studies on cold-hardiness of wheat. Levitt (1941) has presented a critical review of the evidence available on the role of hydrophilic colloids in "binding" water, thus enabling plants better to withstand cold and drought. After carefully examining the numerous pertinent investigations, he concluded that "bound" water is of little significance in prevention of water loss by plants and that most studies purporting to establish the importance of "bound" water are based on misinterpretations and faulty methods.

Osmosis

Osmosis has long been recognized as a major process effecting entry of water into plant cells. The higher the osmotic pressure of the cellular fluids, the higher the intensity with which the cell may attract water from its surroundings. It would appear, therefore, that those plants with the higher osmotic pressure of their tissue fluids would be more capable of survival and growth under conditions of low water availability. Drabble and Drabble (1907) were among the earlier investigators on the relation between the osmotic pressure of the cellular fluids of different species and their environment. Their conclusions have been verified many times and have now become a generalization. They concluded that plants of a given species have the same osmotic pressure of their tissue fluids when growing under identical conditions of water supply, and that the osmotic pressure of the tissue fluids of a given species increases with the physiological scarcity of water. This relationship appears to hold whether the physiological scarcity of water is due to high solute concentration of the soil solution (Eaton, 1927; Fitting, 1911; Harris, 1934; Korstian, 1924; and Martin, 1940) or to depletion of the moisture content of the soil (Hibbard and Harrington, 1916; Iljin, 1929; Kortian, 1924; and Stoddart, 1935) with the accompanying increase in soil-moisture tension.

The extensive observations of Harris and his associates (1916, 1924, 1926, 1930) on the osmotic pressure of the leaf-tissue fluids emphasizes the wide diversity of this characteristic among different species of plants, as well as among plants of the same species growing under various environmental conditions. For example, in their observations on the vegetation of the Tooele Valley, Utah (1924), they found values for the osmotic pressure of the leaf-tissues fluids varying from 7.1 atmospheres for *Claytonia lanceolata* growing in the higher elevations of the Stansbury Mountains to 169 atmospheres for *Atriplex nuttallii* growing on salt flat in the valley floor. The effect that change in environment with the march of the season may have is illustrated by the fact that their observation on *Atriplex muttallii* leaves was made on July 27, whereas leaves of this same species obtained from the same location had an osmotic pressure in these tissue fluids of only 38 atmospheres when sampled 2 months earlier. They also found (1926, 1930) that the osmotic pressure of the tissue fluids of cotton plants growing on saline soil was significantly correlated with the concentration of the soil solution.

It should be noted that some tissues of a given plant undergo greater change in the osmotic pressure of their fluids with the onset of scarcity of water than others. Thus, Beck (1929) observed that the osmotic pressure of the cell sap of assimilatory tissues showed the greatest degree of change with decreasing soil moisture and the onset of drought. Also, environmental conditions other than soil-moisture supply may affect the osmotic pressure of plant tissues. Meyer (1927) found that the osmotic pressure of the fluids in leaves that are in the sun is higher than in leaves on the same plant that are in the shade.

Species differ markedly in the degree to which the osmotic pressure of their tissue fluids will increase as a result of decreasing soil-moisture supply. Stoddart (1935) observed that some upland prairie species may show an increase of 30 atmospheres in the osmotic pressure of their cell sap as the soil dries out, whereas plants indigenous to moist habitats may show an increase of only 2 to 10 atmospheres. Examples of the effect of soil-moisture stress on the osmotic pressure of the cell sap of corn roots are given by the following measurements:

Osmotic pressure of soil solution[1]	Osmotic pressure of cell sap of roots[1]	Water content of soil[2]	Osmotic pressure of cell sap of roots[2]
Atmospheres	Atmospheres	Percent	Atmospheres
1.2	4.6	31	5.9
2.0	5.5	23	7.2
3.4	6.6	16	7.8
5.0	7.5	14	9.2
7.2	8.2	11	12.0

[1] Data of McCool and Millar (1917).
[2] Data of Hibbard and Harrington (1916).

The foregoing observations are pertinent to the relationships in Figure 32. The locus of curve CB in that figure represents the osmotic pressure of the cellular fluids. The locus of this curve will shift in the direction of curve DE as a result of an increase in osmotic pressure of tissue fluids accompanying an increase in the physiological scarcity of water, i.e., an increase in soil-moisture stress. It is doubtful that the osmotic pressure of the tissue fluids or the total diffusion-pressure-deficit difference (DPDD) ever increases space with the increase in soil-moisture stress. As the soil-moisture stress increases, there will be a tendency for the diffusion-pressure deficit to decrease at a given degree of cellular turgescence. Consider an increase of soil-moisture stress of 6 atmospheres in the hypothetical plant of Figure 32. This increase would shift the sum of the diffusion-pressure components inducing outward water transfer from point B to point P at full turgor. In order to maintain full turgor, the diffusion-pressure-deficit difference ($DPDD$) would also have to increase from point B to point P. As previously mentioned, this is unlikely; the accompanying increase in diffusion-pressure-deficit difference might possibly be of the order represented by the distance BQ. Consequently, at water equilibrium there will be a decrease in the relative volume of the cells to some value approximating that of point G. In other words, during soil-moisture depletion the line FG rises on the diagram more rapidly than the compensating vertical shift of curve DE so that the intersection point G moves to the left. This corresponds to decreasing cell volumes. The net result in line with the experimental observations reported in a previous section, is that increasing soil-moisture stress is associated with decreasing amount of growth.

Guttation and exudation from decapitated plants, characterizing their active absorption of water, have long been intriguing physiological phenomena that appear to be partially if not wholly explained by osmotic activity. They take place in most species of plants under conditions of low evaporation and adequate water supply and are indicative of positive hydrostatic pressures in the conductive tissues, especially of the roots. Hence, exudation from decapitated plants and, in some degree, guttation reflect "root pressures." White (1938) reported that excised tomato roots exude sap from their basal ends with pressures of 6 atmospheres or higher. Most observations (see Kramer, 1949) indicate that the osmotic pressure of the fluid in the xylem vessels is usually only 1 to 3 atmospheres. Thus, the question occasionally arises as to how soil moisture may move across extra-stellar tissues whose cellular fluids have osmotic pressures of 5 to 12 atmospheres into a xylem vessel with sap having a concentration of only 2 atmospheres osmotic pressure. Pertinent experimental evidence has been provided by Kramer (1932). He used the hollow petioles of *Carica papaya* as osmometers, in that they were filled with a sugar solution of 2 atmospheres osmotic pressure and immersed in water. The water passed through the living cells of the petiole into the sugar solution, even though the osmotic pressure of the fluids in the intervening cells was about 9 atmospheres. A comparable mechanism of osmotic movement of water may be operative in the roots towards effecting root pressure.

Kramer (1941) reports that when decapitated root systems of tomato and sunflower plants were placed in sucrose with an osmotic pressure greater than 1 atmosphere, a reversal of exudation, i.e., absorption of water through the stumps, took place. When the roots were washed and returned to water, however, exudation was resumed within $\frac{1}{2}$ to 1 minute. He states that this reversal could be continued almost indefinitely with a given root system. In behavior these root systems resembled rather sensitive osmometers, and this supported the concept that root pressure is an osmotic phenomenon. Kramer (1941) also found that a given degree of soil-moisture depletion had the same effect on exudation as immersing the roots in the dilute sugar solution. He found that exudation from decapitated plants of coleus, sunflower, and tomato ceased when about 45 percent of the moisture available to the intact plants was still present. A summary of the data is shown in Table 18.

TABLE 18.—*Soil moisture available for exudation (after Kramer, 1941)*

Species	Soil	Determinations	Moisture equivalent	Wilting	Moisture content[1]	Available water[2]
		Number	*Percent*	*Percent*	*Percent*	*Percent*
Coleus	Sandy loam	29	19.4	5.0	11.48 ± 0.69	55
Tomato	Sandy loam	74	19.4	5.0	11.32 ± 1.78	56
Sunflower	Sandy loam	66	19.4	5.0	11.66 ± 0.45	53
Sunflower	Clay	36	44.0	25.0	33.45 ± 0.48	55
Sunflower	Coarse sand	27	2.04	0.04	0.04 ± 0.42	55

The "Soil-moisture data" heading spans the Moisture equivalent, Wilting, and Moisture content columns.

[1] Limiting moisture content for exudation.

[2] Proportion of water available to detopped root systems in range between wilting percentage and moisture equivalent.

Results shown in Table 19 suggest that the soil-moisture content limiting to exudation is as characteristic of a soil as are the wilting percentage and the moisture equivalent, and that "active" absorption by the plant "osmometer" does not take place against a moisture tension greater than 1 or 2 atmospheres. Furthermore, Kramer (1941) concludes that these results "indicate that water probably is not equally available to plants over the range from moisture equivalent to wilting percentage, but becomes less available with decreasing soil moisture."

In line with Kramer's observations, Eaton (1943) has vigorously supported the view that "active" absorption of water, as characterized by exudation, may be completely explained as an osmotic phenomenon. Some of his observations on exudation by decapitated cotton plants are set forth in Tables 19 and 20.

Data in Tables 19 and 20 certainly provide strong support for the concept presented by Atkins (1916) and Priestly (1922) that "active

TABLE 19.—*Osmotic differentials and exudation of cotton plants grown in nutrient solutions with added chloride salts (Eaton, 1943)*

Treatment	Osmotic pressure			Number of plants exudating
	Nutrient solutions	Exudates	Differentials	
	Atmospheres	*Atmospheres*	*Atmospheres*	
A	0.40	0.92	±0.52	All
B	0.83	1.01	± .18	All
C	2.40	1.28[1]	−1.12	None
D	4.45	2.22[1]	−2.23	None
E	6.56	3.00[1]	−3.56	None

[1] These xylem-vessel solutions were from exudates collected during the succeeding hour after tap water had been substituted for the nutrient solutions.

TABLE 20.—*Osmotic pressure, differentials, and rate of exudation from decapitated cotton plants during the first hour following replacement of culture solutions with tap water (Eaton, 1943)*

Treatment	Osmotic pressure			Exudation—		
	Tap water	Exudates	Differentials	Average area of xylem	Per square centimeter per hour	Per square centimeter per hour per atmosphere of differential
	Atmospheres	*Atmospheres*	*Atmospheres*	*Square centimeters*	*Milliliters*	*Milliliters*
A	0.13	0.92	0.79	0.83	2.57	3.3
B	0.13	1.01	.88	.77	3.28	3.7
C	0.13	1.28	1.15	.56	4.43	3.9
D	0.13	2.22	2.09	.63	9.20	4.4
E	0.13	3.00	2.87	.54	14.01	4.9

entry of water into roots as exemplified by exudation is an osmotic phenomenon."

Metabolism

The wide diversity of opinion that may pervade physiological thinking is well illustrated by studies on the mechanisms of entry of water into plant roots. In contradistinction to the concept supported by Eaton

(1943), Bennet-Clark and this associates (1936, 1943, 1948) have presented extensive experimental evidence that water movement in plant tissues is effected by energy released through oxidative metabolism rather than through osmotic phenomena. Their conclusions are based largely on the evidence of major discrepancies between values for the osmotic pressure of plant cells as determined cryoscopically and comparable values for the internal hydrostatic pressure as determined by plasmolysis or by mechanical means. Mason and Phillis (1939) and Van Overbeek (1942) have presented supporting evidence. Currier (1944) also noted this discrepancy between evaluating osmotic pressure cryoscopically on expressed sap and plasmolytically on the tissue. He attributed this difference in results to inadequacies in the methodology, and, in line with Eaton (1943), he questioned the possibility of nonosmotic forces being involved in the entry of water into plant cells. It is questionable if adequate methods are yet available for determining whether or not plant cells possess secretory powers over and above those which may be explained by osmotic pressure.

Van Overbeek (1944) has shown that auxin increases the water uptake by potato-tuber tissue, and he has concluded that auxin induced this effect by its action on the respiratory mechanism. It is most probable that the energy for the work done in bringing about nonosmotic movement of water would arise from oxidative metabolism. Calculations by Levitt (1947) indicate that respiratory activity in beet cells might supply sufficient energy to maintain a nonosmotic gradient across the extra-stellar tissues of 1.5 atmospheres, but not much more. However, a definite relationship between the rate of respiration and water entry into roots, or exudation from detopped roots, has not been established (Wilson and Kramer, 1949; Skoog et al., 1938; and Lundegardh, 1948). The present status of the evidence suggests that nonosmotic movement of water in plant tissues may take place with energy derived from oxidative metabolism acting as the driving force, but the preponderance of the evidence indicates that this factor is indeed minor in comparison to the effect of osmotic phenomena.

Tension

Although "active" water absorption has been extensively investigated, this process is of minor importance in relation to the total water economy of most plants, since entry of water into the roots is predominantly controlled by transpirational activity within the shoot. Kramer (1937) has shown that the rate of water entry through the roots closely follows changes in the rate of transpiration. He found that on a bright hot summer day water loss by transpiration tends to exceed water entry, bringing about a water deficit in the tissues from about 8 a.m. to 5 p.m.; and that water entry from the soil exceeded water loss by transpiration during the forepart of the night, with the tendency toward eliminating the water deficit in the plant. The desiccating power of the air is by far the predominant factor in controlling the utilization of soil moisture by plants.

Data by Shull (1939) given in Table 21 indicate the maximum tensional force (*DPD*) that can be produced by evaporation at various

TABLE 21.—*Tensional forces required to stop evaporation (dynamic equilibrium) expressed in atmospheres for various relative humidities and temperatures (Shull, 1939)*

Relative humidity	Temperature range		
	10°C.	20°C.	30°C.
Percent	*Atmospheres*	*Atmospheres*	*Atmospheres*
10	2,969.9	3,070.3	3,166.9
20	2,075.9	2,146.0	2,213.6
30	1,552.9	1,605.4	1,655.9
40	1,181.9	1,221.8	1,260.2
50	894.0	924.2	953.3
60	658.9	681.1	702.6
70	460.1	475.6	485.0
80	287.8	297.5	306.9
90	135.9	140.5	144.9
95	66.2	68.4	70.6
96	52.7	54.4	56.1
97	39.3	40.6	41.9
98	26.1	26.9	27.8
99	13.0	13.4	13.8
99.5	6.5	6.7	6.9
99.9	1.28	1.32	1.36

temperatures and relative humidities. Insolation and air movement also greatly modify the desiccating power of the aerial environment, since insolation provides heat to the evaporating surface and air movement increases the turbulence and decreases the thickness of the gaseous film covering the evaporating surface.

Gradmann (1928) and Van den Honert (1948) have presented a significant evaluation of certain aspects of the transpiration process. They point out that the moisture stress about the roots in a moist non-saline soil is only a fraction of an atmosphere. Hence, at a relative humidity of the air of 47 percent, the plant is inserted as a water-conducting system between two media with moisture stresses of 0.1 and

1,000 atmospheres, respectively. A continuous current of water passes inside the plant from the lower to the higher values of diffusion-pressure deficit, successively through root cells, xylem, chlorenchyma, and the gaseous film extending from the air-spaces in the leaf mesophyll out through the stomata and including an adherent air layer on the surface of the leaf of about 0.4 to 10 millimeters thickness. The diffusion-pressure deficit of cells in the leaf mesophyll rarely exceeds 50 atmospheres. In the present example of the 1,000 atmospheres difference in diffusion-pressure deficit between the soil and the atmosphere, the gradient between the leaf cells and the free atmosphere is about 19 times as large as the gradient in diffusion-pressure deficit between the soil moisture and the leaf cells.

Gradmann (1928) applied an analog of Ohm's law to this water transport as a whole, to the effect that the potential drop across a given part of the system is directly proportional to the resistance. Thus, Gradmann drew the conclusion that, in terms of the example just given, resistance to water movement across the gaseous film from leaf cells to the free atmosphere would be 19 times as great as the total resistance within the entire plant system.

Van den Honert (1948) points out that Gradmann's conclusion received little attention because of its seeming improbability. After all, it is known that diffusion processes proceed more rapidly in gases than in fluids. Brown and Escombe (1900) had shown that the velocity of diffusion through multiperforate septa is nearly as great as in the absence of a septum. The conclusion might be drawn that resistance to water-vapor diffusion from the internal surfaces of the leaf out through open stomata would be negligible; but Van den Honert emphasizes that such a conclusion would be erroneous, since resistance to evaporation from even a free-water surface is high. He cites the data in Table 22.

The data in the last column of this table emphasize how very low evaporation rates are, per atmosphere of diffusion-pressure-deficit difference, even in the presence of the accentuating effect of a strong wind. Since treatment of water transport as an analog of Ohm's law implies that resistance to water movement through the plant as a whole is much less than that set up by the stationary air film about the leaves, it is of interest to consider the data given in Table 23 as cited by Van den Honert. He points out that when Huber and Hofler (1930) published their data on the water permeability of protoplasts of *Salvinia auriculata* it seemed surprisingly low, and yet the permeability of a free-water surface is apparently 20 to 500 times smaller, depending on wind velocity. These data are enlightening with respect to the relative impermeability of the stationary air film over the surface of leaves; they explain and clarify the physical processes that make it possible for plants to tolerate conditions where the desiccating power of the air is relatively enormous.

TABLE 22.—*Evaporation from a circular free-water surface of 33 square centimeters under various environmental conditions (Van den Honert, 1948)*

Air movement	Temperature of air and water	Relative humidity	Diffusion-pressure deficit	Evaporation		
				mg./hr.	mg./hr./cm.^{2}	mg./hr./cm.^{2}/atm.
	°C.	*Percent*	*Atmospheres*			
Still air	{ 15	76	364	86	2.6	0.007
	16	52	861	200	6.0	0.007
Slow wind	{ 15	76	364	360	10.9	0.030
	16	52	861	600	18.0	0.021
Strong wind	16	80	293	1,850	56.0	0.191

TABLE 23.—*Relative resistance of various media to water displacement (Van den Honert, 1948)*

Water displacement	Displacement rate (mg./cm.^{2}/hr./atm.)	Relative resistance/cm.^{2}
Through—		
1 meter of foliage wood	100,000	1
1 meter of coniferous wood	20,000	5
Protoplast *Salvinia*	3.3	30,000
Surface water–air:		
In still air	0.007	14,000,000
In slow wind	0.025	4,000,000
In strong wind	0.191	520,000

The evaporation of water that takes place from the cells of the mesophyll of leaves tends to induce a water deficit in these cells, thus producing an increase in the diffusion-pressure deficit of the internal phase of these cells. This diffusion-pressure deficit of the cellular fluids is transmitted through the conducting system of the plant to the absorbing cells of the roots, in accordance with the classical cohesion theory of Dixon and Joly (1894). The cohesive action of water in the conducting systems of plants has been estimated to attain around 300 atmospheres by Ursprung (1916). Also, MacDougal *et al.* (1929) made dendographic measurements on tall trees and calculated the probable existence of tensions within the conducting system of the order of 200 atmospheres. More recently, Briggs (1949) subjected water to tensile stress by a direct centrifuge method and obtained a value of 223 atmospheres before column separation occurred. The cohesive strength of water thus exceeds the water tension which would have to be developed in the conducting system to move water from the roots to the uppermost leaves in the tallest trees.

The importance of tension in the conducting system of rapidly transpiring plants in relation to the entry of soil moisture is indicated by the fact that the osmotic pressure of the absorbing cells of the roots of plants is usually only a few atmospheres. Stocking (1945) evaluated the tensions in squash plants growing in soil and found that they varied from a maximum of 4 atmospheres during the day to a positive pressure of 1 atmosphere at night. When the soil was allowed to dry down to the wilting percentage, the tensions increased 6.3 to 9.1 atmospheres. Since the xylem sap of his plants had an osmotic pressure of about 1.9 atmospheres, the total diffusion-pressure-deficit difference ($DPDD$) of the plant system was 8.2 to 11.0 atmospheres at the wilting stage. Stocking pointed out that this range of values was appreciably less than the value of 16 atmospheres frequently taken (Veihmeyer *et al.*, 1943) as the soil-moisture tension at the wilting percentage. Veihmeyer and Hendrickson (1933) have shown that there are wide variations among various biologically determined wilting percentages as to the actual specific free energy of the moisture at this percentage. This has been confirmed by others (Bodman and Day, 1943; Richards and Weaver, 1944), and the moisture tension at the biologically determined wilting percentage has been reported to vary from 4 to 40 atmospheres.

Diffusion-pressure deficits

As evaporation of water takes place from the walls of the mesophyll cells in leaves, a diffusion pressure deficit (DPD) develops in the walls effecting movement of water out of the cells to the wall and inducing an enhanced diffusion-pressure deficit of water in the cellular fluids. This DPD in the parenchymatous cells further induces movement of water from the tracheids of the leaf veinlets and, consequently, water movement up through the entire conducting system of the plant. Thus, the DPD effected in leaf cells by transpiration tends to be translated to all other tissues of the plant. Since the DPD induced in the leaves is the driving force of "passive" water absorption and the predominant influence in the movement of water up through the plant, it is apparent that there should be a relationship among rate of transpiration, water deficit in the leaves, and rate of water entry from the soil.

Kramer (1937) has studied these interrelationships; pertinent data he obtained on sunflower plants are presented in Figure 35.   During the day the rate of transpiration tended to exceed the rate of absorption, with the reverse relation taking place at night.   As a consequence, the leaves showed a minimum in moisture content during the day and a maximum at night.   Maximov (1929) has reviewed the earlier literature on water balance in plants; it provides extensive evidence for diurnal variations in the water content of leaves resultant from relative rates of transpiration and of absorption analagous to that shown in Figure 35.   Lachenmeier (1932) also reported the lag in water absorption with reference to transpiration, even though the plants were grown

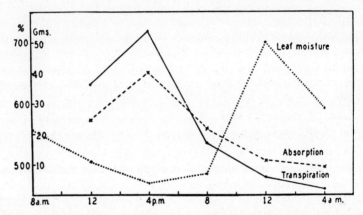

FIGURE 35.—Leaf-moisture content and absorption and transpiration rates of autoirrigated sunflowers.   Leaf moisture in percentages of dry weight; absorption and transpiration in grams of water per plant (Kramer, 1937).

in water cultures.   Halma (1934a, 1934b) has reported that the degree of water deficit developing in citrus leaves is inversely related to the supply of soil moisture, and that when the water deficit is allowed to reach a relatively high value there is a reduction in the growth of the tree.

Water transfer within the plant as a result of a diffusion-pressure deficit initiated in the leaves will tend to effect uniformity in distribution in *DPD* among the various tissues; but since the plant is a dynamic organism, actual uniformity in distribution is seldom attained.   Yet, it is frequently possible to obtain an index of water balance within a plant by the measurement of *DPD* within a given tissue.   For example, Molz (1926) used the *DPD* of the ray florets of the *Chrysanthemum frutescens* as an indicator of the water status of the plant as conditioned by soil moisture.   He allowed a pot culture of a plant of this species to go without water for 8 days. At this time "the soil, which had become extremely dry, was then thoroughly soaked." The marked drop Molz observed in diffusion-pressure deficit is shown as follows:

Time:	Number of hours after watering culture	Diffusion-pressure deficit of ray flower of Chrysanthemum frutescens
10 A.M. (start)............	0	19.1
11 A.M..................	1	14.0
12 A.M..................	2	11.8
1 P.M..................	3	7.4
5 P.M..................	7	6.9
8 A.M..................	22	4.7

The variations in osmotic pressure of the tissue fluids and the diffusion-pressure deficit of the tissues that may occur in plants under environmental stress are well-illustrated by the data of Herrick (1933). His observations on *Ambrosia trifida* (giant ragweed) are given in Table 24.

The data in Table 24 were obtained during hot days early in July when the plants were wilting daily due to depletion of soil moisture.

TABLE 24.—*Diurnal variation in osmotic pressure and diffusion-pressure deficit values in leaves of Ambrosia trifida*

Time	Temperature, °C.	Top leaf	Next to top leaf	Second from top leaf	Lowest leaf
		OSMOTIC PRESSURE			
		Atmospheres	Atmospheres	Atmospheres	Atmospheres
6:00 A.M.	23	12.5	12.5	12.9	10.1
10:00 A.M.	38	15.3	15.6	15.0	13.0
2:00 P.M.	38	17.4	17.2	17.1	15.9
5:00 P.M.	38	16.5	15.7	15.7	14.3
8:00 (sunset)	34	16.3	14.9	14.9	14.0
		DIFFUSION-PRESSURE DEFICIT			
5:15 (sunrise)	23	7.5	8.0	8.0	6.5
7:00 A.M.	27	9.5	9.5	8.5	7.5
9:00 A.M.	33	12.0	12.0	11.0	11.0
11:00 A.M.	38	15.0	15.0	14.5	13.5
1:00 P.M.	39	17.5	17.0	16.5	14.5
3:00 P.M.	38	17.5	17.5	17.0	15.5
4:30 P.M.	38	15.0	16.0	15.5	14.5
7:30 P.M.	35	15.0	15.0	15.0	14.0

At 6:00 A.M., the osmotic pressure of the tissue fluids were distinctly higher than the diffusion-pressure deficits of of the tissues for 5:15 to 7:00 A.M. By 2:00 P.M. the osmotic pressure values reached their diurnal maximum, and the highest value at this time was formed in the top leaf. By 1:00 P.M. the values for *DPD* were nearly identical with those for osmotic pressure, showing complete loss of turgor; and there was a consistently increasing gradient in *DPD* from the lowest to the highest leaf.

Herrick (1933) emphasizes that under conditions of maximum stress for water the *DPD* of any one leaf is essentially equal to the osmotic pressure of the cellular fluids of that same leaf, and that both of these values increase consistently from the lowest to the highest leaves of the plant. He points out that under conditions of drought it is characteristic for the lower leaves of *Ambrosia trifida* to wilt first and for the immature upper leaves to wilt last. Thus, the order of wilting of the various leaves is apparently the inverse of the order of their potential ability to secure water as indicated by values for either osmotic pressure or diffusion-pressure deficit. Since osmotic pressure and diffusion-pressure deficit tend to become equal under conditions of stress, it is apparent that a determination of the osmotic pressure of the various aerial parts of plants provides a reliable index of their relative potential ability to compete for water.

Under conditions inducing a water deficit within the plant, there frequently develops an apparent competition between fruit and leaves for water. Bartholomew (1926) pointed out that when a water deficit develops in a lemon tree, water moves out of the fruit into the leaves, so that loss of turgor by lemon fruits becomes a sensitive index of the water status in the tree. Haas and Klotz (1935) report finding the osmotic pressure of the juice of the pulp in lemon fruits to be 13 atmospheres whereas the osmotic pressure of the tissue fluids of adjacent leaves was found to be 14.4 to 22 atmospheres. Compton (1936) presents data showing that water deficits in naval orange leaves are directly related to the irrigation regime and are modified by diurnal variations in the desiccating power of the atmosphere. Enlargement of fruits was inversely related to the intensity of water deficits in the leaves.

Internal water relationships in cotton plants are somewhat in contrast to those found for citrus. Anderson and Kerr (1943) obtained auxographic records of the development of cotton bolls and found that enlargement of young bolls is not inhibited by even severe wilting of the parent plant. That is, the young bolls showed a constant rate of enlargement, even during the heat of the day when the leaves were showing marked water deficits due to inadequate soil moisture. However, after the bolls are 16 days old, they shrink in size during the day when the parent plants are visibly wilted, but regain their size at night if soil moisture is not sufficiently low to limit reattainment of turgor. The degree of shrinkage of full-size bolls was found to be proportional to the severity of wilting of the parent plant.

Kerr and Anderson (1944) found that the osmotic pressure of the immature seeds in young cotton bolls (0 to 16 days old) markedly exceeds the *DPD* of those seeds. After 16 days, they found a sharp drop in osmotic pressure, which tended gradually to decrease further until maturity. On the other hand, the *DPD* of the immature seeds continued to increase continuously almost to maturity, with the seemingly anomalous condition wherein *DPD* exceeded osmotic pressure after 26 days and greatly exceeded osmotic pressure near maturity. Kerr and Anderson (1944) were not able fully to account for the high *DPD* values found in the older cotton bolls but suggested the imbibitional properties of cellular contents were probably involved. It is pertinent to note, however, that the absence of shrinking in young bolls in the presence of water deficits in the plant was associated with relatively high osmotic pressure for the tissue fluids of the immature seeds, and that the increase in sensitivity of the bolls to water deficits after they were 16 days old was associated with a marked drop in the osmotic pressure of the tissue fluids in the immature seeds.

In the movement of water from soil into plant roots, it is evident that the diffusion-pressure deficits prevailing in the absorbing cells will be a primary consideration. Ursprung and Blum (1921) determined the *DPD* (Saugkraft) of the absorbing cells of the roots of *Vicia faba* growing under various conditions. In one experiment, roots grown in moist sawdust were found to have absorbing cells with a *DPD* of 1.1 atmospheres. When the roots were shifted to water the *DPD* decreased gradually with time, becoming zero after 23 hours. In another experiment, the roots were transferred from moist sawdust to a sucrose solution of 1.1 atmospheres, and the investigators found that the *DPD* of the absorbing cells remained at 1.1 atmospheres over a 2-week period of observation. In a further study, Ursprung and Blum transferred roots having a *DPD* in the absorbing cells of 1.1 atmospheres from moist sawdust to a sucrose solution having an osmotic pressure of 5.3 atmospheres and observed that all the cells of the absorbing zone, i.e., the piliferous layer, died. However, growth of the roots continued, and by the fifth day a new absorbing zone had formed, and the *DPD* of these cells was found to be 5.7 atmospheres. Thus, these data suggest an appreciable degree of adjustment in the *DPD* of absorbing cells, depending on the status of water in the surrounding medium.

It should be emphasized that the *DPD* of absorbing cells of roots may not indicate the *DPD* of the root as a whole. As pointed out by Priestly (1922), the *DPD* of the root as an entity may be quite independent of that found in the surface cells and is largely determined by the concentration of the solution in the root vessels. Thus, potometric methods such as devised by Rosene (1941a, 1941b) and Hayward *et al.* (1942) provide the best method available at present for determining the effective *DPD* of whole roots. Rosene (1941a, 1941b) found roots of onions to have a *DPD* of 4.2 to 5.7 atmospheres; and Hayward and Spurr (1944a) found the *DPD* of roots of young corn plants to be 6.0 to 6.8 atmospheres. Tagawa (1934) found that the osmotic pressure of the culture solution had to be increased to 14.7 atmospheres to prevent entry of water into roots of bean plants. This value may be considered the *DPD* of the roots of his experimental plants.

It is evident that the potential *DPD* that may develop within roots will be largely determined by the prevalence of solutes, i.e., the osmotic pressure of the tissue fluids. Since plants have the capacity to make limited adjustments to changes in environment, increasing soil-moisture stress (*DPD* of soil water) would probably be accompanied by increasing osmotic pressure (potential *DPD*) of the root sap. Data by Hibbard and Harrington (1916) and McCool and Millar (1917), which were cited earlier, verify such a relationship.

Root surface

Imbibition, osmotic pressure, metabolism, and transpirational pull may all be regarded as intensity factors in the entry of water, for they are in varying degrees components of the net water-moving force within the plant, i.e., the resultant *DPD* effecting influx of water. The total quantity of water entering a plant in a given time will also be dependent upon the total effective root surface over which water entry is taking place and on the resistance to flow offered by the histological nature of the root. The latter subject will be briefly reviewed in the subsequent section on Permeability of Roots.

Dittmer (1937) has recorded his measurements on the root system of a single winter rye plant grown in dark loam in the greenhouse during the winter for 4 months in a container 12 inches square and 12 inches deep. The roots were carefully liberated from the soil at the end of the experiment by spraying with water for several hours. From detailed measurements of extensive samplings it was determined that this plant had approximately 13,800,000 roots, with a length of over 385 miles, and a surface area of about 2,550 square feet. The root hairs of this same plant numbered approximately 14,000,000,000, with a total length of over 6,600 miles and a surface area of about 4,320 square feet.

Kramer and Coile (1940) pointed out that this rye plant produced an average of 3.1 miles of new roots per day during the 4-month period. The roots were mostly 120 to 250 microns in diameter and covered with root hairs which were mostly 700 to 800 microns in length. Kramer and Coile reasonably assumed, therefore, that these roots and root hairs showed a daily average increase in contact with soil particles essentially comprising a cylinder of soil 2 millimeters in diameter and 3.1 miles long and having a total volume of approximately 15.7 liters. If the soil mass penetrated by the roots was at field capacity, a volume of water would become available to the plant each day corresponding to the difference between volumes present at field capacity and the wilting percentage. Thus, Kramer and Coile calculated that 1.6 liters of water would be added to the available supply by root growth in a sandy loam; and 2.9 liters, in clay. Accordingly, it might appear that root extension would provide all the water that would be required by a rye plant. However, the calculations of the above authors do not take into account the multiple permeation of a given mass of soil by growth of different portions of the root over a long period of time.

In order to ascertain the relative efficiency with which the roots of different species permeate the soil, Dittmer (1938) determined the number of roots in samples of soil 42 cubic inches in volume. These samples were removed by a cutting tube from soil underneath oats, winter rye, and Kentucky bluegrass growing under normal field conditions. He thereby calculated that in the upper soil levels, oats would expose a surface of 15 square inches per cubic inch of soil; rye, 30; and bluegrass, about 65 square inches. Oats would have approximately 150,000 root hairs per cubic inch of soil; rye, 300,000; and bluegrass, about 1,000,000. These measurements indicate that oats would probably be the least efficient in extracting water from the soil, and that, relatively, bluegrass would be quite superior.

Pavlychenko (1937a, 1937b) has presented comparable data on the extensiveness of root systems. He has stressed (1937b) the effect of competition on the extensiveness of root systems. For example, he found 44.3 miles of roots on a single mature Marquis wheat plant grown free of competition; whereas a comparable plant grown in a 6-inch drill row was found to have only 0.54 miles of roots. In other instance, he found that Marquis wheat plants 40 days old grown in a field without weed competition had root systems that averaged 582 feet in total linear length, but had only 276 feet linear length when wild mustard plants were also growing between the drill rows. The presence of the weed induces a marked decrease in the root surface of the crop plant available for water entry and also decreases the supply of moisture that might otherwise enter roots of the crop plant.

The available evidence emphasizes the tremendous surface area that the roots of even relatively small plants will expose to the soil. In considering the water reservoir available to a plant, it is essential to take into account the total volume of soil penetrated by roots as well as the degree of permeation. The extensive observations of Weaver (1926) and Weaver and Bruner (1927) on the characteristics of root systems of many different crop plants are too well known to be elaborated upon

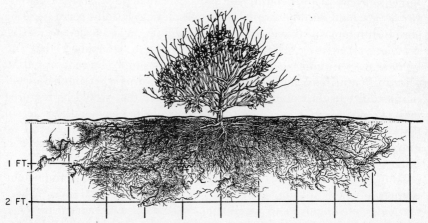

FIGURE 36.—Root system of native guayule about 30 years old on Ector stony loam, Brewster County, Texas (Muller, 1946).

here. However, recent observation by Muller (1946) on root distribution of guayule as affected by ecological conditions are of unusual interest.

Muller's studies show that the root zone, i.e., the potential water reservoir, may vary widely within a given species, depending on soil and cultural conditions. As shown in Figure 36, the roots of a 30-year-old guayule plant growing on Ector stony loam in Brewster County, Tex., was found to have its root system confined to the surface 2 feet of soil because below this depth there were unbroken limestone flagstones alternating with dry shale. By contrast, the roots of 2-year-old guayule plants on Lewisville silty clay at San Antonio, Tex., had penetrated to 16 feet as shown in Figure 37. Thus, the facility with which roots may penetrate the soil may have a major effect on the extent of the usable soil-moisture reservoir.

Permeability of roots

Even though there is evidence that plants have a relatively large amount of root surface, water supply to the conducting tissues of the stem is conditioned by the facility with which water will flow from the exterior of the epidermal cells across compacted layers of living cells to the xylem vessels. There are data indicating that protoplasm is relatively impermeable. Huber and Hofler (1930) obtained a value of 0.79 millimeter per day per atmosphere difference in osmotic pressure for protoplasts of leaf cells of *Salvinia ariculata*. Levitt *et al.* (1936) obtained a value of 0.48 millimeter per day per atmosphere difference in osmotic pressure for the permeability of the protoplasts of the pulp cells of onion plants.

Measurements on the rate of water entry into roots provide values of the same order of magnitude as those given for permeability of protoplasm. These measurements are shown in Table 25.

Although data in Table 25 are all of the same order of magnitude, there are significant variations in resistance to water penetration, depending on the condition of the roots. The observations of Rosene (1941a) and of Hayward *et al.* (1942) show that rate of entry of water is appreciably less near the growing point of a root than some distance back from the tip, corresponding to the region of maximum cell elongation but without development of maturation. Even though mature suberized roots are sometimes regarded as impervious to water, it is evident from studies by Hayward *et al.* (1942) and Kramer (1946) that appreciable amounts of water will enter such roots.

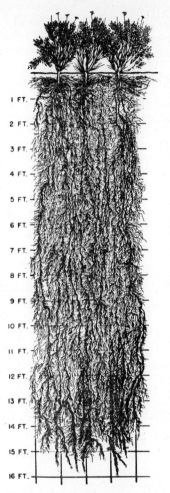

FIGURE 37.—Root systems of 2-year-old guayule transplants spaced at 12 inches within the row and grown without irrigation in Lewisville silty clay at San Antonio, Texas (Muller, 1946).

Addoms (1946) concluded from her studies with dye solutions that water entered older suberized roots by means of lenticels, breaks around branch

TABLE 25.—*Rates of water entry into roots*

Species	Conditions	Entry velocity	Investigator
		Millimeters per day	
Onion	36 millimeters from tip	4.2	Rosene (1941a).
	5 millimeters from tip	1.1	
Corn	10 centimeters from tip	5.0	Hayward *et al.* (1942).
	2 centimeters from tip	1.4	
Barley	Root of seedling in moist air	0.43	
Oats	Root of seedling in moist air	0.72	
Wheat	Root of seedling in moist air	0.72	Rosene and Walthall (1949).
Corn	Root of seedling in moist air	2.4	
Tomato	Root of seedling in moist air	3.3	
Field pea	Root of seedling in moist air	6.3	
Orange	Suberized root	0.86	Hayward *et al.* (1942).
Shortleaf pine	⅖-atmosphere tension on excised root	2.2	
Dogwood	⅖-atmosphere tension on excised root	3.7	
Poplar	⅖-atmosphere tension on excised root	2.4	Kramer (1946).
Shortleaf pine	Intact root	0.81	

TABLE 26.—*A comparison of the volumes of water passing through living and dead root systems under suction*

Species	Living roots	Dead roots	Percentage increase secured by killing root systems
	Cubic centimeters	*Cubic centimeters*	
Fuchsia magellanica	9.66	17.80	84
Helianthus annuus	3.57	67.50	1,790
Pelargonium hortorum	1.48	4.99	237
Phaseolus vulgaris	1.90	5.00	163
Picea excelsa	0	1.85	
Lycopersicum esculentum	3.15	13.64	333

roots, and wounds. Kramer (1946) found that the artificial introduction of even a small tension on the water in the vessels would induce a marked increase in the rate of water-entry penetration through suberized roots.

The data in Table 26 suggests that even the most permeable parts of roots provide a relatively poor facility for transfer of water from the exterior to the conductive tissues. Kramer (1932, 1933) has shown that the presence of living protoplasm in the roots may be an appreciable factor contributing to impermeability. This is illustrated by the data in Table 26 showing the increase in water flow through roots brought about by vacuum pump attached to the designated roots for 12-hour periods before and after killing by heat.

Kramer (1940) has reviewed the literature and made studies of the effect of temperature on the resistance of roots to water absorption. Many investigators have noted that plants may wilt when growing on cold soil, even though an adequate supply of moisture is present. In harmony with this Kramer (1940) found that resistance to water penetration through live roots increased with a lowering of the temperature, whereas the increase was relatively small for killed roots. This indicates that viscosity of protoplasm, as conditioned by temperature, may limit movement of water through the root system.

The apparently low permeability of root tissues is compensated for in most plants by the large area of root surface. Consider the 4-month-old winter rye plant found by Dittmer (1937) to have 4,321 square feet of root-hair surface and assume that water would enter these root hairs with an average velocity over the root surface of 0.72 millimeter per day as reported by Rosene and Walthall (1949) for oats and wheat. Thus, the root hairs alone would be capable of providing for the entry of 289 liters of water per day into this plant—far more than would ever be lost by transpiration. It is possible that the data reported by Dittmer (1937) for the root surface of a single plant are unique, and that plants growing under average conditions have far less root surface. This is suggested by Pavlychenko's (1937b) observations. It is possible that plants growing under conditions conducive to poor root growth may have low root permeability and thus limit the water supply to their top. Vigorously vegetative plants having a high top-to-root ratio are especially likely to show wilting when the roots are relatively cold.

X. SOIL MOISTURE EFFECTS ON PLANT GROWTH NOT RELATED TO THE ENERGY STATUS OF THE MOISTURE

In the preceding section, emphasis was placed on the relation between the moisture content of soil and the energy status of the moisture. Growth responses of plants were in turn interpreted on the basis of the energy status of the soil water. The moisture content of the soil may affect plants through other means. When the soil moisture persists at levels above field capacity as a result of poor drainage or a high water table, many species are adversely affected or even killed. As the pore space of the soil becomes correspondingly filled with water, the air spaces in the soil are correspondingly reduced and the rate of gaseous diffusion through the soil is decreased. Consequently, one effect of high levels of soil moisture on plant growth is to cause inadequate aeration. The effect of soil aeration on plant growth is dealt with elsewhere.

The shallow root system that develops on most plants in wet poorly drained soils is particularly unfortunate under conditions where the soil dries out during the latter part of the growing season. A plant with such a superficial root system is especially susceptible to drought because it lacks roots that permeate the lower strata of soil and is therefore unable to utilize the soil moisture in the lower strata if the water table lowers during the dry season.

Oskamp and Batjer (1932) observed in their studies of soil conditions in relation to fruit growing in New York that the most unfavorable orchard locations are those in which shallow rooting occurs because of a high water table during certain seasons of the year. In some orchards the roots were confined to the surface 30 inches of soil, whereas in others they penetrated to more than 8 feet. The greater depth of root penetration permits the tree to utilize the moisture in a correspondingly greater volume of soil during dry spells. Oskamp (1934) noted that some orchards had a high level of ground water during the fall and winter but that this water usually drained away during the growing season in the summer. In these orchards, even though soil-moisture conditions were favorable to root penetration during the growing season, the occurrence of high water tables during part of the year would asphyxiate the deeper roots. Thus, a large part of the potential supply of water for such trees is actually less available to them. Oskamp (1934) found a marked positive correlation between the performance of apple orchards and the depth to the water table during the fall and winter.

Light frequent irrigations may become disadvantageous to crop production in that they are associated with the development of shallow root systems. Such shallow-rooted plants would suffer seriously if irrigation were discontinued or the frequency decreased during the latter part of the growing season. Stephens et al. (1943) observed during the course of their studies on the water requirement of wheat that "a high moisture content of the surface soil often induces early vigorous vegetative growth and consequent drought injury later if ample moisture is not available."

XI. SOIL MOISTURE AND THE MINERAL NUTRITION OF PLANTS

The relation of soil moisture to the mineral nutrition of plants has recently been reviewed by Wadleigh and Richards (1950). In the treatment that follows frequent use will be made of material from an earlier review.

Excess Moisture

The influence of an excess of water upon nutrient supply and availability in soils may be segregated into three categories: (1) Surface erosion, (2) leaching, and (3) presence of a high water table or other conditions maintaining soil in a relatively wet state. Few soils are devoid of the occasional presence of one of these effects, and frequently two or all three of them may be operative.

Surface erosion

Agriculturists in this country have become increasingly aware of the vast losses in soil fertility incurred by surface runoff. This has been so well publicized that further mention seems superfluous. Yet the enormity of this loss mitigates any danger of overemphasis.

Fippin (1945) presents data to the effect that the Mississippi River carries 475 million tons of silt into the Gulf of Mexico during the average year. This silt load contains 4.5 million tons of the exchangeable bases CaO, MgO, and K_2O and 1.5 million tons of P_2O_5 and N. This is indeed a tremendous quantity of plant nutrients. Fippin also calculated that for the year 1939, the average loss of plant nutrients per acre of row crops in the Tennessee River system was "84.6 pounds of calcium, 97.9 pounds of magnesium, 212.2 pounds of potassium, and 13.0 pounds of phosphorus, all expressed as oxides, and 23.8 pounds of nitrogen." These figures amply indicate that surface runoff may bring about an alarming drain on plant nutrients present in the relatively more fertile topsoil. However, these values are much higher than those reported by Bryant and Slater (1948) for two New York soils subjected to seven different kinds of cover. The small losses of nutrients they found in surface runoff would probably be compensated by contributions from soil-formation processes.

Leaching

Soil-management practices inducing infiltration and curbing nutrient loss through surface runoff tend to increase nutrient loss by percolation. The objection might be raised that prevention of surface runoff merely alters the manner in which plant nutrients are removed from the soil, not the amount. Liquid water moving through a soil always carries solutes with it. A large amount of data on leaching has been provided by lysimeter studies. Kohnke *et al.* (1940) have provided an excellent bibliography and summary of the information available. Since soils have practically no adsorptive capacity for nitrate and chloride ions, these two anions are readily leachable and the quantities of these ions lost by leaching are rather closely related to the quantities present in the soil and the amount of percolate. The sulfate and bicarbonate ions are also readily leachable, whereas phosphate is usually present in leachate in very small quantities, if at all.

Loss of nutrient cations by leaching will be conditioned by base-exchange phenomena. Of the exchangeable bases usually found in soils, sodium has a relatively low energy of retention by adsorption surfaces, and is most readily leachable. Consequently, sodium is not prevalent in the percolate from soils of humid regions. This is in marked contrast to the case for soils of arid regions. Potassium also has a relatively low energy of retention by soil colloids, but it may readily become fixed within the crystal lattice of soil clays. It usually occurs in rather minor quantities in the leachate from soils. Thus, calcium and magnesium are almost invariably the predominant cations in the leachate from lysimeters.

As Kohnke *et al.* (1940) point out, the actual quantity and quality of nutrient loss by leaching depends on many different factors. Coarse-textured soils permit a greater proportional loss of nutrients than fine-textured soils, and a porous crumb structure favors greater percolation than a single-grain structure. The type of soil cover may markedly affect nutrient loss by leaching. Lyon and Bizzell (1936) found that uncropped Dunkirk silty clay loam lost 28 times as much nitrogen by leaching as the same soil continuously cropped to grass. There is much evidence to the effect that a vegetative cover lowers nutrient loss from leaching by effecting a reduction both in the amount of leachate and in the content of nutrients in the leachate. Chapman, Liebig, and Raynor (1949), reporting on a long-time lysimeter study of nitrogen gains and losses under various cropping and fertilization treatments, have given considerable information on nitrogen losses by leaching. They found that leaching losses were highest during the years of heaviest rainfall, especially when the nitrate content of the soil was at a high level from fertilization or the growth of legumes.

Dreibelbis (1946) reported that drainage from elaborately designed monolith lysimeters containing Keene silt loam showed an average annual loss of nutrients in pounds per acre as follows: Calcium, 19.9; magnesium, 10.3; potassium, 13.4; manganese, 0.3; nitrogen, 2.6; and sulfur, 17.8. Losses from Muskinghum silt loam averaged lower for calcium, potassium, and sulfur, but higher for nitrogen. Even though some data indicate that nutrient loss by leaching may be large, these observations do not warrant such a conclusion. Kohnke (1942) has emphasized that losses of plant nutrients in drainage are appreciably less than those possible from surface runoff.

When fertilizer is applied to a soil and conditions conducive to leaching prevail, there is usually found to be an increase in solute in the leachate, but the proportions of the component ions of the solute usually deviate from those in the added fertilizer, owing to base-exchange reactions. This is well illustrated by the observations of Volk and Bell (1947) on lysimeters filled with Lakeland loamy fine sand having a base-exchange capacity of 3.0 milliequivalents per 100 grams. Various sodium, magnesium, and potassium salts were applied to different lysimeters. Though no calcium was applied, it was invariably the predominant cation in the leachate. Even when 16.39 inches of leachate had been collected from the 4-foot columns of soil, only about 1 percent of the potassium applied was found in the leachate, whereas about 65 percent of the applied sodium and about 30 percent of the applied magnesium appeared in the leachate. Chlorides were recovered almost quantitatively; about 50 percent of the applied sulfate appeared in the leachate, and in most instances, more than twice as much nitrate was recovered as was applied. There was practically no difference in the proportions or amounts of cations in the leachate, whether the salts added to the soil were chlorides or nitrates; but when sulfate salts were applied there was a marked decrease in the loss of calcium.

The foregoing data emphasize that leaching losses of nutrients may be high on a light soil under heavy rainfall. The standard treatment of Volk and Bell (1947) corresponded to an application of 31 pounds of nitrogen per acre, and the leachate from this treatment showed a loss of 74 pounds of nitrogen per acre from fallow soil over a 5-month period. It is commonly observed that nitrogen deficiency may readily develop on light soils during wet seasons. There is increasing evidence that these same conditions are conducive to the development of magnesium deficiency. Hester *et al.* (1947) noted that magnesium-deficiency symptoms were quite prevalent on sweetpotatoes and tomatoes growing in sandy soils in New Jersey during the relatively wet season of 1946. They state that extreme magnesium deficiency is not likely to occur on this soil except under conditions of high rainfall or heavy potash fertilization. Boynton *et al.* (1944, 1946) have noted that magnesium-deficiency symptoms are more prevalent in the apple orchards of New York during wet years than dry.

The preponderance of evidence indicates that percolation of water through a soil tends to effect the depletion of sodium, calcium, and magnesium ions with relatively little removal of potassium. Jamison (1946) reports that potassium is readily leached out of certain sandy soils in Florida in which the exchange capacity is largely provided by organic matter because of the inability of organic adsorbents to fix potassium.

It is probable that in many cases, considered over long periods of time, losses of nutrients by leaching do not exceed contributions from soil decomposition and nitrogen fixation.

High water tables and wet soils

It is evident that under certain conditions serious losses of plant nutrients from soil may arise from either surface runoff or downward percolation. In addition, retention of excess soil moisture within the root zone may have a seriously detrimental effect on the nutrition and health of crop plants. Impervious layers in the subsoil that bring about permanent or even temporary water tables affect soil aeration, and, consequently, root growth, microbial activity, nutrient availability, and nutrient entry. As mentioned previously, soils with low permeability may also provide adverse conditions within the rhizosphere following a heavy rain or after an irrigation. As the soil-moisture tension becomes lower, the soil pores become increasingly filled with moisture, and gaseous interchange is inhibited. Observations on the composition of soil air illustrate the result of this relationship.

Furr and Aldrich (1943) studied the composition of the soil atmosphere at various depths under irrigated date palms. The soil-moisture tension at the 6-inch depth dropped from 700 to 800 to 11 to 15 centimeters of water following irrigation and remained low for 4 to 5 days. The oxygen content of the soil atmosphere dropped from about 20 to 5 percent during the period of low moisture tension, but a corresponding increase in carbon dioxide content was not noted. As soon as 100 centimeters of water tension developed following irrigation, a rapid increase in oxygen content of the soil atmosphere was observed. The oxygen content of soil air at the 30-inch depth also was affected by the irrigation, but at the 96-inch depth the oxygen content of the soil atmosphere persisted continuously at 15 to 17 percent. The carbon dioxide content of the soil air at the greater depths maintained itself at about 5 percent. These data illustrate the interrelationship between soil moisture and the composition of the soil air. They are especially striking since they were obtained on a relatively coarse-textured soil—Indio very fine sand loam.

Boynton (1941) found that fluctuations of ground water in relatively fine-textured soils was usually fairly well correlated with fluctuations in oxygen and carbon dioxide percentages of the soil air, particularly in the strata of soil just above the water table. Interestingly enough, sometimes a month or more elapsed between the disappearance of ground water and the rise of oxygen level to a maximum. Boynton and Reuther (1938) recorded oxygen percentages in the soil air as low as 0.1 percent in the second foot of Dunkirk silty clay loam under an apple tree during March and April. On subsidence of the water table during the summer the oxygen content at this depth rose to a level of 17 to 19 percent, whereas the carbon dioxide content remained at about 3 to 4 percent throughout the year. In the fourth foot the carbon dioxide content of the soil air remained at 8 to 10 percent throughout the summer. Excess soil moisture conditions soil aeration, which in turn affects mineral nutrition.

The essentiality of adequate aeration for the development of healthy roots and vigorous plants of most species has been emphasized many times both in soils (Bain and Chapman, 1940; Baver and Farnsworth, 1940; Cannon, 1925; Ellis and Morris, 1945; Goedewaagen, 1941; Loehwing, 1934; Muller, 1946; and Smith and Cook, 1946) and in the solution cultures (Boynton and Compton, 1943; Erickson, 1946; Gilbert and Shive, 1942; and Shive, 1941). Numerous studies by Stewart *et al.* (1933, 1936), Hoagland and Broyer (1936), Lundegardh (1940), and Robertson and Wilkins (1948) have amply shown that a rate of nutrient entry into absorbing tissue is conditioned by the rate of respiration of the absorbing cells, which, in turn, is conditioned by the supply of oxygen. Lawton (1945) grew corn plants on cultures of Clarion loam and Clyde silt loam in which the moisture regime was maintained at near saturation in some of the cultures and at or below field capacity in others. The inferior corn plants produced by the soils maintained at near saturation were found to have a relatively low percentage composition of nitrogen phosphorus, and potash, but with little consistent effect on content of calcium and magnesium.

Modified soil atmospheres resulting from excess soil moisture affect the nutrition of plants not only through reduced oxygen supply but also by increased partial pressure of carbon dioxide. Bradfield (1941) has discussed the influence of increasing partial pressure of carbon dioxide within a system containing calcium carbonate. In general, there is an associated increase in activity of both hydrogen and calcium ions. It is conceivable that these effects could markedly affect the availability not only of calcium but also of other nutrient ions under certain soil conditions. In fact, McGeorge and Breazeale (1931, 1932) conclude from their studies that a supply of carbon dioxide in the soil is the primary consideration in maintaining phosphate availability in alkali soils because of its modulating effect on the high pH of these soils. On the other hand, Parker (1925) found that on a noncalcareous soil, Norfolk sandy loam, there was no consistent effect on the calcium and phosphorus content of plants whether the soil was fortified with carbon dioxide, whether the carbon dioxide of the soil was removed, or whether the soil was left untreated. Chang and Loomis (1945) have presented evidence that increasing the carbon dioxide content of the air which is supplied to nutrient cultures may be toxic *per se* to plants over and above any effect of inadequacy in oxygen supply. Increasing partial carbon dioxide pressure would effect an increase in bicarbonate ion concentration in the aqueous phase.

Harley and Lindner (1945) noted that when certain apple and pear orchards in Wenatchee, Wash., were irrigated a number of years with water high in bicarbonate (200 to 360 parts per million) the trees showed a marked decline in vigor and an increase in incidence of chlorosis. A definite improvement was noted when irrigation water low in bicarbonate was substituted for the water high in bicarbonate. Calcium carbonate concretions developed on the roots of the affected trees when water high in bicarbonate was applied to the calcareous soil present in that area. The data of Lindner and Harley (1944) indicate that the chlorosis which develops under these conditions is characterized by an abnormally high potassium and low calcium content of the leaves.

The evidence appears to indicate that relatively low concentrations of carbon dioxide in the soil air of calcareous soils aid nutrient availability, but that the high carbon dioxide partial pressures which may occur under excessive soil moisture may be deleterious to root activity and nutrient intake.

Excessive soil moisture may have an indirect effect on the supply of nutrients to the plant. Oskamp and Batjer (1932) observed in their studies of soil conditions in relation to fruit growing in New York that the most unfavorable orchard locations are those in which shallow rooting occurs because of high water table during certain seasons of the year. Muller (1946) also noted that claypan soils maintaining a high moisture content of the subsoil restrict root development of guayule and may even asphyxiate those roots which have penetrated the lower strata prior to the prevalence of excess moisture. That is, shallow and restricted root development means that a given plant has a correspondingly smaller volume of soil to draw upon for nutrients. Furthermore, as noted in a preceding section, the moisture reservoir available to the plant is also restricted so that the plant may suffer from drought and be unable to utilize nutrients in the fertile topsoil, even though moisture is present in soil at depths within the normal scope of root penetration by the species.

Under the anaerobic conditions which may prevail in wet, poorly drained soils there tends to be a decrease in the degree of oxidation of both inorganic and organic constituents. Lawton (1945) observed a marked increase in the extractable ferrous iron content of Clarion loam and Clyde silt loam, together with an associated decrease in extractable ferric iron, when the soils were compacted or maintained at high moisture content. Anaerobic conditions resulting from waterlogging of soil may also effect an increase (very large in some soils) in exchangeable divalent manganese (Leeper, 1947; Steenbjerg, 1935). Studies by Fujimoto and Sherman (1948) indicate that the effect of a given level of soil moisture on manganese is complicated by a hydration-dehydration equilibrium. The complex hydrated oxide found in cool moist soil has a much lower activity than dehydrated divalent manganese. There is ample evidence available to lend weight to the suggestion of Hoffer (1945) that a relatively high accumulation of reduced iron and manganese in the soil under anaerobic conditions may well be toxic *per se* to plant roots over and above any effect caused strictly by inadequate aeration of the root surfaces.

There is some evidence to indicate that the reduced forms of certain organic components prevailing under the anaerobiosis of waterlogged soils are specifically toxic to plants (Breazeak, 1924; Pickering, 1917; Schreiner, 1923) and that these substances are readily oxidized and rendered harmless under aerobic soil conditions. The concept that specific toxicity of certain organic substances in soil has an adverse effect in plant nutrition has been scoffed at many times, but it has been adequately demonstrated by recent investigations (Benedict, 1941; Bode, 1940; Gray and Bonner, 1948). Thom and Smith (1938) point out that the anaerobic decomposition of organic matter in waterlogged soils frequently produces hydrogen sulfide. This compound is very toxic to roots.

The presence of accumulations of carbon dioxide in the atmosphere of waterlogged soils exerts a modulating influence over the activities of Fe^{+++} and Fe^{++} and consequently influences plant nutrition over and above the effect of the state of oxidation-reduction in the system. Halvorson (1931) points out that ferrous carbonate is very insoluble, as compared with ferrous bicarbonate, which is readily soluble. Thus, activity of Fe^{++} in a given soil system is conditioned by oxidation-reduction potential, pH, and partial pressure of carbon dioxide within the limitations of the amount and kind of ferruginous mineral present. Halvorson's (1931) analysis of the equilibria related to these components indicates that anaerobic conditions in an alkaline soil in the presence of a relatively high partial pressure of carbon dioxide may actually bring about a reduction in solubility of iron as compared with the aerobic state. On the other hand, increased partial pressure of carbon dioxide under aerobic soil conditions is actually conductive to solubility of ferric hydrate.

There is considerable evidence to support Kliman's (1937) conclusion that iron enters plants mostly in the reduced state. As a consequence, the iron supply to plants on wet soils may be either hindered or accentuated, depending on the status of other prevailing conditions (pH, carbon dioxide pressure); and the activity of iron in the soil appears to affect the relative rate of entry of other plant nutrients into the roots.

In the light of the foregoing, it is of interest to consider the nutritional disturbance known as lime-induced chlorosis. There is a great deal of evidence (Abbott, 1947; Burgess and Pohlman, 1928; Davidson, 1948; Haas and Zentmeyer, 1946; McGeorge, 1949; Mulder, 1948; and Reuther and Crawford, 1947) that this type of chlorosis, which is associated with a disturbance in iron metabolism within the plant, is accentuated by wet weather or heavy irrigation, and is ameliorated when the soil dries. Wet poorly aerated calcareous soils would be conducive to accumulations of the bicarbonate ion. It should be recalled that Harley and Lindner (1945) observed the development of chlorosis on apple trees when they were irrigated with high bicarbonate water. However, Reuther and Crawford (1947) found no relationship between the carbon dioxide content of the soil atmosphere and degree of chlorosis of grapefruit when the intensity of the symptoms varied with soil-moisture content over an irrigation cycle.

Evidently, the primary cause of chlorosis of plants growing on wet calcareous soils has not been resolved, but a consideration of Halvorson's (1931) theoretical treatment along with manganese chemistry and the bicarbonate ion activity might prove fruitful. The status of both iron and manganese in the soil is intimately related to the prevailing biological activity (Halvorson, 1931; Leeper, 1947). Hence, the effect of a high level of soil moisture upon the population of micro-organisms must be taken into account. As a case in point, Jones and Tio (1948) observed that symptoms of frenching on tobacco associated with low iron content of the plant could be eliminated by (1) adding ferrous sulfate to the soil, (2) maintaining a relatively low soil temperature, or (3) autoclaving the soil. The interrelationship between iron availability to the plant and activity of microflora in the soil is implicit in their findings.

It is apparent, a priori, that wet poorly drained soils are favorable to the development of anaerobes and inhibitive to aerobes. Since the anaerobes are capable of using oxygen that is in chemical combination with soil components to meet the needs of their life processes, their activity effects a reduction in iron, manganese, and other reducible compounds (Leeper, 1947). It is also known that denitrification takes place rapidly in waterlogged soils (De and Sarker, 1936; Walliban, 1937; Willis and Sturgis, 1944). There is a rapid loss of applied nitrate under these conditions, but only a fraction of it is recoverable as ammonia. Willis and Sturgis (1944) observed that large quantities of nitrogen as ammonia are lost from waterlogged soil high in nitrogen and maintained at high temperature (100° F.), or from soils high in organic matter. These results indicated that such a soil will tend to reach an equilibrium at which it will maintain a low soluble nitrogen content against losses induced by high temperatures and alkaline reactions.

De and Sarker (1936) found that much of the difference in nitrogen between the amount of nitrate applied to a waterlogged soil and that recoverable as ammonia was due to nitrogen assimilated by the increase population of micro-organisms. Wallihan (1937) confirmed this and pointed out that this condition explains the relatively low loss of nitrogen when waterlogged soils are drained. He found that there was a relatively rapid rate of nitrate production following drainage of such a soil, providing further evidence that the denitrification process actually prevents excessive losses of an important plant nutrient from waterlogged soils. On the other hand, the nitrogen so stored may be withheld from crop plants, as rice for example, growing on such a soil. In fact, Willis and Sturgis (1944) have emphasized the generally poor response to applications of nitrogen observed on rice. They attribute much of this effect to loss of ammonia on denitrification, but the competition for nitrogen by micro-organisms is also undoubtedly involved.

A further effect of wet soils on micro-organisms arises from the fact that wet soils tend to be cold (Baver, 1948). That is, the higher the moisture content of a soil the higher its heat capacity. This means that wet soils warm up more slowly during the spring months. Since relatively low soil temperatures depress microbiological activity, nutrient availability dependent on this activity will be correspondingly depressed.

Mineral Nutrition in the Moisture Range between Field Capacity and the Wilting Percentage

The extent to which growth and, consequently utilization might be limited by water supply

Regardless of how nearly optimal the level of mineral nutrients and other factors may be, growth will be limited by the extent to which water supply to the plant is limited.   Hence, the possibility that growth may be limited by water availability in the available range is quite pertinent to a discussion of mineral nutrition in the available soil-moisture range.

The status of prevailing weather conditions may be a determinant as to whether or not decreasing soil-moisture content within the available range will affect plant growth (Clements, 1940; Stanford, 1947). If the level of soil moisture approaches the wilting percentage while the plant is subjected to a cool humid environment, an associated decrease in growth is much less likely than if the plant is growing in a hot dry environment.   That is, at the lower levels of available moisture the supply of soil moisture in the former case could probably maintain turgescence, whereas it would probably be insufficient in the latter.

There is indication that some species of tree fruits show little response in productiveness to variation in the level of soil moisture, providing it is maintained above the wilting percentage.   There are productive vineyards in the San Joaquin Valley of California that receive neither rain nor irrigation during the entire growing season.   On the other hand, potato fields in the same area are irrigated daily, and successful maintenance of Ladino clover pastures in this Valley requires that the soil-moisture content be kept at near field capacity.   The lower soil temperature prevailing in highly moist soils may be a factor in the need for much more frequent irrigation of potatoes and Ladino clover.

The criterion adopted as the measure of growth response is involved in evaluating the effect of degree of soil-moisture depletion on growth. Adams, Veihmeyer, and Brown (1942) studied the   effect of various irrigation regimes on growth and productiveness of cotton.   The plots maintained at the highest level of soil moisture produced the maximum vegetative growth of the plants, and vegetative growth declined with decreasing soil-moisture reserve at time of irrigation.   Yet, there was practically no difference in yield of seed cotton per acre among the various treatments.   Thus, the plants made a physiological response to increased level of soil-moisture supply, but did not provide a corresponding economic return.   Hendrickson and Veihmeyer (1929) observed the maximum vegetative growth of peach trees on plots that had the most abundant water supply. The production of these trees was not superior to those irrigated less frequently, and the keeping quality of the fruit from the frequently irrigated trees was quite inferior. Here again, maintenance of relatively moist soil produced the maximum physiological response as regards vegetation, but the treatment was actually an economic liability. Guayule has been observed to decline in vegetative growth as soil-moisture depletion prior to irrigation is intensified, but rubber production was found to be increased (Hunter and Kelley, 1946c; Wadleigh, et al., 1945).

The tenability of the concept that all soil moisture above the wilting percentage is equally available to plants is conditioned, therefore, by the criteria used in evaluating the results, in addition to the degree of prevalence of modulating factors. Consequently, the question as to whether or not the soil-moisture content above the wilting percentage will become limiting to full utilization of nutrients available to the plant is correspondingly involved. Unquestionably, conditions frequently prevail in which plant response to fertilization is limited by soil-moisture supply within the available range; but any generalization would be hazardous, considering the present state of our knowledge of the subject.

The effect of the change in the thickness of moisture films on nutrient availability

The discussion in the fore part of this paper pointed out that as the thickness of moisture films on the soil particles decreases, the intensity with which the water is retained on the particles by surface-force action increases. Buehrer and Rose (1943) have discussed the physical properties of adsorbed water, and have designated as "bound" water that portion of the soil water that fails to freeze at $-3°$ C. They state:

Bound water is found to have a dielectric constant of only 2.2 as compared with a value of 81 for normal water. Its low dielectric constant indicates a greatly reduced polarity, and therefore its solvent power and dissociating action on salts and other substances must be considerably less than that of pure, normal water.

This implies, therefore, that with diminishing thickness of moisture films, there is a corresponding decrease in the proportion of water in the film with normal solvent properties.

Reitemeier (1946) determined the dissolved ions in solutions extracted from six soils at four moisture contents and found that the concentration of nitrate and chloride increased as the moisture content decreased. He explained this effect on the basis of existence of "unfree" water in the soil, or negative adsorption of monovalent anions, or a combination of both. This relative concentration of chloride and nitrogen ions in the outer layers of thin moisture films may also be involved in the usually observed accumulation of nitrogen in plants on dry soils. In general, Reitemeier (1946) found the opposite effect for cations and polyvalent anions; i.e., as the thickness of the moisture films decreased there was a relative diminution of the concentration of these ions in the outer layers. It may be coincidental, but plants subjected to low soil-moisture supply also tend to have a relatively low content of these ions (Greaves and Carter, 1922; Greaves and Nelson, 1925).

The diminished amplitude of the cationic swarm about an adsorption surface under a thinning moisture film appears to be conducive to potassium ions present entering the lattice of the clay crystal and becoming fixed. Volk (1934) found that alternate wetting and drying of soils treated with soluble potassium salts caused rapid fixation of potassium in a nonreplaceable form in many soils (depending on the mineralogical nature of the clay); and that very little fixation of this kind took place when the soils were kept continuously moist. This has been verified many times (Attoe, 1946; Raney and Hoover, 1946; Stanford, 1947; Walsh and Cullinan, 1945). Acid soils fix relatively little potassium when moist, but drying effectively increases potassium fixation. Calcareous soils fix potassium when moist, and the extent of fixation increases on drying. Martin *et al.* (1945) suggest that the effect of drying on potassium fixation is that of increased concentration of ions at the adsorption interface, and that dehydration, *per se,* is not involved. It is logical to conclude that the relatively low potassium content of plants subjected to low soil-moisture supply is related to the increased intensity of potassium fixation under such conditions.

Soil-moisture depletion is also conducive to the fixation of phosphorus. Trumble (1947) concludes that this explains the relatively low phosphorus content of plants under inadequate soil-moisture supply. Neller and Comar (1947) report that the extent of phosphorus fixation on drying is directly related to the clay content of soils.

Wilting Range

A partial exhaustion of available soil moisture may affect plant development otherwise than through the effect on soil-moisture tension. A deeply rooted plant may completely exhaust all available moisture in the fertile surface horizon of soil but at the same time may have an adequate supply of moisture available to the deeper roots in the lower strata. There is a possibility that such a plant may suffer from nutrient deficiencies because of inability to absorb nutrients from the fertile but moisture-deficient soil.

For example, the availability of boron to crops is definitely related to soil moisture.   Boron deficiency symptoms are widely observed in New York and Wisconsin in dry years.   Brown and King (1939) in Connecticut and Kostyuchenko (1938) in Russia have reported that boron-deficiency symptoms are more prevalent in dry seasons.   Hobbs and Bertramson (1949) have reported that in Indiana boron-deficiency symptoms on alfalfa appear only in dry years.   Hobbs (1948) found that the available boron content of Indiana soils decreased with depth and that in dry years applications of boron to the surface of the soil did not always prevent deficiency symptoms.   Hobbs and Bertramson (1949) conducted experiments with tomato plants having divided root systems and found that fast-growing plants were not able to obtain enough boron when half the root system was in nondeficient surface soil with a moisture content near wilting.   From their work they concluded that boron-deficiency symptoms observed on alfalfa in Indiana may have resulted from a deficient supply of moisture in the soil rather than from a deficient supply of boron.

Breazeale (1930) presented evidence that wheat seedlings were able to absorb potassium from soil at or below the permanent-wilting percentage when water was available elsewhere to the root system.   Hunter and Kelley (1946a) grew corn plants in tar-paraffin pots filled with moist soil and surrounded with air-dry soil containing radiophosphorus. In all cases the corn roots penetrated the walls of the pot and extended into the dry soil.   The moisture content of the dry soil increased, but values as high as the permanent-wilting percentage were not obtained. The results of the experiment indicated that the roots of corn are able to elongate into dry soil and to build up the moisture content of that soil; but the evidence obtained did not indicate that an absorption of nutrients from dry soil by plants takes place.   A later study by Hunter and Kelley (1946b) provided inconclusive evidence that there was a movement of radiophosphorus into alfalfa roots from surface soil at or below the wilting percentage when moisture was available to the roots below the 2-foot depth.   Volk (1947) has presented evidence that corn roots can absorb potassium and nitrogen from soil at or below the wilting percentage, but his data concerning phosphorus were inconclusive. The problem of nutrient absorption from dry soil has not been recognized as an important one in terms of crop production.   Most evidence indicates that plants grown under the drier soil-moisture regimes have a high percentage composition of the various mineral elements.   The observations of Miller and Duley (1925) are typical.

During protracted periods of drought, the fertile surface soil may dry to less than the wilting percentage.   This may have drastic consequences to shallow-rooted crops.   Even though deep-rooted plants may obtain adequate moisture from the deeper horizons under these conditions, the question immediately arises as to the ability of plants to absorb nutrients from the fertile topsoil when it is drier than the wilting percentage. For example, boron-deficiency symptoms usually become predominant during a drought (Brown and King, 1939; Plant, 1947). There are two alternative explanations for this: (1) Drying of soil may affect the availability of borate, as is the case with potassium and phosphate, or (2) plants are unable to absorb boron when the soil moisture is below the wilting percentage and inadequate supplies of this nutrient are present in the lower horizons.

Breazeale (1930) carried out a number of experiments to ascertain whether or not plants are able to remove nutrients from soil that is drier than the wilting percentage. When the root system of a plant was divided between a moist soil and soil with moisture content below the wilting percentage, Breazeale (1930) noted the root system transported water from the moist to the dry soil, raising the moisture content of the latter to slightly above the wilting percentage. He also found evidence that because of the moisture-transfer phenomenon, the roots were able to absorb potassium from the dry soil. That is, net movement of potassium into the roots was in opposite direction to the net movement of water out of the roots and into the dry soil. This two-way adjustment of moisture between soil and plant roots has recently been demonstrated by Breazeale and McGeorge (1949) by a new technic.

A pertinent consideration in the ability of roots to remove nutrients from dry soils is whether or not the roots are able to grow and proliferate in the dry soil. Loomis and Ewan (1936) found that the roots of 29 different genera of seedlings completely failed to penetrate soil at a moisture content of about the hygroscopic coefficient. Hendrickson and Veihmeyer (1931b) concluded that the roots of sunflower plants would not grow into soil drier than the wilting percentage. Shantz (1927) also concluded that the roots of crop plants lack the ability to penetrate dry soils, but he believed that the roots of xerophytic plants possessed this capacity. Lobanov (1947) found appreciable variation in the dryness of soil limiting to the growth of roots of woody plants. The minimal soil-moisture contents (soil-moisture retentive properties unknown) for root growth were 6.11 percent for *Fraxinus excelsior*, 5.11 percent for *Caragana arborescens*, and 2.07 percent for *Picea abies* and *Pinus sylvestris*.

Although there is some evidence that plants may absorb small quantities of nutrients from dry soils, this source appears to be inadequate for a thriving plant. If moisture is available in unfertile lower horizons of a soil and if most of the fertility is in the surface horizon that has become very dry, the plant may suffer from inadequate mineral nutrition.

XII. NUTRIENT ACCUMULATION IN PLANTS IN RELATION TO THE SOIL MOISTURE SUPPLY

It would be logical to conclude that under conditions of adequate nutrient supply, plants that are limited in growth by a relatively low level of soil moisture would have a higher content of mineral nutrients than plants under comparable fertility but not limited in growth by moisture supply. Miller and Duley (1925) studied this relationship on corn plants. Corn grown at an optimum level of soil moisture made much more growth than comparable plants in soil maintained at a minimum level of soil moisture. The nitrogen, phosphorus, and potassium contents of the plants were appreciably higher under the minimum soil moisture level, but the reverse relationship was observed for calcium. Emmert (1936) found that the smaller tomato plants grown with a relatively low soil-moisture supply were higher in nitrogen and potassium and lower in phosphorus than the larger control plants grown at an optimum level of soil moisture.

Many studies have provided evidence somewhat at variance with that just cited. Haddock[1] found no consistent variation in nitrate content in petioles of sugarbeets subjected to wide differences in irrigation regime. Leamer et al., as shown by the data in Table 13, found that alfalfa irrigated whenever the soil-moisture tension reached 0.4 atmosphere at the 1-foot depth had a slightly higher nitrogen content than comparable alfalfa on which irrigation was delayed until moisture tension reached 4.0 atmospheres at the 1-foot depth. The effect of soil-moisture content on activity of nodule bacteria may be involved here. Most experimental evidence shows that for a given level of fertility, decreasing soil-moisture supply is associated with a definite increase in nitrogen content of the plant tissue, a definite decrease in potassium content, and a variable effect upon content of phosphorus, calcium, and magnesium (Greaves and Carter, 1923; Greaves and Nelson, 1925; Janes, 1948; Maximov, 1929; Thomas et al., 1942, 1943).

In other words, it is well established that when growth of plants is limited by soil-moisture supply, nitrogen tends to accumulate within the plant because rate of entry is approximately maintained in conjunction with the decreased rate of utilization in growth processes. The general tendency for potassium content to be relatively low in plants on the drier soils show that rate of entry of potassium decreases to a greater degree than does rate of utilization in these slower growing plants.

[1] Haddock, J. L. Personal communication concerning an unpublished report.

Hence, availability of potassium to plants may be depressed at the lower soil-moisture contents, depending on the nature of the soil. It is of interest to note, however, that Wimmer *et al.* (1944) studied nutrient content of two varieties of sugarbeets at different soil-moisture levels and reported that one variety showed the conventional decrease in potassium content with decreasing moisture supply, whereas the other variety showed the reverse trend under the same conditions. If this observation is verified, it will indeed be a remarkable case of specificity in ionic entry between two varieties of a given crop.

Although the phosphate ion may accumulate in plants limited in growth by low soil-moisture supply (Janes, 1948; Miller and Duley, 1925) there is also evidence that plants so affected may have a relatively low content of phosphate[2] (Emmert, 1936; Thomas *et al.*, 1942, 1943). Thus, the effect of soil moisture on phosphate nutrition is far less consistent than observed for nitrogen or potassium. This seems to be indicative of the wide variation among soils in their fixing power for phosphorus as conditioned by soil-moisture content. Miller and Duley (1925) grew corn on a fertile silt loam from an alluvial bottom along the Missouri River; and Janes (1948), bean plants on Arredono loamy sand fertilized with 1,200 pounds per acre of 4–7–5. These soils were conducive to phosphate accumulation under low moisture supply.

McMurtrey *et al.* (1947) grew tobacco on Collington fine sandy loam fertilized with 750 pounds per acre of 4–8–12 in the row and found no effect of soil-moisture supply on phosphate content of tobacco leaves. Haddock[2] grew beets on a calcareous soil, Millville silt loam. Thomas *et al.* (1942) studied tomatoes presumably grown on Hagerstown silty clay loam that was variously fertilized. These two experiments yielded evidence that phosphate content of plants was reduced by diminishing the soil-moisture supply. It is quite probable that these various soils differ considerably in their fixing power for phosphate, and that this variation is related to the observed effects of soil-moisture supply on phosphate content of plants.

The available evidence consistently shows magnesium to be relatively high in plants growing under restricted soil-moisture supply (Janes, 1948; McMurtrey *et al.*, 1947; Thomas *et al.*, 1942). This is in line with the inverse tendency for magnesium deficiency to develop in plants during periods of heavy rainfall.

Since entry of calcium and potassium into plants tends to vary reciprocally, it could be inferred that the characteristically low potassium content of plants with inadequate soil-moisture supply would be ac-

[2] See footnote 1, p. 203.

companied by a relatively high content of calcium. McMurtrey *et al.* (1947) and Thomas *et al.* (1942) found this to be the case on fertilized soils, but the latter investigators found the reverse trend on their unfertilized plots. Miller and Duley (1925) and Janes (1948) found virtually no effect of soil-moisture supply on calcium content of their experimental plants. It is evident, therefore, that the status of other constituents in the soil has a modulating effect on calcium availability under varying soil-moisture content.

As pointed out in the first part of this paper, diminishing soil-moisture content effects a concentration of the solutes in the soil solution. Fertilized plants may even intensify this solute concentration as a result of increased rate of moisture extraction. Thus, Jordon *et al.*[3] found that corn plants fertilized with nitrogen during a dry year not only rapidly depleted the soil moisture to the wilting percentage in the surface foot of soil, but also to the 3-foot depth. On the other hand, readily available moisture continuously prevailed in the 3 feet of soil under the unfertilized control plants. In a well-fertilized soil subjected to a prolonged dry spell, this solute concentration may in itself inhibit water availability so that growth on the unfertilized soil may be better than that on which fertilizer was applied.

Neff and Potter (1946) noted that newly transplanted tung trees were injured by mineral fertilization during a dry year. Carolus and Woltz (1944) found that during four dry seasons in eastern Virginia, the more nitrogen fertilizer they added to Sassafras sandy loam, the lower the yield of potatoes. Adding increasing amounts of superphosphate had a moderately beneficial effect, however. The effect of these two fertilizing materials on potato yields under these conditions was directly related to their effect on the solute content of the soil solution. Correspondingly, Rahn (1946) found that during a dry year, fertilization with manure produced a much higher yield of melons than did mineral fertilization, but that during a wet year there was no difference in effect on yield from these two sources of fertility.

The need for taking into account soil-moisture supply in adjusting the fertility program is well recognized in the Hawaiian Islands. Nightingale (1942a, 1942b) emphasized in his studies on the nitrogen, phosphorus, and potassium nutrition of pineapples that the capacity of the plant to utilize efficiently the available supplies of these nutrients was conditioned by soil-moisture supply and other environmental factors. Clements and Kubota (1942, 1943) have developed a technic of following the status of moisture, nutrient, and sugar content of sugar-

---

[3] Personal communication from H. V. Jordon, K. D. Laird, and D. D. Ferguson, concerning an unpublished report.

cane over the course of its development, and of adjusting the irrigation and fertility program in accordance with the trend in the status of the plants.

XIII. EFFECT OF VARIATIONS IN SOIL MOISTURE ON MICROBIOLOGICAL ACTIVITY

The important role of microorganisms in the mineral nutrition of plants, especially with respect to the decomposition and mineralization of the organic constituents of soils, is generally recognized. It follows, therefore, that any effect that varying degrees of soil-moisture tension would have on microbial activity may result in an indirect effect on mineral nutrition. There have been numerous studies (Bollen, 1941; Clark, 1947; Greaves and Carter, 1922; and Waksman, 1932) on the relation of soil moisture to soil micro-organisms, but, as pointed out by Bhaumik and Clark (1947), in most of this work the soil-moisture levels were expressed as a percentage of the maximum water-holding capacity. Also the technics used often failed to insure even moisture distribution throughout the soil sample, or to maintain constant moisture content over the experimental period.

Bhaumik and Clark (1947) adjusted the moisture tension of samples of five different soils at 0, 0.001, 0.01, 0.05, 0.5, and 3.2 atmospheres and collected the carbon dioxide evolved during the course of incubation. In two soils the peak rate of carbon dioxide production was at 0.5 atmosphere of moisture tension, and in the other three soils at 0.05 atmosphere tension. For all soils, the peak rate of carbon dioxide production was observed at or very near to the moisture tension at the aeration porosity limit, taken by convention as 0.05 atmosphere. Total carbon dioxide production was actually at a maximum in Thurman sand at the highest moisture tension used, and it was relatively very low at the lowest two levels of moisture tension. On the other hand, total carbon dioxide production for Wabash silty clay was only slightly less than maximum on the saturated soil but was relatively low at the highest moisture tension. The diverse effect of moisture tension on microbiological activity on these two soil types differing widely in texture is indeed intriguing. This difference may be partially explained by the enormous increase in population of fungi at 3.2 atmospheres tension, as compared to increase in population at zero tension in the sample of Thurman sand.

Novogrudsky (1947) studied the rate of nitrification in a Chestnut soil as a function of moisture content. No nitrification occurred when only hygroscopic water was present, but it did occur when the moisture content was equal to about one and one-half times maximum hygroscopicity (presumably slightly above the wilting percentage). Nitrification reached its greatest intensity when the upper limit of film water equalled twice the maximum molecular water-holding capacity (presumably twice field capacity). That is, these results tend to be in line with those of Bhaumik and Clark (1947) for their fine-textured soils.

Waksman (1932) has reviewed the earlier work on the influence of soil moisture on microbiological activity. Different organisms vary as to the optimum soil-moisture content for their activity. Thus, nitrification is at its highest near the moisture content of field capacity, and excessive quantities of water are much more injurious than too low a moisture content. It is quite evident that to whatever extent the mineral nutrition of plants is dependent upon the activity of soil microorganisms, the soil-moisture level will have an indirect effect on nutrition through its influence on soil microbes.

This aspect of the relation of soil moisture to microorganism activity is concerned with minor-element nutrition. The mineral nutrition of crops on many soils is intimately connected with the organic-matter content of these soils. It is probable that deficiency symptoms in dry years, such as are reported for boron in Wisconsin and Indiana, arise directly from the fact that the surface soil, which contains most of the organic matter, becomes too dry for the mineralization of the organic matter by microbial activity.

XIV. THE INFLUENCE OF SOIL MOISTURE ON PHYSIOLOGICAL PROCESSES

The extent to which soil moisture affects physiological processes of plants is largely dependent upon the degree to which the diffusion-pressure deficit of the water in the various plant tissues has been affected. In other words, soil-moisture stress affects the various processes as a result of its influence on the turgescence of the various tissues as indicated by the relationships in Figure 32. The fundamental phenomena of cell division and enlargement are obviously involved to an intimate degree, especially enlargement. Heyn (1940) has reviewed the literature on the physiology of cell elongation and has proposed a theory that appears to be consistent with available evidence. This theory postulates that plastic extension in the cell wall is the primary factor in cell elongation, and that elastic extensibility of the wall is not involved. It is further postulated from the evidence that the energy necessary for surface enlargement of the wall is derived from turgor pressure.

This conclusion that turgor pressure is essential to growth by cell elongation is in agreement with the observations of Loomis (1934) on the growth of corn. His study indicated that growth was directly dependent upon a liberal supply of water to the growing point. This water supply is reduced and growth checked by the following factors in their order of effectiveness: (1) Direct sunlight, (2) deficient soil moisture, and (3) low humidity. It is of special interest that direct sunlight was found to be even more effective in inducing moisture deficits at the growing point than insufficient soil moisture. Thut and Loomis (1944) present additional data confirming their observation. Thus, light intensity and temperature condition the effect of soil moisture upon terminal elongation. For example, Loomis (1934) found that a well-watered corn plant made most of its growth during the warmer daylight hours of a partly cloudy day, but a comparable corn plant growing under moderate soil-moisture stress made most of its growth at night.

Sayre (1926) has shown that the operation of the guard cells of stomata is an osmotic phenomenon, the degree of opening of the stoma being directly dependent on the turgescence of the guard cells. The effect of light on the opening and closing of the stomata is accomplished by means of osmotic phenomenon, since reversible starch-sugar conversions induce variations in the osmotic pressure of the guard cells, and consequently their degree of turgescence with respect to adjacent cells. Beck (1931) has also presented data on the diurnal variation in the osmotic pressure of the guard cells and its relation to their operation. The guard cells close as a result of loss of turgidity, regardless of the ultimate cause. Veihmeyer and Hendrickson (1927b) state that if the moisture content of the soil is above the wilting percentage no differences can be detected as to stomatal opening, whether the trees are growing on relatively dry soil or at the moisture content of field capacity. Loftfield (1921) and Magness et al. (1935), however, observed that early closing of stomata on apple leaves was about the best indication of the beginning of water shortage. Similarly, Mendel (1945) observed that stomatal opening of orange leaves began to decrease before other outward symptoms of moisture deficiency were apparent.

It was pointed out previously that the rate of transpiration may largely determine the rate of water absorption from the soil. It now becomes apparent that the development of a soil-moisture stress sufficient to induce stomatal closing may affect rate of transpiration. As pointed out by Loftfield (1921), the rate of transpiration is determined by the vapor-pressure deficit in the air when the stomata are fully open or nearly so, but as the stomata close the determinative effect of evaporative conditions is lessened. Knight (1922) and others have shown that this relationship is not consistent. Martin (1940) grew sunflower plants in large containers of soil maintained under various moisture regimes and found that the rate of transpiration was ordinarily affected when about two-thirds of the available soil moisture had been removed. The level of soil moisture at which a decreased rate was observed was dependent upon the rate of transpiration. The various soil-moisture regimes had no effect on stomatal opening unless the rate of transpiration was also affected. There appeared to be a close relationship between stomatal opening and rate of transpiration, but it was not ascertainable whether or not one of these effects was dependent on the other. Martin (1940) observed that decreasing moisture content of the soil induced decreased rate of growth before any effect on stomatal opening or transpiration rate per unit area could be detected.

Dolgov (1947) used observations on the rate of transpiration of oat plants under standard conditions as a measure of the availability of soil moisture. He found that the transpiration rate was greatest, independently of the soil, at field capacity and decreased to a minimum at the wilting point. These observations on the effect of soil-moisture content on rate of transpiration are in line with most of those that have appeared in the literature.

The rate of transpiration by leaves of various trees (Loustalot, 1945; Mandel, 1945; Schneider and Childers, 1941) has been found to decrease markedly with decreasing soil moisture, the decrease in rate of transpiration being evident before any outward symptoms of water deficiency in the trees became apparent. Mendel (1945) found on oranges that this decrease in rate of transpiration began when the "soil suction force" was still low and became very rapid when the "soil suction force" exceeded 3.5 atmospheres. He also noted that rate of transpiration by oranges was conditioned by the specific characteristics of the rootstock. When soil moisture was adequate, leaves of Shamouti orange budded on sweet lime had a higher rate of transpiration than those on sour orange; but where soil moisture was inadequate, this difference tended to be reversed. The low level to which rate of transpiration may be reduced on loss of turgescence in plants at the wilting percentage of soil moisture is indicated by the data of Miller and Saunders (1923). During the heat of the day, they found that the rate of transpiration of wilted cowpea and soybean plants was only one-twentieth that of comparable turgid plants. Loss of water from the leaf mesophyll is very effectively reduced by an increase in the diffusion-pressure deficit of the cellular fluids of this tissue.

Gaseous interchange between the leaf mesophyll and the external atmosphere also takes place in the process of photosynthesis. Presumably this process should also be affected by degree of stomatal opening. Sayre (1939) has studied the stomatal behavior of the corn plant in detail and states that "there is no close relation between stomata and photosynthesis in corn" and that "maximum photosynthesis can go on in the absence of open stomata." Schneider and Childers (1941) observed fairly high rates of photosynthesis on apple leaves when the stomata appeared to be closed. Mitchell (1936) observed on tomato and *Pelargonium* that reduction in diffusive capacity of the stomata does not have a marked effect on photosynthesis. In other words, rate of photosynthesis is not nearly so closely related to stomatal opening as is rate of transpiration. Heinicke and Childers (1936) studied the rates of photosynthesis and transpiration of apple trees on soil that was drying out in relation to the rates of these processes on comparable trees which were well supplied with water. The drying soil induced a reduction in rate of transpiration. Transpiration was one-fourth that of the tree on the well-watered soil, but under these same conditions the rate of photosynthesis was reduced by one-half.

The predominance of evidence indicates that rate of photosynthesis is more closely related to the water content of the leaves than to the diffusive capacity of the stomates. Thus, Dastur (1925) and Dastur and Desai (1933) studied several tropical species and found that there is a direct correlation between the rate of photosynthesis per unit area of leaf and the water content of the leaf. Even on a given plant, Dastur (1925) noted that those tissues first to be affected by a reduced water supply are the first ones to lose the power of photosynthesis. Iljin (1923) also noted that a reduction in rate of photosynthesis occurred when the water content of the leaves was reduced. However, he noted that species varied appreciably in this respect, some undergoing a marked reduction in water content with only a moderate lowering in rate of photosynthesis. For example, a reduction of 34 percent in water content of the leaves of *Phlomis pungens* was associated with only a 13 percent reduction in rate of photosynthesis; whereas a reduction of 44 percent in water content in leaves of *Bidens tripartita* was associated with a reduction of about 65 percent in rate of photosynthesis.

Actually there is some evidence that maximum rate of photosynthesis takes place when the water content of the leaves is less than maximum. Brilliant (1924) observed that rate of photosynthesis for *Hedera helix* and *Impatiens parviflora* was maximum when the water content of the leaves was reduced 5 to 15 percent below maximum. Photosynthesis nearly ceased when the leaves of these species lost 50 percent of their water. Correspondingly, Heinicke and Childers (1936) suggested as a result of their studies that the optimum soil-moisture content for maximum rate of photosynthesis by apple leaves was probably below field capacity. Schneider and Childers (1941) verified this observation.

Chrelashvili (1941) found that the maximum rate of photosynthesis occurred for *Allium victorialis, Primula obconica,* and *Zea mays* at a certain degree of water loss from the assimilating tissue, the degree of loss varying with different species. Schneider and Childers also noted that under conditions of a gradually drying soil transpiration was reduced at least 1 day before there was any reduction in rate of photosynthesis. If evaporation conditions were low, several days elapsed between the first observed reduction in rate of transpiration and a reduction in rate of photosynthesis. However, they noted that before wilting was evident on their young apple trees, rate of photosynthesis had reduced 55 percent as a result of decreasing soil moisture. When the plants showed definite wilting and the soil moisture was at the wilting percentage, they recorded an 87-percent reduction in rate of photosynthesis. When water was applied to the soil in which these wilted apple trees were growing, the leaves usually attained turgidity in 3 to 5 hours. However, they did not reestablish the rate of photosynthesis maintained by the controls until 2 to 7 days after watering.

Iljin (1923) noted in his experiments that wilted plants did not develop the maximum rate of photosynthesis for an appreciable time after they had recovered turgor. Loustalot (1945) also observed that pecan trees subjected to drought did not attain a normal rate of photosynthesis until several days after they were watered. On the other hand, he found that the rate of photosynthesis on flooded trees was reduced to 11 percent of normal, and that 10 days to 2 weeks elapsed after the excess water was drained away before the normal photosynthetic rate was again attained. It is quite evident that soil-moisture conditions may have a major effect upon the process of photosynthesis and that this effect takes place largely through the degree of hydration of the chloroplasts and other protoplasmic constituents rather than by affecting the diffusive capacity of the stomata.

Respiration is the process whereby food reserves accrued through the process of photosynthesis are oxidized with the release of energy and carbon dioxide. Since all structural components of the plant and all organic constituents of the living protoplasm are derived from carbohydrates, depletion of carbohydrates by excessive respiration may seriously jeopardize plant development. For example, death would ensue if the rate of oxidation of carbohydrates by respiration should exceed the rate of carbohydrate formation by photosynthesis for an extended period of time during vegetative growth. Consequently, the effect of environmental factors upon the status of these two processes is a prime consideration in crop production.

Soil-moisture conditions may affect the rate of respiration through its effect on the degree of hydration of tissues. There is a decided paucity of evidence as to the precise effect the degree of hydration has on the activity of oxidative enzymes involved in respiration. Pickler (1919) found that the diastase activity in barley grain increased with increase in water content. There is ample evidence (Appleman and Brown, 1946; Bailey, 1921; Coleman et al., 1928) that the rate of respiration of seeds increases markedly with increase in moisture content. Apparently, this relationship between moisture content of seeds and rate of respiration does not hold for leaves. Schneider and Childers (1941) found that rate of respiration for young apple trees on soil undergoing decreasing moisture content increased by 62 percent before wilting of the trees was evident. That is, decreasing moisture content of the leaf tissue was associated with an increase in respiration. Chrelashvili (1941) found for all species studied—*Allium victorialis*, *Primula obconica*, and *Zea mays*—that a slight hydration of the leaf tissue was associated with an increase in rate of respiration. When the water-loss was considerable, the respiration of *Allium* leaves decreased, but the respiration of leaves of *Primula* and *Zea* continued to exceed that of the controls.

The evidence that inadequate soil moisture induces increased rate of respiration and decreased rate of photosynthesis of leaves implies a potential decrease in the carbohydrate reserves of the plant. This latter possibility may be partially compensated by the decreased vegetative growth and concomitant decrease in utilization of carbohydrates in growth, which is frequently observed to take place with increasing soil-moisture stress.

The available evidence does not permit a generalization as to the effect of soil-moisture conditions upon the status of carbohydrates within plants, for this status is the resultant of several variables that are also partially conditioned by the soil-moisture regime. Spoehr (1919) found that decreasing moisture content of cacti favored the accumulation of polysaccharides rather than soluble sugars. Traub et al. (1946) determined at various times of the year the carbohydrate reserves in guayule plants grown under various degrees of soil-moisture stress. For plants harvested in October, these investigators found a much higher percentage of inulin and levulins in plants grown under high soil-moisture stress than in those from the treatment providing low moisture stress. The difference in content of levulins disappeared during winter, but the plants under high moisture stress maintained the relatively high level of inulin until the following spring. At all samplings there was a higher percentage of pentosans in the plants under higher moisture stress than in those under low. There were no consistent variations in content of reducing sugars as related to moisture stress.

Rosa (1921) reported that the hardening process in plants resulting from inadequate soil moisture was associated with increasing percentage of pentosans, increasing percentage of reducing and total sugars, but decreasing percentage of starch. This disappearance of starch from plants undergoing moisture stress has been observed many times. Molisch (1921) noted that the onset of a water deficit in starch-filled leaves hastens the disappearance of the starch. Schroeder and co-workers (1922, 1931) found that the disappearance of starch from wilting nasturtium leaves was accompanied by an increase in sucrose. Spoehr and Milner (1939) found that the starch dissolution taking place in leaves undergoing moisture stress is due to the increased activity of amylase, i.e., the activity of this enzyme increases with decreased degree of hydration. Eaton and Ergle (1948) also found that leaves of cotton plants grown in a greenhouse and allowed to wilt daily contained four times as much amylolytic activity as comparable leaves on plants maintained on an adequate supply of soil moisture. Correspondingly, there was found to be only one-third as much starch and about one-half as much total carbohydrate in the leaves allowed to wilt daily as compared to the controls. That is, starch dissolution in the wilted leaves was not found to be accompanied by compensating levels of hexoses and sucrose. Comparable data on leaves were observed on field plants grown at Shafter, Calif., but it was also observed that the stems and roots of plants subjected to drought showed a marked relative accumulation of starch in contrast to the situation observed in leaves.

Wadleigh et al. (1943) followed the disappearance of starch from bean plants on diminishing soil-moisture availability and found that starch reappeared within 24 hours after irrigation at a higher percentage than that found in the control plants. Wadleigh and Ayers (1945) also observed the disappearance of starch from bean plants under high moisture stress, but they did not find an increase in percentage of sugars accompanying the lowered levels of starch.

In contrast to the rather consistent observations of moisture stress on the starch reserves in plants, there is little consistent evidence as to the effect upon the sugars. This is undoubtedly related to the transitional nature of sugars in the various plant tissues, the time of day at which sampling occurred frequently being a major factor affecting the percentage of sugars found. Nevertheless, Hartt (1934) presents evi-

214 L. A. RICHARDS AND C. H. WADLEIGH

dence that more sucrose is synthesized in leaves on sugarcane well supplied with water than in leaves on plants undergoing moisture stress.

Little information is available concerning the effect of soil-moisture conditions on nitrogen metabolism in plants. Water deficits within the plant are influenced by the adequacy of the supply of soil moisture. Hydrolysis condensation equilibria within the plant such as those existing between proteins and their constituent amides and amino acids are undoubtedly conditioned by water deficits, and, hence, degree of hydration of hydrophilic constituents of the protoplasm. Obviously, this effect may take place largely through the degree of activation of the pertinent enzymes.

The experiments of Mothes (1926) indicated a relationship between water content of leaves and proteolysis. He observed that a deficiency of water in leaves hastened protein decomposition and the translocation of the soluble products. In general, this effect of a water deficit was more pronounced in old leaves than in young leaves. By studying detached leaves, Mothes found that the rate of proteolysis caused by water deficit was actually faster in young leaves than in old ones, and that the accumulation of the proteolytic products tended to inactivate the enzymes concerned. Translocation of the soluble nitrogenous constituents out of old attached leaves prevented enzyme inactivation and thus proteolysis appears to be more intense in old attached leaves when the plant undergoes moisture stress. The proteolytic products translocated out of the old leaves under such conditions apparently move to meristematic tissues or to developing seeds.

Petrie and Wood (1938) also noted a decreased net formation of protein from amino acids with a reduction in water content of leaves, but they pointed out that the evidence did not show clearly whether this net effect was due to decreased rate of protein synthesis or to increased rate of proteolysis. They point out that Mothes' observations on old leaves are typical, since the process is not reversible with shifts in water content but is partially dependent on senescence in old leaves.

XV. THE INFLUENCE OF SOIL MOISTURE ON THE VARIOUS PHASES OF PLANT GROWTH
Germination

Since absorption of water is the initial activity taking place in the germination of seeds, it is reasonable to assume that availability of water should affect seed germination and seedling growth. The imbibitional power of some seeds is enormous. Shull (1916) found that seeds of *Xanthium pennsylvanicum* imbibed 12 percent as much water from a saturated sodium chloride solution having an osmotic pressure of 375 atmospheres as from pure water. Intake of water from a solution with an osmotic pressure of 19 atmospheres was 75 percent that of the control. Even though some seeds have this remarkable power of imbibition, very few of them will germinate if the soil-moisture content is below the wilting percentage. The data of Doneen and MacGillivray (1943) are the most inclusive on this point and are presented in detail in Table 27.

Data in Table 27 indicate a remarkable specificity in seed germination by various species at different levels of soil moisture. Thus, germination of cabbage seeds was excellent when the soil-moisture content was slightly below the wilting percentage, whereas the germination of celery seed was inhibited when the soil-moisture content was slightly below field capacity. Doneen and MacGillivray (1943) state that the germination of seeds of all of the crops studied took place in a shorter period of time at high soil moisture than at low. Since rate of germination is dependent upon rate of water intake, this observation implies that the imbibitional power of the seed is conditioned by the moisture content within the range of available moisture.

Stiles (1948) studied water absorption by seeds of two varieties of cotton and three varieties of corn during the early stages of germination. She found that the embryo and seed of Drought Resistant No. 293 cotton absorbed about half as much water during the first 96 hours of germination as those of Rogers Acala; and concluded that the low proportion of water in the embryo of Drought Resistant No. 293 cotton seeds, the rapid initial and extended absorption of water, and the high proportion of water in the endosperm were factors adapting this variety to germination under dry land conditions, whereas Rogers Acala cotton, its seeds requiring almost twice as much water, is adapted to germination under a mesophytic habitat. Differences among varieties of corn were less clear-cut. Seeds of Yellow Dent absorbed considerably more water than did those of Sure Cropper or Gehu Flint, yet a much higher proportion of the water absorbed during the first 24 hours entered the embryos of seeds of the Sure Cropper and Gehu Flint varieties than the seeds of Yellow Dent. Thus, of the three varieties, Yellow Dent is considered to be the least adapted to germination under dry land conditions.

Uhvits (1946) studied the germination of alfalfa seeds on artificial substrates supplied with sodium chloride and mannitol solutions at various osmotic pressures. The rate at which the seeds absorbed water was continuously decreased by increasing the concentration of either sodium chloride or mannitol. Rate of germination was also decreased by increasing the osmotic pressure of the substrate. Germination was almost completely inhibited by 15 atmospheres of sodium chloride, but 84

TABLE 27.—*Germination (emergence) of vegetable seed in Yolo fine sandy loam at different soil moistures*

[Vegetables grouped with reference to germination near permanent-wilting percentage (field capacity 15.7 percent; permanent-wilting percentage 8.6 percent)]

Seeds tested	Percent germination by official methods	Percent germination at soil moisture of —									Least significant difference
		7%	8%	9%	10%	11%	12%	14%	16%	18%	
Group A:											
Cabbage, Copenhagen Market	93	0	80	94	95	92	93	93	91	86	7.7
Sunflower, dwarf	..	0	73	89	90	90	92	92	82	90	9.2
Turnip, Purple Top White Globe	92	0	72	89	88	91	91	87	90	87	7.7
Radish, Scarlet Globe	95	0	64	94	89	95	92	95	94	90	9.7
Summer squash, Zucchini	98	0	31	98	98	99	99	99	98	97	2.3
Sweet corn, Golden Bantam	95	2	35	90	95	93	93	89	93	95	6.9
Watermelon, Striped Klondike (Blue Ribbon)	86	1	39	82	83	83	84	87	85	85	8.8
Tomato, Essar	97	0	31	79	88	95	93	95	91	93	8.4
Winter squash, Hubbard	99	1	22	86	94	93	96	96	95	96	8.9
Cantaloup, Mildew Resistant No. 45	99	0	7	92	99	97	99	97	97	96	3.7
Pepper, Pickling Wax	89	0	19	75	75	73	76	79	80	74	9.6
Cucumber, Short Colorado	90	0	0	84	97	99	98	98	99	98	4.7
Onion, Yellow Sweet Spanish	96	0	0	75	90	91	90	91	91	85	7.6
Spinach, Viroflay	87	0	0	74	90	93	94	94	95	85	6.1
Group B:											
Carrot, Imperator	91	0	3	57	75	87	76	78	77	78	10.4
Snap beans, Stringless Greenpod	82	0	0	57	80	86	92	89	88	89	7.5
Spinach, New Zealand (seed balls)	..	..	4	42	64	76	81	83	80	61	8.7
Spinach, New Zealand (seedlings)	..	0	5	63	87	117	119	141	132	96	16.6
Group C:											
Lettuce, Hanson	93	0	0	29	65	81	91	91	90	88	8.2
Lima beans, Baby Potato	88	0	0	23	79	89	86	86	89	91	5.5
Peas, Laxton's Progress	91	0	3	19	73	86	87	89	86	90	16.6
Beets, Detroit Dark Red (seed balls)	91	0	3	4	52	82	90	91	93	92	6.0
Beets, Detroit Dark Red (seedlings)	..	0	3	5	77	129	156	167	179	172	32.7
Group D:											
Celery	80	0	0	0	0	29	43	62	73	82	

percent of the seeds germinated at 7 atmospheres osmotic pressure of salt. On the mannitol substrates 57 percent of the seeds germinated even in the presence of 15 atmospheres osmotic pressure. The relatively adverse effect of the sodium chloride at a given osmotic pressure appears to be related to the excess intake of chloride during germination when this ion is present in the substrate in high concentration.

Decreased physiological availability of water arising from increased concentration of solutes in the soil solution affects the germination of seeds of various crops quite differently. Ayers and Hayward (1948) point out soil salinity impedes the rate at which seeds germinate and also decreases the number of seeds that do germinate. Evaluation of their data indicates that the following concentrations of the soil solution were found to bring about a 50 percent depression in number of seeds germinating:

Osmotic pressure of soil solution

Atmospheres

Crop:

California common alfalfa	9.0
U.S. 22 M sugarbeets	5.8
Mexican June corn	12.0[1]
Red kidney beans	7.6
California Mariout barley	20.0

[1] Approximate.

The sensitivity of sugarbeets to saline soil during germination and the relatively high tolerance of barley were especially emphasized.

Vegetative Growth

The English plant physiologists have placed considerable emphasis on the analysis of agricultural yields in terms of quantitative evaluation of the effect of various environmental factors on growth under field conditions. The "unit leaf rate" of West, Briggs, and Kidd (1920), now usually designated as "net assimilation rate," has received extensive study. This net assimilation rate is defined as the rate of increase in dry matter per unit area of leaf surface. The concept assumes that accumulation of dry matter is the most satisfactory criterion of crop growth. Such accumulation is the net resultant of total photosynthate produced in the leaves less total loss in the entire plant due to respiratory activity. The rate of accumulation of dry matter, i.e., rate of growth, is thus expressed at the product of the leaf area and the net assimilation rate. In other words, the growth taking place over a given period of time in terms of increase in dry weight is the integral of the product of net assimilation rate and leaf area. Growth, therefore, is segregated into two components: (1) Total leaf area within which photosynthesis may take place and (2) the efficiency with which additional dry matter is produced in this leaf area.

Heath and Gregory (1938) have reviewed the earlier observations within this field of inquiry and have concluded that during the vegetative phase of growth the mean net assimilation rate was essentially constant for all the kinds of plants and environmental conditions investigated. Consequently, they point out that variations in growth as measured by dry matter are preponderantly determined by variations in leaf area. Heath (1937) reported that net assimilation rate of cotton leaves is practically constant from early stages of growth to maximum leaf area beginning with flowering. This would indicate that during vegetative development net assimilation rate was independent of the age of the plant. This would indeed be surprising if substantiated, but Watson and Baptiste (1938), Watson (1947), and Williams (1937, 1946) have presented evidence that net assimilation rate does shift with age of leaves, environmental conditions, and species. Nevertheless, after studying five field crops over a period of 6 years Watson (1947) concluded that "in general, variation in leaf area was the main factor determining differences in yield; variation in net assimilation rate was of minor importance." It is immediately apparent, therefore, that an analysis of the degree to which environmental factors condition development of leaf area during vegetative growth would provide a direct basis for evaluating yield response to treatment or environment.

The recent work of Morton and Watson (1948) presenting a physiological study of the growth of sugarbeet leaves is especially pertinent to the above. They arbitrarily segregated the process of leaf initiation and development into three separate stages: (1) Formation of the leaf initial in the apical meristem; (2) active cell division by which the initial gives rise to the cells and tissues of the leaf; and (3) extension of cells accompanied by appearance of intercellular spaces and final differentiation. These investigators studied the effect of nitrogen and water supply on leaf growth of sugarbeets in a pot experiment. A resume of their observations is presented in Table 28.

Every measurement that was influenced by the experimental conditions showed the greatest response to level of nitrogen. Leaf characteristics showing a response to water supply did so mainly in the presence of added nitrogen. Morton and Watson reasoned that a higher level of water supply should have effected a decrease in number of cells per unit area (increase in cell size) and regarded their observations as presented in Table 28 as inconclusive on that point. The reviewers concur with this conclusion. It is to be hoped, however, that this type of investigation will be continued, since little evidence from controlled experiments is available showing the influence of water supply on histological development of leaves.

Crowther (1934) made a detailed study of the vegetative growth of cotton plants in field plots under three different irrigation regimes at Wad Medani, Sudan. The experiment also involved three levels of

TABLE 28.—*Growth of sugarbeet leaves of Hilleshög variety (after Morton and Watson, 1948)*

Treatment	Leaves produced per plant	Cells per leaf (all leaves)	Cells in 20th leaf	Palisade cells per unit area (0.00035 cm.^{2}) in 20th leaf	Mean leaf area per plant	Net assimilation rate (latter part of growing period)
	Number	Mean number	Mean number	Number	Cm.^{2}	
No nitrogen added to soil; plants allowed to wilt before watering	32.0	31.0	19.1	75.8	672	0.333
No nitrogen added to soil; soil kept moist	28.3	31.9	25.5	83.0	710	0.297
1 gram nitrogen, as $(NH_4)_2SO_4$, added to 10.5 kilograms of soil; plants allowed to wilt before watering	37.0	60.9	73.2	51.8	1,540	0.343
1 gram nitrogen, as $(NH_4)_2SO_4$, added to 10.5 kilograms of soil; soil kept moist	40.0	75.4	108.7	56.6	2,068	0.421

nitrogen application. Each treatment combination was replicated six times. The treatments are listed in the first two columns of Table 29.

No data were presented on the status of soil moisture under the various treatments, and no information was given as to whether or not the light irrigations were sufficient to prevent soil moisture depletion to the extent of inducing wilting of the plants. Crowther (1934) stated, however that:

In the periods between irrigations, the water supply apparently never falls so low as to prevent the laying down of new parts, and meristematic activity, as measured by flower production, shows no periodicity corresponding with the periods of irrigation.

The data in Table 29 emphasize the interdependence of water and nitrogen supply for maximum vegetative growth. In the absence of added nitrogen, an increasing supply of irrigation water is essentially without effect on any of the criteria of vegetative growth. By contrast, at the high level of applied nitrogen, increasing quantities of irrigation water were associated with marked responses for each of the various criteria of growth, with the exception of the number of nodes in the

TABLE 29.—*Vegetative growth of cotton plants under irrigation in the Sudan (after Crowther, 1934)*

$(NH_4)_2SO_4$ applied per acre	Water applied at fortnightly irrigations	Final height of main stem	Final node number	Final internode lengths	Relative mean leaf weights
Pounds	Inches	Centimeters		Centimeters	
0	2	63.6	25.3	2.52	100
0	3.5	71.6	26.9	2.67	88
0	5	70.3	27.7	2.53	126
286	2	71.1	30.0	2.38	131
286	3.5	78.8	31.1	2.53	147
286	5	83.2	31.8	2.63	193
572	2	78.1	34.7	2.25	157
572	3.5	84.8	35.4	2.40	198
572	5	95.1	36.1	2.65	265
S. E.	...	1.7	1.1	.07	

main stems. Crowther emphasizes that "the main function of nitrogen consists in initiating meristematic activity, whereas that of water is the expansion of the parts thus laid down."

Maturation

Soil-moisture conditions frequently have a different effect upon the quality and quantity of the plant product than they have upon vegetative growth. In their previously mentioned experiments on cotton, Adams *et al.* (1942) found during the years 1934 and 1935 that increasing amounts of irrigation water applied were associated with marked increases in vegetative growth but were without effect on yield of seed-cotton. Barker and Berkley (1946) found that cotton lint produced on dry soil is shorter and stronger than when grown in the presence of adequate soil moisture. That is, cotton lint produced under moisture stress is actually superior for some purposes, as for example, tire cord.
Hendrickson and Veihmeyer (1929, 1934) present data from their

irrigation experiments on peaches and prunes showing that observed maximum vegetative growth of the trees takes place under their maximum frequency of irrigation. However, in each study all treatments except one permitted the soil moisture to fall below the permanent-wilting percentage for various lengths of time. As these investigators point out, it is detrimental to a plant to undergo wilting. They state that the decreased growth associated with their lower levels of moisture supply is indicative of the duration of soil-moisture conditions below the permanent-wilting percentage. The yields of peaches and prunes tended to be higher on the frequently irrigated plots, but storage tests on peaches showed that those grown at a continuously high level of soil moisture showed more bruising and decayed more rapidly than those grown on soil having a generally lower moisture content.

Irrigation studies on Jonathan apples in Washington by Overley *et al.* (1932) showed that the lightly irrigated plots produced the highest quality apples. The medium and heavily irrigated plots produced fruit with less red overcolor and a lower percentage of extra-fancy grade. Although the fruits were larger on these latter medium and heavily irrigated plots, they were more readily bruised by handling and they decayed more rapidly when stored at room temperature.

Ryall and Aldrich (1938) found that Bartlett pears produced by trees on a continuously high level of soil moisture were lower in percentage of dry matter, less firm according to the pressure test, and higher as to frequency of core breakdown than fruit from trees at a lower level of soil-moisture supply. A moderate moisture stress during the latter part of the season was conducive to the production of higher quality fruit.

There is evidence that the quality of grain is improved by the presence of a moisture stress during maturation. High quality wheat has a high protein content, and most studies indicate an inverse relationship between moisture availability during maturation and protein content of the grain (Greaves and Nelson, 1925; Harris, 1914; Hopkins, 1935; Meyers, 1946; Neidig and Snyder, 1926). Part of this effect may be brought about by decreased nutrient supply under conditions of higher rainfall or supplemental irrigation, but moisture stress is unquestionably a factor. Neidig and Snyder (1924) state that under conditions in Idaho, a high soil-moisture content properly distributed during the growing period will produce on the average soil a high-yielding wheat of low protein content. Increasing the level of nitrogen supply will increase protein content. A relatively lower moisture content of the soil produces a lower yield but a higher protein content of the kernel.

Although a low level of moisture stress is conducive to maximum vegetative growth of guayule, it is evident that the accumulation of rubber in this plant is greatly enhanced by being subjected to a period of high moisture stress (Benedict *et al.*, 1947; Hunter and Kelley, 1946c; Wadleigh *et al.*, 1946). On the other hand, Loustalot *et al.* (1947) found a high level of moisture stress to be associated with a decrease in the percentage of quinine sulfate in the roots of *Cinchona ledgeriana* in addition to a decrease in vegetative growth.

The foregoing observations indicate that the economic value of a crop is frequently increased by the presence of a moderate moisture stress during the period of maturation. The quality of some crops is lowered by maturation of tissues induced by moisture stress. This is the case with forage crops that are actually harvested, or should be, during a period of active vegetative growth. If maturation of the tissues takes place, the quality of the herbage is lowered. The importance of this fact has been well emphasized by Willoughby (1944). He points out that the economy of Australia is closely allied to the quality of their export wool. High quality wool involves fibers of smooth uniform growth. Such fibers are produced on animals continuously supplied with high quality herbage. Herbage that has undergone a moisture stress usually develops increased lignification of the cell walls and an accompanying decrease in the availability of the contained protein to the sheep. This decreased protein-quality of the feed resulting from high soil-moisture stress brings about an aberrant growth of the wool fibers if the feed is supplied to the animal for an extended period.

XVI. DROUGHT TOLERANCE

Most agricultural areas over the earth's surface experience a drought some time during the growing season. In many areas a serious drought is the normal expectancy rather than the exception. Drought and its effect on crop plants can become a major economic concern and occasionally lead to mass starvation. The selection of varieties and species of plants that have the capacity to endure drought and still produce may thus be a primary consideration.

Drought, in its limited sense, designates the period between rainfalls. With reference to plants, the term "drought" has two aspects: (1) The desiccating power of the aerial environment and (2) the availability of moisture from the soil reservoir. Both of these aspects may impinge upon the plant at the same time, for a period of deficient rainfall is often characterized by high temperature and low humidity that hasten the depletion of the soil moisture. In the present review, drought will be considered mainly to be a state of insufficient soil moisture.

Newton and Martin (1930) have reviewed the earlier literature on the drought tolerance (resistance) of crop plants. Their summary of the principal factors affecting drought resistance in plants is as follows:

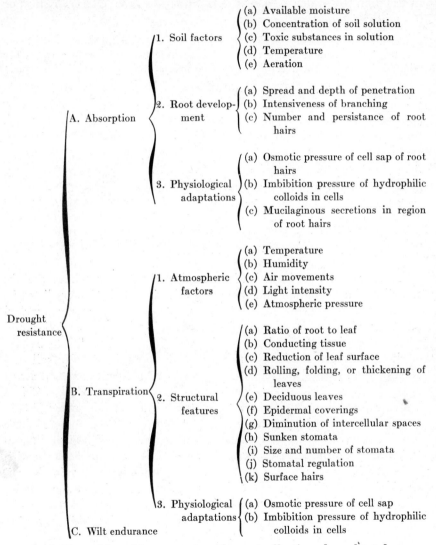

Drought resistance

A. Absorption
1. Soil factors
   - (a) Available moisture
   - (b) Concentration of soil solution
   - (c) Toxic substances in solution
   - (d) Temperature
   - (e) Aeration
2. Root development
   - (a) Spread and depth of penetration
   - (b) Intensiveness of branching
   - (c) Number and persistance of root hairs
3. Physiological adaptations
   - (a) Osmotic pressure of cell sap of root hairs
   - (b) Imbibition pressure of hydrophilic colloids in cells
   - (c) Mucilaginous secretions in region of root hairs

B. Transpiration
1. Atmospheric factors
   - (a) Temperature
   - (b) Humidity
   - (c) Air movements
   - (d) Light intensity
   - (e) Atmospheric pressure
2. Structural features
   - (a) Ratio of root to leaf
   - (b) Conducting tissue
   - (c) Reduction of leaf surface
   - (d) Rolling, folding, or thickening of leaves
   - (e) Deciduous leaves
   - (f) Epidermal coverings
   - (g) Diminution of intercellular spaces
   - (h) Sunken stomata
   - (i) Size and number of stomata
   - (j) Stomatal regulation
   - (k) Surface hairs
3. Physiological adaptations
   - (a) Osmotic pressure of cell sap
   - (b) Imbibition pressure of hydrophilic colloids in cells

C. Wilt endurance

As indicated by this summary, factors affecting drought tolerance by virtue of their effect on rate of entry or loss of water have been fairly well worked out. At the time of their review, however, it was evident that practically nothing was known concerning the physiological basis of wilt endurance; i.e., "the still obscure physiological adaptation which enables the plant to maintain life when the moisture content of the tissues becomes abnormally low." This is essentially the same conclusion reached by Maximov (1929) from his extended study of plants in relation to water. Maximov summarizes the characteristics of drought resistance in plants as follows:

From what we already know of these anatomical peculiarities, we may suppose that they will be those which characterize a zerophilous structure, namely, other things being equal, small cells, a dense network of veins, numerous (but small) stomata per unit area, a relatively great development of the root system, and so on. Physiologically these peculiarities are for the most part associated with intense assimilation, intense transpiration, reduced growth in height, high osmotic pressure, etc. But these relatively easily observable peculiarities appear of secondary importance as compared with the capacity to endure without injury as intense loss of water— one of the most important properties of true drought resistant plants. This property is connected with the capacity of the protoplasm to endure considerable fluctuations in its degree of swelling, without the loss of vital activity and without the appearance of irreversible coagulation. This capacity of enduring water loss may completely mask the significance of the other anatomical and physiological peculiarities, and thus mystify investigators who endeavour to find a strict correlation between drought resistance and these external peculiarities. Such forms alone are really drought resistant, and we may consider that the anatomical and physiological peculiarities of these plants are in some way connected with protection from drought.

Numerous recent investigations on drought tolerance have mainly contributed a validation and some amplification of the factors listed in segments *A* and *B* of the diagram on page 223. That there are marked differences in drought tolerance between strains, between varieties, and between species has received considerable verification of late by the work of Calvert (1935), Aamodt and Johnston (1936), Birdsall and Neatby (1944), and Bartel (1947) on wheat; Haber (1938) on sweet corn; Dexter (1942) Mueller and Weaver (1942), Cook (1943), Weaver and Albertson (1944), McAlister (1944), and Julander (1945) on grasses; and Shirley and Meuli (1939) on conifers. Some of these investigators sought to correlate anatomical and physiological characteristics with drought resistance. In general, it was found that modification which better enable a plant to draw upon the water in the soil or aid in protecting the plant tissues against excessive water loss increased drought resistance. No information was presented on the specific nature of protoplasm that enabled it to survive while enduring abnormally low moisture levels.

Northen (1943) has reviewed the literature and studied the effect of incipient drought on the structural viscosity of protoplasm and its relation to physiological processes. He found that incipient drought conditioned a decrease in the structural viscosity of the leaf cells of *Mnium* sp. and *Bryum* sp. as a consequence of protein dissociations. He suggested that this dissociation of the cellular protein effected increased protoplasmic swelling pressure and accelerated the rates of certain enzymatically controlled processes such as respiration and polysaccharide hydrolysis. This would appear to be a fruitful line of research to ascertain the fundamental basis that enables certain species of plants or selections thereof to endure long periods of seriously low water content of the tissues as a result of drought.

XVII. EFFICIENCY OF WATER USE BY PLANTS

Crop production in arid regions has focused attention on means of obtaining maximum yields with the limited supply of water available. The cost of irrigation water frequently makes this problem a consideration in irrigated areas. The amount of water used by the plant in the production of a unit amount of dry matter in the top or in the crop product has been termed the "water requirement." This term is unsatisfactory in certain respects. It implies that a given amount of water is necessary for the growth of the plant, but actually it merely denotes the amount of water transpired from the leaves, in addition to that retained in the plant, in producing a given amount of dry matter under prevailing environmental conditions. Widtsoe (1912) used the term "transpiration ratio" for a similar concept; his term deviates from the term "water requirement" only in that the small fraction of water retained in the plant body is not included. Israelsen (1932) presented a good evaluation of the engineering importance of this concept in irrigation agriculture and proposed the term "transpiration efficiency," which he defined on a percentage scale as the dry weight of plant product per 100 weight-units of water transpired. Transpiration efficiency is thus equal to 100 divided by the transpiration ratio (water requirement).

Numerous experiments have been conducted on the water requirement, or the efficiency of water use by crops. There does not appear to be much activity in this field at the present time, although comparatively recent reports on the water requirements of wheat, sorgums, and alfalfa have been given by Stephens, Oveson, and Mitchell (1943); Kanitkar, Gode, and Gokhale (1943); and Scofield (1945a). The early literature and methods of measurement were reviewed by Montgomery (1911), Briggs and Shantz (1913b), Kiesselbach (1916), and more recently by Miller (1938). Work conducted at the Great Plains field stations by the United States Department of Agriculture has been reported by Briggs and Shantz (1913a, 1914, 1916a, 1916b, 1917),

Shantz and Piemeisel (1927), and Dillman (1931) and is of special significance, since carefully standardized measuring methods were used over a period of many years and with a considerable number of species and varieties of plants.

Water requirement depends on both growth and transpiration and should be related to environmental factors such as climate, soil fertility (mineral nutrition), and soil-moisture stress.   Of these factors, climate is by far the most important and has already been mentioned in an earlier section.   The data of Briggs and Shantz (1917) given in Table 8 showed the effect of climate on the water requirement of alfalfa at widely separated stations in the Great Plains region.   The ratio of water requirement to shallow-pan evaporation was substantially constant, and this indicates that those climatic factors influencing the evaporative power of the aerial environment are principally involved in the climatic effect.   This is illustrated also by the effect on water requirement of the year-to-year variation in climate at the same location. Table 30, adapted from the extensive report of Shantz and Piemeisel (1927), shows in the first column the average water requirement of a number of species at Akron, Colo., for the years 1913–17.   Individual values for the various years are expressed in the remaining columns as percentage of the average for the whole period.   The averages at the bottom of the table indicate that the variation in water requirement is related to the variation in the evaporation from the shallow-pan evaporimeter.   The relation is not perfect but is certainly significant. Kiesselbach (1929) and Scofield (1945a) found an analogous climatic effect on the water requirement of crops over different parts of the growing season.   From experiments with alfalfa at Riverside, Calif., Scofield found in 1942 that the water requirements for cuttings before and after mid-July were 619 and 1,159, respectively, while for 1943 corresponding values were 625 and 1,018.

The effects of soil fertility and soil-moisture stress on the water requirement are less marked than for climate, and the experimental coverage is less complete.   Present data seem to indicate that large decreases in growth and yield resulting from deficiencies of nutrients and moisture may cause only nominal increases in water requirement.   For example, Kiesselbach (1916) grew corn in an infertile soil, in a mixture of this soil and a fertile soil, and in the fertile soil.   The dry matter produced and the water-requirement values obtained were, respectively, 113 and 184, 270 and 550, 479 and 392.   Dry-matter production was increased respectively by 194, 79, and 41 percent by the use of sheep manure, but the water requirement under this treatment was reduced respectively by 29, 17, and 8 percent.   Scofield (1945a) found similar results for alfalfa grown in cans. Adding mineral nutrients to one set produced a 14-percent increase in yield, but the water requirement for the fertilized and unfertilized sets were 792 and 802, respectively. During the following year, the yield difference was 33 percent, and the water requirement values were 661 and 706, respectively. The significance of these differences was not tested statistically.

TABLE 30.—*Water requirement-evaporation index numbers for crops; indices of their average water requirements and average evaporation; and ratio of average water requirement to average evaporation (Shantz and Piemeisel, 1927)*

[Water requirement based on dry matter; mean value of 100 taken as base for index numbers]

	Average water requirement	Water requirement–evaporation index numbers					
Item		1913	1914	1915	1916	1917	Mean
Crop:							
Alfalfa, ADIE-23	858	97	104	81	122	96	100
Oats, Swedish select	635	97	94	71	138	100	100
Oats, Burt CI-293	624	99	99	71	130	102	100
Barley, Hannchen	521	98	96	78	127	100	100
Wheat, Kubanka, CI-1440	505	98	103	80	126	93	100
Corn, Northwestern Dent	372	107	99	68	133	93	100
Millet, Kursk	287	100	103	70	128	99	100
Sorghum, Minnesota Amber	271	110	105	75	109	100	100
Cotton, Triumph	562	117	102	79	109	93	100
Cowpea, SPI-29282	578	99	114	71	133	83	100
Pigweed	300	107	102	76	113	102	100
Grama grass	343	113	113	91	98	85	100
All crops:							
Index of average water requirement	. . .	104	103	76	122	96	100
Index of average evaporation	. . .	103	101	80	113	103	100
		Ratio	Ratio	Ratio	Ratio	Ratio	
Average water–requirement index to average–evaporation index	. . .	1.01	1.02	.95	1.08	.93	

Also, variations in soil moisture within the available range apparently do not have an important effect on the efficiency of water use by plants. Kiesselbach (1916) found that if the soil-moisture content approached either extreme, above field capacity or wilting percentage, the water requirement was increased, but he also stated that this increase was usually associated with a relatively greater decrease in yield.

Thom and Holtz (1917) also concluded that variations in soil-moisture content had little effect on water requirement, provided that the moisture content did not approach the wilting percentage.

Information on this subject is contained in data previously referred to in this chapter. For example, Beckett and Dunshee (1932), as shown by the data in Table 10, found that the seed cotton produced per inch of water applied was the same for wet treatment W–1 as for dry treatment W–3. The low dependence of water requirement on the amount of water applied to cotton is further suggested by the positive linear relation shown by the data in Figure 20. Also from Table 31 it

TABLE 31.—*Comparison of water use and cotton yield in field plots and tanks receiving the same irrigation treatments in the seasons 1928, 1929, and 1930 (Beckett and Dunshee, 1932)*

	Irrigation treatment					
	W–1 (low stress)		W–2 (medium stress)		W–3 (high stress)	
Item	Field plot	Tanks	Field plot	Tanks	Field plot	Tanks
Average surface inches of water used per season	29.5	40.3	20.6	30.5	18.9	27.4
Average yield of seed cotton in pounds per plant	.328	.433	.237	.339	.182	.292
Water requirement in inches of water per pound of seed cotton per plant	90	83	87	90	104	94

is seen that for 3-year averages for these experiments on cotton, moisture-stress sufficient to cause 50 to 80 percent yield reductions caused relatively smaller effects on the water requirement. Essentially similar relations are shown in Figures 22 and 23, the field data for alfalfa in the Salt River Valley. The yield is seen to change rapidly, whereas the tons of alfalfa per foot of irrigation water applied is seen to be relatively independent of the depth of water applied as irrigation during the growing season. Scofield (1945a) found similar results for alfalfa grown in cans. Low, medium, and high soil-moisture levels in the irrigation treatments gave, respectively, yields of 537, 790 and 1,105 grams of dry weight per can, but the corresponding water requirement values were, respectively, 743, 794, and 781.

Veihmeyer (1927) grew prune trees in tanks and found, as shown by the data in Table 14, that the length of shoot growth per pound of irrigation water applied was essentially independent of the soil-moisture conditions maintained in the various moisture treatments. The moisture stress and yield differences for the experiment on potatoes reported in Table 16 are small, but the low change in water requirement with soil-moisture level in the available range is indicated for potatoes also.

Adequate data are not available for a quantitative evaluation, but the foregoing evidence indicates that the effect of nutrient deficiencies and soil-moisture stress on the water requirement of crops is small.

Literature Cited

AAMODT, O. S., and JOHNSTON, W. H. 1936. Studies on drought resistance in spring wheat. *Can. J. Research* **C14:** 122–152.

ABBOTT, E. V. 1947. Influence of certain environmental conditions on chlorotic streak of sugar cane. *Phytopathology* **37:** 162–173.

ADAMS, F., VEIHMEYER, F. J., and BROWN, N. 1942. Cotton irrigation investigations in San Joaquin Valley, California, 1926 to 1935. *Calif. Agr. Expt. Sta. Bull.* **668.**

ADDOMS, R. M. 1946. Entrance of water into suberized roots of trees. *Plant Physiol.* **21:** 109–111.

ALDRICH, W. W., LEWIS, M. R., and WORK, R. A. 1940. Anjou pear responses to irrigation in a clay adobe soil. *Ore. Agr. Expt. Sta. Bull.* **374, pt. I.**

ALDRICH, W. W., and WORK, R. A. 1932. Preliminary report of pear tree responses to variations in available soil moisture in clay adobe soil. *Proc. Am. Soc. Hort. Sci.* **29:** 181–187.

ALDRICH, W. W., WORK, R. A., and LEWIS, M. R. 1935. Pear root concentration in relation to soil-moisture extraction in heavy clay soil. *J. Agr. Research* **50:** 975–988.

ALLYN, R. B., and WORK, R. A. 1941. The availameter and its use in soil moisture control. The instrument and its use. *Soil Sci.* **51:** 307–321.

ALWAY, F. J. 1913. Studies on the relation of the nonavailable water of the soil to the hygroscopic coefficient. *Nebr. Agr. Expt. Sta. Bull.* **3.**

ANDERSON, D. B., and KERR, T. 1943. A note on the growth behavior of cotton bolls. *Plant Physiol.* **18:** 261–269.

APPLEMAN, C. O., and BROWN, R. G. 1946. Relation of anaerobic to aerobic respiration in some storage organs with special reference to the Pasteur effect in higher plants. *Am. J. Botany* **33:** 170–181.

ATKINS, W. R. G. 1916. Some recent researches in plant physiology. Whittaker and Co., London.

ATTOE, O. J. 1946. Potassium fixation and release in soils occurring under moist and drying conditions. *Soil Sci. Soc. Am. Proc.* **11:** 145–149.

AYERS, A. D., and HAYWARD, H. E. 1948. A method for measuring the effects of soil salinity on seed germination with observations on several crop plants. *Soil Sci. Soc. Am. Proc.* **13:** 224–226.

AYERS, A. D., WADLEIGH, C. H., and MAGISTAD, O. C. 1943. The interrelationship of salt concentration and soil moisture content with growth of beans. *J. Am. Soc. Agron.* **35:** 796–810.

BACHMANN, F. 1922. Studien über dickenänderungen von laubblättern. *Jahrb. wiss. Botan.* **61:** 372–429.

BAILEY, C. H. 1921. Respiration of shelled corn. *Minn. Agr. Expt. Sta. Tech. Bull.* 3.

BAIN, F. H., and CHAPMAN, H. D. 1940. Nitrate fertilizer additions to water-logged soils in relation to oxygen deficiency. *Soil Sci.* 50: 357–367.

BARK, D. H. 1916. Experiments on the economical use of irrigation water in Idaho. *U. S. Dept. Agr. Bull.* 339.

BARKER, H. D., and BERKLEY, E. E. 1946. Fiber and spinning properties of cotton, with special reference to varietal and environmental factors. *U. S. Dept. Agr. Tech. Bull.* 931.

BARTEL, A. T. 1947. Some physiological characteristics of four varieties of spring wheat presumbly differing in drought resistance. *J. Agr. Research* 74: 97–112.

BARTHOLOMEW, E. T. 1923. Internal decline of lemons. II. Growth rate, water content, and acidity of lemon at different stages of maturity. *Am. J. Botany* 10: 117–126.

BARTHOLOMEW, E. T. 1926. Internal decline of lemons. III. Water deficit in lemon fruits caused by excessive leaf evaporation. *Am. J. Botany* 13: 102–117.

BAVER, L. D. 1948. Soil physics. John Wiley and Sons, Inc., New York.

BAVER, L. D., and FARNSWORTH, R. B. 1940. Soil structure effects in the growth of sugar beets. *Soil Sci. Soc. Am. Proc.* 5: 45–48.

BECK, W. A. 1929. The effect of drought on the osmotic value of plant tissue. *Protoplasma* 8: 70–126.

BECK, W. A. 1931. Variations in the O_g of plant tissues. *Plant Physiol.* 6: 315–323.

BECKETT, S. H., and DUNSHEE, C. F. 1932. Water requirements of cotton on sandy loam soils in southern San Joaquin Valley. *Calif. Arg. Expt. Sta. Bull.* 537.

BECKETT, S. H., and ROBERTSON, R. D. 1917. The economical irrigation of alfalfa in Sacramento Valley, California. *Calif. Agr. Expt. Sta. Bull.* 280.

BENEDICT, H. M. 1941. The inhibiting effect of dead roots on the growth of bromegrass. *J. Am. Soc. Agron.* 33: 1108–1109.

BENEDICT, H. M., McRORY, W. L., and SLATTERY, M. C. 1947. Response of guayule to alternating periods of low and high moisture stresses. *Botan. Gaz.* 108: 535–549.

BENNET-CLARK, T. A. 1948. Non-osmotic water movement in plant cells. *Faraday Soc. Discussions* No. 3: 134–139.

BENNET-CLARK, T. A., and BEXON, D. 1943. Water relations of plant cells. III. The respiration of plasmolysed tissues. *New Phytologist* 42: 65–92.

BENNET-CLARK, T. A., GREENWOOD, A. D., and BARKER, J. W. 1936. Water relations and osmotic pressures of plant cells. *New Phytologist* 35: 277–291.

BHAUMIK, H. D., and CLARK, F. E. 1947. Soil moisture tension and microbiological activity. *Soil Sci. Soc. Am. Proc.* 12: 234–238.

BINNS, C. F. 1922. The potter's craft. D. Van Nostrand, New York.

BIRDSALL, J. E., and NEATBY, K. W. 1944. Researches on drought resistance in spring wheat. *Can. J. Research* C22: 38–51.

BLAIR, G. Y., RICHARDS, L. A., and CAMPBELL, R. B. 1950. Rate of elongation of sunflower plants in relation to available soil moisture. *Soil Sci.* 69. [In press.]

BODE, H. R. 1940. Über die blattausscheidungen des wermuts und ihre wirkung auf andere pflanzen. *Planta* 30: 567–589. [*Biol. Abstracts* 15: 2993.]

BODMAN, G. B. 1942. Nomograms for rapid calculation of soil density, water content, and total porosity relationships. *J. Am. Soc. Agron.* 34: 883–893.

BODMAN, G. B., and COLMAN, E. A.   1943.   Moisture and energy conditions during downward entry of water into soils.   *Soil Sci. Soc. Am. Proc.* **8:** 116–122.

BODMAN, G. B., and DAY, P. R.   1943.   The freezing points of a group of California soils and their extracted clays.   *Soil Sci.* **55:** 225–246.

BOLLEN, W. B.   1941.   Soil respiration studies on the decomposition of native organic matter.   *Iowa State Coll. J. Sci.* **15:** 353–374.

BOUYOUCOS, G. J., and MICK, A. H.   1947.   Improvements in the plaster of Paris absorption block electrical resistance method for measuring soil moisture under field conditions.   *Soil Sci.* **63:** 455–465.

BOUYOUCOS, G. J., and MICK, H. H.   1948.   A fabric absorption unit for continuous measurement of soil moisture in the field.   *Soil Sci.* **66:** 217–232.

BOWER, C. A., and PETERSEN, R. K.   1950.   Technic for determining the permeability of soil cores obtained with the Lutz sampler.   *J. Agron.* **42:** 55–56.

BOYNTON, D.   1937.   Soil moisture and fruit growth in an orchard situated on shallow soil in the Hudson Valley, New York, in 1936.   *Proc. Am. Soc. Hort. Sci.* **34:** 169–172.

BOYNTON, D.   1941.   Soils in relation to fruit growing in New York.   XV. Seasonal and soil influences on oxygen and carbon-dioxide levels of New York orchard soils.   *N. Y. (Cornell) Agr. Expt. Sta. Bull.* **763:** 3–43.

BOYNTON, D., and CAIN, J. C.   1946.   Magnesium nutrition of apple orchards.   *Am. Fertilizer* **105:** 7–8.

BOYNTON, D., CAIN, J. C., and COMPTON, O. C.   1944.   Soil and seasonal influences on the chemical composition of Mcintosh apple leaves in New York.   *Proc. Am. Soc. Hort. Sci.* **44:** 15–24.

BOYNTON, D., and COMPTON, O. C.   1943.   Effect of oxygen pressure in aerated nutrient solution on production of new roots and on growth of roots and tops of fruit trees.   *Proc. Am. Soc. Hort. Sci.* **42:** 53–58.

BOYNTON, D., and REUTHER, W.   1938.   A way of sampling soil gases in dense subsoils, and some of its advantages and limitations.   *Soil Sci. Soc. Am. Proc.* **3:** 37–42.

BOYNTON, D., and SAVAGE, E. F.   1938.   Soils in relation to fruit growing in New York.   Part XIII.   Seasonal fluctuations in soil moisture in some important New York orchard soil types.   *N. Y. (Cornell) Agr. Expt. Sta. Bull.* **706.**

BRADFIELD, R.   1941.   Calcium in the soil.   I. Physico-chemical relations.   *Soil Sci. Soc. Am. Proc.* **6:** 8–15.

BRADFIELD, R., and JAMISON, V. E.   1939.   Soil structure—attempts at its quantitative characterization.   *Soil Sci. Soc. Am. Proc.* **3:** 70–76.

BREAZEALE, J. F.   1924.   The injurious after-effects of sorghum.   *Am. Soc. Agron.* **16:** 689–700.

BREAZEALE, J. F.   1930.   Maintenance of moisture equilibrium and nutrition of plants at and below the wilting percentage.   *Ariz. Agr. Expt. Sta. Tech. Bull.* **29:** 137–177.

BREAZEALE, J. F., and McGEORGE, W. T.   1932.   Nutritional disorders in alkaline soils as caused by deficiency of carbon dioxide.   *Ariz. Agr. Expt. Sta. Tech. Bull.* **41:** 113–153.

BREAZEALE, J. F., and McGEORGE, W. T.   1949.   A new technic for determining wilting percentage of soil.   *Soil Sci.* **68:** 371–374.

BRIGGS, D. R.   1931.   Water relationships in colloids.   I. Vapor pressure measurements on elastic gels.   *J. Phys. Chem.* **35:** 2914–2929.

BRIGGS, D. R. 1932. Water relationships in colloids. II. "Bound water in colloids. *J. Phys. Chem.* **36:** 367–386.

BRIGGS, L. J. 1897. Mechanics of soil moisture. *U. S. Dept. Agr., Div. of Soils Bull.* **10:** 1–24.

BRIGGS, L. J. 1949. A new method for measuring the limiting negative pressure in liquids. (Abstract) *Science* **109:** 440.

BRIGGS, L. J., and McLANE, J. W. 1907. The moisture equivalent of soils. *U. S. Dept. Agr., Bur. of Soils Bull.* **45:** 1–23.

BRIGGS, L. J., and SHANTZ, H. L. 1911. Application of wilting coefficient determinations in agronomic investigations. *J. Am. Soc. Agron.* **3:** 250–260.

BRIGGS, L. J., and SHANTZ, H. L. 1912a. The wilting coefficient and its indirect determination. *U. S. Dept. Agr., Bur. Plant Ind. Bull.* **230.**

BRIGGS, L. J., and SHANTZ, H. L. 1912b. The wilting coefficient and its indirect determination. *Botan. Gaz.* **53:** 20–37.

BRIGGS, L. J., and SHANTZ, H. L. 1912c. The relative wilting coefficient for different plants. *Botan. Gaz.* **53:** 229–235.

BRIGGS, L. J., and SHANTZ, H. L. 1913a. The water requirements of plants. I. Investigations in the Great Plains in 1910 and 1911. *U. S. Dept. Agr., Bur. Plant Ind. Bull.* **230.**

BRIGGS, L. J., and SHANTZ, H. L. 1913b. The water requirement of plants. II. A review of the literature. *U. S. Dept. Agr., Bur. Plant Ind. Bull.* **285.**

BRIGGS, L. J., and SHANTZ, H. L. 1914. Relative water requirements of plants. *J. Agr. Research* **3:** 1–64.

BRIGGS, L. J., and SHANTZ, H. L. 1916a. Hourly transpiration rate on clear days as determined by cycle environment factors. *J. Agr. Research* **5:** 583–650.

BRIGGS, L. J., and SHANTZ, H. L. 1916b. Daily transpiration during the normal growth period and its correlation with the weather. *J. Agr. Research* **7:** 155–212.

BRIGGS, L. J., and SHANTZ, H. L. 1917. The water requirement of plants as influenced by environment. *Proc. 2d Pan-Amer. Sci. Congr.* **3:** 95–107, Washington, D. C.

BRILLIANT, B. 1924. Le teneur en eau dans les feuilles et l'energie assimilatrice. *Compt. rend.* **178:** 2122–2125.

BROWN, B. A., and KING, A. 1939. Soil conditions under which alfalfa responded to boron. *Soil Sci. Soc. Am. Proc.* **4:** 310–313.

BROWN, H. T., and ESCOMBE, F. 1900. Static diffusions of gases and liquids in relation to the assimilation of carbon and translocation in plants. *Trans. Roy. Soc. London* **B.193:** 223–291.

BROYER, T. C. 1947a. The movement of materials into plants. Part I. Osmosis and the movement of water into plants. *Botan. Rev.* **13:** 1–58.

BROYER, T. C. 1947b. The movement of materials into plants. Part II. The nature of solute movement into plants. *Botan. Rev.* **13:** 125–167.

BROYER, T. C. 1950. On the theoretical interpretation of turgor pressure. *Plant Physiol.* **25:** 135–139.

BRYANT, J. C., and SLATER, C. S. 1948. Runoff water as an agent in the loss of soluble materials from certain soils. *Iowa State Coll. J. Sci.* **22:** 269–297.

BUCKINGHAM, E. 1907. Studies on the movement of soil moisture. *U. S. Dept. Agr., Bur. of Soils Bull.* **38:** 1–61.

BUEHRER, T. F., and ROSE, M. S. 1943. Studies in soil structure. V. Bound water in normal and puddled soils. *Ariz. Agr. Expt. Sta. Tech. Bull.* **100.**

BUREAU OF RECLAMATION. 1948. Land classification report. Welton-Mohawk Division, Gila Project, Arizona. U. S. Dept. Interior, 130 pp. [Processed.]

BURGESS, P. S., and POHLMAN, G. G. 1928. Citrus chlorosis as affected by irrigation and fertilizer treatments. *Ariz. Agr. Expt. Sta. Bull.* **124:** 183–232.

BURSTRÖM, H. 1948. A theoretical interpretation of the turgor pressure. *Physiologia Plantarum* **1:** 57–64.

CALVERT, J. 1935. Drought resistance in wheat. *Protoplasma* **24:** 505–524.

CANNON, W. A. 1925. Physiological features of roots with especial reference to the relation of roots to aeration of the soil. *Carnegie Inst. Wash. Pub.* **368:** 1–168.

CAROLUS, R. L., and WOLTZ, W. G. 1944. Nitrogen and phosphate fertilizer in relation to potato yields and to soil constituents during dry seasons. *Soil Sci. Soc. Am. Proc.* **9:** 194–199.

CHANDLER, R. C. 1941. Nature of bound water in colloidal systems. *Plant Physiol.* **16:** 273–292.

CHANG, H. T., and LOOMIS, W. E. 1945. Effect of carbon dioxide on absorption of water and nutrients by roots. *Plant Physiol.* **20:** 221–232.

CHAPMAN, H. D., LIEBIG, G. F., and RAYNER, D. S. 1949. A lysimeter investigation of nitrogen gains and losses under various systems of cover cropping and fertilization, and a discussion of error sources. *Hilgardia* **19:** 57–128.

CHILDS, E. C. 1940. The use of soil moisture characteristics in soil studies. *Soil Sci.* **50:** 239–252.

CHRELASHVILI, M. N. 1941. The influence of water content and carbohydrate accumulation on the energy of photosynthesis and respiration. *Trudy Inst. Bot. Nauk. Akad. Nauk S.S.S.R. I zv., Ser. 4., Eksperimental'naia Botanika* **5:** 101–137. [*Biol. Abstracts* **15:** 22669.]

CHRISTENSEN, H. R. 1944. Permeability-capillary potential curves for three prairie soils. *Soil Sci.* **57:** 381–390.

CHRISTIANSEN, J. E. 1943. Ground-water studies in relation to drainage. *Agr. Eng.* **24:** 339–342.

CLARK, F. E. 1947. Rhizosphere microflora as affected by soil moisture changes. *Soil Sci. Soc. Am. Proc.* **12:** 239–242.

CLEMENTS, H. F. 1940. Integration of climatic and physiologic factors with reference to the production of sugar cane. *Hawaiian Planter's Record* **44:** 201–233.

CLEMENTS, H. F. 1948. Managing the production of sugar cane. *Repts. Hawaiian Sugar Technol.* 6th meeting, 1948.

CLEMENTS, H. F., and KUBOTA, T. 1942. Internal moisture relations of sugar cane. The selection of a moisture index. *Hawaiian Planter's Record* **46:** 17–35.

CLEMENTS, H. F., and KUBOTA, T. 1943. The primary index, its meaning and application to crop management with special reference to sugar cane. *Hawaiian Planter's Record* **47:** 257–297.

COLE, J. S. 1938. Correlations between annual precipitation and the yield of spring wheat in the Great Plains. *U. S. Dept. Agr. Tech. Bull.* **636.**

COLEMAN, D. A., ROTHGEB, B. E., and FELLOWS, C. H. 1928. Respiration of sorghum grains. *U. S. Dept. Agr. Tech Bull.* **100.**

COLMAN, E. A. 1947. A laboratory procedure for determining the field capacity of soils. *Soil Sci.* **63:** 277–283.

COLMAN, E. A., and BODMAN, G. B. 1944. Moisture and energy conditions during downward entry of water into moist and layered soils. *Soil Sci. Soc. Am. Proc.* **9**: 3–11.

COLMAN, E. A., and HENDRIX, T. M. 1949. The fiberglas electrical soil-moisture instrument. *Soil Sci.* **67**: 425–438.

COMPTON, C. 1936. Water deficit in citrus. *Proc. Am. Soc. Hort. Sci.* **34**: 91–95.

CONRAD, J. P., and VEIHMEYER, F. J. 1929. Root development and soil moisture. *Hilgardia* **4**: 113–134.

COOK, C. W. 1943. A study of the roots of *Bromus inermis* in relation to drought resistance. *Ecology* **24**: 169–182.

CRAFTS, A. S., CURRIER, H. B., and STOCKING, C. R. 1949. Water in the physiology of plants. Chronica Botanica Co., Waltham, Mass.

CROWTHER, F. 1934. Studies in growth analysis of the cotton plant under irrigation in the Sudan. I. The effects of different combinations of nitrogen applications and water-supply. *Ann. Botany* **48**: 877–913.

CULLINAN, F. P., and WEINBERGER, J. H. 1932. Studies on the influence of soil moisture on growth of fruit and stomatal behavior of Elberta peaches. *Proc. Am. Soc. Hort. Sci.* **29**: 28–33.

CURRIER, H. B. 1944. Water relations of root cells of *Beta vulgaris*. *Am. J. Botany* **51**: 378–387.

CYKLER, J. F. 1946. Effect of variations in available soil water on yield and quality of potatoes. *Agr. Eng.* **27**: 363–365.

DARCY, H. 1856. Les fontaines publique de la ville de Dijon. Dalmont, Paris, 570 pp.

DASTUR, R. H. 1925. The relation between water content and photosynthesis. *Ann. Botany* **39**: 769–786.

DASTUR, R. H., and DESAI, B. L. 1933. The relation between water content, chlorophyll content, and the rate of photosynthesis in some tropical plants at different temperatures. *Ann. Botany* **47**: 69–88.

DAVIDSON, A. L. C., and SCHOFIELD, R. K. 1942. Measurement of the suction of soil water by Portland stone absorbers calibrated by a new method for determining vapour pressures near saturation. *J. Agr. Sci.* **32**: 413–427.

DAVIDSON, J. M. 1940. Infiltration of water into the soil. U. S. Dept. Agr. Soil Conserv. Biblog. No 3, October 1940. [Mimeographed.]

DAVIDSON, J. R. 1948. Lime-induced chlorosis of fruit trees on the Murrumbidgee irrigation area. *Agr. Gaz. N. S. Wales* **59**: 410–413.

DAVIS, C. H. 1940. Absorption of soil moisture by maize roots. *Botan. Gaz.* **101**: 791–805.

DAVIS, C. H. 1942. Response of *cyperus rotundus* (*L.*) to five moisture levels. *Plant Physiol.* **17**: 311–316.

DAVIS, W. E., and SLATER, C. S. 1942. A direct weighing method for sequent measurements of soil moisture under field conditions. *J. Am. Soc. Agron.* **34**: 285–287.

DAY, P. R. 1947. The moisture potential of soils. *Soil Sci.* **54**: 391–400.

DE, P. K., and SARKAR, S. N. 1936. Transformation of nitrate in waterlogged soils. *Soil Sci.* **42**: 143–155.

DEXTER, S. T. 1942. Seasonal variations in drought resistance of exposed rhizomes of quack grass. *J. Am. Soc. Agron.* **34**: 1125–1136.

DILLMAN, A. C. 1931. The water requirement of certain crop plants and weeds in the northern Great Plains. *J. Agr. Research* **42**: 187–238.

DITTMER, H. J. 1937. A quantitative study of the roots and root hairs of a winter rye plant (*secale cereale*). *Am. J. Botany* 24: 417–419.

DITTMER, H. J. 1938. A quantitative study of the subterranean members of three field grasses. *Am. J. Botany* 25: 654–657.

DIXON, H. H., and JOLY, J. 1894. On the ascent of sap. *Ann. Botany* 8: 468–470.

DOLGOV, S. I. 1947. On the availability of soil moisture to the plant. *Compt. rend. acad. sci. U.R.S.S.* 55: 449–451. [Abstract in *Soils and Fertilizers* 11: 65 1948.]

DONAT, J. 1937. Das Gefüge des bodens und dessen kennzeichung. *Trans. 6th Intern. Congr. Soil Sci. Zurich* B: 423–439.

DONEEN, L. D. 1942. Some soil moisture conditions in relation to growth and nutrition of the sugar-beet plant. *Proc. Am. Soc. Sugar Beet Technol.* 54–62.

DONEEN, L. D., and MacGILLIVRAY, J. H. 1943. Germination (emergence) of vegetable seeds as affected by different soil moisture conditions. *Plant Physiol.* 18: 524–529.

DONEEN, L. D., and MacGILLIVRAY, J. H. 1946. Suggestions on irrigating commercial truck crops. *Calif. Agr. Expt. Sta. Lithoprint* 5m-9, '46 (9938).

DONEEN, L. D., PORTER, P. R., and MacGILLIVRAY, J. H. 1939. Irrigation studies with watermelon. *Proc. Am. Soc. Hort. Sci.* 37: 821–824.

DRABBLE, E., and DRABBLE, H. 1907. The relation between the osmotic strength of cell sap in plants and their physical environment. *Biochem. J.* 2: 117–132.

DREIBELBIS, F. R. 1946. Some plant nutrient losses in gravitational water from monolith lysimeters at Coshocton, Ohio. *Soil Sci. Soc. Am. Proc.* 11: 182–188.

EATON, F. M. 1927. The water requirement and cell-sap concentration of Australian salt bush and wheat as related to the salinity of the soil. *Am. J. Botany* 14: 212–226.

EATON, F. M. 1941. Water uptake and root growth as influenced by inequality in the concentration of the substrate. *Plant Physiol.* 16: 545–564.

EATON, F. M. 1943. The osmotic and vitalistic interpretation of exudation. *Am. J. Botany* 30: 663–673.

EATON, F. M., and ERGLE, D. R. 1948. Carbohydrate accumulation in the cotton plant at low moisture levels. *Plant Physiol.* 23: 169–187.

EDLEFSEN, N. E. 1934. A new method of measuring the aqueous vapor pressure of soils. *Soil Sci.* 38: 29–35.

EDLEFSEN, N. E. 1941. Some thermodynamic aspects of the use of soil moisture by plants. *Trans. Union Am. Geophys.* pt. III, pp. 917–926.

EDLEFSEN, N. E., and ANDERSON, B. C. 1943. Thermodynamics of soil moisture. *Hilgardia* 15: 31–298.

EDLEFSEN, N. E., and BODMAN, G. B. 1941. Field measurements of water movement through a silt loam soil. *J. Am. Soc. Agron.* 33: 713–731.

ELLIS, N. K., and MORRIS, R. 1945. Preliminary observations on the relation of yield of crops grown on organic soil with controlled water table and the area of aeration in the soil and subsidence of the soil. *Soil Sci. Soc. Am. Proc.* 10: 282–283.

EMMERT, E. M. 1936. Effect of drought on the nutrient levels in the tomato plant. *Soil Sci.* 41: 67–70.

ERICKSON, L. C. 1946. Growth of tomato roots as influenced by oxygen in the nutrient solution. *Am. J. Botany* 33: 551–561.

FIPPIN, E. O. 1945. Plant nutrient losses in silt and water in the Tennessee River system. *Soil Sci.* 60: 223–239.

FIREMAN, M. 1944. Permeability measurements on disturbed soil samples. *Soil Sci.* **58:** 337–353.

FITTING, H. 1911. Die wasserversorgung und die osmotischen druckverhältnisse der wüstenpflanzen. *Botan. Ztg.* **3:** 209–275.

FUJIMOTO, C. K., and SHERMAN, G. D. 1948. Behavior of manganese in the soil and the manganese cycle. *Soil Sci.* **66:** 131–145.

FURR, J. R., and ALDRICH, W. W. 1943. Oxygen and carbon-dioxide changes in soil atmosphere of an irrigated date garden on calcareous very fine sandy loam soil. *Proc. Am. Soc. Hort. Sci.* **42:** 46–52.

FURR, J. R., and REEVE, J. O. 1945. The range of soil-moisture percentages through which plants undergo permanent wilting in soils from semi-arid irrigated areas. *J. Agr. Research* **71:** 149–170.

FURR, J. R., and TAYLOR, C. A. 1939. Growth of lemon plants in relation to the moisture content of soil. *U. S. Dept. Agr. Tech. Bull.* **640:** 1–72.

GARDNER, R. 1937. A method of measuring the capillary tension of soil moisture over a wide moisture range. *Soil Sci.* **43:** 277–283.

GARDNER, W. 1920. The capillary potential and its relation to soil moisture constants. *Soil Sci.* **10:** 357–359.

GAUCH, H. G., and WADLEIGH, C. H. 1945. Effect of high concentrations of sodium, calcium, chloride, and sulfate on ionic absorption by bean plants. *Soil Sci.* **59:** 139–153.

GILBERT, G. S., and SHIVE, J. W. 1942. The significance of oxygen in nutrient substrates for plants. I. The oxygen requirement. *Soil Sci.* **53:** 143–152.

GOEDEWAAGEN, M. A. J. 1941. Water conditions in the soil and root development. *Landbouwkund, Tidschr.* **53:** 118–146. [*Soils and Fertilizers* **10:** 139–140. 1947.]

GORTNER, R. A. 1932. The role of water in the structure and properties of protoplasm. *Ann. Rev. Biochem.* **1:** 21–54.

GRADMANN, H. 1928. Untersuchungen über die wasserverhältnisse des bodens als grundlage des pflanzenwachstums. *Jahrb. wiss. Botan.* **69:** 1–100.

GRAY, R., and BONNER, J. 1948. An inhibitor of plant growth from the leaves of *encelia farinosa*. *Am. J. Botany* **35:** 52–57.

GREAVES, J. E., and CARTER, E. G. 1922. The influence of moisture and soluble salts on the bacterial activities of the soil. *Soil Sci.* **13:** 251–270.

GREAVES, J. E., and CARTER, E. G. 1923. The influence of irrigation water on the composition of grains and the relationship to nutrition. *J. Biol. Chem.* **58:** 531–541.

GREAVES, J. E., and NELSON, D. H. 1925. The influence of irrigation water and manure on the composition of the corn kernel. *J. Agr. Research* **31:** 183–191.

GROLLMAN, K. 1931. The vapour pressures of aqueous solutions with special reference to the problem of the state of water in biological fluids. *J. Gen. Physiol.* **14:** 661–683.

HAAS, A. R. C., and KLOTZ, L. J. 1935. Physiological gradients in citrus fruits. *Hilgardia* **9:** 179–217.

HAAS, A. R. C., and ZENTMEYER, G. A. 1946. Control of chlorosis in citrus leaves. *Calif. Citrograph* **31:** 334–335, 346–348.

HABER, E. S. 1938. A study of drought resistance in inbred strains of sweet corn *zea mays* var. *rugosa*. *Iowa Agr. Expt. Sta. Research Bull.* **243.**

HADDOCK, J. L., and KELLEY, O. J. 1948. Interrelations of moisture, spacing and fertility to sugar beet production. *Proc. Am. Soc. Sugar Beet Technol.* 1–19.

HAINES, W. B. 1930. Studies in the physical properties of soils. V. The hysteresis effect in capillary properties and the modes of moisture distribution associated therewith. *J. Agr. Sci.* **20**: 97–116.

HALMA, F. F. 1934a. Some phases in the water relation of citrus. *Proc. Am. Soc. Hort. Sci.* **31**: 108–109.

HALMA, F. F. 1934b. Trunk growth and the water relation in leaves of citrus. *Proc. Am. Soc. Hort. Sci.* **32**: 273–276.

HALVERSON, H. O. 1931. Studies on the transformations of iron in nature. III. The effect of CO_2 on the equilibrium in iron solutions. *Soil Sci.* **32**: 141–165.

HARLEY, C. P., and LINDNER, R. C. 1945. Observed responses of apple and pear trees to some irrigation waters of north central Washington. *Proc. Am. Soc. Hort. Sci.* **46**: 34–44.

HARLEY, C. P., and MASURE, M. P. 1932. Studies on the interrelation of leaf area, soil moisture, and nitrogen to fruit growth and fruit bud formation in the apple. *Proc. Wash. State Hort. Assoc.* **28**: 212–216.

HARLEY, C. P., and MASURE, M. P. 1938. Relation of atmospheric conditions to enlargement rate and periodicity of winesap apples. *J. Agr. Research* **57**: 109–124.

HARRIS, F. S. 1914. Effects of variations in moisture content on certain properties of a soil and on the growth of wheat. *N. Y. (Cornell) Agr. Expt. Sta. Bull.* **352**.

HARRIS, J. A. 1926. The relationship between the concentration of the soil solution and the physico-chemical properties of the leaf-tissue fluids of Egyptian and upland cotton. *J. Agr. Research* **32**: 605–649.

HARRIS, J. A. 1934. The physico-chemical properties of plant saps in relation to phytogeography. 339 pp. Univ. of Minnesota Press.

HARRIS, J. A., GORTNER, R. A., HOFFMAN, W. F., LAWRENCE, J. V., and VALENTINE, A. T. 1924. The osmotic concentration, specific electrical conductivity, and chloride content of the tissue fluids of the indicator plants of Tooele Valley, Utah. *J. Agr. Research* **27**: 893–924.

HARRIS, J. A., and LAWRENCE, J. V. 1916. The cryoscopic constants of expressed vegetable saps as related to local environmental conditions in the Arizona deserts. *Physiol. Research* **2**: 1–49.

HARRIS, J. A., and PASCOE, T. A. 1930. Further studies on the relationship between the concentration of the soil solution and the physico-chemical properties of the leaf-tissue fluids of cotton. *J. Agr. Research* **41**: 767–789.

HARTT, C. E. 1934. Water and cane ripening. *Hawaiian Planter's Record* **38**: 193–206.

HAYNES, J. L. 1948. The effect of availability of soil moisture upon vegetative growth and water use in corn. *J. Am. Soc. Agron.* **40**: 385–395.

HAYWARD, H. E., BLAIR, W. M., and SKALING, P. E. 1942. Service for measuring entry of water into roots. *Botan. Gaz.* **104**: 152–160.

HAYWARD, H. E., and LONG, E. M. 1941. Anatomical and physiological responses of tomato to varying concentrations of sodium chloride, sodium sulphate, and nutrient solutions. *Botan. Gaz.* **102**: 437–461.

HAYWARD, H. E., and LONG, E. M. 1943a. Some effects of sodium salts on the growth of the tomato. *Plant Physiol.* **18**: 556–569.

HAYWARD, H. E., and SPURR, W. B. 1943b. Effects of osmotic concentration of substrate on the entry of water into corn roots. *Botan. Gaz.* **105**: 152–164.

HAYWARD, H. E., and SPURR, W. B. 1944a. Effects of isosmotic concentrations of inorganic and organic substrates on entry of water into corn roots. *Botan. Gaz.* **106**: 131–139.

HAYWARD, H. E., and SPURR, W. B. 1944b. The tolerance of flax to saline conditions: effect of sodium chloride, calcium chloride, and sodium sulfate. *J. Am. Soc. Agron.* **36:** 287–300.

HEATH, O. V. S. 1937. Effect of age on net assimilation and relative growth rates in the cotton plant. *Ann. Botany* **1:** 565–566.

HEATH, O. V. S., and GREGORY, F. G. 1938. The constancy of the mean net assimilation rate and its ecological importance. *Ann. Botany* **2:** 811–818.

HECK, A. F. 1934. A soil hygrometer for irrigated cane lands of Hawaii. *J. Am. Soc. Agron.* **26:** 274–278.

HEINICKE, A. J., and CHILDERS, N. F. 1936. The influence of water deficiency in photosynthesis and transpiration of apple leaves. *Proc. Am. Soc. Hort. Sci.* **33:** 155–159.

HENDRICKSON, A. H., and VEIHMEYER, F. J. 1929. Irrigation experiments with peaches in California. *Calif. Agr. Expt. Sta. Bull.* **479.**

HENDRICKSON, A. H., and VEIHMEYER, F. J. 1931a. Irrigation experiments with grapes. *Proc. Am. Soc. Hort. Sci.* **28:** 151–157.

HENDRICKSON, A. H., and VEIHMEYER, F. J. 1931b. Influence of dry soil on root extension. *Plant Physiol.* **6:** 567–576.

HENDRICKSON, A. H., and VEIHMEYER, F. J. 1933. Maintenance of predetermined soil moisture conditions in irrigation experiments. *Proc. Am. Soc. Hort. Sci.* **30:** 421–425.

HENDRICKSON, A. H., and VEIHMEYER, F. J. 1934. Irrigation experiments with prunes. *Calif. Agr. Expt. Sta. Bull.* **573.**

HENDRICKSON, A. H., and VEIHMEYER, F. J. 1936. The irrigation of pears on a clay adobe soil. *Proc. Am. Soc. Hort. Sci.* **34:** 224–226.

HENDRICKSON, A. H., and VEIHMEYER, F. J. 1941a. Moisture distribution in soil containers. *Plant Physiol.* **4:** 821–826.

HENDRICKSON, A. H., and VEIHMEYER, F. J. 1941b. Some factors affecting the growth rate of pears. *Proc. Am. Soc. Hort. Sci.* **39:** 1–7.

HENDRICKSON, A. H., and VEIHMEYER, F. J. 1942a. Irrigation experiments with pears and apples. *Calif. Agr. Expt. Sta. Bull.* **667.**

HENDRICKSON, A. H., and VEIHMEYER, F. J. 1942b. Readily available soil moisture and sizes of fruits. *Proc. Am. Soc. Hort. Sci.* **40:** 13–18.

HENDRICKSON, A. H., and VEIHMEYER, F. J. 1945. Permanent wilting percentage of soils obtained from field and laboratory trials. *Plant Physiol.* **20:** 517–539.

HERRICK, E. M. 1933. Seasonal and diurnal variations in the osmotic values and suction tension values in the aerial portions of *Ambrosia trifida*. *Am. J. Botany* **20:** 18–34.

HESTER, J. B., SMITH, G. E., and SHELTON, F. A. 1947. The relation of rainfall, soil type and replaceable magnesium to deficiency symptoms. *Proc. Am. Soc. Hort. Sci.* **40:** 304–308.

HEYN, A. N. J. 1940. The physiology of cell elongation. *Botan. Rev.* **6:** 515–574.

HIBBARD, R. P., and HARRINGTON, O. E. 1916. The depression of the freezing point in triturated plant tissue and the magnitude of this depression as related to soil moisture. *Physiol. Research* **1:** 441–454.

HILGARD, E. W. 1906. Soils, their formation, properties, composition, and relations to climate and plant growth in the humid and arid regions. Macmillan Co., New York, 593 pp.

HILGEMAN, R. H. 1948. Changes in soil moisture in the top eight feet of bare soil during 22 months after wetting. *J. Am. Soc. Agron.* **40:** 919–925.

HOAGLAND, D. E., and BROYER, T. C. 1936. General nature of the process of salt accumulation by roots with description of experimental methods. *Plant Physiol.* **11:** 471–507.

HOBBS, J. A. 1948. Boron needs of Indiana soils. (Thesis, Ph. D., Graduate School, Purdue Univ., Lafayette, Ind.)

HOBBS, J. A., and BERTRAMSON, R. B. 1949. Boron uptake by plants as influenced by soil moisture. *Soil Sci. Soc. Am. Proc.* **14:** 257–261.

HOFFER, G. N. 1945. Some ways and wherefores for air-conditioning soils. *Better Crops with Plant Food* **29** (2): 19–21.

HÖFLER, K. 1920. Ein schema für die osmotische leistung der pflanzenzelle. *Ber. deut. botan. Ges.* **38:** 288–298.

HOPE, C., KING, C. J., and PARKER, O. 1936. The effect of crazy top disorder on cotton plants and its control by irrigation management. *U. S. Dept. Agr. Tech. Bull.* **515**, pp. 1–43.

HOPKINS, J. W. 1935. Influence of weather conditions on the nitrogen content of wheat. *Can. J. Research* **12:** 228–237.

HUBER, B., and HÖFLER, K. 1930. Die wasserpermeabilitat des protoplasmas. *Jahrb. wiss. Botan.* **73:** 351–511.

HUNTER, A. S., and KELLEY, O. J. 1946a. The extension of plant roots into dry soil. *Plant Physiol.* **21:** 445–451.

HUNTER, A. S., and KELLEY, O. J. 1946b. A new technique for studying the absorption of moisture and nutrients from soil by plant roots. *Soil Sci.* **62:** 441–450.

HUNTER, A. S., and KELLEY, O. J. 1946c. The growth and rubber content of guayule as affected by variation in soil moisture stress. *J. Am. Soc. Agron.* **38:** 118–134.

ILJIN, W. S. 1923. Der einfluss des wassermangels auf die kohlenstoff = assimilation durch die pflanzen. *Flora* **116:** 360–378.

ILJIN, W. S. 1929. Der einfluss der standortsfeuchtigkeit auf den osmotischen wert bei pflanzen. *Planta* **7:** 45–58.

ISRAELSEN, O. W. 1950. Irrigation principles and practices. John Wiley and Sons, Inc., New York.

ISRAELSEN, O. W., and WEST, F. L. 1922. Water holding capacity of irrigated soils. *Utah Agr. Expt. Sta. Bull.* **183.**

JAMISON, V. C. 1946. Chemical relationships of potassium and magnesium in organic and sandy soils of central Florida. *Soil Sci.* **61:** 443–453.

JANES, B. E. 1948. The effect of varying amounts of irrigation on the composition of two varieties of snap beans. *Proc. Am. Soc. Hort. Sci.* **51:** 457–462.

JONES, L. H., and TIO, M. A. 1948. Unavailability of iron as a cause of frenching of tobacco (*nicotiana tabacum* L.). *Plant Physiol.* **23:** 576–594.

JULANDER, O. 1945. Drought resistance of range and pasture grasses. *Plant Physiol.* **20:** 573–599.

KANITKAR, N. V., GODE, R. B., and GOKHALE, D. H. 1943. Water requirement of *rabi jowar* in the scarcity tracts of the Bombay-Deccan. *Indian J. Agr. Sci.* **13:** 235–251.

KELLEY, O. J., HUNTER, A. S., HAISE, H. R., and HOBBS, C. H. 1946. A comparison of methods of measuring soil moisture under field conditions. *J. Am. Soc. Agron.* **38:** 759–784.

KELLEY, O. J., HUNTER, A. S., and HOBBS, C. H. 1945. The effect of moisture stress on nursery-grown guayule with respect to the amount and type of growth and growth response on transplanting. *J. Am. Soc. Agron.* **37:** 194–216.

KENWORTHY, A. L. 1948. Effect of soil moisture on the growth of apple trees. (Pullman, Wash. Thesis, Ph. D., Washington State College.)

KENWORTHY, A. L. 1949. Soil moisture and growth of apple trees. *Proc. Am. Soc. Hort. Sci.* **54:** 29–39.

KERR, T., and ANDERSON, D. B. 1944. Osmotic quantities in growing cotton bolls. *Plant Physiol.* **19:** 338–349.

KIESSELBACH, T. A. 1916. Transpiration as a factor in crop production. *Nebr. Agr. Expt. Sta. Research Bull.* 6.

KIESSELBACH, T. A. 1929. Varietal, cultural and seasonal effects upon the water requirement of crop. *Proc. Intern. Congr. Plant Sci. 1st Congr. Ithaca* **1:** 87–105.

KIESSELBACH, T. A., and WEIHING, R. M. 1935. The comparative root development of selfed lines of corn and their F_1 and F_2 hybrids. *J. Am. Soc. Agron.* **27:** 538–541.

KING, F. H. 1907. Irrigation and drainage. The Macmillan Co., New York, 171 pp.

KING, F. H. 1914. Soil management. Orange Judd Co., New York, pp. 1–311.

KIRKHAM, D., and FENG, C. L. 1949. Some tests of the diffusion theory and laws of capillary flow in soils. *Soil Sci.* **67:** 29–40.

KLIMAN, S. 1937. The importance of ferrous iron in plants and soil. *Soil Sci. Soc. Am. Proc.* **2:** 385–392.

KNIGHT, R. C. 1922. Further observations on the transpiration, stomata, leaf water-content and the wilting of plants. *Ann. Botany* **36:** 361–385.

KOHNKE, H. 1942. Runoff chemistry: an undeveloped branch of soil science. *Soil Sci. Soc. Am. Proc.* **6:** 492–500.

KOHNKE, H. 1946. The practical use of the energy concept of soil moisture. *Soil Sci. Soc. Am. Proc.* **11:** 64–66.

KOHNKE, H., DREIBELBIS, F. R., and DAVIDSON, J. M. 1940. A survey and discussion of lysimeters and a bibliography on their construction and performance. *U. S. Dept. Agr. Misc. Pub.* **372:** 1–68.

KOKETSU, R. 1928. Variation of the water content of leaves as related to the wilting of plants. *Dept. Agr. J.* **2:** 93–116, Kyuschu Imp. Univ. [*Expt. Sta. Rec.* **61:** 627.]

KORSTIAN, C. F. 1924. Density of cell sap in relation to environmental conditions in the Wasatch mountains of Utah. *J. Agr. Research* **28:** 845–909.

KOSTYUCHENKO, A. D. 1938. The influence of soil moisture and boron on the effectiveness of liming on flax. *Chemisation Socialistic Agr. U.S.S.R.* **2:** 82–91. [*Chem. Abstracts* **32:** 5980 (1938).]

KRAMER, P. J. 1932. The absorption of water by root systems of plants. *Am. J. Botany* **19:** 148–164.

KRAMER, P. J. 1933. The intake of water through dead root systems and its relation to the problem of absorption by transpiring plants. *Am. J. Botany* **20:** 481–492.

KRAMER, P. J. 1937. The relation between rate of transpiration and rate of absorption of water in plants. *Am. J. Botany* **24:** 10–15.

KRAMER, P. J. 1940. Root resistance as a cause of decreased water absorption by plants at low temperatures. *Plant Physiol.* **15:** 63–80.

KRAMER, P. J. 1941. Soil moisture as a limiting factor for active absorption and root pressure. *Am. J. Botany* **28:** 446–451.

KRAMER, P. J. 1944. Soil moisture in relation to plant growth. *Botan. Rev.* **10:** 525–559.

KRAMER, P. J. 1945. Absorption of water by plants. *Botan. Rev.* **11**: 310–355.

KRAMER, P. J. 1946. Absorption of water through suberized roots of trees. *Plant Physiol.* **21**: 37–41.

KRAMER, P. J. 1949. Plant and Soil Water Relationships. McGraw-Hill Book Co., New York.

KRAMER, P. J., and COILE, T. S. 1940. An estimation of the volume of water made available by root extension. *Plant Physiol.* **15**: 743–747.

KUMMER, F. A., and COOPER, A. W. 1945. Soil porosity determinations with air pressure picnometer as compared with tension method. *Agr. Eng.* **26**: 21–23.

LACHENMEIER, J. 1932. Transpiration und wasserabsorption intakter pflanzen noch vorangsgegrangem verdunkelung bei konstanz der jahrb. *Jahrb. wiss. Botan.* **76**: 765–827.

LAWTON, K. 1945. The influence of soil aeration on the growth and absorption of nutrients by corn plants. *Soil Sci. Soc. Am. Proc.* **10**: 263–268.

LEAMER, R. W., and SHAW, B. 1941. A simple apparatus for measuring non-capillary porosity on an extensive scale. *J. Am. Soc. Agron.* **33**: 1003–1008.

LEEPER, G. W. 1947. The forms and reactions of manganese in the soil. *Soil Sci.* **63**: 79–94.

LEVITT, J. 1941. Frost killing and hardiness of plants. Burgess Publishing Co., Minneapolis.

LEVITT, J. 1947. The thermodynamics of active (non-osmotic) water absorption. *Plant Physiol.* **22**: 514–525.

LEVITT, J., SCARTH, G. W., and GIBBS, R. D. 1936. Water permeability of isolated protoplasts in relation to volume change. *Protoplasma* **26**: 237–248.

LEWIS, M. R. 1937. Rate of flow of capillary moisture. *U. S. Dept. Agr. Tech. Bull.* **579**.

LEWIS, M. R., WORK, R. A., and ALDRICH, W. W. 1934. Studies of the irrigation of pear orchards on heavy soil near Medford, Oregon. *U. S. Dept. Agr. Tech. Bull.* **432**.

LINDNER, R. C., and HARLEY, C. P. 1944. Nutrient interrelations in lime-induced chlorosis. *Plant Physiol.* **19**: 420–439.

LIVINGSTON, B. E., and KOKETSU, R. 1920. The water-supplying power of the soil as related to the wilting of plants. *Soil Sci.* **9**: 469–485.

LIVINGSTON, B. E., and NOREM, W. L. 1937. Water-supplying power and water-absorbing power of soils as related to wilting of wheat and coleus in greenhouse pot cultures. *Soil Sci.* **43**: 177–204.

LOBANOV, N. V. 1947. A method for investigating the growth of roots in woody plants under various conditions of soil moisture. *Compt. rend. acad. sci. U. R. S. S.* **55**: 547–550. [Soils and Fertilizers (1948) **11**: 169.]

LOEHWING, W. F. 1934. Physiological aspects of the effect of continuous soil aeration of plant growth. *Plant Physiol.* **9**: 567–583.

LOFTFIELD, J. V. G. 1921. The behavior of stomata. *Carnegie Inst. Wash. Pub.* **314**.

LONG, E. M. 1943. The effect of salt additions to the substrate on intake of water and nutrients by roots of approach-grafted tomatoes. *Am. J. Botany* **30**: 594–601.

LOOMIS, W. E. 1934. Daily growth of maize. *Am. J. Bot.* **21**: 1–6.

LOOMIS, W. E., and EWAN, L. M. 1936. Hydrotropic responses of roots in soil. *Botan. Gaz.* **97**: 728–743.

LOUSTALOT, A J. 1945. Influence of soil moisture conditions on apparent photosynthesis and transpiration of pecan leaves. *J. Agr. Research* **71**: 519–532.

LOUSTALOT, A. J., WINTERS, H. F., and CHILDERS, N. F. 1947. Influence of high, medium, and low soil moisture on growth and alkaloid content of *cinchona ledgeriana*. *Plant Physiol.* **22**: 613–619.

LUNDEGARDH, H. 1940. Investigations as to the absorption and accumulation of inorganic ions. *Ann. Sweden Agr. Coll.* **8**: 234–404.

LUNDEGARDH, H. 1948. On the mechanism of active movement of water and solutes through plant roots. *Faraday Soc. Discussions* No. **3**: 139–146.

LUTHIN, J. N., and KIRKHAM, D. 1949. A piezometer method for measuring permeability of soil *in situ* below a water table. *Soil Sci.* **68**: 349–358.

LUTZ, J. F., et al. 1946. Effects of cover crops on pore-size distribution in a coastal plain soil. *Soil Sci. Soc. Am. Proc* **11**: 43–46.

LYON, T. L., and BIZZELL, J. A. 1936. Lysimeter experiments. IV. Records for tanks 17 to 20 during the years 1922 to 1933 and for tanks 13 to 16 during the years 1913 to 1928. *N. Y. (Cornell) Agr. Expt. Sta. Mem.* **194**: 3–59.

McALISTER, D. F. 1944. Determination of soil drought resistance in grass seedlings. *J. Am. Soc. Agron.* **36**: 324–336.

McCOOL, M. M., and MILLAR, C. E. 1917. The water content of the soil and the composition and concentration of the soil solution as indicated by the freezing-point lowerings of the roots and tops of plants. *Soil Sci.* **3**: 113–138.

MacDOUGAL, D. T. 1920. Hydration and growth. *Carnegie Inst. Wash. Pub.* **297**.

MacDOUGAL, D. T., OVERTON, J. B., and SMITH, G. B. 1929. The hydrostatic-pneumatic system of certain trees; movement of liquids and gases. *Carnegie Inst. Wash. Pub.* **397**.

McGEORGE, W. T. 1949. A study of lime-induced chlorosis in Arizona orchards. *Ariz. Agr. Expt. Sta. Tech. Bull.* **117**: 341–388.

McGEORGE, W. T., and BREAZEALE, J. F. 1931. The relation of phosphate availability, soil permeability, and carbon dioxide to the fertility of calcareous soils. *Ariz. Agr. Expt. Sta. Tech. Bull.* **36**: 361–412.

MacGILLIVRAY, J. H. 1949. Effect of irrigation on the growth and yield of sweet corn. *Proc. Am. Soc. Hort. Sci.* **54**: 330–338.

MacGILLIVRAY, J. H., and DONEEN, L. D. 1942. Soil moisture conditions as related to the irrigation of truck crops on mineral soils. *Proc. Am. Soc. Hort. Sci.* **40**: 483–492.

McMURTREY, J. E., JR., BOWLING, J. D., BROWN, D. E., and ENGLE, H. B. 1947. Effects of controlled soil moisture on growth, composition, yield, and quality of Maryland tobacco. *J. Agr. Research* **75**: 215–249.

MAGISTAD, O. C., AYERS, A. D., WADLEIGH, C. H., and GAUCH, H. G. 1943. Effect of salt concentration, kind of salt and climate on plant growth in sand cultures. *Plant Physiol.* **18**: 151–166.

MAGNESS, J. R., DEGMAN, E. S., and FURR, J. R. 1935. Soil moisture and irrigation studies in eastern apple orchards. *U. S. Dept. Agr. Tech. Bull.* **491**.

MARR, J. C. 1927. The use and duty of water in the Salt River Valley. *Ariz. Agr. Expt. Sta. Bull.* **120**.

MARSHALL, T. J., and STIRK, G. B. 1949. Pressure potential of water moving downward into soil. *Soil Sci.* **68**: 359–370.

MARTIN, E. V. 1940. Effect of soil moisture on growth and transpiration in *helianthus annus*. *Plant Physiol.* **15**: 449–466.

MARTIN, J. C., OVERSTREET, R., and HOAGLAND, D. R. 1945. Potassium fixation in replaceable and nonreplaceable forms in relation to chemical reactions in the soil. *Soil Sci. Soc. Am. Proc.* **10:** 94–101.

MASON, T. G., and PHILLIS, E. 1939. Experiments on the extraction of sap from the vacuole of the leaf of the cotton plant and their bearing on the osmotic theory of water absorption by the cell. *Ann. Botany* **3:** 531–533.

MAXIMOV, N. A. 1929. The plant in relation to water. Translated by R. H. Yapp, George Allen and Unwin, Ltd., London.

MENDEL, L. 1945. Orange leaf transpiration under orchard conditions. II. Soil moisture content decreasing. *Palestine J. Bot. Ser. R Jerusalem* **5:** 59–85. [*Biol. Abstracts* **20:** 11132.]

MEYER, B. S. 1927. Studies on the physical properties of leaves and leaf saps. *Ohio J. Sci.* **27:** 263–288.

MEYER, B. S. 1945. A critical evaluation of the terminology of diffusion phenomena. *Plant Physiol.* **20:** 142–164.

MEYER, B. S., and ANDERSON, D. B. 1939. Plant physiology. D. Van Nostrand Co., New York.

MEYERS, H. D. 1946. Soil quality and wheat quality. *Northwestern Miller* **228:** 4a. [*Biol. Abstracts* **21:** 9793.]

MILLER, E. C. 1938. Plant Physiology. McGraw-Hill Book Co., New York.

MILLER, E. C., and SAUNDERS, A. R. 1923. Some observations on the temperature of the leaves of crop plants. *J. Agr. Research* **26:** 15–43.

MILLER, M. F., and DULEY, F. L. 1925. The effect of a varying moisture supply upon the development and composition of the maize plant at different periods of growth. *Mo. Agr. Expt. Sta. Research Bull.* **76:** 3–36.

MITCHELL, J. W. 1936. Effect of atmospheric humidity on rate of carbon fixation by plants. *Botan. Gaz.* **98:** 87–104.

MOLISCH, H. 1921. Über den einfluss der transpiration auf das verschwinden der stärke in den blattern. *Ber. deut. botan. Ges.* **39:** 334–339.

MOLZ, F. J. 1926. A study of suction force by the simplified method. I. Effect of external factors. *Am. J. Botany* **13:** 433–463.

MONTGOMERY, E. G. 1911. Methods of determining the water requirements of crops. *J. Am. Soc. Agron.* **3:** 261–283.

MOORE, R. E. 1939. Water conduction from shallow water tables. *Hilgardia* **12:** 383–426.

MORTON, A. G., and WATSON, D. J. 1948. A physiological study of leaf growth. *Ann. Botany* **12:** 281–310.

MOTHES, K. 1926. Ein beitrag zur kenntnis des *n*-stoffwechsels höherer pflanzen. *Planta* **1:** 472–552.

MUELLER, I. M., and WEAVER, J. E. 1942. Relative drought resistance of seedlings of dominant prairie grasses. *Ecology* **23:** 387–398.

MULDER, D. 1948. De gevolgen van onevenwichtige voeding van vruchtbomen. *Mededeel Direct. Tuinb.* **11:** 187–195. [The effects of unbalanced nutrition of fruit trees. *Soils and fertilizers* (1948) **11:** 276.]

MULLER, C. H. 1946. Root development and ecological relations of guayule. *U. S. Dept. Agr. Tech. Bull.* **923:** 1–113.

MUSKAT, M. 1937. Flow of homogeneous fluids through porous media. McGraw-Hill Book Co., New York.

NEFF, M. S., and POTTER, G. F. 1946. Factors affecting growth of newly transplanted tung trees during dry weather. *Proc. Am. Soc. Hort. Sci.* **47:** 153–160.

NEIDIG, R. E., and SNYDER, R. S. 1924. The relation of moisture and available nitrogen to the yield and protein content of wheat. *Soil Sci.* **18:** 173–179.

NEIDIG, R. E., and SNYDER, R. S. 1926. The relation of the yield and protein content of wheat to the nitrogen content of the soil under ten years of different systems of cropping. *Idaho Agr. Expt. Sta. Research Bull.* **5.**

NELLER, J. R., and COMAR, C. L. 1947. Factors affecting fixation of phosphorus in soils as determined with radioactive phosphorus. *Soil Sci.* **64:** 379–387.

NEWTON, R. 1924. Colloidal properties of winter wheat plants in relation to frost resistance. *J. Agr. Sci.* **14:** 178–191.

NEWTON, R., and BROWN, W. R. 1926. Seasonal changes in the composition of winter wheat plants in relation to frost resistance. *J. Agr. Sci.* **16:** 522–538.

NEWTON, R., and GORTNER, R. A. 1922. A method for estimating hydrophilic colloid content of expressed plant tissue fluids. *Botan. Gaz.* **74:** 442–446.

MULDER, D., and MARTIN, W. M. 1930. Physico-chemical studies on the nature of drought resistance in crop plants. *Can. J. Research* **3:** 336–427.

NIGHTINGALE, G. T. 1942a. Nitrate and carbohydrate reserves in relation to nitrogen nutrition of pineapple. *Botan. Gaz.* **103:** 409–456.

NIGHTINGALE, G. T. 1942b. Potassium and phosphate nutrition of pineapple in relation to nitrate and carbohydrate reserves. *Botan. Gaz.* **104:** 191–223.

NORTHEN, H. T. 1943. Relationship of dissociation of cellular proteins by incipient drought to physiological processes. *Botan. Gaz.* **104:** 481–485.

NOVOGRUSDKY, D. M. 1947. Microbiological processes in semi-desert soils. III. Category of soil moisture and nitrification. *Pedology,* pp. 27–31. [*Soils and Fertilizers* (1947) **10:** 291.]

OSKAMP, J. 1934. Ground water as a measure of the suitability of soil for orchard purposes. *Proc. Am. Soc. Hort. Sci.* **30:** 410–414.

OSKAMP, J., and BATJER, L. P. 1932. Soils in relation to fruit growing in New York. II. Size, production, and rooting habit of apple trees on different soil types in the Hilton and Morton areas, Monroe County. *N. Y. (Cornell) Agr. Expt. Sta. Bull.* **550:** 3–45.

OVERLEY, F. L., *et al.* 1932. Irrigation of orchards by sprinkling. *Wash. Agr. Expt. Sta. Bull.* **268.**

PAGE, J. B. 1947. Advantages of the pressure pycnometer for measuring the pore-space of soils. *Soil Sci. Soc. Am. Proc.* **12:** 81–84.

PARKER, F. W. 1925. The carbon dioxide content of the soil air as a factor in the absorption of inorganic elements by plants. *Soil Sci.* **20:** 39–44.

PAVLYCHENKO, T. K. 1937a. The soil-block washing method in quantitative root study. *Cand. J. Research* **C15:** 33–57.

PAVLYCHENKO, T. K. 1937b. Quantitative study of the entire root systems of weed and crop plants under field conditions. *Ecology* **18:** 62–79.

PEELE, T. C., BEALE, O. W., and LESESNE, F. F. 1948. Irrigation requirements of South Carolina soils. *Agr. Eng.* **29:** 157–159.

PETRIE, A. H. K., and WOOD, J. G. 1938. Studies on the nitrogen metabolism of plants. *Ann. Botany* **2:** 33–59, 729–750, 887–898.

PICKERING, S. 1917. The effect of one plant on another. *Ann. Botany* **31:** 181–187.

PICKLER, W. E. 1919. Water content and temperature as factors influencing diastase formation in barley grain. *Plant World* **22:** 221–238.

PLANT, W. 1947. A survey of trace element and magnesium deficiencies of crops in some counties of England. *Sci. Hort.* **5:** 23–26.

POST, K., and SEELEY, J. G. 1947. Automatic watering of roses, 1943–1946. *Proc. Am. Soc. Hort. Sci.* **49**: 433–436.

PRESTON, R. D. 1948. Mechanism of movement of solutions in plants. *Faraday Soc. Discussion No.* **3**: 130–133.

PRIESTLY, J. H. 1922. Further observations upon the mechanism of root pressure. *New Phytologist* **21**: 41–47.

RAHN, E. M. 1946. The influence of rainfall on the response of cantaloupes to manures and commercial fertilizers. *Proc. Am. Soc. Hort. Sci.* **47**: 343–346.

RANEY, W. A. 1949. Oxygen diffusion as a criterion of soil aeration. *Soil Sci. Soc. Am. Proc.* **14**: 61–65.

RANEY, W. A., and HOOVER, C. D. 1946. The release of artificially fixed potassium from a kaolinitic and montmorillonitic soil. *Soil Sci. Soc. Am. Proc.* **11**: 231–237.

REEVE, R. C., and JENSEN, M. C. 1949. Use of piezometers for ground water flow studies and measurement of subsoil permeability. *Agr. Eng.* **30**: 435–438.

REITEMEIER, R. F. 1946. Effect of moisture content on the dissolved and exchangeable ions of soils of arid regions. *Soil Sci.* **61**: 195–214.

REITEMEIER, R. F., CHRISTIANSEN, J. E., MOORE, R. E., and ALDRICH, W. W. 1948. Effect of gypsum, organic matter and drying on infiltration of a sodium water into a fine sandy loam. *U. S. Dept. Agr. Tech. Bull.* **937**.

RENNER, O. 1912. Versuche zur Mechanik der Wasserversorgung. I. Der Druck in den Leitungsbahnen von Freilandpflanzen. II. Über wurzeltatigkeit. *Ber. deut. botan. Ges.* **30**: 576–580, 642–648.

REUTHER, W., and CRAWFORD, C. L. 1947. Effect of certain soil and irrigation treatments on citrus chlorosis in a calcareous soil. II. Soil atmosphere studies. *Soil Sci.* **63**: 227–240.

RICHARDS, L. A. 1928. The usefulness of capillary potential to soil moisture and plant investigators. *J. Agr. Research* **37**: 719–742.

RICHARDS, L. A. 1931. Capillary conduction of liquids through porous mediums. *Physics* **1**: 318–333.

RICHARDS, L. A. 1936. Capillary conductivity data for three soils. *J. Am. Soc. Agron.* **28**: 297–300.

RICHARDS, L. A. 1940. Concerning permeability units for soils. *Soil Sci. Soc. Am. Proc.* **5**: 49–53.

RICHARDS, L. A. 1941a. Uptake and retention of water by soil as determined by distance to a water table. *J. Am. Soc. Agron.* **33**: 778–786.

RICHARDS, L. A. 1941b. A pressure-membrane extraction apparatus for soil solution. *Soil Sci.* **51**: 377–386.

RICHARDS, L. A. 1947. Pressure-membrane apparatus, construction and use. *Agr. Eng.* **28**: 451–454, 460.

RICHARDS, L. A. 1948. Porous plate apparatus for measuring moisture retention and transmission by soil. *Soil Sci.* **66**: 105–110.

RICHARDS, L. A. 1949a. Methods for mounting porous plates used in soil moisture measurements. *J. Agron.* **41**: 487–490.

RICHARDS, L. A. 1949b. Methods of measuring soil moisture tension. *Soil Sci.* **68**: 95–112.

RICHARDS, L. A., and CAMPBELL, R. B. 1948a. Use of thermistors for measuring the freezing point of solutions and soils. *Soil Sci.* **65**: 429–436.

RICHARDS, L. A., and CAMPBELL, R. B. 1948b. The freezing point of moisture in soil cores. *Soil Sci. Soc. Am. Proc.* **13**: 70–74.

RICHARDS, L. A., CAMPBELL, R. B., and HEALTON, L. H. 1949. Some freezing-point-depression measurements on cores of soil in which cotton and sunflower plants were wilted. *Soil Sci. Soc. Am. Proc.* **14:** 47–50.

RICHARDS, L. A., and FIREMAN, M. 1943. Pressure-plate apparatus for measuring moisture sorption and transmission by soils. *Soil Sci.* **56:** 395–404.

RICHARDS, L. A., and HUBERTY, M. R. 1941. Moisture studies under citrus using tensiometers. *Proc. Am. Soc. Hort. Sci.* **39:** 73–79.

RICHARDS, L. A., and LOOMIS, W. E. 1942. Limitations of auto-irrigators for controlling soil moisture under growing plants. *Plant Physiol.* **17:** 223–235.

RICHARDS, L. A., NEAL, O. K., and RUSSELL, M. B. 1939. Observations on moisture conditions in lysimeters. *Soil Sci. Soc. Am. Proc.* **4:** 55–59.

RICHARDS, L. A., and WEAVER, L. R. 1943a. The sorption block soil moisture meter and hysteresis effects related to its operation. *J. Am. Soc. Agron.* **35:** 1002–1011.

RICHARDS, L. A., and WEAVER, L. R. 1943b. Fifteen-atmosphere-percentage as related to the permanent wilting percentage. *Soil Sci.* **56:** 331–339.

RICHARDS, L. A., and WEAVER, L. R. 1944. Moisture retention by some irrigated soils as related to soil moisture tension. *J. Agr. Research* **69:** 215–235.

RICHARDS, L. A., and WILSON, B. D. 1936. Capillary conductivity measurements in peat soils. *J. Am. Soc. Agron.* **28:** 427–431.

RICHARDS, S. J. 1938. Soil moisture content calculations from capillary tension records. *Soil Sci. Soc. Am. Proc.* **3:** 57–64.

RICHARDS, S. J., and LAMB, J., JR. 1937. Field measurements of capillary tension. *J. Am. Soc. Agron.* **29:** 772–780.

ROBERTSON, L. S., and KOHNKE, H. 1946. The pF at the wilting point of several Indiana soils. *Soil Sci. Soc. Am. Proc.* **11:** 50–52.

ROBERTSON, R. N., and WILKINS, M. J. 1948. Studies in the metabolism of plant cells. VII. The quantitative relation between salt accumulation and salt respiration. *Australian J. Sci. Research* **1B:** 17–49.

ROSA, J. T. 1921. Investigations on the hardening process in vegetable plants. *Mo. Agr. Expt. Sta. Research Bull.* **48.**

ROSENE, H. F. 1941a. Comparison of rates of water intake in contiguous regions of intact and isolated roots. *Plants Physiol.* **16:** 19–38.

ROSENE, H. F. 1941b. Control of water transport in local root regions of attached and isolated roots by means of the osmotic pressure of the external solution. *Am. J. Botany* **28:** 402–409.

ROSENE, H. F., and WALTHALL, A. M. J. 1949. Velocities of water absorption by individual root hairs of different species. *Botan. Gaz.* **111:** 11–21.

RUSSELL, M. B. 1939. Soil moisture sorption curves for four Iowa soils. *Soil Sci. Soc. Am. Proc.* **4:** 51–54.

RUSSELL, M. B. 1949. A simplified air-pycnometer for field use. *Soil Sci. Soc. Am. Proc.* **14:** 73–76.

RUSSELL, M. B., DAVIS, F. E., and BAIR, R. A. 1940. The use of tensiometers for following soil moisture conditions under corn. *J. Am. Soc. Agron.* **32:** 922–930.

RUSSELL, M. B., and RICHARDS, L. A. 1938. The determination of soil moisture energy relations by centrifugation. *Soil Sci. Soc. Am. Proc.* **3:** 65–69.

RYALL, A. L., and ALDRICH, W. W. 1938. The effects of water supply to the trees upon water content, pressure test and quality of Bartlett pears. *Proc. Am. Soc. Hort. Sci.* **35:** 283–288.

SAYRE, J. D. 1926. Physiology of the stomata of *rumex patientia. Ohio J. Sci.* **26:** 233–267.

SAYRE, J. D. 1939. Corn stomata. *Ohio Agr. Expt. Sta.* Quoted by Schneider and Childers. [Mimeographed.]

SCHNEIDER, G. W., and CHILDERS, N. F. 1941. Influence of soil moisture on photosynthesis, respiration, and transpiration of apple leaves. *Plant Physiol.* 16: 565–584.

SCHOFIELD, R. K. 1935. The pF of the water in soil. *Trans. 3d Intern. Congr. Soil Sci.*, Pt. II, pp. 37–48.

SCHOFIELD, R. K., and DA COSTA, B. 1935. The determination of the pF at permanent wilting and at the moisture equivalent by the freezing point method. *Trans. 3d Intern. Congr. Soil Sci.*, 1: 6–17.

SCHREINER, O. 1923. Toxic organic soil constituents and the influence of oxidation. *J. Am. Soc. Agron.* 15: 270–276.

SCHROEDER, H., and HERRMAN, F. 1931. Über die kohlenhydrate und den kohlenhydratstoffwechsel des laubblatter. I. Die zunahme des saccharosegehaltes beim welken. *Biochem. Z.* 235: 407–425.

SCHROEDER, H., and HORN, T. 1922. Das gegenseitige mengenverhaltnis der kohlenhydrate im laubblatt im seiner abhangigheit vom Wassergehalt. *Biochem. Z.* 130: 165–198.

SCHWALEN, H. C., and WHARTON, M. F. 1930. Lettuce irrigation studies. *Ariz. Agr. Expt. Sta. Bull.* 133.

SCOFIELD, C. S. 1945a. The water requirement of alfalfa. *U. S. Dept. Agr. Circ.* 735: 1–11.

SCOFIELD, C. S. 1945b. The measurement of soil water. *J. Agr. Research* 71: 375–402.

SHANKS, J. B., and LAURIE, A. 1949. A progress report of some rose root studies. *Proc. Am. Soc. Hort. Sci.* 53: 473–488.

SHANTZ, H. L. 1925. Soil moisture in relation to the growth of crop plants. *J. Am. Soc. Agron.* 17: 705–711.

SHANTZ, H. L. 1927. Drought resistance and soil moisture. *Ecology* 8: 145–157.

SHANTZ, H. L., and PIEMEISEL, L. N. 1927. The water requirement of plants at Akron, Colo. *J. Agr. Research* 34: 1093–1190.

SHAW, C. F. 1927. The normal moisture capacity of soils. *Soil Sci.* 23: 303–317.

SHAW, B., and BAVER, L. D. 1939. An electrothermal method for following moisture changes of the soil *in situ*. *Soil Sci. Soc. Am. Proc.* 4: 78–83.

SHIRLEY, H. L., and MEULI, L. J. 1939. Influence of moisture supply on drought resistance of conifers. *J. Agr. Research* 59: 1–21.

SHIVE, J. W. 1941. The balance of ions and oxygen tension in nutrient substrates for plants. *Soil Sci.* 51: 445–457.

SHULL, C. A. 1916. Measurement of the surface forces in soils. *Botan. Gaz.* 62: 1–31.

SHULL, C. A. 1924. Imbibition in relation to absorption and transportation of water in plants. *Ecology* 5: 230–240.

SHULL, C. A. 1939. Atmospheric humidity and temperature in relation to the water system of plants and soils. *Plant Physiol.* 14: 401–422.

SKOOG, F., BROYER, T. C., and GROSSENBACHER, K. A. 1938. Effects of auxin on rates, periodicity, and osmotic relations in exudation. *Am. J. Botan.* 25: 749–759.

SMITH, F. W., and COOK, R. L. 1946. The effect of soil aeration, moisture, and compaction on nitrification and oxidation and the growth of sugar beets following corn and legumes in pot cultures. *Soil Sci. Soc. Am. Proc.* 11: 402–406.

SMITH, R. M., and BROWNING, D. R. 1947. Soil moisture tension and pore space relations for several soils in the range of the "field capacity." *Soil Sci. Soc. Am. Proc.* **12:** 17–21.

SPOEHR, H. A. 1919. The carbohydrate economy of cacti. *Carnegie Inst. Wash. Pub.* 287.

SPOEHR, H. A., and MILNER, H. W. 1939. Starch dissolution and amylolytic activity of leaves. *Proc. Am. Phil. Soc.* **81:** 37–78.

STANFORD, G. 1947. Fixation of potassium in soils under moist conditions and on drying in relation to type of clay mineral. *Soil Sci. Soc. Am. Proc.* **12:** 167–171.

STEENBJERG, F. 1935. The exchangeable manganese in Danish soils and its relation to plant growth. *Trans. 3d Intern. Congr. Soil Sci.,* **1:** 198–201.

STEPHENS, D. E., OVESON, M. M., and MITCHELL, G. A. 1943. Water requirements of wheat at the Sherman Branch Experiment Station. *Ore. Agr. Expt. Sta. Tech. Bull.* 1.

STEWARD, F. C. 1933. The absorption and accumulation of solutes by living plant cells. V. Observations upon the effects of time, oxygen and salt concentration upon absorption and respiration by storage tissue. *Protoplasma* **18:** 208–242.

STEWARD, F. C., BERRY, W. E., and BROYER, T. C. 1936. The absorption and accumulation of solutes by living plant cells. VIII. The effect of oxygen upon respiration and salt accumulation. *Ann. Botany* **50:** 345–366.

STILES, I. E. 1948. Relation of water to the germination of corn and cotton seeds. *Plant Physiol.* **23:** 201–222.

STOCKING, C. R. 1945. The calculation of tensions in *cucurbita pepo. Am. J. Botany* **32:** 126–134.

STODDART, L. A. 1935. Osmotic pressure and water content of prairie plants. *Plant Physiol.* **10:** 661–680.

STOECKELER, J. H., and AAMODT, E. 1940. Use of tensiometers in regulating watering in forest nurseries. *Plant Physiol.* **15:** 589–607.

SWEZEY, J. A., and WADSWORTH, H. A. 1940. Irrigation interval as an aid in lowering production costs. *Hawaiian Planter's Record* **44:** 49–69.

TAGAWA, T. 1934. The relation between the absorption of water by plant root and the concentration and nature of the surrounding solution. *Japan J. Botany* **7:** 33–60.

TAYLOR, C. A., BLANEY, H. F., and MCLAUGHLIN, W. W. 1934. The wilting point in certain soils and the ultimate wilting point. *Trans. Am. Geophys. Union* Pt. II, pp. 436–444.

TAYLOR, S. A. 1949. Oxygen diffusion in porous media as affected by compaction and moisture content. *Soil Sci. Soc. Am. Proc.* **14:** 55–61.

THODAY, D. 1918. On turgescence and the absorption of water by the cells of plants. *New Phytologist* **17:** 108–113.

THOM, C. C., and HOLTZ, H. F. 1917. Factors influencing the water requirements of plants. *Wash. Agr. Expt. Sta. Bull.* **116.**

THOM, C., and SMITH, N. R. 1938. Fauna and flora of the soil. *U. S. Dept. Agr. Yearbook,* 1938, pp. 940–947.

THOMAS, W., MACK, W. B., and COTTON, R. H. 1942. Foliar diagnosis in relation to irrigation. *Proc. Soc. Hort. Sci.* **40:** 531–535.

THOMAS, W., MACK, W. B., and COTTON, R. H. 1943. Nitrogen, phosphorus, and potassium nutrition of tomatoes at different levels of fertilizer application and of irrigation. *Proc. Am. Soc. Hort. Sci.* **42:** 535–544.

THORNE, M. D. 1949. Moisture sorption characteristics of some Hawaiian soils. *Soil Sci. Soc. Am. Proc.* **14:** 38–41.

THORNE, D. W., and PETERSON, H. B. 1949. Irrigated soils. The Blakiston Co., Philadelphia and Toronto.

THUT, H. F., and LOOMIS, W. E. 1944. Relation of light to the growth of plants. *Plant Physiol.* **19:** 117–130.

TORSTENSEN, G., and ERICKSON, S. A. 1936. A new method for determining the porosity of the soil. *Soil Sci.* **42:** 405–417.

TRAUB, H. P., SLATTERY, M. D., and McRARY, W. L. 1946. The effect of moisture stress on nursery-grown gauyule with reference to changes in reserve carbohydrates. *Am. J. Botany* **33:** 699–705.

TRUMBLE, H. C. 1947. Some factors affecting the nutrition of herbage plants. *Australian Inst. Agr. Sci.* **13:** 198.

UHVITS, R. 1946. Effect of osmotic pressure on water absorption and germination of alfalfa seeds. *Am. J. Botany* **33:** 279–285.

URSPRUNG, A. 1916. Dritter beitrag zur demonstration der flussigkeitskohäsion. *Ber. deut. botan. Ges.* **34:** 475–487.

URSPRUNG, A., and BLUM, G. 1921. Zur kenntniss der saugkraft. V. Eine methode zur bestimmung des widerstandes, den der boden der wasserabsorption durch die wurzel entgegensetzt. *Ber. deut. botan. Ges.* **39:** 139–148.

URSPRUNG, A., and BLUM, G. 1924. Eine methods zur messung des wand und turgordruckes der zelle, nebst anwendunges. *Jahrb. wiss. Botan.* **63:** 1–110.

VAN DEN HONERT, T. H. 1948. Water transport in plants as a catenary process. *Faraday Soc. Discussions* No. **3:** 146–153.

VAN DOREN, C. A., and KLINGEBIEL, A. A. 1949. Permeability studies on some Illinois soils. *Soil Sci. Soc. Am. Proc.* **14:** 51–55.

VAN OVERBEEK, J. 1942. Water uptake by excised root systems of the tomato due to non-osmotic forces. *Am. J. Botany* **29:** 677–683.

VAN OVERBEEK, J. 1944. Auxin, water uptake, and osmotic pressure in potato tissue. *Am. J. Botany* **31:** 261–269.

VEIHMEYER, F. J. 1927. Some factors affecting the irrigation requirements of deciduous orchards. *Hilgardia* **2:** 125–288.

VEIHMEYER, F. J. 1929. An improved soil-sampling tube. *Soil Sci.* **27:** 147–152.

VEIHMEYER, F. J. 1939. The validity of the assumption that it is possible to produce different moisture percentages in field soils. *Trans. Am. Geophys. Union* Pt. IV, pp. 543–545.

VEIHMEYER, F. J., EDLEFSEN, N. E., and HENDRICKSON, A. H. 1943. Use of tensiometers in measuring availability of water to plants. *Plant Physiol.* **18:** 66–78.

VEIHMEYER, F. J., and HENDRICKSON, A. H. 1927a. The relation of soil moisture to cultivation and plant growth. *Proc. 1st Intern. Congr. Soil Sci. Washington* **3:** 498–513.

VEIHMEYER, F. J., and HENDRICKSON, A. H. 1927b. Soil-moisture conditions in relation to plant growth. *Plant Physiol.* **2:** 71–82.

VEIHMEYER, F. J., and HENDRICKSON, A. H. 1933. Some plant and soil-moisture relations. *Am. Soil Survey Assoc. Bull.* **15:** 76–80.

VEIHMEYER, F. J., and HENDRICKSON, A. H. 1936. Essentials of irrigation and cultivation of orchards. *Calif. Agr. Expt. Sta. Circ.* **50.**

VEIHMEYER, F. J., and HENDRICKSON, A. H. 1938. Soil moisture as an indication of root distribution in deciduous orchards. *Plant Physiol.* **13:** 169–177.

VEIHMEYER, F. J., and HENDRICKSON, A. H. 1948a. The permanent wilting percentage as a reference for the measurement of soil moisture. *Trans. Union Am. Geophys.* 29: 887–891.

VEIHMEYER, F. J., and HENDRICKSON, A. H. 1948b. Soil density and root penetration. *Soil Sci.* 65: 487–493.

VEIHMEYER, F. J., and HENDRICKSON, A. H. 1949. Methods of measuring field capacity and permanent wilting percentage of soils. *Soil Sci.* 68: 75–94.

VEIHMEYER, F. J., and HOLLAND, A. H. 1949. Irrigation and cultivation of lettuce. *Calif. Agr. Expt. Sta. Bull.* 711.

VOLK, G. M. 1947. Significance of moisture translocation from soil zones of low moisture tension to zones of high moisture tension by plant roots. *J. Am. Soc. Agron.* 39: 93–106.

VOLK, G. M., and BELL, C. E. 1947. Effect of anion balance on the leaching of ions from sandy soils. *Soil Sci. Soc. Am. Proc.* 12: 188–190.

VOLK, N. J. 1934. The fixation of potash in difficultly available form in soils. *Soil Sci.* 37: 267–287.

WADLEIGH, C. H. 1946. The integrated soil moisture stress upon a root system in a large container of saline soil. *Soil Sci.* 61: 225–238.

WADLEIGH, C. H., and AYERS, A. D. 1945. Growth and biochemical composition of bean plants as conditioned by soil moisture tension and salt concentration. *Plant Physiol.* 20: 106–132.

WADLEIGH, C. H., and FIREMAN, M. 1948. Salt distribution under furrow and basin irrigated cotton and its effect on water removal. *Soil Sci. Soc. Am. Proc.* 13: 527–530.

WADLEIGH, C. H., and GAUCH, H. G. 1948. Rate of leaf elongation as affected by the intensity of the total soil moisture stress. *Plant Physiol.* 23: 485–495.

WADLEIGH, C. H., GAUCH, H. G., and DAVIES, V. 1943. The trend of starch reserves in bean plants before and after irrigation of a saline soil. *Proc. Am. Soc. Hort. Sci.* 43: 201–209.

WADLEIGH, C. H., GAUCH, H. G., and MAGISTAD, O. C. 1946. Growth and rubber accumulation in guayule as conditioned by salinity and irrigation regime. *U. S. Dept. Agr. Tech. Bull.* 925: 1–34.

WADLEIGH, C. H., GAUCH, H. G., and STRONG, D. G. 1947. Root penetration and moisture extraction in saline soil by crop plants. *Soil Sci.* 63: 341–349.

WADLEIGH, C. H., and RICHARDS, L. A. 1950. Soil moisture and mineral nutrition of plants. Mineral Nutrition Symposium. Univ. of Wisconsin Press, Madison, Wis.

WADSWORTH, H. A. 1934. Soil moisture and the sugar cane plant. *Hawaiian Planter's Record* 38: 111–119.

WADSWORTH, H. A. 1936. Some aspects of the internal water economy of the sugar cane plant. *Hawaiian Planter's Record* 40: 21–33.

WAKSMAN, S. 1932. Principles of soil microbiology. The Williams and Wilkins Co., Baltimore, Md.

WALLIHAN, E. F. 1937. The effect of water-logging on the rate of nitrification in soils subsequent to drainage. *Soil Sci. Soc. Am. Proc.* 2: 259–262.

WALSH, T., and CULLINAN, S. J. 1945. The effect of wetting and drying on potash-fixation in soils. *Empire J. Exptl. Agr.* 13: 203–212.

WATSON, D. J. 1947. Comparative physiological studies on the growth of field crops. I. Variation in net assimilation rate and leaf area between species and varieties, and within and between years. *Ann. Botany* 11: 41–76.

WATSON, D. J., and BAPTISTE, E. C. D. 1938. A comparative physiological study of sugar-beet and mangold with respect to growth and sugar accumulation. I. Growth analysis of the crops in the field. *Ann. Botany* **2:** 437–480.

WEAVER, J. E. 1926. Root development of field crops. McGraw-Hill Book Co., New York.

WEAVER, J. E., and ALBERTSON, F. W. 1944. Nature and degree of recovery of grassland from the great drought of 1933 to 1940. *Ecol. Monographs* **14:** 393–479.

WEAVER, J. E., and BRUNER, W. E. 1927. Root development of vegetable crops. McGraw-Hill Book Co., New York.

WEST, C., BRIGGS, G. E., and KIDD, F. 1920. Methods and significant relations in a quantitative analysis of plant growth. *New Phytologist* **19:** 200–207.

WHITE, P. R. 1938. "Root-pressure" an unappreciated force in sap movement. *Am. J. Botany* **25:** 223–227.

WIDTSOE, J. A. 1912. The production of dry matter with different quantities of irrigation water. *Utah Agr. Expt. Sta. Bull.* **116.**

WIDTSOE, J. A., and McLAUGHLIN, W. W. 1912. The movement of water in irrigated soils. *Utah Agr. Expt. Sta. Bull.* **115.**

WILLIAMS, R. F. 1937. Drift of net assimilation rate in plants. *Nature* **140:** 1099.

WILLIAMS, R. F. 1946. The physiology of plant growth with special reference to the concept of net assimilation rate. *Ann. Botany* **10:** 41–72.

WILLIS, W. H., and STURGIS, M. B. 1944. Loss of nitrogen from flooded soil as affected by changes in temperature and reaction. *Soil Sci. Soc. Am. Proc.* **9:** 106–113.

WILLOUGHBY, W. M. 1944. Irrigation and the wool industry. *J. Australian Inst. Agr. Sci.* **10:** 102–107.

WILSON, B. D., and RICHARDS, S. J. 1938. Capillary conduction of peat soils at different capillary tensions. *J. Am. Soc. Agron.* **30:** 583–588.

WILSON, C. C., and KRAMER, P. J. 1949. Relation between root respiration and absorption. *Plant Physiol.* **24:** 55–59.

WIMMER, G., SAMMET, K., and LESCH, W. 1944. The influence of the fluctuating moisture content of the soil on the yield and quality of various varieties of sugar beet. *Z. Wirtschaftsgruppe Zuckerind.* **94:** 2–25. [*Chem. Abstracts* **41:** 7033 (1947).]

WOODRUFF, C. M. 1940. Soil moisture and plant growth in relation to pF. *Soil Sci. Soc. Am. Proc.* **5:** 36–41.

WORK, R. A., and LEWIS, M. R. 1936. The relation of soil moisture to pear tree wilting in a heavy clay soil. *J. Am. Soc. Agron.* **28:** 124–134.

CHAPTER 4

SOIL AERATION AND PLANT GROWTH
By M. B. Russell

THE AMOUNT and composition of the gaseous constituents found in soil are generally believed to influence crop growth. Despite this wide acceptance of its importance, the soil atmosphere has received relatively little attention by investigators, even though numerous experiments in liquid and sand cultures have shown that marked changes in plant growth may be effected by artificially altering the composition of the gaseous phase in the root zone.

Differences in crop growth that have been observed following different cultural practices and management schemes are frequently attributed to differences in soil aeration. With few exceptions, however, such interpretation of the results are based solely on preconceived ideas rather than factual information. Ample evidence has been collected to show that such cultural practices do bring about changes in the physical properties of field soils. The nature of such changes has been discussed in an earlier chapter of this monograph. It is commonly accepted that changes in such physical properties as bulk density, pore-size distribution, and aggregate stability result in changes in soil aeration. It is on the basis of such assumptions that the results of most field experiments have been interpreted in terms of aeration and its effect on plant growth.

There is a surprising lack of quantitative data to support the hypothesis that bulk density, pore-size distribution, and other soil physical properties bear a causal relationship to soil aeration. In this chapter, the existing information on such relationships is presented, but no attempt is made to discuss the influence of such cultural practices as tillage, drainage, and manuring on aeration. Instead, the discussion will be limited to the relation of such physical properties as bulk density, porosity, degree of aggregation, and pore-size distribution to soil aeration. From this information and from the previous discussion of the effects of tillage and other cultural practices on these properties, the reader will be able to deduce the probable significance of specific cultural practices as factors affecting aeration.

I. CHARACTERIZATION OF THE SOIL ATMOSPHERE

In attempting to characterize the soil atmosphere and to understand the relationship of this soil constituent to the other soil properties and to the behavior of plants being grown on the soil, it is well to review briefly certain general features of the soil. Under natural conditions, soils are composed of solid, liquid, and gaseous constituents in various proportions. The solid constituents consist of particles ranging widely in size and composition. These are so arranged that a considerable portion of the macroscopic soil volume is available for the liquid and gaseous constituents. The interparticle voids are normally filled with the liquid and gaseous constituents of the soil in reciprocally varying amounts. Many of the properties of the soil that determine its mechanical behavior and suitability for plant growth arise as a consequence of the proportion of the void space that is occupied by the liquid and gaseous constituents.

From the standpoint of the mechanical behavior of soils, this relationship is readily understood when attention is called to the significant differences that exist between the physical properties of the liquid and the gaseous constituents. The soil atmosphere, for example, exhibits all the characteristics of a gas. It has a low density, is highly compressible and, in comparison with liquids such as water, has a low viscosity. The specific heat of soil air is intermediate between that of the solid and liquid soil components. However, on a volume basis, the contribution of the gaseous components to the heat capacity of the soil is negligible. The thermal conductivity of the soil air also is very low. As a consequence of these features of the soil atmosphere, the ability of a soil to support loads without rapid deformation, to retain its shape when molded, to change its temperature when heat is applied, and to transmit heat, water, and air, as well as many other of its physical characteristics, can be roughly predicted in terms of the proportion of the total soil volume that is occupied by the gaseous phase. Therefore, one of the most straightforward ways of characterizing the soil atmosphere is to specify the fraction of the total soil volume that is occupied by gaseous constituents. This can be done by calculation from data on the bulk density and moisture content of the soil on the assumption that the densities of the gaseous constituents are negligibly small.

The volume of the gaseous constituents can be determined directly on a sample of soil by the use of an air-pycnometer (Page, 1947 and Russell, 1949). This device applies the principle of Boyle's law to a sample of soil in a closed system and permits the direct determination of the volume of the gaseous constituents by measurement of pressure-volume relationships at constant temperature.

Knowledge of the volume fraction occupied by the gaseous constituents is sufficient information to predict certain mechanical properties of soil. Such information is not sufficient, however, to understand the influence of aeration on chemical properties of soil and on plant growth, since each of these groups of phenomena are also strongly influenced by the composition of the soil atmosphere. Numerous studies have established that the composition of the soil atmosphere, while quite variable, is in general similar to that of atmospheric air, but differs from it in two or three important respects (Boussingault and Lewy, 1853; Boynton and Reutner, 1938, 1939; Compton and Boynton, 1944; Howard, 1918; Howard and Howard, 1915; Letts and Blake, 1900; Russell and Appleyard, 1915). The carbon dioxide content of the soil atmosphere is characteristically from 10 to 1,000 times that of atmospheric air. The oxygen content is usually slightly lower, and the water vapor content is significantly higher. With some notable exceptions, the sum of carbon dioxide and oxygen content of the soil atmosphere is very near that of atmospheric air.

Russell and Appleyard (1915) summarized their extensive investigation of the soil atmosphere as follows:

1. The free air in the pores of the soil at a depth of six inches is very similar in composition to the atmospheric air but differs in two respects: (a) It contains more CO_2 and correspondingly less oxygen, the average in 100 volumes being 0.25 volume CO_2 and 20.6 of oxygen against 0.03 volume CO_2 and 20.96 oxygen in atmospheric air. (b) It shows greater fluctuations in composition. Usually the sum of CO_2 and oxygen is only slightly less than in atmospheric air, but in periods when nitrates rapidly increase, there is a perceptible falling off of oxygen, and a still greater one in waterlogged soils.

2. Besides this free air there is another atmosphere dissolved in the water and colloids of the soil. This consists mainly of CO_2 and nitrogen and has practically no oxygen.

3. The fluctuations in composition of the free soil air are mainly due to fluctuations in the rate of biochemical change in the soil, the curves being similar to those showing the amount of nitrate and bacterial counts as far as they were taken . . .

4. Grass land usually contains more CO_2 and less oxygen than arable land but we cannot attribute the difference to the crop owing to the large differences in soil composition and conditions . . .

5. Such weather conditions as barometric pressure, wind velocity, variations in temperature from the mean, small rainfall, etc., seem to have but little effect on the soil atmosphere.

The composition of the soil air exhibits marked seasonal variations, the intensity of which is affected by the texture of the soil and the posi-

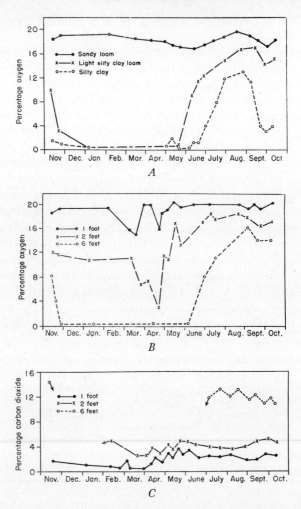

FIGURE 38.—Variations in oxygen and carbon dioxide in orchard soils. A, Oxygen percentage at 5-foot depth as affected by texture. B, Oxygen percentage at three depths in a light silty clay loam. C, Carbon dioxide percentages at three depths in a silty loam. (Boynton and Reuther, 1939.)

tion of the water table. The seasonal changes in oxygen and carbon dioxide percentages in orchard soils are shown in Figure 38, adapted from the work of Boynton and Reuther (1939). These curves indicate that the oxygen content in heavy subsoils is normally low in early spring and increases as the season advances. The carbon dioxide percentage fluctuates over narrower limits and normally reaches a maximum in summer when the soil temperature and moisture conditions are favorable for biological activity. The minimum oxygen content and the maximum carbon dioxide percentage do not occur simultaneously.

Marked reductions in oxygen content of the soil air have been shown to occur following rains and irrigation (Furr and Aldrich, 1943). The addition of manure or plant materials to the soil stimulates the production of carbon dioxide and results in an increase in the concentration of this compound in the soil air (Lundegardh, 1927). Except insofar as they affect biological activity in the soil, tillage practices have not shown any clearly defined effect on the composition of the soil air.

The underlying principle that governs the diurnal, seasonal, and spatial variations in the composition of the soil air as well as the influence of changes in physical properties on such variations is that the composition of the soil air is the resultant of two sets of processes that function simultaneously. The first of these include the chemical and biological reactions that occur in soils and result in the production of carbon dioxide and the consumption of oxygen. The second set of processes of significance are those physical processes that affect the interchange of gaseous constituents between the soil voids and the atmosphere. These latter processes tend to minimize the differences between the composition of the soil air and the atmosphere, whereas the former tend to accentuate those differences.

Two distinct types of mechanisms are involved in the interchange of gases between the soil and the atmosphere. The first of these involves the mass flow of gaseous constituents into and out of the soil as a consequence of gradients in the total pressure between the soil air and the atmosphere. The second mechanism of importance is that of diffusion, in which individual gaseous constituents move in response to gradients in the partial pressure of that particular constituent.

Interchange of gases between the soil voids and the atmosphere will occur by the process of mass flow whenever a difference in total pressure exists between the soil air and the atmosphere. Pressure differences of this type may arise by several causes (Keen, 1931 and Romell, 1935). Since the specific volume of a gas is strongly temperature dependent, the existence of temperature gradients between the air and the soil atmosphere will create density and pressure gradients that will tend to cause flow. In considering the significance of pressure changes that arise owing to differences in temperature, it should be remembered that the variation is proportional to the absolute temperature and that the depth to which diurnal fluctuations in temperature are significant is not great. Hence, the volume of soil that would be influenced by diurnal gaseous interchange arising from temperature gradients is relatively small.

Changes in barometric pressure also tend to cause a mass flow of gaseous constituents through the soil. The insignificant influence of changes in barometric pressure can be more clearly understood by remembering that it is the variation in the total barometric pressure that is responsible for the resultant pressure gradient. The kinetic effects of wind blowing over the soil surface may, under certain circumstances, result in pressure gradients and gas transport. The penetration of zones of saturation through the soil profile following rains or irrigation is effective in bringing about the displacement of the soil atmosphere and its renewal by atmospheric air.

Careful examination of the pressure gradients that can be established by temperatures and barometric pressure changes reveal that the volume of gaseous transport arising from such causes is negligibly small (Romell, 1935). The same conclusion is reached as to the effect of wind blowing over the surface of the ground and of the flushing action associated with penetration of zones of saturation into the soil. Even in regions where frequent rainfall occurs, the total volume of gaseous interchange that can be attributed to the flushing action of water is much too small to account for the observed composition of the soil air. Thus we are led to the conclusion that the interchange of gases between the soil and the atmosphere as the result of mass flow in response to gradient of the total pressure is of minor significance.

The physical process most important in bringing about interchange of gases between the soil and the atmosphere is that of diffusion. In this process, the individual gases move in response to their own partial pressure gradients. In most soils this process is a continuously operating one for both carbon dioxide and oxygen, since biological activity in the soil tends to maintain a difference in partial pressure of these two gases between the soil atmosphere and the air. In field soils, particularly during the growing season, considerable quantities of oxygen are consumed and appreciable amounts of carbon dioxide are produced by biological processes. As a result, the partial pressure of oxygen in the soil is reduced below that of the atmosphere and the partial pressure of the carbon dioxide is increased above its normal atmospheric value. Since these partial pressure differences tend to be maintained or even accentuated by biological processes, the stage is set for a continuous interchange of oxygen and carbon dioxide between the soil and the atmosphere by the process of diffusion.

A limited number of studies (Buckingham, 1904; Penman, 1940; and Taylor, 1949a) have established that the rate of diffusion is a function of the volume of air-filled voids. The more recent investigations have shown that the functional relationship is linear over a rather wide range of diffusion rates and porosities (Penman, 1940 and Taylor, 1949a). The validity of this statement undoubtedly is limited to those instances where the volume of air-filled voids is a valid measure of the volume of such voids accessible for diffusion. In some instances it may be in error because of the existence of isolated soil pores cut off from direct connection to the atmosphere by water-filled necks.

It is of interest to note that the rate of diffusion is a linear function of the available pore space, whereas air permeability, that is, the rate of mass flow under unit pressure gradient, is proportional to a higher power of the porosity (Dalla Valle, 1948). This indicates that changes in soil porosity result in a relatively smaller change in rate of diffusion than in rate of mass flow. This further emphasizes the importance of diffusion as a process responsible for gaseous interchange in field soils. Recent investigations (Taylor, 1949a) have shown conclusively that oxygen diffusion is strongly influenced by degree of compaction and moisture content of soil samples and that the effects of these variations in compaction and moisture content can be summarized in terms of their influence on the total air-filled pore space of the sample.

The use of the rate of carbon dioxide evolution as a means of characterizing soil aeration has been proposed (Humfield, 1930; Lundegardh, 1927; and Marsh, 1928). Measurements made in the laboratory are of little value in evaluating field conditions because of the marked effects of temperature, structure, and plant cover on the rate of carbon dioxide evolution. Field measurements are also difficult to interpret because of solubility effects and the indefinite nature of the soil volume that is being measured. Smith and Brown (1931, 1932, 1933) concluded that such measurements did not give a valid picture of carbon dioxide diffusion through the soil and were of little value in determining the rate of soil respiration. Carbon dioxide production is likewise a poor measure of the oxygen status of the soil because of the existence of anaerobic respiration.

Since the composition of the soil atmosphere represents a dynamic equilibrium between the processes of respiration in the soil and diffusion between the soil and the atmosphere, it is not surprising to find rather wide diurnal and seasonal fluctuations of the type shown in Figure 38 in the percentage of carbon dioxide and oxygen in the soil atmosphere. Such fluctuations have been described by several investigators who have shown that conditions that favor high biological activity and/or restricted gaseous interchange lead to high concentrations of carbon dioxide and reduced concentrations of oxygen in the soil atmosphere. Conversely, conditions that reduce the intensity of biological activity in the soil and/or favor the rapid exchange of soil gases with the atmosphere tend to result in oxygen and carbon dioxide percentages in the soil air that approach those of the atmosphere. In situations where gas interchange is prevented, as in waterlogged soils or where sufficient anaerobic biological activity occurs, the accumulation of such products as methane, carbon monoxide, and hydrogen sulfide may result.

As will be pointed out in a later section of this chapter, the use of oxygen and carbon dioxide concentrations as a means of characterizing soil aeration for plant growth has not been entirely satisfactory. This may arise from the fact that the rates at which oxygen can be supplied to and carbon dioxide removed from the root zone are more important than the instantaneous concentrations of the type normally measured in characterizing the composition of the soil atmosphere.

Hutchins (1926) measured the rate at which oxygen was supplied to a porous absorber buried in the soil and found that a correlation existed between the values obtained and seed germination. Preliminary work (Raney, 1949) has indicated that measurements of oxygen diffusion rates under field conditions are more useful in predicting plant response than are measurements of the partial pressure of oxygen in the soil atmosphere. It is hoped that further work along this line will lead to the development of a more quantitatively expressed theory of the influence of aeration on plant growth.

Other methods of characterizing soil aeration than those already mentioned have been proposed. Of these, the measurement of oxidation-reduction potentials, both *in situ* and on soil samples have received the most attention (Batjer and Oskamp, 1934; Gillespie, 1920; Kohnke and Bradfield, 1935; Pearsall and Mortimer, 1939; Starkey and Wight, 1945; Sturgis, 1936). To date, however, such measurements have not given very close or consistent relationships to plant response. This may partly be explained on the very complex and indefinite nature of the oxidation-reduction reactions that occur in soils and the dependence of these results on variables that are not of direct consequence to plant growth (Peech and Batjer, 1935). Since the oxidation-reduction potential measures only the intensity of such reactions, the interpretation is more significant if supporting information on the capacity factor of the reaction also is available. Such information can be obtained from potentiometric titrations of the soil with an oxidizing agent such as potassium permanganate (Reed, 1946). It is possible that further work along these lines may yield a useful means of characterizing the crop-producing potentialities for soils in which the nature of the oxidation-reduction system can be more definitely identified.

It is generally agreed that the evaluation of the conditions at the interface between the root and the soil system offers the greatest possibility of establishing the influence of soil aeration on plant growth. For this reason, measurement on a system in which the plant and soil are both constituent parts seem to offer great possibilities. The existence of difference in electrical potential between living plants and their growth medium is well established (Arnon, 1937; Osterhout, 1936; Tendeloo, Vervelde and Voorspuij, 1944). Those potentials have been shown to respond to changes in the aeration status of the medium and it is reasonable to expect that such bio-electric potentials would be a measure of the oxidation-reduction reactions occurring at the plant root-soil interface. A careful study of the utility of this approach as a means of characterizing soil aeration has shown, however, that such bio-electric potentials are not solely dependent upon aeration, but are strongly influenced by all other environmental factors that influence cell respiration (Taylor, 1949b). Their use as a criterion of soil aeration, therefore, seems to be limited to those situations in which all other environmental factors are either constant or measurable to the extent that their influence on the observed potential can be evaluated. The realization of such a condition in a complex medium such as soil is not now in sight.

Other indirect methods of characterizing the aeration status of soil have been proposed, based upon the relationships that exist between aeration conditions and the chemical properties of the soil. The presence of an appreciable amount of ferrous iron has been used as an index of inadequate aeration (Lawton, 1945 and Lemon, 1948). The content of this soil constituent is also conditioned, to a certain extent at least, by other factors; therefore its usefulness as a diagnostic tool depends upon the establishment of a high degree of correlation between the presence of ferrous iron and crop growth on the particular soil that is being studied. Since qualitative tests for the presence of ferrous iron can be quickly made, this technique has some merit as a qualitative index of aeration conditions as they apply to plant growth. The possibility of using similar tests involving other ions should not be overlooked, although the probability of finding such a test that will give quantitative information on the influence of aeration on plant growth in such a complicated system as soil seems to be remote.

II. SOIL PROCESSES AND PROPERTIES AFFECTED BY AERATION

Variations in the composition of the soil atmosphere normally bring about characteristic changes in the chemical and biological reactions occurring in the soil. In the absence of adequate amounts of oxygen, anaerobic reactions predominate, with the formation of large amounts of reduced soil constituents.   Some of the changes in state of oxidation of certain soil constituents are given by Bradfield, Batjer, and Oskamp (1934) as follows:

	Normal form in well-oxidized soils	Reduced form in waterlogged soils
Element:		
Carbon	CO_2	CH_4
Carbon	—	Complex aldehydes, etc.
Nitrogen	NO_3^-	N_2 and NH_3
Sulfur	SO_4^{--}	H_2S
Iron	Fe^{+++} (ferric)	Fe^{++} (ferrous)
Manganese	Mn^{+++} (manganic)	Mn^{++} (manganous)

The presence of anaerobic conditions frequently results in the development of characteristic coloration in the soil.   When the anaerobic processes are periodically replaced by aerobic reactions, certain soil constituents such as iron and manganese may accumulate in the form of concretions.

Among the soil reactions that are most strongly influenced by changes in aeration conditions are those involving manganese.   Although the complete chemistry of the manganese reactions in soils is not established, it is evident that this element can occur in several different stages of oxidation.   Since both chemical and biological oxidation and reduction reactions are involved in this cycle, it is apparent that the proportion of the various types of manganese ions in soil will be a highly dynamic function and will be influenced by aeration, temperature, the presence of readily oxidizable organic material, pH, and the total manganese content of the soil (Dion and Mann, 1946; Hopkins, Pagan and Silva, 1944; Leeper, 1935, 1947; Leeper and Swaby, 1940; McCool, 1934; Robinson, 1930; Samuel and Piper, 1928).

The absence of sufficient amounts of manganese in soluble form results in manganese deficiency in crops grown on those soils.   This problem occurs most frequently in soils low in total manganese content and high in pH.   Manganese deficiency in such soils may often be corrected by lowering the pH or by subjecting the soil to a period of anaerobic condition by waterlogging and/or the addition of large amounts of readily decomposable organic matter.   Manganese toxicity also may occur in soils having unusually high concentrations of soluble manganese.   This condition can frequently be corrected by increasing the pH or by bringing about better oxidation conditions in the soil by drainage and/or tillage operations.   Present information seems to give a fairly satisfactory qualitative picture of the relationships between manganese and soil aeration.   It is hoped that future work will elucidate the quantitative nature of this relationship so that levels of aeration tolerance for plant growth may be established.

The reactions involving iron in the soil also are strongly influenced by aeration conditions (Halverson, 1931; Lemon, 1948; Olsen, 1935; Robinson, 1930). Iron, unlike manganese, exhibits only two valance forms. It is less stable in the reduced condition but, like manganese, the ferrous compounds are more stable under acid than alkaline conditions. In general, iron and manganese are much alike in their behavior under varying conditions in the soil. Iron in the reduced form is highly unstable, water soluble, and subject to the influence of organic matter, soil reaction, biological oxidation-reduction processes, temperature, and total iron content. The oxidation-reduction reactions of iron and manganese are strongly interdependent as indicated by the influence of high contents of manganese on the occurrence of iron deficiencies (Hopkins, Pagan and Silva, 1944; Johnson, 1917; Pearse, 1944; Somers and Shive, 1942). Iron deficiency occurs most commonly in calcareous soils. The condition can usually be alleviated by lowering the pH of the soil and/or subjecting it to a period of anaerobic biological activity (Brewer and Carr, 1927; Kliman, 1937; Willis, 1932). In practice, however, it is usually more economical to supply the plant with iron directly in the form of sprays rather than to attempt to correct the soil condition. Although the amount of iron in soluble form in the soil may be great enough to result in toxicity, the presence of such large amounts of iron probably is of significance because of the reaction between this constituent and the phosphate ion in the soil. The presence of high concentrations of ferrous iron will favor the formation of iron phosphate compounds, which are so slightly soluble that the phosphorus is essentially unavailable to plants.

In addition to the importance of the composition of soil atmosphere on such oxidation-reduction reactions as those involved in iron and manganese, the soil atmosphere also influences other chemical reactions in the soil. The importance of carbon dioxide in the chemistry of soil-mineral weathering is well known (Lyon and Buckman, 1947; Robinson, 1932). The release of such acid-forming ions as nitrate and sulfate by aerobic bacteriological activity and the creation of organic acids by such reactions also may play an important role in the weathering of primary minerals in soil. The agronomic significance of the carbon dioxide effect on the solubility of phosphate minerals has been studied by McGeorge and Breazeale (1931) and Buehrer (1932) who found that, in general, carbon dioxide increased the solubility of phosphorus. They attributed this to the presence of a carbonate-phosphate complex in the soil which was probably a carbonate-apatite.

The partial pressure of carbon dioxide strongly influences the calcium relationships in the soil (Johnston and Williamson, 1916; Simmons, 1938). The distribution of calcium between the hydroxide, the carbonate, and the bicarbonate can be expressed as a function of the partial pressure of carbon dioxide. The direct significance of this reaction to the problem of liming, and indirectly to the whole field of soil fertility, has been recently emphasized by Bradfield (1941).

Perhaps the greatest effects of aeration conditions on soil processes arise through the relation of such conditions to the microbiological activities of the soil (Lyon and Buckman, 1947; Robinson, 1932; Waksman, 1932). The decomposition of organic materials and the mineralization of the elements arising therefrom are primarily microbiological processes. Nitrogen fixation by symbiotic and nonsymbiotic organisms also is of great importance in soil and is strongly influenced by soil aeration.

In the presence of ample amounts of oxygen a large number of soil micro-organisms participate in the decomposition of organic matter. In this process the complex organic compounds of the original tissue are reduced to progressively simpler forms, largely by oxidative processes. The final products of such aerobic decomposition include carbon dioxide, water, nitrates, sulfates, phosphates, and compounds of calcium, magnesium, potassium, iron, and so on. In the absence of sufficient oxygen, the products of decay are quite different. Thus such compounds as methane, hydrogen sulfide, ammonia, aldehydes, and reduced forms of iron will be found.

This condition arises from the fact that although certain of the decomposition processes can be performed by a wide variety of micro-organisms, some of which can function in anaerobic media, other transformations are performed by specific groups of aerobic organisms. The absence of oxygen prevents such organisms from functioning and thereby blocks further decomposition along the path followed in aerated media. *Bact. nitrosomonas* and *B. nitrobacter*, the organisms responsible for the oxidation of ammonia to nitrites and/or nitrates, are examples of the type just mentioned. The decomposition processes leading to the production of ammonia can be performed by a large number of organisms, some of which function under anaerobic conditions. If oxygen is present, the ammonia is oxidized to nitrate at a rate limited by the rate of ammonia production. Thus, under these conditions, ammonia does not accumulate in the system as it does when the nitrification process is stopped through lack of oxygen. In the absence of free oxygen the oxidation to nitrates is prevented and ammonia accumulates.

A similar situation applies to the sulfur transformations that occur during decomposition. Aerobic organisms perform the oxidation to sulfate of the sulfur released in the decomposition process. In the absence of oxygen this transformation is stopped and reduced forms of sulfur such as hydrogen sulfide are formed.

The fixation of atmospheric nitrogen is performed by soil organisms that are usually classified as symbiotic and nonsymbiotic. The amount of nitrogen fixed symbiotically by the rhizobia is strongly conditioned by soil aeration. The same is true of the nonsymbiotic nitrogen fixing organisms, such as Azotobacter. The other important members of the non-symbiotic group, which belong to the genus Clostridium, are either anaerobic or facultative in nature and therefore not inhibited by lack of free oxygen.

III. AERATION AND PLANT GROWTH

The importance of aeration as a factor affecting plant growth has been recognized since the respiration process of plants was established. It was shown at an early date that all plant organs possessed this function in common; hence, the importance of aeration of the rooting medium was established. Direct evidence of the necessity of oxygen for the proper functioning of roots was obtained by a number of early investigators who showed that the respirational behavior of roots, tubers, and other underground parts was significantly curtailed or stopped by the absence of oxygen from the medium. Differential responses to aeration were found among species, the differences observed being greatest when aquatic species were contrasted with plants indigenous to well-drained sites.

A comprehensive review of the extensive literature on the early work in this field was prepared in 1921 by Clements (1921). From the material contained in that review, it may be concluded that oxygen is of importance for root growth and absorption of water and salts. Although rather crude techniques were used in most of the early investigations, the data obtained were sufficient to establish the qualitative importance of aeration for plant growth.

Since the majority of the studies reported by Clements as well as those conducted since 1921 have been conducted in liquid cultures, their application to the problem of aeration in soils must be made with caution in view of the complex interactions between aeration conditions and the chemical composition of the soil as discussed in the preceding section of this chapter. The influence of aeration on plant growth has been most commonly studied in terms of the dry-matter production of the plant. Recently, however, more attention has been given to the influence of aeration on specific physiological processes and anatomical responses. Several investigations of the latter type will be discussed in a later section of this chapter.

Many investigators (Allison, 1922; Andrews, 1921; Arrington and Shive, 1936; Gilbert and Shive, 1942, 1945; Hall, Brenchley and Underwood, 1914; Knight, 1924; Rich and Hunter, 1925; Shive, 1941; Steward and Street, 1947) have shown that the aeration of nutrient cultures results in highly significant increases in plant growth of a rather large number of species. In a comparison of various methods of supplying oxygen to nutrient solutions (Allison and Shrive, 1923b) it was found that marked differences existed among the methods, and that the increase in dry weight of the plants grown in such media was in general agreement with the abilities of the technique to supply oxygen to the roots. Measurements of the dissolved oxygen content of unaerated cultures indicate that plants deplete the oxygen content to a very low level in the medium (Allison and Shrive, 1923a). Because of the relatively low solubility of oxygen in water, intermittent-aerating techniques or a technique that does not bring about an intimate contact between the aerating gas and the liquid medium usually result in failure to maintain a sufficiently high concentration of dissolved oxygen in cultures containing significant quantities of actively growing roots.

Results of a number of experiments on the effect of relatively low oxygen concentrations on the growth of roots were summarized by Cannon (1925). A large number of plant species were studied in these investigations. Most of the conclusions drawn were based on observations of rates of root growth as measured over relatively short periods of time in sand or soil cultures to which various static gas treatments had been applied. As pointed out by Compton (1947) and Seeley (1948), there are certain objections to such a technique, since experience has shown that the composition of the gases in such sealed containers may change rapidly in response to root respiration with the result that the effective gas composition may differ significantly from that initially present. The same authors also point out that no provision was made for standardizing the environmental conditions affecting top growth, which are known to have an important bearing on root response. In spite of these criticisms, the work of Cannon established certain relationships that probably are qualitatively correct, although they may be quantitatively questionable in the light of the experimental techniques employed.

One of the major conclusions Cannon made was that root growth at various levels of oxygen was strongly influenced by temperature.

When the oxygen concentration was of the order of 3 percent, root growth was inhibited at all temperatures between 18° and 30° C. Normal growth occurred with 10 percent oxygen at 18°, but at 30° C. the rate was reduced, indicating that at the higher temperature, 10 percent oxygen was deficient. Thus, within the temperature limits for root growth, the greater the temperature of the soil, the higher must be the concentration of oxygen in the soil atmosphere for normal root growth. Cannon attributed this relationship to the decreasing solubility of oxygen in the soil solution with increasing temperature. Although this may be a factor, the effect of increasing temperature on the respirational demands of the roots for oxygen certainly plays an important part.

Cannon also concluded that various species differ in their response to a soil atmosphere of low oxygen content, but that in the absence of oxygen, root growth ceased in all species. Many species maintained a slow growth rate at as low as 0.5 percent oxygen for a limited period of time, and all species appeared to be able to maintain root growth in an atmosphere containing 2 percent oxygen, provided the carbon dioxide did not exceed 30 to 50 percent. Another significant observation from Cannon's work was that root growth could be maintained at a low oxygen level, providing a constant supply could be maintained. In this way it was demonstrated that the rate of supply as well as the partial pressure of oxygen was important.

The existence of critical oxygen concentrations for different phases of root activity was further substantiated by the work of Boynton *et al.* (Boynton, 1940; Boynton and Compton, 1943; Boynton and Reutner, 1939). These investigators recognized four levels of root activity. The lowest, or subsistence level, for apple tree roots larger than 1 millimeter in diameter corresponded to an oxygen concentration of less than 3 percent for trees in active growth. At oxygen concentration of less than 1 percent the roots apparently lost weight. Oxygen contents between 5 and 10 percent were found necessary for growth of existing root tips, whereas an oxygen level of greater than 12 percent was required for root initiation. Progressive decreases in absorption and accumulation, as expressed in terms of ash content, were found for oxygen contents below 15 percent. Since the dry weight of the root tissue was less at oxygen concentrations below 10 percent, it was probable that absorption and accumulation were inhibited at such low values.

In root studies on apple seedlings grown in sand cultures through which various gas mixtures of known oxygen concentration were supplied, it was found that at 1 percent oxygen, root growth, as judged by dry weight, was only 35 percent of that made with normal air (De-Villiers, 1938). With 5 percent oxygen, the growth was 50 percent as great as with air. Growth, as measured by green weight, number of leaves, leaf area, root growth, and percentage of ash, decreased with decreasing oxygen in the soil atmosphere. Below 15 percent oxygen, the decrease in root growth and the decrease in total ash was very nearly proportional to the oxygen content of the soil.

Girton (1927) reported significantly greater root elongation of orange seedlings in aerated than in nonaerated liquid cultures. In sand cultures he found that no growth was made in 17 days when the aerating gas contained 1.5 percent oxygen. With 4.6 to 6.1 percent oxygen the growth rate was one-half normal. No root growth was observed in cultures aerated for 8 days with 37 percent carbon dioxide or for 17 days with 55 percent carbon dioxide.

The limited value of measurements of oxygen and carbon dioxide concentrations for predicting the response of plants to differences in aeration conditions is illustrated by the work of Boicourt and Allen (1941). These investigators studied the effect of artificially aerating rose-garden soils by placing 4-inch tiles beneath the rose beds and forcing air through the tile for a 1 hour period each day. The soil moisture was maintained at a high level. The soil atmosphere was sampled at a depth of 8 inches and analyzed for oxygen and carbon dioxide. The oxygen content of the unaerated plot ranged from 18.8 to 19.3 percent, with 1.5 to 1.9 percent carbon dioxide; whereas the aerated soils contained 20.2 to 20.3 percent oxygen and 0.3 to 0.6 percent carbon dioxide. Despite these relatively minor differences in the composition of the soil atmosphere for the two plots, the total linear growth of roses on the aerated soil was about double that on the nonaerated soils.

In view of the work of Seeley (1948), who found that normal growth of roses was obtained in liquid cultures for all oxygen levels above 10 percent, it would appear that the results of Boicourt and Allen can best be explained on the basis that the composition of the soil atmosphere, as they measured it, was probably a very poor estimate of the aeration conditions at the root-soil interface. This interpretation is supported by the work of other investigators who have shown that marked growth responses may occur in soils in which the measured oxygen concentration is far above the critical level as established in sand and liquid cultures. This is not surprising in view of the existing techniques by which samples of the soil air are obtained for analysis. The gas analyzed is undoubtedly withdrawn from the large voids in the soil, which quite likely have a higher concentration of oxygen and a lower concentration of carbon dioxide than occurs at the root-soil interface.

As emphasized by the work of Cannon on soil temperatures, the relationship between aeration and plant growth response may be strongly conditioned by other environmental factors. The possibilities of such interactions is illustrated by experiments reported by Arnon (1937). With barley plants grown at pH 6, lack of aeration limited the growth of those plants receiving ammonium nitrogen but had little effect on similar plants that were fertilized with nitrates. The effect on ammonium plants was greatest during those periods when growth was most rapid. It was also observed that the addition of manganese to the nutrient solution greatly increased the growth of nonaerated ammonium plants. Such additions were without effect on aerated nitrate plants, improved the growth of nonaerated nitrate plants grown in the fall, and did not improve growth of nonaerated nitrate plants grown in the spring. Additions of copper had little effect on nitrate plants, regardless of aeration conditions, but marked responses were obtained when copper was added to aerated ammonium plants. These results were explained on the basis that the nitrate ion served as a source of oxygen as well as nitrogen. These results are not in accord with those of Bain and Chapman (1940), who found that the addition of nitrate fertilizer to waterlogged soils was harmful to avocados. They attributed their results partly to osmotic effects, partly to the possible production of toxic amounts of nitrate, and partly to the stimulating effect of the fertilizers on root-attacking organisms. The role of nitrates as an oxygen supply for root respiration has also been demonstrated by Gilbert and Shive (1945).

The mutual effects of carbon dioxide and oxygen concentrations on root growth of cotton have been studied by Leonard and Pinckard (1946). On the basis of daily measurements of root elongation, it was concluded that the growth of cotton roots in liquid cultures in which the carbon dioxide content was maintained constantly at 10 percent was not affected by variations in oxygen percentage between 10 and 21 percent. Oxygen concentration less than 5 percent reduced appreciably the rate of growth, as did concentrations of 90 and 100 percent oxygen. When oxygen was maintained at 21 percent and carbon dioxide was varied from 0 to 100 percent, cotton root elongation over a period of 2 weeks was not affected at carbon dioxide concentrations of 15 percent or less. The rate of growth was reduced approximately one-half at 30 percent carbon dioxide, and no growth took place at 60 percent or above. In these experiments precautions were taken to prevent pH changes in the nutrient solution arising from the high concentration of carbon dioxide.

In a similar study (Erickson, 1946) of the effect of oxygen and carbon dioxide contents on the growth of tomatoes in aerated and un-

aerated 8-liter three-plant cultures, it was found that in aerated cultures, dissolved oxygen remained practically constant at 1 m.e./l.,
while carbon dioxide decreased to a small fraction of a milliequivalent.
In nonaerated cultures exposed to normal diffusion of the air, dissolved
oxygen decreased progressively to about 0.1 m.e./l. in 5 weeks, while
carbon dioxide increased from 0 to 1 milliequivalent in 3 weeks, then to
6 milliequivalents 2 weeks later. These differences in oxygen and
carbon dioxide concentrations were reflected in top and root weights
of the plants. At 25° C. and with five oxygen concentrations ranging
from 0.05 to 1 m.e./l., the length of roots increased progressively, with
significant differences as the concentrations increased. The dry
weight of tops and roots showed the same progressive increases.

By the use of an iron tannate root-staining technique, root growth
for 24-hour periods was followed at oxygen concentrations of 1, 1.8,
2.7, 3.5 and 4.6 m.e./l. Only at the highest value was there any
significant reduction in root growth. In another trial in which oxygen
concentration was held constant at 1 m.e./l., the growth of roots was
not limited, except at the highest carbon dioxide concentration. This
retardation was highly significant, but the value was thought to be
confused by a slight increase in hydrogen ion concentration. At a
concentration of 9.1 percent carbon dioxide, growth of tomato roots was
slightly reduced from that of the lower carbon dioxide treatments. At
the highest concentration, corresponding to 28.8 percent carbon dioxide,
there was a significant reduction in growth. It is of interest that this
corresponds closely to the value of 30 percent found by Leonard and
Pinckard (1946) for cotton roots.

Erickson (1946) emphasized that if aeration is used to supplement
the oxygen content of the solution, no response will be obtained if the
solution is already well supplied with this gas. He is of the opinion
that the failure on the part of some investigators to demonstrate the
need for aerating liquid cultures merely indicates that the oxygen content of these cultures was not a limiting factor of growth.

In a study of growth response of corn to various degrees of aeration
in soil cultures, Reed (1946) found that the growth in unaerated sealed
cultures was greatly reduced below that of cultures that received relatively slow rates of air flow. Daily measurements of oxygen and carbon dioxide concentrations of the gas contained in the unaerated cultures showed that the oxygen content ranged from 0 to 12 percent, and
the carbon dioxide content from 12 to 29 percent. When aerated at
the rate of one-third the volume of the available pore space per day, the
range of oxygen concentration was from 1 to 15 percent, and carbon
dioxide from 6 to 31 percent. The growth of corn in cultures aerated

at this low rate was approximately 90 percent that of similar cultures aerated at a rate 200 times as great.

From the experiments reported above and others of similar nature (Childers and White, 1942; Childs, 1940; Clark and Shive, 1932; Durell, 1941) it can be concluded that while there is a significant interaction between the influence of oxygen and carbon dioxide concentration at the extreme limits of two constituents, the interaction can be largely neglected for the range of concentrations that are normally encountered in field soil.

In addition to its effect on the over-all growth of plants, aeration may also affect the composition of the roots and tops. Loehwing (1934) found that for sunflowers and soybeans the dry weight and total amount of sugars, starch, nitrogen, ash, calcium, potassium, magnesium, and phosphorus were greater in the aerated cultures than in those that were not aerated. When expressed in terms of percentage of the dry weight, however, these constituents in general were higher in the unaerated cultures in both the tops and roots, although some slight variations were observed when the analyses were made at different stages of growth. Sap pressed from the roots and tops was more alkaline when the plants were grown in well-aerated media. When the plants were grown in well-aerated media the sap from plant tops had a higher buffer capacity, whereas that from the roots was lower.

Studies on the influence of nitrogen carriers and oxygen levels on the organic acid content of oats showed that oxygen levels ranging from 0 to 16 parts per million in nutrient cultures resulted in significant variations in the organic-acid content (Pepkowitz and Shive, 1944). The total organic-acid content was higher in plants grown at low oxygen levels than in well-aerated or nitrate-containing cultures. Oxalic acid production was largely dependent upon the presence of nitrate and was inversely related to oxygen content of the culture solution. Malic acid was also higher in plants receiving nitrate nitrogen but was not significantly affected by the oxygen level. Unidentified acids constituted the most important fraction, and their variations determined the results observed.

These results differ from those of Ulrich (1942), who found that the organic-acid content of excised barley roots decreased approximately 27 percent when they were subjected to a zero oxygen treatment for 8 hours. Sugar losses amounted to 33 percent during this same period, and the combined ammonia and amide contents were slightly reduced. In part the losses were attributed to injury of the roots by the anaerobic conditions. At oxygen levels of 3.2 percent and higher, the organic-acid content was independent of the oxygen treatment.   Ulrich found that the total nonvolatile organic-acid content of excised barley roots containing an ample supply of available sugar remained constant unless a change in the ion balance took place within the roots.   When roots absorbed an excess of anions over cations, organic acid disappeared.   Conversely, when cations were absorbed in excess of anions, organic acids were formed.   Failure of the total organic-acid content to be affected by temperature and oxygen content was attributed to the lack of influence of those factors upon ionic balance in the root cells.   No evidence was present that the acids arose primarily from the oxidative deamination of amino acids.   Indirect evidence indicated that they were derived from carbohydrates.

In a study of the causes for unusual shedding of very young cotton-fruit buds (Albert and Armstrong, 1931), it was found that this condition was associated with periods of high rainfall.   In field experiments in which the moisture content of the soil was maintained high by excessive irrigation, it was found that the carbon dioxide content of the soil air rose as high as 7.8 percent, that the oxygen content fell to 3.6 percent, and that these effects were associated with an increased shedding of young cotton squares.

Germination of seeds of many plant species is strongly affected by the concentrations of oxygen and carbon dioxide in the medium (Meyer and Anderson, 1939; Miller, 1938).   It is a commonly expressed view that faulty aeration conditions are the cause of poor germination and spotty stands for many field crops when they are sown in soils having poor structure and/or excessive water content.   Studies of factors responsible for seeding failure of peas revealed that in crusted soil having high moisture content, germination was greatly reduced and was highly correlated with low oxidation-reduction potentials in the soil adjacent to the seed.   Varieties having the highest sugar content gave the lowest potentials and the poorest germination.

The results of many investigators on the influence of oxygen and carbon dioxide on germination of seeds of several plants have been reviewed by Mack (1930).   In all cases cited, low oxygen and/or high carbon dioxide reduced germination, although the limits of tolerance were variable among the species studied.   In a series of experiments on the effects of oxygen concentration and temperature on the germination of wheat in aerated culture solutions Mack found a high interaction between the two environmental factors.   A double peak in the oxygen versus germination curve was recorded.   The first maximum occurred at from 6 to 9 percent oxygen in tests at 30° C.; the second maximum was at 90 to 96 percent oxygen.   In a similar study Tang (1931) confirmed the existence of a bimodal aeration-germination relationship.

The nature and importance of certain excretory germination inhibitors is the subject of a recent review by Evenari (1949). Considerable evidence is cited indicating that many such inhibitors exist and that they effectively reduce or prevent seed germination of many plant species. Certain of the germination inhibitors, such as the aldehydes and organic acids, are known to result from anaerobic respiration. The absence of ample oxygen may therefore result in the production of respiratory products that act as germination inhibitors. This hypothesis is in accord with the results of Thornton (1943–45) who reported that secondary dormancy can be induced in many seeds by low oxygen supply. The same author attributes the depressing effect of high storage temperature on germination to the relatively higher activity of the hydrolyzing than the oxidizing system in the seeds.

IV. AERATION AND ROOT MORPHOLOGY

In studies of aeration and plant growth, many investigators have observed differences in the appearance of the plant roots (Loehwing, 1937; Weaver and Himmel, 1930). In general, roots growing is well-aerated media are long, light-colored, and well supplied with root hairs. In the absence of adequate amounts of oxygen, the roots are thickened, shorter, darker, and have less than the normal number of root hairs. Aquatic plants and those indigenous to poorly drained soils frequently develop specialized structures, such as the knees of the cypress tree, which serve to supply oxygen for normal aerobic respiration of the submerged tissues (Bergman, 1920; Clements, 1921; Dean, 1933; Sifton, 1945).

Examination of the internal structure of corn roots by Beal (1918) and Andrews and Beal (1919) revealed that the cortical cells of aerated roots were uniform in size with no conspicuous air cavities, whereas the cortical cells of the nonaerated roots contained large air cavities separated by narrow strands of tissue. In a similar study on the development of cortical modifications of corn and wheat as a consequence of differences in aeration, it was found that the openings first developed by separation of adjacent cells in the cortical tissues. In later stages the openings appeared to have enlarged through the disintegration of adjoining cells. Such differentiation did not occur when these plants were grown in well-aerated soils or nutrient solutions.

In comparing the anatomical and histological characteristics of roots of barley grown in aerated and nonaerated cultures, Bryant (1934) found that barley grown in nonaerated cultures had 225 roots per plant, averaging 10.9 centimeters in length, whereas aerated plants had 75 roots per plant, averaging 37.4 centimeters. The nonaerated roots were 15 percent thicker than the aerated. Microscopic examination of the root tissues showed that the cortex of roots in aerated solutions consisted of uniformly compact parenchyma with no intercellular spaces. That of nonaerated roots was composed of large air passages separated by narrow strands of parenchyma.

Chronologically, the first tissue to differentiate was the xylem vessels in nonaerated roots. Secondary thickening started at 5 millimeters from the tip. The next tissue to differentiate was xylem vessels of aerated roots 15 millimeters from root tips. This was followed by pericycle of the nonaerated roots at 35 millimeters from the tip. At 45 millimeters from the root tip, pericycle cells of aerated roots had begun to thicken, as had the central ducts of nonaerated roots. Endodermal cells of plants from both aerated and nonaerated soils showed secondary thickening, but the walls of aerated roots were twice as thick as those for nonaerated roots. It was found that respirable sugars were less in the aerated roots.

These observations can be summarized as follows: Tissues in non-aerated roots started to differentiate nearer the tip than in aerated roots. Starting at 25 millimeters from the root tips, however, the cell walls of aerated roots thickened more rapidly than for nonaerated roots. In mature regions of the root, these walls were twice as thick as for nonaerated roots. Thus, aerated plants have a longer portion of the root over which absorption of water and salts may occur.

Similar results have also been observed for wheat and oat roots, in the study of which it was further observed that the production of air spaces was preceded by deterioration and death of the protoplasm in groups of cells (McPherson, 1939). During this deterioration the cells lost their rigidity, and their walls, being normally soft owing to the loss of calcium pectate, became crumpled and finally collapsed.

The hypothesis that the presence of air passages in the stems and roots of plants can serve as an important method of supplying oxygen to the roots is supported by the work of Zimmerman, Hitchcock, and Crocker (1930) who showed that ethylene gas entered and moved fairly rapidly through the tissues of tomato, rose, lily, ivy, and Boston fern plants. It was suggested that possibly oxygen likewise could diffuse through these tissues. Recent results by Brown (1947) have demonstrated a definite transfer mechanism between the shoot and root of Cucurbita pepo.

Measurements of the composition of gas found in the air-space systems of plants growing in swamps show oxygen concentrations as high as 15 percent. This led Conway (1940) to conclude that such plants are not dependent for their oxygen supply on that in the medium surrounding them. The effects of interfering with the air-space system were strikingly exhibited by the development of low oxygen values for the gas in the internal spaces of the roots.

In a study of the effects of different oxygen tensions on certain physiological responses in rice, wheat, and barley, it was found that when excised roots were used, all three plants responded alike with respect to accumulation of potassium and bromide under varying oxygen tensions (Vlamis and Davis, 1943, 1944). However, when intact plants were subjected to aeration with nitrogen, air, and carbon dioxide, tomato roots failed to accumulate bromide, barley roots were greatly inhibited, and rice roots accumulated nearly as much as they did when the culture was well aerated.

The existence of specialized air-conducting tissues in rice serves to explain why this crop is able to grow with submerged roots but fails to explain why normal growth is not attained by this crop on well-drained soils. Lin (1946) attributed such reduced growth to low availability of iron and was able to show that normal growth resulted following the addition of a reducing substance such as sodium thioglycollate, which presumably increased the concentration of soluble iron in well-drained soil. The work of Taylor (1942) also suggests that rice possesses a highly functional anaerobic respiration mechanism and as compared with other cereals such as wheat, a less active aerobic system. It is suggested that this respiration mechanism is responsible for the marked difference in germination observed between rice and wheat under conditions of limited oxygen supply. The importance of algae in supplying oxygen to the roots of paddy rice has also been suggested (Dobbs, 1915; Harrison and Aiyer, 1913).

Zimmerman (1930) found that willow cuttings would root in water having an oxygen content of 1 part per million or more. English ivy and tomatoes required higher contents than willows. The fact that green stems would partially substitute for aeration, provided the light intensity was sufficiently high, was attributed to oxygen released by photosynthesis in the submerged green tissues. It was also observed that hypertrophied lenticels were larger in willow stems submerged in nonaerated water than in similar stems in aerated cultures. Rooting was induced in nonaerated cultures by the addition of such oxidizing agents as hydrogen peroxide and potassum permanganate.

V. AERATION AND WATER ABSORPTION BY ROOTS

Inadequate soil aeration decreases the intake of water by plants directly through its effect on absorption and indirectly by reducing root growth. The latter phenomenon is discussed elsewhere in this chapter.   Numerous investigators have reported wilting of plants grown in liquid cultures aerated with gas mixtures containing high amounts of carbon dioxide and/or low concentration of oxygen.   In many of the early experiments the effects of low oxygen and high carbon dioxide were not separated.   In interpreting the influence of aeration on the water economy of plants, the picture is further complicated by the existence of two types of water entry.   In the first of these, called passive absorption, the entry of water into the plant roots is independent of respirational activity.   The second mechanism is designated as active absorption and is dependent upon aerobic respiration in the plant roots.   It is believed that the former process is by far the more important and that active absorption can account for only a small percentage of the water needed by actively transpiring plants.   Since the reduction in water absorption that results from inadequate aeration is much greater than can be attributed to active absorption, it must be concluded that aeration has an influence on both mechanisms.

Kramer (1938, 1940, 1945) found that the transpiration of tomatoes and sunflowers was reduced by 50 percent or more within an hour following saturation of the culture solution with carbon dioxide, but that saturation with nitrogen reduced transpiration by only about 10 percent.   These and similar data led to the conclusion that the early reduction in water absorption was more a consequence of the increased carbon dioxide than of the low oxygen content.   Some increase in water uptake occurred in the high carbon dioxide cultures, but no recovery was observed in those having low oxygen.   Similar results were obtained by Chang and Loomis (1945), who studied both the water absorption and nutrient absorption of maize, rice, and wheat in culture solutions through which carbon dioxide and nitrogen were bubbled. Since no reductions were observed when nitrogen was used as the aerating gas, these authors concluded that carbon dioxide has a specific effect on water and nutrient uptake.

The work of Whitney (1942) indicated, however, that for longer periods, oxygen deficiency may be of greater consequence in reducing water absorption than excessive carbon dioxide.   This investigator grew tomatoes, tobacco, sunflower, coleus, cotton, and corn in artificially aerated sand cultures.   Four aerating gases were used in what was essentially a factorial combination in two levels of oxygen and carbon dioxide.   These levels were zero and 20 percent of each gas, with the balance of the mixture being made up of nitrogen.   Measurements and treatments were extended over a 7- to 14-day period, with water uptake being evaluated in terms of transpiration losses.   The low oxygen mixtures gave a 70 percent reduction in relative transpiration of tobacco the first day, followed by a slight decrease and then a gradual increase. The relative transpiration of tomatoes decreased approximately 10 percent the first day and steadily thereafter. In the case of the corn, the initial decrease was 40 percent, after which there was little change. Twenty percent of carbon dioxide had little effect if the oxygen content was high and produced little additional effect when superimposed on low oxygen treatments.

The detrimental effects of high concentrations, 50 percent or more, of carbon dioxide on the water absorption of roots grown in liquid cultures seems to be well established. This effect is attributed primarily to the influence of carbon dioxide on the permeability of the plant roots. The increase in water uptake that occurs when the treatments are continued for long periods of time is believed due to the breakdown of the root tissue which follows the lethal action of the high concentrations of carbon dioxide. Since reductions in water uptake occur only at relatively high carbon dioxide concentrations and are greatly reduced by the presence of oxygen, even in relatively small concentrations, it is probable that the effects of carbon dioxide on water economy of plants grown in field soils is of minor significance except in those cases where the roots are grown in waterlogged soils in the presence of large amounts of readily decomposable organic matter.

The conclusions regarding the influence of oxygen concentration on water uptake are less definite. Thus Kramer found a 10 percent reduction in transpiration loss following a one-hour treatment with nitrogen. Chang and Loomis reported that the same treatment gave a 10 percent increase, whereas Whitney observed a decrease ranging up to 70 percent in cultures aerated with nitrogen. Since all these studies were conducted in liquid cultures, some of the discrepancies may be traced to the differences in method used for aerating the cultures. The use of intermittent gas streams to control the oxygen level in liquid cultures is open to question, for in all studies of this kind, it is assumed that the composition of the aerating gas is a valid criterion for characterizing the substrate at the root-liquid interface. In quiescent unaerated solutions, the replenishment of oxygen in this zone will be by diffusion or slow convection. In aerated solutions the resultant circulation of the solution may be effective in supplying fresh solution to the root surfaces at a rate sufficient to meet the oxygen needs of the plants, even though the concentration of oxygen in the aerating gas may be relatively low. On a volume basis, the amount of the dissolved oxygen in liquid cultures is large when compared with the amount supplied by slow or intermittent aeration with air or gas mixtures containing lower concentrations of oxygen; therefore, information relative to the concentration of dissolved oxygen and the degree of agitation effected in the culture solution would be helpful in any attempt to rationalize seemingly divergent results reported above.

Reduction in the permeability of plant roots grown in unaerated cultures is presumed to be a consequence of the accumulation of toxic products of anaerobic respiration as well as the possible effects of carbon dioxide on the permeability. Hoagland and Broyer (1936, 1942) also suggest that root permeability is related to metabolism through the influence of the latter process on the maintenance of protoplasmic membranes. Thus it would appear that metabolism, salt absorption, permeability, and possibly active absorption of water are closely related and subject to the influence of all those factors that have been shown to influence metabolic processes.

VI. THE EFFECT OF AERATION ON NUTRIENT ABSORPTION BY PLANTS

The absorption of ions by roots is one of the most important physiological functions of living plants. It represents the connecting link between soil conditions and plant growth; hence, the nature of the process is of great interest to all those who are concerned with soil and plant interrelations. Of the many environmental factors that have been shown to have an effect on this important process, this discussion will be limited to the influence of aeration on nutrient uptake by plant roots.

In preceding sections of this chapter evidence has been presented to show that adequate amounts of oxygen must be supplied to plant roots if normal growth is to result. Failure to obtain normal plant development in cultures receiving inadequate amounts of oxygen is related to restricted ion uptake by the roots; this is well established from the work of many investigators (Hoagland, 1940, 1944; Hoagland and Broyer, 1936; Hoagland and Davis, 1929; Lundegardh, 1947; Osterhout, 1947; Prevot and Steward, 1936; Robertson, 1941; Steward, 1932, 1933, 1935; Steward, Barry and Broyer, 1937) who have shown that the presence of insufficient quantities of oxygen or high concentrations of carbon dioxide result in restricted nutrient uptake by the roots of a large number of plant species. Although a high proportion of these studies have been conducted in liquid cultures, comparable investigations in soil and sand cultures have shown that the principles established from the liquid culture studies apply to the more complex media, although the limits of deficiency and toxicity may be altered appreciably. Unfortunately, many of the results obtained on the soil and sand cultures have been interpreted in terms of the influence of aeration on nutrient absorption without the quantitative evaluation of the actual aeration conditions involved. In several studies the influence of tillage, drainage, and other management practices on crop growth have been interpreted in terms of the effect of those treatments on aeration, although no factual information is given to support the hypothesis that these treatments resulted in differences in the aeration status of the soil. Therefore, the validity of the conclusions that have been drawn can only be established when evidence has been presented to substantiate the hypothesis used.

The results of many tillage experiments have shown that differences in the method of seedbed preparation result in highly significant differences in crop growth on certain soils (Baver and Farnsworth, 1940; Bushnell, 1935; Raney, 1949; Reuther and Crawford, 1947; Smith and Cook, 1946). Significant differences in nutrient uptake by plants grown under different tillage practices also have been reported (Bower, Browning, and Norton, 1944). Potassium and nitrogen are the nutrient elements that are most commonly reported as being influenced by such tillage treatments. Since the observed effects on growth and nutrient uptake are most strongly expressed in soils that are poorly drained or in a poor state of tilth, it has been assumed that the observed effects were a consequence of inadequate aeration. Although this seems a reasonable assumption, final evaluation of the results and their interpretation in terms of aeration must be reserved until the aeration conditions actually obtained under such treatments have been evaluated.

The influence of aeration on the growth and nutrient absorption of corn has been reported recently by Lawton (1945). It was found that the order of reduction in nutrient absorption by corn from Clyde silt loam as a consequence of restricted aeration was $K > Ca > Mg > N > P$. Similar results were obtained when aeration was inhibited by waterlogging the soil or by reducing the porosity by compaction. An increase in top and root growth resulted when air was forced through the pots having high moisture content. The increases in nutrient absorption associated with this forced aeration were in the order of $K > N > Ca > Mg > P$. No quantitative data for specifying the aeration conditions were given other than the relative amounts of ferrous or ferric iron. The ferrous iron was highest in those pots having high moisture contents and high states of compaction. Ferrous iron was absent or present in only small amounts in the aerated pots and those having normal packing and moisture. The concentrations of ferrous and ferric iron varied inversely.

The modes of entry of solutes into plant roots is by no means completely understood. Certain characteristics of this important reaction has been established, however, and serve to explain the influence of aeration conditions on salt absorption. Early investigators postulated that the entry of solutes into the plant was merely a process of diffusion and that the necessary activity gradients were maintained by the removal of ions from the roots to other parts of the plants and by combination or precipitation of the ions in osmotically inactive forms. Subsequent studies of the ion concentration of the cell sap obtained from such large cells, as *Valonia* and *Nitella*, revealed that the concentration of ions within the vacuoles of the living cells may greatly exceed that of the external solution. Such a study is summarized in Table 32.

Data in Table 32 and other data obtained by many other workers emphasized the inadequacy of the simple diffusion theory of nutrient absorption.

TABLE 32.—*Ratio of ion concentration in the cell sap to the concentration outside for four species growing in fresh water (Osterhout, 1947)*

Ion	Chara ceratophylla	Tolypellopsis stelligera	Nitella flexilis	Nitella gracilis
Cl	294	1,150	1,300	1,600
Na	400	90	390	31
K	650	3,200	2,500	13,000
Mg	50	42	—	—
Ca	4	7	77	49

Although the concentration of ions against activity gradients is well established for such large-celled plants as those mentioned in Table 32, the frequency with which this situation exists in tissues of crop plants is not known. It is true than many workers have reported data which have been interpreted to indicate that the concentration of osmotically active salts in plant tissue is significantly higher than that in the nutrient medium. It should be pointed out, however, that this may not be a completely correct picture of the situation in living tissue, since it is possible that many of the ions which appear as inorganic forms in analyses as they are now made may actually exist in the living plants in rather unstable combination with organic constituents from which they are released during the preparation of the sample for analysis.

Despite this uncertainty of the present information, it is generally agreed that many plants accumulate ions against concentration gradient under certain circumstances. It is also agreed that the energy that must be supplied to transport ions against such gradients is derived from aerobic respiration in the roots. Therefore, the accumulation of ions in root tissue is strongly influenced by the concentration of oxygen in the culture solution. As an example of the influence of oxygen on salt absorption, the results of Hoagland and Broyer (1936) are shown in Figure 39.

Hoagland and Broyer (1936, 1942) found that the rate of oxygen absorption was a better index of respiratory metabolism in relation to salt absorption than the rate of carbon dioxide production. Treatment of the roots with dilute cyanide and with methylene blue greatly reduced the oxygen absorption and salt accumulation but had little or no effect on the carbon dioxide production. The authors state, "The

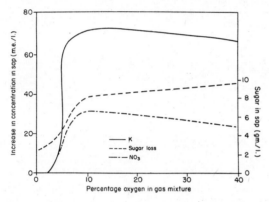

FIGURE 39.—Effect of oxygen content of aerating gas on accumulation of ions and sugar loss by excised barley roots (Hoagland and Broyer, 1936).

general suggestion is that a metal-catalyzed respiratory system is linked in some way with the process of salt accumulation although preliminary experiments have not revealed the exact nature of the system involved."

The same authors also reported that under anaerobic conditions salts were not accumulated by barley roots even when immersed in a solution having a higher solute content than the cell sap. In the absence of aerobic respiration, the cells behave as though their permeability to salt was very low. Salt accumulation was negligible even though an inward concentration gradient existed between the medium and the cell sap.

A certain amount of ionic exchange that is independent of metabolic activity probably occurs between the cell sap and the external solution. This reaction is similar in character to the ionic exchange phenomenon of soils and other materials. By the use of radioactive potassium Broyer and Overstreet (1940) demonstrated that considerable exchange of potassium occurred when *Nitella* was placed in a dilute solution of potassium chloride. Little or no outward movement of cations occurred, however, when such a cell was placed in distilled water. This exchange appeared to be independent of metabolic activity, except to the extent that such activity results in the removal of internal ions from the exchanging surface.

Although the dependence of salt accumulation on aerobic respiration is generally accepted, no general agreement has been reached as to the nature of the mechanism involved. Hoagland and his colleagues agree that aerobic metabolism is necessary for salt accumulation but

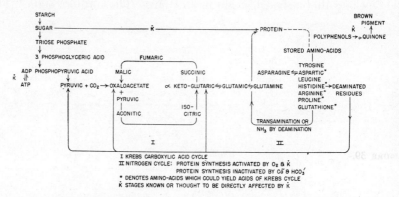

FIGURE 40.—A speculative scheme relating respiration and protein synthesis (Steward and Street, 1947).

that no functional relationship between the two processes can be established. Steward and his colleagues have demonstrated that salt accumulation was dependent upon metabolic processes that are intimately associated with protein synthesis. Steward and Preston (1940) reported that the accumulation of potassium in potato-tuber tissue was accompanied by oxidase activity and the oxidation of phenolic compounds. A possible mechanism by which respiration and protein synthesis may be linked has been suggested by Steward and Street (1947) and is shown in Figure 40. It is suggested that under conditions of ample carbon dioxide and low oxygen the Krebs respiratory cycle is supplied with carbon via pyruvic acid, with respiration proceeding without reference to nitrogen metabolism. When carbon dioxide is limiting, as it may be in well-aerated cultures of the type used by Steward and his colleagues, it is postulated that the Krebs cycle is supplied via glutamic acid arising from the deamination of amino acids during the protein-synthesis cycle. This cycle is activated by oxygen and potassium and is inactivated by bicarbonate and calcium. Although this multiple cycle is admittedly speculative it is not in disagreement with the observed effects of oxygen, carbon dioxide, and specific ions on respiration and nitrogen metabolism. The existence of certain phosphorylated nitrogen compounds in the protein synthesis cycle has been suggested as a means whereby the salt accumulation process could be energized as a byproduct of the nitrogen metabolism.

In contrast with these views, Lundegardh (1947) contends that salt accumulation is a consequence of a specific respiratory reaction that is activated by anions. This fraction of the total respirational activity of the plant is distinguished from the so-called ground respiration by the fact that it is cyanide sensitive. Lundegardh is of the opinion that

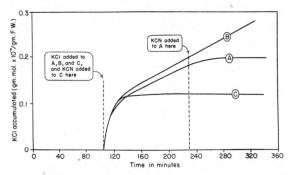

FIGURE 41.—Rate of respiration of carrot tissue as influenced by additions of KCL and KCN. The increased respiration of *A* and *B* following addition of KCL is attributed to salt respiration. This fraction of the total respiration is cyanide sensitive as shown by curve *A* (Robertson and Turner, 1945).

the prevailing anionic character of the protoplasm creates a permanent absorption potential for cations. The accumulation of sufficient anions to maintain electrical neutrality is then accomplished by means of an absorption mechanism energized by anion respiration.

The existence of a cyanide-sensitive respiratory mechanism in root tissue that is intimately related to salt accumulation has recently been shown in a convincing manner by Robertson (Milthrope and Robertson, 1948; Robertson, 1941, 1944; Robertson and Thorn, 1945; Robertson and Turner, 1945; Robertson, Turner and Wilkins, 1947; Robertson and Wilkins, 1948). Typical results showing the relationship between oxygen uptake and salt absorption for carrot tissue are shown in Figure 41. These data support the Lundegardh hypothesis that accumulation of salt by plant tissue is accompanied by increased respirational activity which is sensitive to cyanide.

Similar data summarized in terms of KCL accumulated as a function of time and added salt are shown in Figure 42. The KCL accumulation data for this figure were obtained from conductivity measurements on the nutrient solution. It was noted that following an initial rapid increase, KCL accumulation continued at a steady rate until the cyanide-sensitive respiratory metabolism was stopped by the addition of KCN. From Figure 42 it can be seen that the initial rapid uptake of salt was independent of salt respiration. This apparent accumulation of salt without respiratory energization was attributed to the equalization of salt concentrations between the tissues and the culture solution. Following this equalization, further accumulation occurred only if energy was supplied by respiration.

Lundegardh (1947) suggests that the energy obtained from aerobic metabolism is utilized in the concentration of anions against the activity gradient through the mechanism of a cytochrome-cytochrome oxidase

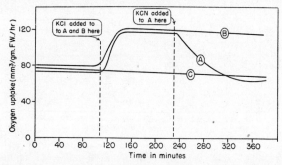

FIGURE 42.—Rate of accumulation of KCL by carrot tissue as influenced by additions of KCL and KCN (Robertson and Turner, 1945).

system in which the active components are iron ions which undergo cyclic valency changes. Since hydrogen ions are produced in this process, it is postulated that cation absorption occurs by a process of exchange between the cations and the hydrogen ions produced by the cyclic process. The nature of this enzyme system as it pertains to anion accumulation is given in Figure 43.

When a hydrogen atom liberated by the dehydrogenase stage of respiration reaches the cytochrome system, it loses an electron to the cytochrome and is converted into a hydrogen ion. The electron unites with the ferric iron of the ferricytochrome, reducing it to the ferrous form. In this process an anion, indicated as Cl^- in Figure 43, is released. In the presence of cytochrome oxidase, the reduced cytochrome gives up an electron which combines with oxygen from the medium and a hydrogen ion to form a hydroxyl radical and ferricytochrome which, having a positive charge, unites with an anion and returns to the starting point of the cycle.

In a recent analysis of the movements of materials into plants, Broyer (1947) discussed the characteristics and limitations of each of several possible modes of solute flux between the root tissue and surrounding media. He described simple diffusion as the movement of solute from regions of high concentration to regions of lower concentration, and he points out that the process has a low temperature coefficient and is not directly affected by aerobic respiration. The diffusion rate may be influenced by such respiration, however, through the influence of cell activity on the diffusion constant or permeability of the root tissue and possibly through effects on cytoplasmic streaming. For diffusion to account for the continued entry of ions from the medium,

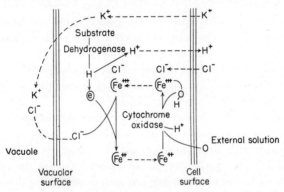

FIGURE 43.—Schematic representation of the electron and anion transport system: Solid lines represent chemical reactions; broken lines, movements of substances; (Fe^{+++}, oxidized cytochrome; (Fe^{++}, reduced cytochrome. (Robertson and Wilkins, 1948.)

it is necessary to postulate that entering ions are rendered inactive due to precipitation or conversion into insoluble forms inside the roots. The process of simple diffusion is therefore unable to account for the observed accumulation of ions by cells having higher concentrations of ions than the surrounding medium. The low temperature coefficient of this process also is at variance with the observed marked increases in accumulation at elevated temperatures.

Under Donnan diffusion Broyer considers the entry of ions into a system in which one of the constituent ions is restrained. The typical restraint is a membrane through which certain particles cannot pass. Broyer is of the opinion that Donnan equilibrium is inadequate for explaining the observed concentration in large-celled algae and that the existence of an impermeable complex has yet to be established experimentally.

Under the heading of pressure effects, Broyer points out that an increase in pressure results in an increase in the free energy of both the solvent and solute constituents. Hence, the existence of the differences in hydrostatic pressure between the solutions on the outside and inside of the plant root will give rise to a free-energy gradient that will favor the movement of solute and solvent constituents. Under most conditions, however, the pressure in the root is greater than in the surrounding medium so that the driving force rising from this effect would be directed outward from the roots.

Under electrical and thermal effects it was observed that although electrical phenomenon undoubtedly are connected with plant growth, the exact manner in which these phenomena are involved in the uptake of solutes is obscure. With respect to thermal effects, it is pointed out that although temperature differences might cause modifications of the specific free energy of the solute in such a manner as to favor the movement of material, the existence of the necessary temperature gradients across the root-soil interface have not been observed. The effect of temperature on metabolic processes and upon the pressure-volume relations of the medium also are considered.

Broyer defines the process of adsorption as the process whereby substances are concentrated at an interface regardless of the mechanisms by which this accumulation occurs. Since such a process will be accompanied by a reduction in the free energy of the adsorbed particles, it is possible to account for ion entry, providing a mechanism is postulated whereby the adsorbed constituents are continuously removed or inactivated from the adsorbing medium. Exchange reactions between the adsorbed ions and those in the surrounding media also are possible, but here also it is necessary to provide a mechanism whereby the exchangeable ions are replenished if a continuously operative adsorption mechanism is to be established. Broyer is of the opinion that under certain conditions exchange adsorption alone may account for a large portion of the net influx of solutes. He points out, however, that maintained exchange adsorption of this type is dependent on the outward movement of solutes derived from metabolic activity or through the continued increase in the exchange capacity of the adsorbing surface. He points out that hydrogen, bicarbonate ions, and possibly organic cations and anions may be important in supplying exchangeable ions to activate exchange adsorption.

Broyer also discusses the phenomenon of the accumulation of ions against the concentration gradient by living cells and points out that such accumulation is associated with aerobic respiration. That such accumulation is probably of greatest importance is indicated by the following statement taken from the summary of Broyer's paper.

The metabolic accumulation of solute is probably a universal mode of net influx. The accumulation is directly related to the oxidative catabolism for its source of energy. This energy is applied to the solute molecules through some type of solute-cytoplasmic interaction increasing their free energy such that the molecules of a solute species tend to move with and against the direction in which their concentration in solution decreases. The mechanism for conversion or transfer of chemical into mechanical energy remains to be elucidated.

That the entry of ions into plant cells is associated with an electrical potential gradient is suggested by the work of Blinks *et al.* (1938). Osterhout (1936, 1947), and Tendeloo *et al.* (1944). Potential differences of the order of 70 to 80 millivolts exist between the cell sap and the external solution of such large cells as *Halicystis* and *Valonia.* This potential remains constant as long as an adequate oxygen supply is maintained but drops to 20 millivolts or less when the aerating gas contains 0.2 percent oxygen or less. Recovery occurs when the oxygen content of the aerating gas is raised to 2 percent or more. Cells of

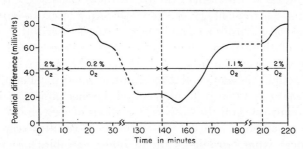

FIGURE 44.—The effect of oxygen concentration of the aerating gas on the bioelectric potential of *Halicystis ovalis* (Blinks, Darsie, and Skow, 1938).

Halicystis engaged in active aerobic respiration can drive a current of 5 to 10 microamperes through a completed external circuit, indicating that a source of energy, undoubtedly metabolic in nature, is involved in the electrical properties of these cells. The effects of variation of oxygen content on the potential differences of *Halicystis* are shown in Figure 44. Effects similar to those shown in Figure 44 were obtained when the oxygen content of the cell sap was altered, indicating that the direction of the oxygen gradient per se is not involved in the restoration of the potential difference of the cell. The reduction in the potential difference that accompanies the lowering of oxygen difference cannot be interpreted from these measurements alone as being due either to a reduction of mobility of the faster ion or to an increase in the mobility of the slower anions. A considerable decrease in total ionic permeability is indicated, however, by a greatly increased direct current resistance of the cells during periods of low oxygen tension. Low re-

sistance is regained on aeration; thus, the reduction in potential difference appears to be largely the result of the greatly reduced cation
mobility during periods of restricted aerobic respiration.

The fundamental relationship that governs the motion of solutes
into and out of plant roots is that the motion will be in such a direction
as to result in a reduction in the specific free energy of the solute in
question. Thus the existence of a free-energy gradient between two
points in the root-soil environment is a necessary condition for solute
transport. The other condition that must be satisfied for solute intake
is that the permeability of the plant root to the constituent in question
be finite.

Since the specific free energy of a given solute is a function of temperature, pressure, composition, and such body forces as those arising
from gravitational and electrical fields that may be operative, it follows
that differences in specific free energy between two points in the system
may arise owing to differences in any of these variables. It is highly
unlikely that the free-energy gradient necessary to cause ion transport
between the soil environment and the root can be ascribed to variations
in any one of these parameters, rather it is to be expected that such
gradients result from the integrated effects of differences in several of
the variables that determine the specific free energy. For this reason
it appears that any attempt to understand the mechanism of ion movement into plant roots on the basis of variations of any one of the above
mentioned parameters will not yield consistent results except in those
rare instances where gradients in all other variables are negligible.
Hence, the assumption that the entry of a given ion can be predicted
on the basis of the chemical potential or ion activity of that ion in the
external and internal parts of the system can only hold in those cases
where temperature, pressure, and other composition variables are constant and where there are no contributions to the specific free energy
from electrical or other body forces. That such conditions do not exist
in all cells is well demonstrated by the significant electrical potentials
that have been measured across the cells of certain algae and the observed differences in pressure that exist between turgid cells and the
external solution.

Since the accumulation in cells of ions in greater concentration than
in the external solution occurs only when accompanied by aerobic
respiration, it is generally assumed that the specific free energy of the
ions in the plant tissue is greater than that in the external medium and
that the accumulation process represents the movement of solutes
against an over-all specific free-energy gradient. In Figure 45 is shown
a schematic diagram of a mechanism whereby such movement could

be realized and the fundamental conditions necessary for solute movement can be satisfied.

The over-all effect in the process shown in Figure 45 is the transport of an ion from the external medium having an energy of ΔF_e to a higher specific free energy state ΔF_i in the root tissue. For such transport to take place in accordance with the principles of ion motion in the direction of a decreasing free energy, it is necessary to postulate the existence of two energy states for the ion designated in Figure 45 as A and B. Providing the permeability of the tissue to the ion is finite, ion transport would occur spontaneously from the external solution to the lower energy state A and spontaneously from the high energy level B to the internal energy level ΔF_i. The increase in specific free energy

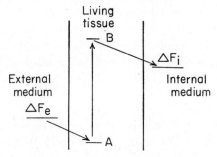

Figure 45.—Schematic energy–level diagram pertaining to the entry of ions into plant roots.

of the solute ion corresponding to a transformation from energy level A to B can occur only if energy is added to the system. A reaction similar to the cytochrome-cytochrome oxidase cycle proposed by Lundegardh would fulfill the requirement of such an energy transformation. An analogous series of reactions seem to occur by a cyclic chain of phosphorylation and dephosphorylations in muscle tissue. Since these and similar mechanisms are fundamentally electron-transfer phenomena, it is not unreasonable to expect that such ions as iron, manganese, copper, and zinc may act as the active component of the catalyst involved in such reactions.

VII. SOIL AERATION AND THE INCIDENCE OF PLANT DISEASES

In addition to the more or less direct influence of soil aeration on plant growth it may also exert an important indirect effect as a factor in the occurrence and severity of certain plant diseases. Such effects are of two kinds, namely: (1) The lack of oxygen and/or excess of carbon dioxide on the growth and longevity of the pathogen and (2) the increased susceptibility of the host plant when grown in poorly aerated soils. Pathogens that attack plant roots are the ones that are most influenced by soil conditions. The importance of temperature, pH, and moisture content are widely discussed as factors affecting root-attacking organisms (Berkeley, 1944; Garrett, 1937a, 1939; Simmonds, 1941; Wingard, 1941). It is assumed by some that the principal effect of high moisture content arises from the attendant poor aeration. Although some direct evidence of the influence of aeration on certain phytopathogens will be cited below, most of the evidence to be discussed is based on the assumption made above.

The importance of soil aeration as a factor in the control of take-all disease of cereals has been established by experiments of Garrett (1937b and 1942) and Griffiths (1933). These investigators found that forced aeration greatly increased the growth rate of *Ophiobolus graminis*. Growth rate of the runner hyphae along the roots of wheat seedlings was greatly reduced when the soil was firmly packed but was increased when the soil was well granulated and loose or when it was diluted with sand. These results led Garrett to suggest that the growth of the runner hyphae was largely controlled by the accumulation of carbon dioxide in the micro-environment of the root. Other respiratory products of antagonistic micro-organisms may also be involved. From these results it would appear that soil conditions conducive to good aeration would give greatest infection by the take-all organism. Since root initiation and growth of the host plant are also stimulated by good aeration, the resultant influence of the pathogen on the host may actually be most severe under poor aeration conditions. Studies of the survival of *Ophiobolus graminis* in the absence of the host plant have established that its viability declines most rapidly in well-aerated soil, providing temperature, pH, and energy materials are such as to favor rapid microbiological activity (Fellows, 1941). Similar results have been obtained on survival studies with tobacco mosaic virus (McKinney, 1946).

In reviews of the root rot of cereal (Simmonds, 1941) and non-cereal crops (Berkeley, 1944) considerable attention was given to the influence of water content of soils as a factor affecting the occurrence and severity of most root rots. The following remarks are taken from these reviews, to which the reader is referred for references to the original publications.

Fusarium rot of pineapple is capable of attacking the tips of roots growing on wet soil but does not infect roots in dry soil. The disease occurs most often in low-lying fields having faulty drainage. Similar observations have been made regarding red stele and black root rot of strawberries. These root rots are also strongly affected by soil temperature conditions.

The clitocybe rot of grapes, rhizoctonia and aphanomyces root rot of peas, phoma and fusarium root rots of sugarbeets, the several root rots of sugarcane, peppers, sweetclover, cauliflower, citrus, chestnut, beech, and the violet root rot of tea are all most severe under conditions of poor drainage. Some evidence has been given that poor aeration *per se* is not important but that certain toxic products of anaerobic decomposition are involved. Practically all root rots are favored by excessive soil moisture because the fungi involved are favored by such high moisture content and the plant roots are adversely affected and hence are more susceptible to attack.

Chupp (1946) has discussed the significance of soil conditions including aeration as factors in disease incidence. He discussed the sensitivity of verticillium wilt to soil moisture conditions as well as the sensitivity of several of the root rot organisms listed in paragraphs just preceding. It also was pointed out that the most common cause of lack of aeration is the presence of excessive free water in the soil. This gives the impression that the author considers soil aeration as a factor in disease incidence but that its influence is confounded with that of high water content.

In a discussion of factors affecting pathogenic damping-off Beach (1946) also implies the possible effect of soil aeration but emphasizes the difficulties in attempting to separate the effects of the other factors that influence the parasitic fungi involved.

SUMMARY

In this chapter the significance of soil aeration as a factor in crop growth has been reviewed. It has been shown that the amount and composition of the soil atmosphere influences plant production in a large number of ways. Much of the information relating soil aeration to crop growth is based on inference rather than quantitative data. For example, many authors have attributed the observed effects of drainage, tillage, and other soil management practices on crop growth to the influence of those factors on soil aeration. Only in a limited number of cases, however, has the validity of that assumption been established by means of direct measurements of soil aeration. This situation undoubtedly is a consequence of the lack of satisfactory methods of characterizing soil aeration in terms of parameters that are of significance in plant growth. Despite the lack of quantitative verification, the large volume of qualitative information seems to justify the conclusion that soil aeration is a major factor in plant growth in many instances. The quantitative evaluation of this interaction, however, must await the accumulation of much more data on the parameters involved.

With regard to the composition of the soil air, we can say that in general it is similar to the atmosphere, except that the content of carbon dioxide and water vapor are significantly higher. The composition of the soil air undergoes characteristic variations both in time and in space. These fluctuations are conditioned by temperature, soil conditions and composition, and the presence of living organisms in the soil. The underlying principle governing such variations is that the soil atmosphere is the resultant of the reaction rates of two sets of processes. The first tends to accentuate the differences in composition between the soil air and the atmosphere; the second, or gaseous transport processes, tends to eliminate these differences. Thus it is possible to predict the influence of any environmental factor or cultural practice on the composition of the soil air in terms of the influence that factor or process will have on the respiratory activities in the soil and on the process of diffusion.

One of the important ways in which soil aeration indirectly influences plant growth is through its effect on the chemical composition and biological processes of the soil. Thus the amount of soluble iron and manganese are strongly influenced by the oxygen concentration of the soil air. In a similar fashion the concentration of carbon dioxide affects the rate of mineral weathering and distribution of various forms of calcium in the soil. In calcareous soils carbon dioxide concentration also is a significant factor influencing phosphate availability. The oxygen content of the soil air is a major factor controlling certain very important biological reactions. Thus, in the absence of oxygen, the oxidation of nitrogen and sulfur to forms readily utilizable by living plants is prevented, and as a result reduced forms of these elements may accumulate in toxic concentrations. Under aerobic conditions the decomposition stages of the carbon cycle lead predominantly to carbon dioxide. Under anaerobic conditions, however, reduced forms such as methane and certain complex aldehydes may be the end products.

Since aerobic respiration is a vital process for all living plant roots, the presence of oxygen in the root zone is required for normal growth. In certain aquatic species, oxygen for root respiration is supplied through specialized air-conducting tissues in the shoot and root which render the root independent of oxygen conditions of the medium. In species that are indigenous to well-drained soils, the low levels of oxygen in the rooting medium result in greatly restricted growth or death of the roots.   Certain species exhibit greater tolerance to low oxygen concentrations than others, but all fail to survive in the absence of oxygen.

Aeration conditions influence the water economy of plants in two ways.   Of minor importance is the influence of lack of oxygen on root respiration, which is required for the active absorption of water by plant roots.   Of greater significance is the effect of high concentrations of carbon dioxide and low oxygen on root permeability.   Toxic concentrations of carbon dioxide presumably reduce permeability through their lethal action on the root cells.   A low oxygen concentration on the other hand results in decreased water permeability of plant roots through its inhibition of root respiration.

The importance of aeration as a factor regulating the accumulation of nutrients by plant roots has been the subject of the most extensive investigations of any of the topics discussed in this review.   Although many mechanisms may be involved in the entry of nutrients into plant roots, it is clear that the accumulation of such nutrients in concentrations higher than those in the external medium can be effected only by the addition of energy to the accumulating mechanism.   The evidence appears to be conclusive that this energy is derived from aerobic respiration of the root tissues and is therefore dependent upon the presence of oxygen.   Certain plausible mechanisms for conversion of the respirationally derived energy into the increased electrochemical potential of the ion being accumulated have been proposed.   It is probable that several mechanisms based on the catalytic transfer of electrons may be operative in the accumulation of nutrients by plants.   It is not possible at this time to establish the relative significance of such possible mechanisms, but the evidence seems to support the hypothesis that many of them will involve the cyclic oxidation and reduction of heavy metals such as iron, manganese, copper, or possible others. Until it is demonstrated that such reactions can be energized by anaerobic respiration or by other mechanisms, it is reasonable to expect that all such accumulation processes will be dependent upon the presence of oxygen in the tissues involved.

Soil aeration may indirectly influence crop production through its effect on disease incidence, although direct evidence of the importance of soil aeration on the incidence and survival of such diseases as root rots is scanty.   Many investigators have expressed the view that the often described importance of excessive soil moisture on the pathogenicity of root-infesting fungi may be partially due to the absence of adequate amounts of oxygen.   Considerable evidence is available to show that the survival of such pathogens in fallow soil is greatly reduced by practices which encourage the activity of antagonistic aerobic micro-organisms.

In conclusion, it can be said that soil aeration undoubtedly is an important factor in plant growth, although the quantitative evaluation of its effects remain to be established. In this connection the importance of developing means of measuring soil aeration in terms of parameters that are meaningful must be emphasized. It also should be emphasized that many of the effects of the soil aeration mentioned in this chapter are strongly influenced by other environmental conditions, including the physical and chemical nature of the soil, the nature of the plant and its stage of growth, and climatic variables such as temperature and light intensity. A complete understanding of the significance of soil aeration as a factor influencing plant growth therefore cannot be expected until additional quantitative information concerning the direct effect of this edaphic factor and of its interactions with other factors influencing plant growth has been obtained.

Literature Cited

ALBERT, W. B., and ARMSTRONG, G. M. 1931. Effects of high soil moisture and lack of soil aeration upon fruiting behavior of young cotton plants. *Plant Physiol.* 6: 585–591.

ALLISON, R. V. 1922. Effect of aeration and continuous renewal of nutrient solutions upon the growth of barley and buckwheat in artificial culture. *N. J. Agr. Expt. Sta. Ann. Rept.* pp. 402–407.

ALLISON, R. V., and SHIVE, J. W. 1923a. Micro–sampling for the determination of dissolved oxygen. *Soil Sci.* 15: 489–491.

ALLISON, R. V., and SHIVE, J. W. 1923b. Studies on the relation of aeration and continuous renewal of nutrient solution to the growth of soybeans in artificial cultures. *Am. J. Botany*, 10: 554.

ANDREWS, F. M. 1921. The effect of aeration on plants. *Proc. Indiana Acad. Sci.* 1920: 147–148.

ANDREWS, F. M., and BEAL, C. C. 1919. The effect of soaking in water and of aeration on the growth of Zea mays. *Bull. Torrey Botan. Club* 46: 91–100.

ARNON, D. I. 1937. Ammonium and nitrate nitrogen nutrition of barley at different seasons in relation to hydrogen–ion concentration, manganese, copper, and oxygen supply. *Soil Sci.* 44: 91–121.

ARRINGTON, L. B., and SHIVE, J. W. 1936. Oxygen and carbon dioxide content of culture solutions in relation to cation and anion nitrogen absorption by tomato plants. *Soil Sci.* 42: 341–357.

BAIN, F. M., and CHAPMAN, H. D. 1940. Nitrate fertilizer additions to waterlogged soils in relation to oxygen deficiency. *Soil Sci.* 50: 357–367.

BAVER, L. D., and FARNSWORTH, R. B. 1940. Soil structure effects in the growth of sugar beets. *Proc. Soil Sci. Soc. Am.* 5: 45–48.

BEACH, W. S. 1946. Pathogenic and physiogenic damping off. *Soil Sci.* 61: 37–46.

BEAL, C. C. 1918. The effect of aeration on the roots of Zea mays L. *Proc. Indiana Acad. Sci.* 1917: 177–180.

BERGMAN, H. F. 1920. The relation of aeration to the growth and activity of roots and its influence on the ecesis of plants in swamps. *Ann. Botany* 34: 13–33.

BERKELEY, G. H. 1944. Root–rots of certain non–cereal crops. *Botan. Rev.* 10: 67–123.

BLINKS, L. R., DARSIE, M. L., JR., and SKOW, R. K. 1938. Bioelectric potentials in *Halicystis*. VII. The effects of low oxygen tension. *J. Gen. Physiol.* 22: 255–279.

BOICOURT, A. W., and ALLEN, R. C. 1941. Effect of aeration on growth of hybrid tea roses. *Proc. Am. Soc. Hort. Sci.* 39: 423–425.

BOUSSINGAULT and LEWY. 1853. Memore sur la composition de l'air confine dans la terre vegetale. *Ann. Chim. et Ann. Phys.* 37: 5–50.

BOWER, C. A., BROWNING, G. M., and NORTON, R. A. 1944. Comparative effects of plowing and other methods of seedbed preparation on nutrient element deficiencies in corn. *Proc. Soil Sci. Soc. Am.* 9: 141–146.

BOYNTON, D. 1940. Soil atmosphere and the production of new rootlets by apple tree root systems. *Proc. Am. Soc. Hort. Sci.* 37: 19–26.

BOYNTON, D., and COMPTON, O. C. 1943. Effect of oxygen pressure in aerated nutrient solution on production of new roots and on growth of roots and tops by fruit trees. *Proc. Am. Soc. Hort. Sci.* 42: 53–58.

BOYNTON, D., DEVILLIERS, J. I., and REUTNER, W. 1938. Are there different critical oxygen concentrations for the different phases of root activity? *Science* 88: 569–570.

BOYNTON, D., and REUTNER, W. 1938. A way of sampling soil gases in dense subsoil and some of its advantages and limitations. *Proc. Soil Sci. Soc. Am.* 3: 37–42.

BOYNTON, D., and REUTNER, W. 1939. Seasonal variation of oxygen and carbon dioxide in three different orchard soils during 1938 and its possible significance. *Proc. Am. Soc. Hort. Sci.* 36: 1–6.

BRADFIELD, R. 1941. Calcium in the soil. I. Physico–chemical relations. *Proc. Soil Sci. Soc. Am.* 6: 8–15.

BRADFORD, R., BATJER, L. P., and OSKAMP, J. 1934. Soils in relation to fruit growing in New York. IV. The significance of the oxidation-reduction potential in evaluating soils for orchard purposes. *N.Y. State (Cornell) Agr. Expt. Sta. Bull.* 592.

BREWER, P. H., and CARR, R. H. 1927. Fertility of a soil as related to the forms of its iron and manganese. *Soil Sci.* 23: 165–173.

BROWN, R. 1947. The gaseous exchange between the root and the shoot of the seedling *Cucurbita pepo*. *Ann. Botany* 11: 417–437.

BROYER, T. C. 1947. The movement of materials into plants. Part II. The nature of solute movement into plants. *Botan. Rev.* 13: 125–167.

BROYER, T. C., and OVERSTREET, R. 1940. Cation exchange in plant roots in relation to metabolic factors. *Am. J. Botany* 27: 425–430.

BRYANT, A. E. 1934. Comparison of anatomical and histological differences between roots of barley grown in aerated and in nonaerated culture solutions. *Plant Physiol.* 9: 389–391.

BUCKINGHAM, E. 1904. Contributions to our knowledge of the aeration of soils. *U. S. Dept. Agr. Bur. Soils Bull.* 25.

BUSHNELL, J. 1935. Sensitivity of the potato plant to soil aeration. *J. Am. Soc. Agron.* 27: 251–253.

CANNON, W. A. 1925. Physiological features of roots with especial reference to the relation of roots to the aeration of soil. *Carnegie Inst. Wash. Pub.* 368: 1–168.

CHANG, H. T., and LOOMIS, W. E. 1945. Effect of carbon dioxide on absorption of water and nutrients by roots. *Plant Physiol.* **20:** 221–232.

CHILDERS, N. F., and WHITE, D. G. 1942. Influence of submersion of the roots on transpiration, apparent photosynthesis and respiration of young apple trees. *Plant Physiol.* **17:** 603–618.

CHILDS, W. H. 1940. Photosynthesis, transpiration and growth of apple trees as influenced by various concentrations of oxygen and carbon dioxide in the soil atmosphere. (Thesis, Ph.D., Cornell Univ.)

CHUPP, CHARLES. 1946. Soil temperature, moisture, aeration and pH as factors in disease incidence. *Soil Sci.* **61:** 31–36.

CLARK, H. E., and SHIVE, J. W. 1932. Influence of continuous aeration upon the growth of tomato plants in solution cultures. *Soil Sci.* **34:** 37–42.

CLEMENTS, F. E. 1921. Aeration and air content. The role of oxygen in root activity. *Carnegie Inst. Wash. Pub.* **315:** 1–183.

COMPTON, O. C. 1947. Aeration and salt absorption by young apple trees. (Thesis, Ph.D., Cornell Univ.)

COMPTON, O. C., and BOYNTON, D. 1944. Normal seasonal changes of oxygen and carbon dioxide percentages in gas from the larger pores of three orchard subsoils. *Soil Sci.* **57:** 107–117.

CONWAY, V. M. 1940. Aeration and plant growth in wet soils. *Botan. Rev.* **6:** 149–163.

DALLAVALLE, J. M. 1948. Micromeritics. Ed. 2. Pitman Publishing Corp., New York.

DEAN, B. E. 1933. Effect of soil type and aeration upon root systems of certain aquatic plants. *Plant Physiol.* **8:** 203–222.

DEVILLIERS, J. I. 1938. Some responses of McIntosh apple seedlings growing with the roots in various concentrations of oxygen. *Proc. Am. Soc. Hort. Sci.* **36:** 86.

DION, H. G., and MANN, P. J. G. 1946. Three–valent manganese in soils. *J. Agr. Sci.* **36:** 239–245.

DOBBS, A. C. 1915. Green manuring in India. *Pusa Agr. Research Inst. Bull.* **56:** 55.

DURELL, W. D. 1941. The effect of aeration on growth of the tomato in nutrient solution. *Plant Physiol.* **16:** 327–341.

ERICKSON, L. C. 1946. Growth of tomato roots as influenced by oxygen in the nutrient solution. *Am. J. Botany* **33:** 551–561.

EVENARI, MICHAEL. 1949. Germination inhibitors. *Botan. Rev.* **15:** 153–194.

FELLOWS, H. 1941. Effect of certain environmental conditions on the prevalence of *Ophiobolus graminis* in the soil. *J. Agr. Research* **63:** 715–726.

FURR, J. R., and ALDRICH, W. W. 1943. Oxygen and carbon dioxide changes in the soil atmosphere of an irrigated date garden on calcareous very fine sandy loam soil. *Proc. Am. Soc. Hort. Sci.* **42:** 46–52.

GARRETT, S. D. 1937a. Soil conditions and the root infecting fungi. *Biol. Revs.* **13:** 159–185.

GARRETT, S. D. 1937b. Soil conditions and the "take-all" disease of wheat. II. The relation between soil reaction and soil aeration. *Ann. Applied Biol.* **24:** 747–751.

GARRETT, S. D. 1939. Soil–borne fungi and the control of root disease. *Imp. Bur. Soil Sci. Tech. Commun.* No. 38.

GARRETT, S. D. 1942. The take–all disease of cereals. *Imp. Bur. Soil Sci. Tech. Commun.* No. 41.

Gilbert, S. G., and Shive, J. W. 1942. The significance of oxygen in nutrient substrates for plants. I. The oxygen requirements. *Soil Sci.* **53**: 143–152.

Gilbert, S. G., and Shive, J. W. 1945. The importance of oxygen in the nutrient substrate for plants–relation of the nitrate ion to respiration. *Soil Sci.* **59**: 453–460.

Gillespie, L. J. 1920. Reduction potentials of bacterial cultures and of water-logged soils. *Soil Sci.* **9**: 199–216.

Girton, R. E. 1927. The growth of citrus seedlings as influenced by environmental factors. *Univ. Calif. (Berkeley) Pubs. Agr. Sci.* **5**: 83–117.

Griffiths, R. L. 1933. Take-all. Incidence and control in the lighter soils of the mallee. *Dept. Agr. S. Australia* **36**: 774–778.

Hall, A. D., Brenchley, W. E., and Underwood, L. M. 1914. The soil solution and the mineral constituents of the soil. *J. Agr. Sci.* **6**: 278–301.

Halverson, H. O. 1931. Studies on the transformations of iron in nature. III. The effect of CO_2 on the equilibrium in iron solutions. *Soil Sci.* **32**: 141–165.

Harrison, W. H., and Aiyer, P. A. S. 1913. The gases of swamp rice soils: their composition and their relationship to the crop. *Mem. Dept. Agr. India, Chem. Ser.* **3**: 65–106.

Hoagland, D. R. 1940. Salt accumulation by plant cells with special reference to metabolism and experiments on barley roots. *Cold Spring Harbor Symposia Quant. Biol.* **8**: 181–194.

Hoagland, D. R. 1944. Lectures on the Inorganic Nutrition of Plants. Chronica Botanica Co., Waltham, Mass.

Hoagland, D. R., and Broyer, T. C. 1936. General nature of the process of salt accumulation by roots with description of experimental methods. *Plant Physiol.* **11**: 471–507.

Hoagland, D. R., and Broyer, T. C. 1942. Accumulation of salt and permeability in plant cells. *J. Gen. Physiol.* **25**: 865–880.

Hoagland, D. R., and Davis, A. R. 1929. The intake and accumulation of electrolytes by plant cells. *Protoplasma* **6**: 610–626.

Hopkins, E. F., Pagan, V., and Silva, F. J. R. 1944. Iron and manganese in relation to plant growth and its importance in Puerto Rico. *J. Agr. Univ. Puerto Rico* **28**: No. 2, 43–101.

Howard, A. 1918. Recent investigations on soil aeration. *Indian Forester* 1918: 187.

Howard, A., and Howard, G. L. C. 1915. Soil ventilation. *Pusa Agr. Research Inst. Bull.* **52**: 1–35.

Humfeld, H. 1930. A method for measuring carbon dioxide evolution from soil. *Soil Sci.* **30**: 1–11.

Hutchins, L. M. 1926. Studies on the oxygen–supplying power of the soil together with quantitative observations on the oxygen–supplying power requisite for seed germination. *Plant Physiol.* **1**: 95–150.

Johnson, M. O. 1917. Manganese as a cause of the depression of the assimilation of pineapple plants. *J. Ind. Eng. Chem.* **9**: 47–49.

Johnston, J., and Williamson, E. D. 1916. The complete solubility curve of calcium carbonate. *J. Am. Chem. Soc.* **38**: 975.

Keen, B. A. 1931. The Physical Properties of the Soil. Longmans, Green and Co., London.

Kliman, S. 1937. The importance of ferrous iron in plants and soils. *Soil Sci. Soc. Am. Proc.* **2**: 385–392.

KNIGHT, R. D.   1924.   The response of plants in soil and water culture to aeration of the roots.   *Ann. Botany* **38:** 305–325.

KOHNKE, H., and BRADFIELD, R.   1935.   Factors affecting the redox potential of soils.   *Rept. Am. Soil Survey Assoc.* **16:** 85.

KRAMER, P. J.   1938.   Root resistance as a cause of the absorption lag.   *Am. J. Botany* **25:** 110–113.

KRAMER, P. J.   1940.   Causes of decreased absorption of water by plants in poorly aerated media.   *Am. J. Botany* **27:** 216–220.

KRAMER, P. J.   1945.   Absorption of water by plants.   *Botan. Rev.* **11:** 310–355.

LAWTON, K.   1945.   The influence of soil aeration on the growth and absorption of nutrients by corn plants.   *Soil Sci. Soc. Am. Proc.* **10:** 263–268.

LEEPER, G. W.   1935.   Manganese deficiencies in cereals.   Plot experiments and a new hypothesis.   *Proc. Roy. Soc. Victoria* **47:** 225–261.

LEEPER, G. W.   1947.   The forms and reactions of manganese in the soil.   *Soil Sci.* **63:** 79–94.

LEEPER, G. W., and SWABY, R. J.   1940.   The oxidation of manganous compounds by micro–organisms in the soil.   *Soil Sci.* **49:** 163–169.

LEMON, E. R.   1948.   The effect on plant growth of manganous and ferrous ions as related to soil aeration.   (Thesis, M.S. in Agr., Cornell Univ.)

LEONARD, O. A., and PINCKARD, J. A.   1946.   Effect of various oxygen and carbon dioxide concentrations on cotton root development.   *Plant Physiol.* **21:** 18–36.

LETTS, E. A., and BLAKE, R. F.   1900.   The carbonic anhydride of the atmosphere.   *Proc. Roy. Dublin Soc. Sci.* **9:** 107–270.

LIN, C. K.   1946.   Effect of oxygen and sodium thioglycollate on growth of rice.   *Plant Physiol.* **21:** 304–318.

LOEHWING, W. F.   1934.   Physiological aspects of the effect of continuous soil aeration on plant growth.   *Plant Physiol.* **9:** 567–583.

LOEHWING, W. F.   1937.   Root interactions of plants.   *Botan. Rev.* **3:** 195–239.

LUNDEGARDH, H.   1927.   Carbon dioxide evolution of soil and crop growth.   *Soil Sci.* **23:** 417–453.

LUNDEGARDH, H.   1947.   Mineral nutrition of plants.   *Ann. Rev. Biochem.* **16:** 503–528.

LYON, T. L., and BUCKMAN, H. O.   1947.   The Nature and Properties of Soils.   Ed. 4.   Macmillan Co., New York.

McCOOL, M. M.   1934.   Effects of various factors on soluble manganese in soils.   *Contribs. Boyce Thompson Inst.* **6,** No. 2, pp. 147–164.

McGEORGE, W. T., and BREAZEALE, J. F.   1931.   The relation of phosphate availability, soil permeability and carbon dioxide to the fertility of calcareous soils.   *Ariz. Expt. Sta. Tech. Bull.* **36.**

McKINNEY, H. H.   1946.   Soil factors in relation to incidence and symptom–expression of virus diseases.   *Soil Sci.* **61:** 93–100.

McPHERSON, D. C.   1939.   Cortical air spaces in the roots of *Zea mays* L.   *New Phytologist* **38:** 190–202.

MACK, W. B.   1930.   The relation of temperature and the partial pressure of oxygen to respiration and growth in germinating wheat.   *Plant Physiol.* **5:** 1–68.

MARSH, F. W.   1928.   A laboratory apparatus for the measurement of carbon dioxide evolved from soils.   *Soil Sci.* **25:** 253–261.

MEYER, B. S., and ANDERSON, D. B.   1930.   Plant Physiology.   D. Van Nostrand Co., Inc., New York.

MILLER, E. C. 1938. Plant Physiology. Ed. 2. McGraw-Hill Book Co., Inc., New York.

MILTHORPE, J., and ROBERTSON, R. N. 1948. Studies in the metabolism of plant cells. VI. Salt respiration and accumulation in barley roots. *Australian J. Exptl. Biol. Med. Sci.* **26:** 189–197.

OLSEN, R. B. 1935. Iron absorption and chlorosis in green plants. Carlsberg Lab. *Compt. rend. trav. lab. Carlsberg. Ser. chim.* **21,** No. 3.

OSTERHOUT, W. J. V. 1936. Electrical phenomena in large plant cells. *Physiol. Revs.* **16:** 216–237.

OSTERHOUT, W. J. V. 1947. The absorption of electrolytes in large plant cells II. *Botan. Rev.* **13:** 194–215.

PAGE, J. B. 1947. Advantages of the pressure pycnometer for measuring the pore space in soils. *Soil Sci. Soc. Am. Proc.* **12:** 81–84.

PEARSALL, W. H., and MORTIMER, C. H. 1939. Oxidation reduction potentials in waterlogged soils, natural waters and muds. *J. Ecol.* **27:** 483–501.

PEARSE, H. L. 1944. Iron and manganese in plant nutrition. *Farming in S. Africa* **19:** 688–694.

PEECH, M., and BATJER, L. P. 1935. A critical study of the methods for measuring oxidation–reduction potentials of soils, with special reference to orchard soils. *N. Y. State Agr. Expt. Sta. Bull.* **625:** 1–23.

PENMAN, H. L. 1940. Gas and vapour movements in the soil. II. The diffusion of carbon dioxide through porous solids. *J. Agr. Sci.* **30:** 570–581.

PEPKOWITZ, L. P., and SHIVE, J. W. 1944. The importance of oxygen in the nutrient substrate for plants—ion absorption. *Soil Sci.* **57:** 143–154.

PREVOT, P., and STEWARD, F. C. 1936. Salient features of the root system relative to the problem of salt absorption. *Plant Physiol.* **11:** 509–534.

RANEY, W. A. 1949. Field measurement of oxygen diffusion through soil. *Soil Sci. Soc. Am. Proc.* **14:** 61–65.

REED, W. E. 1946. The effect of plants on the physical properties of a Dundirk silty clay loam and the effect of soil aeration on plant growth and composition. (Thesis, Ph.D., Cornell Univ.)

REUTHER, W., and CRAWFORD, C. L. 1947. Effect of certain soil and irrigation treatments on citrus chlorosis in a calcareous soil. II. Soil atmosphere studies. *Soil Sci.* **63:** 227–240.

RICH, E. M., and HUNTER, C. 1925. The effect of artificial aeration of the soil on *Impatiens balsamina* L. *New Phytologist* **24:** 257–271.

ROBERTSON, R. N. 1941. Studies in the metabolism of plant cells. I. Accumulation of chlorides by plant cells and its relation to respiration. *Australian J. Exptl. Biol. Med. Sci.* **19:** 265–278.

ROBERTSON, R. N. 1944. Studies in the metabolism of plant cells. II. Effects of temperature on accumulation of potassium chloride and on respiration. *Australian J. Exptl. Biol. Med. Sci.* **22:** 237–245.

ROBERTSON, R. N., and THORN, M. 1945. Studies in the metabolism of plant cells. IV. The reversibility of the salt respiration. *Australian J. Exptl. Biol. Med. Sci.* **23:** 305–309.

ROBERTSON, R. N., and TURNER, J. S. 1945. Studies in the metabolism of plant cells. III. The effects of cyanide on the accumulation of potassium chloride and on respiration: the nature of the salt respiration. *Australian J. Exptl. Biol. Med. Sci.* **23:** 63–73.

ROBERTSON, R. N., TURNER, J. S., and WILKINS, M. J. 1947. Studies in the metabolism of plant cells. V. Salt respiration and accumulation in red beet tissue. *Australian J. Exptl. Biol. Med. Sci.* **25**: 1–8.

ROBERTSON, R. N., and WILKINS, M. J. 1948. Studies in the metabolism of plant cells. VII. The quantitative relations between salt accumulation and salt respiration. *Australian J. Sci. Research* **B1**: 17–37.

ROBINSON, G. W. 1932. Soils, Their Origin, Constitution and Classification. Thomas Murphy & Co., London.

ROBINSON, W. O. 1930. Some chemical phases of submerged soil conditions. *Soil Sci.* **30**: 197–217.

ROMELL, L. G. 1935. Mechanism of soil aeration. *Ann. agron.* 5 [N.S.]: 373–384.

RUSSELL, E. J., and APPLEYARD, A. 1915. The atmosphere of the soil: its composition and the causes of variation. *J. Agr. Sci.* **7**: 1–48.

RUSSELL, M. B. 1949. A simplified air–picnometer for field use. *Soil Sci. Soc. Am. Proc.* **14**: 73–76.

SAMUEL, G., and PIPER, C. S. 1928. "Grey speck" (manganese deficiency) disease in oats. *J. Dept. Agr. S. Australia* **31**: 696–705.

SEELEY, J. G. 1948. Some responses of greenhouse roses to various oxygen concentrations in the substratum. (Thesis, Ph.D., Cornell Univ.)

SHIVE, J. W. 1941. The balance of ions and oxygen tension in nutrient substrates for plants. *Soil Sci.* **51**: 445–459.

SIFTON, H. B. 1945. Air–space tissues in plants. *Botan. Rev.* **11**: 108–143.

SIMMONDS, P. M. 1941. Root rots of cereals. *Botan. Rev.* **7**: 308–331.

SIMMONS, C. F. 1938. The effect of carbon dioxide pressure upon equilibrium of the system: hydrogen colloidal clay–H_2O–$CaCO_3$. Abs. Doctor's Dissertation 25: 417. Ohio State Univ. Press, Columbus, Ohio.

SMITH, F. B., and BROWN, P. E. 1931. Soil respiration. *J. Am. Soc. Agron.* **23**: 909–916.

SMITH, F. B., and BROWN, P. E. 1932. Oxygen absorption in soils. *Iowa State Coll. J. Sci.* **7**: 153–159.

SMITH, F. B., and BROWN, P. E. 1933. The concentration of carbon dioxide in the soil air under various crops and in fallow soils. *Iowa State Coll. J. Sci.* **8**: 1–16.

SMITH, F. W., and COOK, R. L. 1946. The effect of soil aeration, moisture and compaction on nitrification and oxidation and the growth of sugar beets following corn and legumes in pot cultures. *Soil Sci. Soc. Am. Proc.* **11**: 402–406.

SOMERS, I. I., and SHIVE, J. W. 1942. The iron–manganese relation in plant metabolism. *Plant Physiol.* **17**: 582–602.

STARKEY, R. L., and WIGHT, K. M. 1945. Anaerobic corrosion of iron in soil. Final Rpt. Am. Gas Assoc. Iron Corrosion Fellowship. Am. Gas Assoc. New York.

STEWARD, F. C. 1932. The absorption and accumulation of solutes by living plant cells. I. Experimental conditions which determine salt absorption by storage tissue. *Protoplasma* **15**: 29–56.

STEWARD, F. C. 1933. The absorption and accumulation of solutes by living plant cells. V. Observations upon the effects of time, oxygen and salt concentration upon absorption and respiration by storage tissue. *Protoplasma* **18**: 208–242.

STEWARD, F. C. 1935. Mineral nutrition of plants. *Ann. Rev. Biochem.* **4**: 519–544.

STEWARD, F. C., BERRY, W. E., and BROYER, T. C. 1937. Salt accumulation by plants—the roles of growth and metabolism. *Trans. Faraday Soc.* **33**: 1006–1016.

STEWARD, F. C., and PRESTON, G. 1940. Metabolic processes of potato discs under conditions conducive to salt accumulation. *Plant Physiol.* 15: 23–61.

STEWARD, F. C., and STREET, H. E. 1947. The nitrogenous constituents of plants. *Ann. Rev. Biochem.* 16: 471–502.

STURGIS, M. B. 1936. Changes in the oxidation–reduction equilibrium in soils as related to the physical properties of the soil and the growth of rice. *La. Agr. Expt. Sta. Bull.* 271: 1–37.

TANG, P. 1931. An experimental study of the germination of wheat seed under water, as related to temperature and aeration. *Plant Physiol.* 6: 203–248.

TAYLOR, D. L. 1942. Influence of oxygen tension on respiration, fermentation and growth in wheat and rice. *Am. J. Botan.* 29: 721–738.

TAYLOR, S. A. 1949. Oxygen diffusion in porous media as affected by compaction and moisture content. *Soil Sci. Soc. Am. Proc.* 14: 55–61.

TAYLOR, S. A. 1949b. Soil air–plant growth relationships with emphasis on means of characterizing soil aeration. (Thesis, Ph.D., Cornell Univ.)

TENDELOO, H. J. C., VERVELDE, G. J., and ZWART-VOORSPUIJ, A. J. Z. 1944. Electrochemical behavior of ion exchanging substances. Potential measurements of plant roots. *Rec. trav. chim.* 63: 97–104.

THORNTON, N. C. 1943–45. Importance of oxygen supply in secondary dormancy and its relation to the inhibiting mechanism regulating dormancy. *Contribs. Boyce Thompson Inst.* 13: 487–500.

ULRICH, A. 1942. Metabolism of organic acids in excised barley roots as influenced by temperature, oxygen tension and salt concentration. *Am. J. Botany* 29: 220–227.

VLAMIS, J., and DAVIS, A. R. 1943. Germination, growth and respiration of rice and barley seedlings at low oxygen pressures. *Plant Physiol.* 18: 685–692.

VLAMIS, J., and DAVIS, A. R. 1944. Effects of oxygen tension on certain physiological responses of rice, barley and tomato. *Plant Physiol.* 19: 33–51.

WAKSMAN, S. A. 1932. Principles of Soil Microbiology. Williams and Wilkins Co., Baltimore, Md.

WEAVER, J. E., and HIMMEL, W. J. 1930. Relation of increased water content and decreased aeration to root development in hydrophytes. *Plant Physiol.* 5: 69–92.

WHITNEY, J. B., JR. 1942. Effects of the composition of the soil atmosphere on the absorption of water by plants. Ohio State Univ. Abs. Doctor's Dissertation 38: 97–103.

WILLIS, L. G. 1932. The effect of liming soils on the availability of manganese and iron. *J. Am. Soc. Agron.* 24: 716–726.

WINGARD, S. A. 1941. The nature of disease resistance in plants I. *Botan. Rev.* 7: 59–109.

ZIMMERMAN, P. W. 1930. Oxygen requirements for root growth of cuttings in water. *Am. J. Botany* 17: 842–861.

ZIMMERMAN, P. W., HITCHCOCK, A. E., and CROCKER, W. 1930. The movement of gases into and through plants. *Contribs. Boyce Thompson Inst.* 3: 313–320.

CHAPTER 5

SOIL TEMPERATURE AND PLANT GROWTH

By S. J. Richards, R. M. Hagan, and T. M. McCalla

INTRODUCTION

TEMPERATURE is one of the primary factors controlling the growth of plants and their distribution over the earth. Many studies have been made of the influence of the aerial environment on plants. Discussions of this subject can be found in a number of reference books on plant ecology, including those by Weaver and Clements (1929), Klages (1942), and Daubenmire (1947). The growth of higher plants, however, is a function of both the aerial and the soil temperatures. The activities of the soil microflora have an important bearing on the growth and well being of higher plants and are dependent entirely upon soil temperature. Nevertheless, comparatively little attention has been given to evaluating the importance of soil temperature as a factor in plant growth. The purpose of this chapter is to summarize existing knowledge of soil temperature and its effects on the growth of plants and micro-organisms.

Man's desires to grow both crop and ornamental plants in environments far different from those of their indigenous habitats have greatly magnified the importance of temperature as a factor in plant growth. Frequently, cultivated plants are forced to attempt their life processes under unfavorable temperature conditions both in the air and in the soil. The importance of soil temperature in this connection was recognized many years ago by Hedrick (1905) who wrote: "In our efforts to till the soil [and] to grow plants, we increase rather than diminish the importance of soil heat as a factor in plant life." He urged that studies be undertaken to provide accurate knowledge of the relation of soil temperature to growth of cultivated plants.

While many investigations have been undertaken on the relationship of climate to plant growth, they shed but little light on the influence of soil temperature on their growth. This situation arises because climatic factors normally affect similarly the temperature of both the aerial and the subterranean environment of growing plants. Accordingly, it is very difficult and in most cases impossible to evaluate from published ecological data the contribution of soil temperature to

303

the observed plant-growth responses.   With the exception of the period during seed germination, its importance remains obscure.

The effect of soil temperature on plant growth can be determined adequately only in controlled experiments providing the desired variation in soil temperature while maintaining constant aerial conditions. It is surprising to find such a paucity of well-designed experiments on this subject.   It will be necessary in many cases, therefore, to make use of information drawn from studies in which the relation of soil temperature to growth was not the primary objective.   Thus, a considerable portion of the data included in this review have been extracted from a great variety of experiments in a number of fields, and in many cases these data are incomplete.   Field studies are a disappointing source for elucidating the influence of soil temperature on plant growth.   In drawing upon these sources for this purpose, one must face not only the usual variability inherent in field work, but also, and far more serious, the fact that the environmental factors that produced the observed soil temperatures also influenced directly the resultant plant growth.

Reported soil-temperature data are often inadequate.   A satisfactory record of soil temperature is extremely cumbersome to present, inasmuch as the temperature varies with both depth and time.   Root temperatures are believed to approach closely those of their immediate surroundings (Daubenmire, 1947, p. 186).   This means that at any given time a single root system is exposed to a considerable range in temperature between its various parts and that each part is subject to a continually changing temperature.   This continual variation in soil temperature with depth and with time poses a formidable obstacle in attempting to relate soil temperatures to the observed growth of higher plants and micro-organisms.

The following sections summarize the present knowledge of the factors influencing soil temperature; the relation of temperature to physical, chemical, and physiological processes involved in growth; the effect of soil temperature on plant growth from germination through maturity; extreme soil temperatures as a cause of plant damage; the indirect effects of soil temperature on plant growth; the influence of soil temperature on the growth and activities of soil micro-organisms; and the relation of soil temperature to crop management.

I. SOIL TEMPERATURE

By S. J. Richards

Soil Temperature Measurements

Soil-temperature measurement is a subject of wide interest.   References to soil-temperature measurements are found in the literature dealing with plant physiology, ecology, pathology, horticulture, agronomy, and soils. In addition soil-temperature measurements are of interest to civil and highway engineers, particularly as they relate to frozen soils.

Because of this wide variety of interests, an adequate survey of soil-temperature measurements becomes a difficult undertaking. Sources of information are widely scattered, and measurements and methods of reporting are so diversified that comparisons and summaries are almost impossible. Certain conventions for measuring air temperature have made possible comparison of records taken at various places. No similar set of conventions has been extensively used in soil-temperature work. Shreve (1918) wrote about a committee appointed by the Ecological Society of America to establish conventions for measuring soil temperature in the United States and Canada. He reported that in 1917 about 30 stations were making measurements at 3-inch and 12-inch depths. A review of the literature, however, does not indicate that the convention to measure soil temperature at these depths was widely adopted. More recently the Conference of Directors of the Organization Meteorologique International, at its meeting in Washington, D. C., on September 22 to October 11, 1947, adopted the resolution:

137 (CIMO Toronto 1947:XX) Earth Temperature Measurements. The Conference recommends that: (1) the standard depths for earth temperature measurements should be 10, 20, 50 and 100 cm. (4, 8, 20 and 40 in.). Where other depths have been employed and a large amount of data collected they may be maintained; (2) the character of the soil and cover [be] described.

Because of the varied subjects relating to soil temperatures, many of the variable factors cannot be eliminated by adopting common practices. For example, studies relating to engineering and climatology will tend to use bare soil and thereby eliminate the plant influence. However, where the effect of soil temperature on plant environment is under consideration, measurements will have to be made while the plants are growing because of the effects of shading by the plants themselves. If, however, the depths suggested by the above resolution become widely used, the comparing of records made at various locations will be greatly facilitated.

Terminology

The expression soil temperature as used in the title of this chapter implies a knowledge of the temperature values at any time and at every location in the root zone of the plants being grown. To adequately measure, record, and make use of the soil temperature records in one localized area is a major undertaking. Figure 46 illustrates the variations in soil temperature occurring at various depths during a single day. Equipment for automatically recording such records is expensive, and the storage and interpretation of the data soon become burdensome.

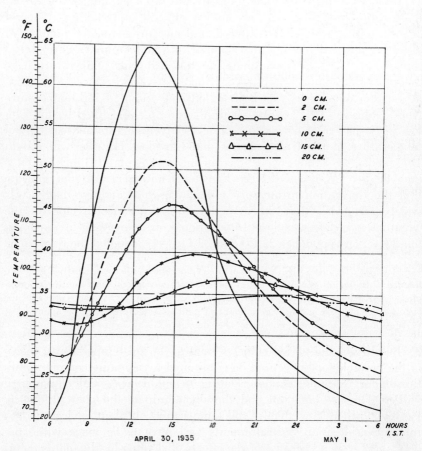

FIGURE 46.—Soil temperature variations at depths of 0, 2, 5, 10, 15, and 20 centimeters taken during a single day (6 A.M. April 30, to 6 A.M. May 1, 1935) at Poona, India. (Dravid, 1940.)

Every investigation of soil temperature is a compromise between the desired completeness of the records and the facilities available for obtaining them.

To summarize long records of temperature, or to obtain a single index that will show an effect of treatment or will correlate with plant response, various summarizing terms are used:

(1) The *daily maximum* and *minimum* values at a given depth are perhaps the best values used to characterize the temperature for a given day. For longer periods of time, *weekly*, *monthly*, or *annual* means of these daily values are used. Where equipment for recording temperature has not been available, soil temperatures have been observed at a given time each day. Such records may be useful to show relative effects of certain treatments, but they are not so valuable as maximum and minimum values in connection with heat-exchange studies.

(2) A *daily mean* value of the soil temperature is usually the average of the maximum and minimum values. A. Smith (1939) has indicated there may be a significant difference between this daily mean and the average of temperature values taken at short intervals throughout the day. However, his data show differences of less than one degree when hourly or 15-minute values are averaged and compared with a weekly mean.

Where continuous records of soil temperatures are available the true mean is defined by

$$\bar{T} = \frac{1}{\tau} \int_0^{\tau} T dt \tag{1}$$

where T is the instantaneous value of temperature, t is time, and τ is the period of time for which the mean is taken. This mean is best obtained using a planimeter as was done by Bliss (1944) and Bliss, Moore, and Bream (1942) for weekly mean values.

(3) The *daily range* of soil temperature is the difference between the maximum and minimum values. The mean daily range is often given in conjunction with weekly and monthly mean temperatures.

None of the summary terms heretofore listed will satisfactorily indicate the variation of temperature with time. When all other environmental conditions are controlled to such extent that plant response to soil temperature is measurable, it may be necessary to devise an index that will show the length of time soil temperature exceeds or falls below a certain temperature interval considered optimum for the particular plant being studied.

Measurements

Chapters dealing with soil temperature have been written by Schubert (1930), Keen (1931), and Baver (1948). Each of these authors has given illustrations of soil-temperature measurements, but none has attempted to summarize and indicate the ranges of the soil-temperature values reported. Baver (1948) gives a list of literature citations for some of the pioneering work done by European workers on soil-temperature measurements.   Some of the early American publications are cited by Seeley (1901), MacDougal (1903), and Carter (1928).

Fitton and Brooks (1931) obtained data from as many sources as possible in the United States.   Table 33 gives selected values of the mean monthly temperatures found in the surface soil at the various

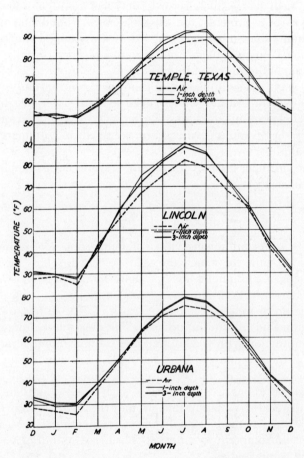

FIGURE 47.—Comparison of monthly mean air and soil temperature values at Temple, Texas, Lincoln, Nebr., and Urbana, Ill.   (Fitton and Brooks, 1931.)

locations as indicated.   References to the original sources of these data are given by the authors of this noteworthy summary.   In many instances the supplementary data were not adequately given.

Figure 47 is also taken from Fitton and Brooks (1931).   It shows a comparison of monthly mean soil and air temperatures from Temple, Texas, Lincoln, Nebr., and Urbana, Ill.

TABLE 33.—*Monthly mean temperature values observed in surface soils at various locations in the United States (Fitton and Brooks, 1931)*

Location	Soil	Vegetative cover	Year	Depth	Jan.	Feb.	Mar.	Apr.	May	June	July	Aug.	Sept.	Oct.	Nov.	Dec.
				Inches	°F.	°F.	°F.	°F.	°F.	°F.	°F.	°F.	°F.	°F.	°F.	°F.
New Haven, Conn.	Sandy	Bare soil	1926	3	....	....	....	....	60.7	68.4	81.2	74.9	67.0	54.4	46.1	
Auburn, Ala.	Sandy Bottom-land	Cultivated	1889	3	48.5	50.5	55.2	65.5	72.2	74.0	86.5	82.2	75.5	64.8	52.2	52.0
	Loam	Stream bank	1889	3	48.0	51.0	55.2	64.0	73.8	75.0	87.5	83.2	76.2	64.8	52.8	51.8
East Lansing, Mich.	Sand	....	1914–15	4	32.0	32.1	33.9	53.0	56.4	66.4	72.8	68.1	65.9	52.8	41.4	33.6
	Clay	....	1914–15	4	31.3	32.7	34.5	54.4	58.1	68.6	75.0	70.0	67.4	54.0	41.5	31.8
		....	1914–15	4	32.0	32.3	33.7	52.0	55.3	65.5	71.6	68.2	65.5	52.3	41.2	33.0
	Peat	....	1914–15	4	31.9	31.7	31.6	46.6	55.0	64.6	71.5	67.5	64.7	51.5	40.7	34.0
Wooster, Ohio		....	1924–25	6	35.0	37.2	41.0	44.8	51.8	65.3	68.8	69.6	....	50.6	40.6	34.4
Lexington, Ky.		....	1922–27	3	32.7	35.5	42.1	56.0	62.8	74.6	77.1	76.7	73.1	58.3	45.6	39.2
		Cultivated, winter cover	1913–15	6	33.3	35.9	36.4	47.8	57.6	68.8	73.5	73.9	66.0	57.4	45.6	40.6
Purdue, Ind.		Straw mulch	1913–15	6	36.3	36.2	35.4	42.6	52.4	61.6	67.3	68.2	64.1	57.3	48.0	43.3
		Grass	1913–15	6	35.0	35.6	35.1	49.7	55.5	66.0	71.9	70.6	62.7	54.9	45.6	41.4
Urbana, Ill.		....	1897–1916	3	31.0	30.6	39.5	50.6	62.2	72.2	77.8	75.8	69.0	56.8	43.0	33.4
		....	1897–1916	6	32.6	31.5	39.3	49.2	60.5	70.5	75.8	74.8	68.8	57.0	44.0	35.0
Lincoln, Nebr.		Bare soil	1900–04	3	30.0	28.7	41.1	59.3	72.1	81.2	88.6	85.3	72.9	61.4	44.3	31.6
		Bare soil	1900–04	6	29.6	28.0	37.9	54.5	68.7	77.5	83.6	82.0	71.0	60.2	44.1	31.9
Temple, Texas		....	1918–24	3	53.2	52.3	58.6	67.9	78.3	86.5	92.2	93.3	83.9	73.1	60.2	52.8
		....	1918–24	6	53.3	52.7	58.7	67.5	77.3	85.6	91.7	92.3	83.8	73.3	60.9	53.4
Moscow, Idaho		....	1898–1901	3	30.8	28.8	34.4	41.2	51.2	58.0	64.1	67.5	54.6	47.8	40.8	33.8
Fort Collins, Colo		....	1889–1927	3	27.7	29.6	36.5	46.6	56.5	66.7	71.4	69.3	61.1	48.3	36.7	29.7
Pullman, Wash.		....	1912–13	6	32.3	....	....	44.7	54.9	62.3	64.8	70.2	57.2	42.4	40.4	34.5
Pendleton, Ore.	Sandy	Grass	1890	4	26.7	37.3	44.9	62.2	72.3	74.2	84.6	83.3	73.2	57.4	45.8	
Davis, Calif.	Loam	Bare	1925–27	3	48.2	49.9	55.2	61.9	72.9	78.9	86.6	83.2	76.4			

The wide variety of data published on soil-temperature measurements may be illustrated by a few examples. Hinton (1944) made daily readings of the temperature at a single depth of 5 feet in Newfoundland from November 1942 to December 1943. A maximum reading of 50°F. was found in September, and a minimum of 33° occurred in April. Thompson (1934) reported the soil temperature at eight depths for the years 1929–34 at Winnipeg, Manitoba. Average values for 3 years are given by the author to show the "overturn" of soil temperatures (reversal of the temperature gradient) that takes place each spring and fall. The annual ranges of temperature values at depths of 4, 10, 20, and 40 inches are, respectively, 42, 36, 34, and 26°F. Soil temperatures in Kansas and Saskatchewan, Canada, can be compared by using data from McColloch and Hayes (1923) and Harrington (1928). Both of these publications give temperature readings at depths of 1-foot intervals down to 6 and 8 feet, respectively. In Kansas the maximum temperature at 1 foot was 85°F., and the annual range was 52°. Corresponding values at the 1-foot level in Saskatchewan were 65° maximum and 67° annual range.

Sinclair (1922) reported soil-temperature values under desert conditions in Arizona. Just below the soil surface in June, 1915, the maximum soil temperature was 71.5°C., which was much higher than the maximum air temperature of 42.5°. At 10- and 20-centimeter depths the maximum values were, respectively, 42 and 35°. For the same two depths the annual range of values was approximately 40 and 30°.

In Egypt, Taylor and Burns (1924) measured average monthly maximum values for July at depths of 10 and 20 centimeters. The average maximum at 10 centimeters depth was 41.7°C., and at 20 centimeters depth, the average maximum was 35.1°. Smith (1929a) gave a detailed report of the soil and air temperatures at Davis, Calif., from February to September, 1925, and from December to June, 1927. In a later publication, Smith (1929b) gave the same data in terms of maximum, minimum, and average values for day and night periods. Rigg (1947) measured the temperature at a depth of 6 inches in a sphagnum bog in Washington and found the values to range from 46 to 68°F. during the growing season.

The published works dealing with soil-temperature measurements just referred to are examples of the material available. Most of these publications cite further literature on the subject.

Instrumentation

A wide variety of instruments has been used to indicate and record soil temperatures. The mercury-in-glass thermometer is undoubtedly the most common one.   Although subject to certain errors, which will be noted later, its greatest asset is reliability.   The mercury thermometer does not lend itself to the automatic recording of temperatures, but it is used as a secondary standard for checking recording equipment. Smith (1926) and Penman (1943) used strips of metal in conjunction with thermometers for measuring the temperature of surface soils.   To observe maximum and minimum values without being present at the time they occurred, Toumey and Stickel (1925) used standard maximum and minimum thermometers developed for air-temperature measurements.   These thermometers were fastened to a wooden paddle and inserted into a horizontal hole from a trench.

Glass thermometers are subject to error in measuring soil temperatures at shallow depths because part of the glass is exposed to radiation and air temperature.   For deeper installations, the hole necessary for inserting the thermometer and removing it for reading provides a parallel path for heat exchange and influences the temperature of the soil where the thermometer bulb rests.

Soil thermographs that continuously record soil temperatures on paper charts have been used for many years.   One of the interesting early models of such equipment, the operation of which was based on the differential expansion of solids, is described by Keen and Russell (1921).   Mail (1937) gives some results of tests made on a commercial thermograph and makes certain recommendations for its use. Thermograph elements are not suitable for measuring surface temperatures, for the bulb will absorb radiant energy and has other thermal properties unlike the soil.   Because its thermal-sensitive unit has a relatively large heat capacity, a thermograph will lag behind rapid changes in the soil temperature.   In installing a thermograph unit, several feet of the flexible cable should be buried in the soil at the same depth as the bulb.   If this is done the heat transmitted by the cable as it passes to the air will be dissipated in the soil without affecting the region where the temperature is being measured.   In testing a thermograph for accuracy before installation, the bulb should be carried through a range of temperature values and the recording instrument itself should be exposed to the full range of temperatures at which it is expected to operate.   Every thermograph should have a built-in mechanism that compensates for changes in ambient temperature. This mechanism should be tested, as well as the reaction due to changes of the bulb temperature.

Thermocouples have been used in soil-temperature studies.   In using them to make freezing-point-depression measurements, Bodman and Day (1937) showed that a thermojunction, because of its low heat capacity, will indicate rapid changes in temperature with little effect on the heat exchange of the system.   By using commercial recording potentiometers and motor-driven switching arrangements, Brooks *et al.* (1941) devised equipment for soil- and air-temperature measurements that would automatically record temperatures at 75 locations. A reading was made at each station every 10 minutes.   Brooks and Kelly (1951) used a "touch" thermocouple for accurately indicating the surface temperature of soils.   One of the disadvantages of using thermocouples is that a reference junction must be maintained at some known temperature or a compensating type reference junction must be used.

The resistance thermometer is another instrument commonly used for measuring soil temperature.   Electrical bridge circuits for measuring resistance are as versatile as potentiometers for adaptation to the automatic recording of multiple stations, as has been shown by the work of W. O. Smith (1939) and White (1946).   The sensitive units are often coils of wire made of nickel alloy.   One commercial variety of this unit has the trade name of Thermohm.   The measurements of Thompson (1934), White (1946), and many others make use of these resistance thermometers.   A more recent development in this type of indicator is called a Thermister.   The properties of this unit are described by Becker, Green, and Pearson (1946).   Richards and Campbell (1948) and Colman and Hendrix (1949) have used them in soil-temperature studies.

Factors Influencing Soil Temperatures

Basically the temperature of an object is determined by the amount of heat or energy associated with the materials comprising the object. If, during an interval of time, there is a net gain or loss of heat to or from the object, then its temperature will increase or decrease a given amount, depending on the heat capacity of the object.   This statement is not valid if chemical reactions or changes in phase occur at the same time, since heat energy which would otherwise affect temperature is released or absorbed by such processes.   A study of the factors influencing soil temperature is therefore largely a study of the various ways in which heat is gained or lost by the soil.

Insolation

Radiation from the sun is considered the only source of heat large enough to influence soil temperatures significantly.   Exothermic chemical reactions within the soil and the conduction of heat from deeper strata within the earth supply some heat to the soil, but at rates too slow to be effective.

The rate at which radiant energy reaches the earth's atmosphere from the sun is called the solar constant. This constant has the value 1.94 calories per minute per square centimeter normal to the direction of the radiation. This value is obtained by extrapolation from several measurements taken at various elevations within the atmosphere. There are slight seasonal variations in the solar constant depending on the earth's distance from the sun, but these variations are small compared with the variable scattering and absorption of the sun's radiation within the atmosphere.

Kimball (1931) reproduces some curves showing the variations in the spectral distribution of the sun's radiation as it passes through various fractions of the atmosphere. These curves show that solar radiation is distributed over the range of wave lengths from 300 to 2,300 millimicrons, and a greater reduction occurs in the shorter, or blue, region of the spectrum. The reduction of the direct radiation in these wave lengths takes place largely by the scattering of light from dust and water particles suspended in the atmosphere. Multiple scattering from all parts of the atmosphere accounts for the blue color of the sky and makes some contribution to the radiant energy received by the soil. This is the so-called diffuse portion of the incoming radiation.

In addition to scattering, absorption of the sun's radiant energy by the earth's atmosphere is the cause of large variations in the rate at which radiant energy reaches the soil. Pure air absorbs a relatively small fraction of the energy, but air laden with dust and water vapor is capable of absorbing variable fractions up to practically 100 percent, as in the case of dense storm clouds. Since the length of path traversed in the earth's atmosphere is much greater during the early and late daylight hours, the fraction of energy absorbed during these periods is greatly increased. Energy absorbed by water in the air may be dissipated when some of the water evaporates, or it is remitted as long-wave-length radiation, which will be considered later.

The amount of solar radiation or insolation has long been recognized as an important part of climatology. The *Monthly Weather Review* publishes periodically numerous instantaneous values and weekly average values of the daily insolation measured at various locations over the United States. Table 34 gives monthly averages of daily insolation values at several stations selected from a paper by Hand (1949). At Poona, India, Dravid (1940) reported that the average daily insolation

TABLE 34.—*Monthly mean values of the daily total solar and sky radiation in calories per square centimeter at various locations (Hand, 1949)*

Month	Blue Hill, Mass.	Fairbanks, Alaska	Ithaca, N. Y.	Lincoln, Nebr.	Miami, Fla.	Madison, Wis.	New Orleans, La.	Riverside, Calif.	Twin Falls, Idaho	Washington, D. C.
January	160	13	120	189	304	150	220	264	165	158
February	236	64	186	249	349	221	267	299	226	223
March	327	196	255	343	421	314	356	434	346	320
April	394	360	311	415	471	403	426	481	464	406
May	471	456	427	491	499	471	455	540	568	483
June	515	507	494	553	476	524	479	577	616	511
July	506	450	505	577	473	540	425	586	604	500
August	467	306	456	481	468	456	430	536	530	444
September	359	174	357	405	405	345	375	468	458	369
October	282	84	243	302	374	245	378	362	320	293
November	171	29	122	205	318	150	284	284	175	202
December	139	8	103	163	347	118	205	211	125	146

for March, April, and May, 1935, was 761 calories per square centimeter of horizontal surface. Similar data for various European stations are given by Knoch (1929).

Long-wave radiation

As was heretofore stated, radiation from the sun is the primary source of heat influencing soil temperature. The next step is to consider the various ways that this heat energy is lost from the soil, for the net rate of heat gain or loss determines whether the soil temperature is being raised or lowered. Radiation from the soil surface is an effective way of losing heat to the atmosphere. Stefan's law is well known; it states that any surface loses heat by radiation at a rate proportional to the fourth power of its absolute temperature. For a good radiator, commonly called a black body, the proportionality constant, σ, is 13.70×10^{-13} calories/cm.^{2} sec. (deg. $A)^4$. In other words, the rate of radiant heat loss from a square centimeter of surface equals σT^4.

The surface characteristics of soils vary greatly, but Brooks (1936) lists data from various sources to show that the soils for which data are available emit long-wave radiations at rates varying between 0.4 and 0.5 of a black body surface. Although the instantaneous rate of long-wave radiation is much smaller than the peak value of solar radiation, long-wave radiation is still important, since it operates continuously and not just during the daylight hours. Assuming a surface emissivity of 0.5 and an average temperature of 30°C., the amount of heat radiated from one square centimeter of soil surface in 24 hours amounts to approximately 500 calories. A further characteristic of the radiation from the soil surface is obtained from Wien's displacement law, which states that the wave length of maximum intensity varies inversely with the absolute temperature of the surface. At 30°C. the wave length of maximum intensity is 10 microns. Since the radiant energy passes from the earth's surface in a range of wave lengths near the value indicated by Wien's law, in contrast to solar radiation, it is called long-wave radiation.

All of the long-wave radiation occurring at the soil surface is not lost to the outer atmosphere. Water vapor, carbon dioxide, and ozone in the atmosphere are good absorbers of radiation in the range of wave lengths that comes from the soil surface. Water vapor is by far the most important because of its broad absorption bands occurring at approximately 6 and 20 microns. These absorbers in turn become emitters of radiation as well.

Elsasser (1942), using temperature and water-vapor data obtained from balloon soundings in the atmosphere, has developed a chart from which long-wave radiation from the sky is given. A summary statement is given by the following quotation from Elsasser:

> With clear skies the incoming radiation is practically always between 50 and 85 percent of the black body flux corresponding to the temperature of the air near the ground and is most commonly between 65 and 75 percent of this flux, . . . any cloud present greatly reduces the heat loss of the ground and with a solid overcast the outgoing flux is only of the order of 5–10 percent of the black body flux.

This same paper gives a review of the measurements made by various workers relating the incoming long-wave-length sky radiation to the temperature and the water-vapor pressure of the air near the ground. One of the several empirical formulas used is

$$R/F_b = a + b \sqrt{e} \qquad (2)$$

where R is the incoming sky radiation, F_b equals σT^4 from Stefan's law, and using the air temperature, e is water-vapor pressure in the air expressed in millibars, and a and b are constants having values of approximately 0.50 and 0.059, respectively.

Radiation measurements

A variety of instruments for measuring and recording radiation has been described. Hand (1937) reviewed the solar radiation investigations made by the United States Weather Bureau. The Epply pyrheliometer is the instrument most commonly used. Other instruments mentioned by Hand are the Callendar electrical resistance pyrheli-ometer, the Marvin pyrheliometer, and the Smithsonian silver disk pyrheliometer. Sprague and Williams (1943) described a simplified integrating light recorder for field use. Such instruments using photo-electric-sensitive elements are limited in their application to visible, or short-wave length, radiation. Elsasser (1942) reviewed the charac-teristics of several instruments that have been used to measure atmos-pheric, or long-wave, radiation.

In most of the instruments listed in the preceding paragraph the sensitive element is a surface designed to absorb as much as possible of the incident radiation, and the temperature of this plate is observed relative to a similar plate that is not exposed. Absolute rates of radia-tion are sometimes indicated by supplying measured heat inputs to the nonradiated plate in order to maintain no difference in temperature between the two. Thermopiles are usually used to indicate tempera-ture differences between the two plates. Brooks, Lorenzen, and Boelter (1939) used a radiometer with 150 junctions to measure the difference between incoming and outgoing radiation above a soil during the night. During one series of measurements the outgoing radiation exceeded the incoming by 25 British thermal units per square foot hour for several hours until a cloud overcast developed, at which time the rates very nearly balanced.

There are advantages and disadvantages to enclosing the absorbing surface of a radiometer. The Epply pyrheliometer has its absorber enclosed and is therefore an instrument with long life characteristics that is relatively insensitive to air movements and surface contamina-tion. However, the enclosing cover limits the range of radiation to which it is sensitive, since some of the long-wave radiation will be absorbed in the enclosing cover.

Gier, Dunkle, and Possner (1949) have recently developed an open-type radiometer. To eliminate the effects of varying air currents, a stream of air is supplied continuously to the radiometer by a blower. In comparison with a pyrheliometer this open type radiometer gave higher readings during the daylight and continued to give a reading of about 100 British thermal units per square-foot hour after nightfall. Brooks and Kelley (1950) also used this instrument in connection with microclimatological studies.

Exposure

The intensity of solar radiation per unit of surface area is propor-tional to the cosine of the angle between the direction of radiation and the normal to the surface. This relation accounts for the continual diurnal change in radiation intensity as the sun's position changes, and it also is one of the factors in soil temperature relations, since the angle indicated above depends on the latitude and the slope of the soil surface. During May and June at the Arizona station, Shreve (1924b) measured the temperature at 3-inch depths on the north and south slopes of an artificial hill 10 feet high with slopes of 30 percent. The average weekly maximum value was 5° to 7°C. higher on the southern slope. Shreve (1924a) observed higher mean values and greater ranges of temperatures on southern slopes under natural forest conditions. This same paper indicated a decrease in mean temperature values with higher elevations. The basis for such observations should be accounted for in terms of radiation and air temperature. Variations in average moisture conditions in the air would probably be the basic explanation for variations in soil temperature with elevation.

Data are not sufficient for conclusive proof, but it is indicated that some of the effects soil temperature and exposure have on natural vegetation are secondary. In certain mountainous regions the difference in the kind and amount of natural vegetation on northern and southern slopes is very great. It is likely, however, that this difference in vegetation is primarily caused by differing soil-moisture conditions brought about by earlier snow melt and faster drying out of the soil on the southern exposure. Shreve (1924a) points out that this relationship of vegetation to exposure is most marked in an intermediate rainfall zone. Under higher or lower rainfall the vegetation is not so greatly influenced by factors relating to slope.

Shade and insulation

Shade and insulation are important in influencing soil temperatures, largely to the extent they affect the exchange of heat at the soil surface by radiation. The interception of radiation by the commercial crops grown on soils is probably the greatest single factor to be considered. In general, the shading by crops grown on the soil has the effect of reducing the annual range in soil-temperature values. When the soil is warming the plants intercept radiation and lower the amount of radiant heat arriving at the soil surface. During other seasons of the year, when the soil is losing heat, a close-growing crop or mulch will reduce the heat loss by long-wave radiation and convection. Factors such as artificial shading and mulching will be mentioned in a later section dealing with cultural practices.

Evaporation and condensation

It is a well known phenomenon that a given amount of heat is associated with any change of phase. For every gram of water evaporating from the soil surface, a quantity of heat energy equivalent to approximately 580 calories is lost by the soil. This same effect also occurs when water is transpired by leaves, although the effect on soil temperature is effective only to the extent that this heat loss cools the surrounding air.

Evaporation of water from a soil surface is too complicated a process to be expressed in terms of the various factors influencing it, although several noteworthy attempts have been made. At the two extremes in the soil-moisture range, evaporation rates are controlled by two entirely different conditions. When the soil surface is wet, evaporation is dependent on vapor-pressure gradients and wind velocity in the air just above the surface, as well as the amount of radiant heat energy available. For such conditions Penman (1948) developed a complicated empirical relation which seemed to agree with several sets of observed data. Under such conditions the evaporation rate from a bare soil was 90 percent of the rate from a water surface, and from sod the rate was only 75 percent of that from water. At the other extreme of soil moisture conditions, when the soil surface is very dry, the rate at which water evaporates from the soil surface depends on the rate at which water is transported from the lower layers of soil to the surface. The effect of temperature gradients on the movement of soil moisture will be considered later. Between the two extremes of soil moisture, both sets of conditions must be considered.

Keen, Crowther, and Coutts (1926) made a study of evaporation rates under laboratory conditions and even here found that the environmental conditions are very complex and liable to irregular change from one experiment to another. Ramdas and Katte (1934) studied the temperature and vapor pressure of the air just above the soil during the clear season at Poona, India. From 0 to 2 meters above the soil, the vapor pressure decreased with height during the day and increased during the night, indicating that the soil was a source and sink for atmospheric moisture. No such variations were found above a surface impermeable to water and moisture. Samplings confirmed the fact that the surface soil gained and lost 3 to 7 percent during the night and day periods.

Russel (1939) gave data to show that mulching and tillage can influence the evaporation loss of water in a fallow soil. Hide (1942) found in one set of soil-temperature readings at Manhattan, Kan., that evaporation can have a significant effect on heat transfers at the soil surface. Fortier (1926) reviewed some of the many attempts to measure evaporation rates from blocks of soil in tanks that were periodically weighed. The degree of wetness of the soil was controlled in some experiments by varying the depths to a free water surface, and this wetness was shown to influence evaporation rates. Several results were reviewed that showed the effects soluble salts in the soil had in decreasing evaporation.

Convection

Convection is another process whereby heat is transferred to or away from the soil surface. The direction and rate of heat transfer by the air will depend on the relative temperature of the soil surface and the air just above the soil. For a given temperature gradient, this transfer rate will also be affected by the wind velocity and turbulence. Direct measurement of heat transfer by convection is rather difficult. It is usually evaluated as the remaining net exchange of heat at the surface when all other factors have been measured. Data are not sufficient to establish the extent to which this form of heat transfer is effective in causing the air temperature inversions that occur during radiation frosts. Guild (1950) presented measurements to show that the magnitude of this convective term was 20 to 40 percent of the net radiation term on clear nights at Gila Bend in the Arizona desert in April 1947. The rate of heat convection and values of the eddy diffusivities were shown to correlate with wind speed.

Thermal Properties of Soils

The foregoing has been a review of the factors influencing the rate at which heat is gained or lost at the soil surface. This section will consider soil properties that influence the disposition of the heat after it reaches the soil surface. Disposition of heat will in turn determine how soil temperature is affected. In dealing with the thermal properties of soils, relations and definitions strictly valid only for homogeneous materials will be used. Solutions of the general equation of heat conduction, for example, are very complicated unless certain assumptions are made. The values obtained when these assumptions are made represent average, or effective, values for the mass of soil being considered.

Surface absorptivity and emissivity

The nature of the soil surface determines what fraction of the solar radiation reaching the soil is absorbed. The surface also affects the rate of long-wave emission. In general a good absorbing surface is also a good emitter. This, however, is not strictly true, for color is a factor in solar radiation, whereas in the long-wave region of the spectrum, color is meaningless. The term "albedo" is often used to characterize the absorptivity of a soil. By definition, however, this term compares a given surface to a "white surface" or poor absorber. Brooks (1936) lists several references to measurements of soil absorptivity and long-wave emissivity values. In general soils will absorb 50 to 80 percent of the radiation to which they are exposed. Since changing the soil surface is one means of influencing soil temperature, this subject will be mentioned again later.

Heat capacity

The amount of heat required to produce a given change in the temperature of a body is, by definition, the heat capacity of the body. A more general statement which relates to the property of the material comprising the object is given by

$$\Delta Q = cM\Delta T \tag{3}$$

where ΔQ is the change in heat content, c is the specific heat capacity of the material, M is the mass of the material, and ΔT is the change in temperature. In this connection c has the same numerical value as the specific heat. It is convenient to define the heat capacity per unit volume by

$$c_v = c\rho \tag{4}$$

where ρ is the grams of the material per unit volume of the soil. For a nonhomogeneous material such as soil, the heat capacity per unit volume is

$$c_v = c_1\rho_1 + c_2\rho_2 + \cdots \tag{5}$$

The subscripts 1, 2, ... refer to each of the individual constituents forming the mixture. Measurements on dry soil and soil constituents by Lang and Ulrich referred to by Baver (1948), and also work reported by Bouyoucos (1913), and Kersten (1949), indicate that the specific heat capacity of soils varies between 0.17 and 0.26 calories per gram per degree centigrade. For many purposes the value 0.2 is used as an approximate average value for the specific heat capacity of the mineral portion of soil.

Applying equation (5) to soils, it may be written

$$c_v = \rho_B \left(c + \frac{P_w}{100} \right) \tag{6}$$

where ρ_B is the bulk density, c is the specific heat capacity of the dry soil and P_w is the percent water. This simplification is possible, since by definition the specific heat capacity of water is unity. If ρ_B and P_w are known at various depths, it is possible to calculate the amount of heat, Q, entering or leaving a unit of soil surface for a given time interval from temperature measurements at the beginning and end of the period, t_1 to t_2. If we let $T(x, t_2) - T(x, t_1)$ represent the change in temperature at depth x we may set down the equation

$$Q = \int_0^{x'} c_v(T_{(x,t_2)} - T_{(x,t_1)})dx \qquad (7)$$

The integration is made from the surface, where x equals zero, to a depth x' where $T(x, t_2) - T(x, t_1)$ is negligible.

Heat of wetting.—The heat of wetting is not generally useful in dealing with heat-exchange problems under field conditions, since in most agricultural soils only the very thin surface of soil becomes sufficiently dry to produce appreciable amounts of heat on wetting. This property is important when making laboratory determinations of the specific heat capacity. In most experimental procedures a known mass of dry soil is heated to a known temperature and poured into a known mass of water at a known temperature, usually near room temperature. To correct for the heat of wetting, a separate sample of soil of equal dryness, but at the water temperature, is wetted and the amount of heat evolved deducted from the former determination. Further details of these procedures are given by Kersten (1949).

Heat-of-wetting values of any significance are associated only with the fine-textured soils. Values reported by Kersten vary from less than 0.5 calories per gram for sands to 2.60 for a silt loam. Janert (1934) reported values as high as 5.27 calories per gram. He gives data to show that the values obtained depend on the temperature at which the soil is dried and on the exchangeable cations. He concludes that the "heat of wetting must be regarded as a portion of the heat of hydration of the adsorbed cations."

Thermal conductivity

The basis for defining the thermal conductivity, κ is an attempt to evaluate that property of a soil which relates to the transfer of heat away from or toward the soil surface. For most applications κ is defined by

$$Q = \kappa At \frac{T_2 - T_1}{x_1 - x_2} \qquad (8)$$

where Q is the amount of heat transferred across the area, A, in time, t, T_1 and T_2 are values of the temperature at points x_1 and x_2, lying on a flow line. The area A is taken at right angles to the flow line. A more accurate definition is

$$\frac{dQ}{dt} = -\kappa A \frac{dT}{du} \qquad (9)$$

where dT/du is the temperature gradient. The negative sign indicates that flow occurs in the opposite direction to the increase in temperature.

In common with most soil properties, κ varies from point to point in the soil, hence any numerical value will represent an average or effective value for the given volume of soil being considered. Measurements of thermal conductivity are rather tedious to make and not many data are available. Various units are in common use for expressing thermal conductivity as well as other thermal properties of soil; therefore the summary of conversion factors listed below will be found useful in comparing the results obtained by various individuals.

A SUMMARY OF DEFINITIONS AND SYMBOLS, AND CONVERSION FACTORS FOR THE VARIOUS UNITS OF MEASUREMENT

Length—L
$$1 \text{ cm.} = 0.3937 \text{ in.} = 3.281 \times 10^{-2} \text{ ft.}$$

Area—A
$$1 \text{ cm.}^2 = 0.1550 \text{ in.}^2 = 1.076 \times 10^{-3} \text{ ft.}^2$$

Volume—V
$$1 \text{ cm.}^3 = 6.102 \times 10^{-2} \text{ in.}^3 = 3.493 \times 10^{-5} \text{ ft.}^3$$

Bulk density—ρ_B and Particle density—ρ_P
$$1 \text{ gm./cm.}^3 = 0.0361 \text{ lbs./in.}^3 = 62.4 \text{ lb./ft.}^3$$

Temperature—T
$$°C. = \tfrac{5}{9}(°F. - 32) = °K. - 273.2$$

Heat—Q
$$1 \text{ cal.} = 3.968 \times 10^{-3} \text{ B.t.u.}$$

Flow density—$\dfrac{dq}{dt} = \dfrac{1}{A}\dfrac{dQ}{dt}$
$$1 \frac{\text{cal.}}{\text{sec. cm.}^2} = 3.686 \frac{\text{B.t.u.}}{\text{sec. ft.}^2}$$

Heat capacity of a body—C
$$1 \frac{\text{cal.}}{°C.} = 2.20 \times 10^{-3} \frac{\text{B.t.u.}}{°F.}$$

Specific heat capacity—c
$$1 \frac{\text{cal.}}{\text{gm. }°C.} = 1 \frac{\text{B.t.u.}}{\text{lb. }°F.}$$

Heat capacity per unit volume—$c_v = \rho c$
$$1 \frac{\text{cal.}}{\text{cm.}^3 °C.} = 62.4 \frac{\text{B.t.u.}}{\text{ft.}^3 °F.}$$

Heat equivalent for latent heat

$$1 \frac{\text{cal.}}{\text{gm.}} = 1.8 \frac{\text{B.t.u.}}{\text{lb.}}$$

Thermal conductivity—$\kappa = \dfrac{dQ}{dt} \bigg/ A \dfrac{dT^*}{dx}$

$$1 \frac{\text{cal.}}{\text{sec. cm. °C.}} = 0.8062 \frac{\text{B.t.u. in.}}{\text{sec. ft.}^2 \text{°F.}} = 6.718 \times 10^{-2} \frac{\text{B.t.u.}}{\text{sec. ft.°F.}}$$

$$= 2{,}902 \frac{\text{B.t.u. in.}}{\text{hr. ft.}^2 \text{°F.}} = 241.8 \frac{\text{B.t.u.}}{\text{hr. ft. °F.}}$$

Thermal diffusivity—$a = \dfrac{k}{\rho c} = \dfrac{k}{c_v} = \dfrac{dT}{dt} \bigg/ \dfrac{d^2 T^*}{dx^2}$

$$1 \frac{\text{cm.}^2}{\text{sec.}} = 1.291 \times 10^{-2} \frac{\text{in. ft.}}{\text{sec.}} = 1.076 \times 10^{-3} \frac{\text{ft.}^2}{\text{sec.}} = 3.87 \frac{\text{ft.}^2}{\text{hr.}}$$

As an indication that thermal conductivity depends on the soil moisture, as well as other things, Shaw and Baver (1939a, 1939b) and Johnston (1942) have described techniques for indicating soil-moisture relations based on the effect of moisture on heat transference. This technique has promise of being a useful soil-moisture indicator, but the measurement cannot be readily identified with numerical values of the thermal properties of soils.

Smith and Byers (1938) assembled equipment for measuring the thermal conductivity of dry soil samples. The method involved the introduction of a given rate of heat flow into one side of a soil sample, and the measurement of the thermal gradient after the temperatures became constant. Suitable guard rings prevented lateral flow of heat. In spite of a rather wide variety of soils used, they found the general relation

$$\kappa = 0.000057P + 0.00080(1 - P)$$

where P is air porosity expressed as a fraction of the total volume.

Later, Smith (1942) included measurements of thermal conductivity on undisturbed monolith samples as compared with fragmented samples. He emphasizes the effect of orientations and arrangement of the soil particles, but in most cases where the fragmented sample showed a much lower conductivity, the bulk density was lower as well.

W. O. Smith (1939) reported direct measurements of thermal conductivity on soil samples at various moisture levels. Because his samples were wetted and then packed in the hard-rubber container, some variation also occurs in the bulk density values obtained. Se-

* For the x coordinate chosen parallel to the direction of heat flow.

TABLE 35.—*Selected values for thermal properties of soils*

Soil type	Particle size			Bulk density	Water	Specific heat capacity	Heat capacity per cubic centimeter	Thermal conductivity	Diffusivity	Reference
	Sand	Silt	Clay							
	Pct.	*Pct.*	*Pct.*	*Gm. per cubic cm.*	*Pct.*	*Cal. gm. °C.*	*Cal. cm.³ °C.*	*Cal. sec. cm. °C.*	*Cm.² sec.*	
Hudson River sand	91	8	1	0.90	4.5	0.176	0.20	0.0091	0.0045	Patton (1909)
				0.94	18.1	.176	.336	.0300	.0089	
Podunk fine sandy loam	90	8	2	0.89	6.6	.182	.221	.0012	.0058	
				0.965	20.2	.182	.371	.0026	.0069	
Leonardtown silt loam	27	58	15	0.99	9.0	.229	.316	.0018	.0058	
				0.83	18.4	.226	.338	.0021	.0061	
Muck soil				0.65	23.0	.156	.251	.00076	.0030	
				0.43	59.0	.156	.321	.00108	.0034	
				0.42	69.4	.156	.315	.00086	.0024	
Yolo clay				1.18	0	.194	.236	.0014	.0062	Johnston (1937)
				1.47	29.0	.194	.720	.0083	.0116	
Granitic sandy loam	55	40	5	1.29	0	.226	.291	.0017	.0059	
				1.56	22.7	.226	.706	.0071	.0101	
Fine calcareous loam	72	26	2	1.14	0	.154	.175	.00079	.0049	
				1.08	24.4	.154	.430	.0048	.0110	
Granitic sand	74	23	3	1.32	0	.204	.269	.00137	.0052	
				1.90	18.1	.204	.636	.0108	.0147	
Barns loam	42	25	33	1.16	5.1	.20	.29	.00041	.0014	Smith (1939)
				1.15	8.9	......	.33	.00045	.0014	
				1.07	13.0	......	.35	.00049	.0014	
				1.18	26.6	......	.55	.00086	.0016	

Soil										Reference
Chester loam	27	41	32	1.44	2.0		.32	.00045	.0014	Smith (1939)
				1.19	4.7		.29	.00051	.0017	
Herman sandy loam	80	16	4	1.12	13.4		.37	.00087	.0023	
				1.42	1.3		.30	.00049	.0016	
				1.24	4.4		.30	.00060	.0020	
				1.23	8.7		.35	.00086	.0024	
Kalkaska loamy sand				1.55	0.8		.32	.00060	.0018	
				1.43	2.6		.32	.00069	.0021	
				1.44	5.7	.18	.37	.00124	.0033	
Northway silt loam	14	64	21	1.56	6.6		.384	.0013	.0034	Kersten (1949)
				1.54	16.4		.530	.0021	.0040	
				1.57	22.5		.636	.0025	.0039	
				1.43	16.5		.493	.0018	.0036	
				1.82	14.5	.18	.592	.0030	.0051	
Fairbanks silty clay loam	9	64	27	1.44	12.3		.436	.0020	.0046	
				1.44	18.0	.18	.518	.0025	.0048	
				1.44	25.4		.625	.0028	.0045	
				1.45	30.0		.696	.0029	.0042	
				1.28	12.3		.388	.0015	.0039	
				1.62	12.5		.494	.0026	.0053	
Dakota sandy loam	58	21	10	1.35	1.9	.18	.269	.00059	.0022	
				2.11	4.9		.483	.0054	.0112	
Black cotton soil: Depth in centimeters:										Dravid (1940)
0 to 5				1.45		.22	.336	.00037	.0011	
5 to 10				2.00			.447	.00067	.0015	
10 to 15				2.2			.500	.00060	.0012	
15 to 20				2.3			.52	.00052	.0010	
Loam								.0024	.011	Shubert (1930)
Sand								.0016	.0063	
Loamy sand								.0043	.0079	

lected values of the data reported by W. O. Smith (1939) are given in Table 35.

One of the difficulties experienced in Smith's direct measurement of the thermal conductivity of moist soil samples was that moisture as well as heat moved in response to the thermal gradient. Differences of 5 to 15 percent moisture were found for the soil at the two edges of samples only 0.75 inch thick.

Kersten (1949) used procedures based on the direct measurement of thermal conductivity. The soil samples were adjusted for moisture and packed by tamping into a chamber, which in cross section was an annulus. His equipment provided for measuring conductivity values at various temperature ranges, including a range below the freezing point. Some of the values from this paper are given in Table 35. Other general conclusions were reported as follows:

> At a constant moisture content . . . on the average, for each 0.016 gm./cm.^{3} increase in density, the conductivity increases 2.8 percent for unfrozen and 3 percent for frozen soils. At a constant density, an increase in moisture content causes an increase in conductivity. This is true up to the point of saturation and holds for frozen as well as unfrozen soils.

Thermal diffusivity

Thermal diffusivity is defined, for convenience, as a combination of thermal properties in the equation

$$\frac{dT}{dt} = \frac{\kappa}{\rho c}\left(\frac{d^2 T}{dx^2} + \frac{d^2 T}{dy^2} + \frac{d^2 T}{dZ^2}\right) \tag{10}$$

This equation is the basis for the analytic treatment of the relation of temperature to heat flow in solids and its use is extensively illustrated in standard texts such as Carslaw (1945). The equation holds for any homogeneous, isotropic medium, whose thermal conductivity is κ, density is ρ, and specific heat capacity is c. In the following example of the use of this equation, it will be assumed that the temperature varies only in the x direction and ρc may be replaced by c_v as defined earlier:

$$\frac{dT}{dt} = \frac{\kappa}{c_v}\frac{d^2 T}{dx^2} = a\frac{d^2 T}{dx^2} \tag{11}$$

The thermal diffusivity, a, is the ratio of κ and c_v:

$$a = \frac{\kappa}{c_v} \tag{12}$$

When thermal conductivity is measured as was done by W. O. Smith (1939) and Kersten (1949), and other soil properties such as bulk density and moisture content are known, values for a may be calculated.   Such calculated values are also included in Table 35.

Patten (1909) used a simple method for evaluating diffusivity directly.   This method has been reviewed by Keen (1931), Johnston (1937), and Baver (1948).   By applying heat to one end of a box of soil and observing temperature values at various locations in the soil as they vary with time, the derivatives appearing in equation 11 may be evaluated.   Thermal diffusivity is then calculated from the ratio

$$\frac{dT/dt}{d^2T/dx^2}$$

Patten's method has the advantage that it does not require a long wait for thermal gradients to become constant, hence the movement of moisture in response to thermal gradients is minimized.   As used by Patten (1909) and Johnston (1937) the soil samples were adjusted for moisture content before being packed into the box.

Patten (1909) emphasized that for a given boundary condition, temperature changes within the soil are simply related to diffusivity rather than conductivity alone.   This explains the conditions commonly observed in the field where a moist soil is slower to respond to temperature changes even though conductivity is higher than it would be in the same soil when dry.   Johnston (1937) measured thermal diffusivities for several soils in which an oil line was laid.   Using equation 12 he then calculated heat conductivities and found that the values for the various soils correlated very well with the rates at which heat was lost from the pipeline as the heated oil moved through it.

One further method of evaluating the thermal diffusivity of soil is based on temperature observations under field conditions similar to those shown in Figure 46.   If it is assumed that equation 11 holds for a semi-infinite solid and a sinesoidal variation of temperature given by

$$T_{(o,t)} = T_m \cos 2\pi \frac{t}{\tau} \tag{13}$$

occurs at the surface, then the solution applicable to this problem is given by

$$T_{(x,t)} = T_m e^{-\sqrt{\frac{\pi}{\tau a}}x} \cos\left(\frac{2\pi t}{\tau} - \sqrt{\frac{\pi}{\tau a}}x\right) \tag{14}$$

where τ is period of the variation, in this case 1 day, or 86,400 seconds, and π equals 3.1416.   Boelter et al. (1948) give the intermediate steps which show that a may be calculated from the relation

$$a = 6.86 \times 10^{-6} \frac{(x_2 - x_1)^2}{G^2} \tag{15}$$

where G is the logarithm of the ratio of the maximum deviations of the temperature from the means (i.e. amplitudes) at depths x_1 and x_2. Still another calculation for a is

$$a = 6870 \frac{(x_2 - x_1)^2}{(t_2 - t_1)^2} \tag{16}$$

where $t_2 - t_1$ is the shift or time interval between maxima or minima of temperature at depths x_2 and x_1.

The values of a in Table 35 from Dravid (1940) are calculated, using equation 15, from values taken from Figure 46.

Data from various sources are combined in Table 35, but in order to express the values given by the various workers in the same units, repeated use was made of the conversion factors given in the summary on page 324.

Cultural Practices Used to Influence Soil Temperature

As indicated in earlier sections, the sun is the only significant source of heat influencing soil temperature, and insolation and net radiation at the soil surface are determined by climatic factors difficult to modify. Lyon and Buckman (1947) wrote: "The temperature of field soils is subject to no radical human regulation, yet soil management methods, especially those that influence soil moisture, provide for small but biologically vital modifications." It will be of interest to enumerate some of the cultural practices that directly or indirectly influence soil temperature.

Shading

Artificial shading to reduce the intensity of the direct radiation from the sun is a common practice. Lath houses are used for some ornamental plants, cloth shade is sometimes provided for tobacco plants, and in some locations coffee plants are grown in the shade of larger trees. Such practices are used primarily to reduce the insolation on the plants involved, but the effects of the shading will influence soil temperature as well.

Several studies of the influence of plant shading on soil temperature have been reported. Zon (1941) observed in Michigan that compared to a similar soil without the forest cover, a soil under a birch-beech-maple forest was at a 6-inch depth about 2°F. warmer in winter and 5 to 9° cooler in summer. Hursh (1948) reported that the daily range of soil temperature values at a depth of 2 inches was increased from 10.9 to 33.5°F. by the removal of vegetation in Tennessee. Julander (1945) compared temperature values at a 2-inch depth under overgrazed and protected areas in semidesert grasslands of New Mexico. He found as much as 10°F. difference in the maximum temperature values.

Brown (1943) reported 4-year average values of temperature at a depth of ½ inch under bare soil and bluegrass sod. During summer months under climatic conditions in Missouri he found that semi-monthly mean values of the daily maxima were as much as 10°F. higher and minima were as much as 5° lower for bare soil than for blue-grass sod. Reeder (1920) reported a similar study of the effect of blue-grass sod on soil temperature as compared with a bare soil and a sand. However, he attempted to measure surface temperatures with mercury thermometers only partially buried in the soil; so, for reasons already noted, his values are somewhat in error, although he made additional refinements of his study by separating his data for periods of clear and cloudy weather and for conditions when the soil was moist and dry. The above references relating to shading by crops have been listed as though shading were the only variable involved, but soils with and without vegetation will have other differences, such as soil moisture, in addition to those caused by shading.

Shading is not always used to reduce the amount of the sun's radiation reaching the soil. Where winter vegetables are grown under semidesert conditions, inclined shades are erected over the rows so that direct radiation from the sun will reach the soil but long-wave radiation from the soil to the atmosphere will be intercepted and reduced as much as possible. By reducing air movement near the soil use of inclined shades also reduces convection loss of heat from the soil.

Mulching

Mulch refers to any material spread over and allowed to remain on the soil surface. In addition, the practice of repeated shallow cultivation is said to produce a dust mulch. Mulching is practiced for various reasons—weed control, protection of the soil surface from the erosive action of rain and wind, reduction of water loss by evaporation, and also for its effect on soil temperature. With a dust mulch, the stirring action of the cultivator tends to dry out the surface soil as well as reduce its bulk density. Both of these changes are in the direction of reducing the thermal conductivity of the surface soil so that less heat will be transferred between the lower layers and the soil surface.

An organic mulch acts as an absorber of short-wave radiant energy when the area is unshaded and reduces the rate of exchange of heat at the soil surface by insulating it. While comparing the effects of three cultural practices in southern Indiana, Oskamp (1915) observed that temperature values at a 9-inch depth under a straw mulch were in between those under clean-tilled and grassland types of culture. From unpublished data taken at Marlboro, N. J., during July and August, 1939, daily maximum temperatures 4 inches below the soil surface were on the average 4.5°F. lower under a salt hay mulch, and the average daily minima were 2.9° higher. McCalla and Duley (1946) reported the effects of straw mulch on soil temperatures at a depth of 1 inch in a cornfield. Two and eight tons per acre of straw reduced the mean weekly maximum values for the summer of 1944 from 31.2° to 26.5° and 23.6°C., respectively, and increased the mean minimum temperatures from 17.9 to 19.7°, respectively. Further data were obtained to show the effects of similar treatments at a 4-inch depth. Nevertheless, these authors also gave data showing that the amount of plant residues returned to the soil surface under the common practice of subsurface tillage are not sufficient to influence soil temperature a few months after the residues are added. These authors indicate that straw mulches applied to cornfields in June did not retard the warming up of the soil enough to impair the yield of corn.

The use of paper mulch has been common in Hawaii. Experimenting with paper mulch, Stewart, Thomas, and Horner (1926) reported finding a 12 to 15°F. increase in maximum daytime temperatures during hot days in July, August, and September. Shaw (1926) experimented with asphalt-coated paper at Berkeley, Calif. He measured soil temperature 3 inches below the soil surface and reported his results in degree-hours above 60°F. During a period of 2,419 hours from May 17 to August 25, a total of 25,489 degree-hours was observed under the mulch, and 24,456 with no mulch. Smith (1927) also observed the effects of paper mulches in California. The following quotation from Smith's paper shows the relative effects of paper on radiation and convection:

Temperatures taken at a depth of 3 inches in five plots, where different mulches were used, varied considerably. The warmest plot was covered with solid black paper. Where the perforated black paper was used the temperaturs were about the same as in the bare plot. The coldest plots were those covered with gray paper; in this case the perforated paper was again colder than the nonperforated.

Smith (1931) reported a 4-year study confirming the above-noted effects of paper mulches on soil temperatures, but concluded the effect on the crops at Davis did not justify the cost of mulching. Magistad, Farden, and Baldwin (1935) compared the effects on soil temperature of paper and bagasse mulches. The mean annual maximum values at 2 inches under no mulch, paper, and bagasse were 91.4, 88.5, and 80.4°F., respectively, and corresponding mean minimum values were

75.5°, 71.2°, and 71.2°. Before shading by the plants occurred, daily maximum values were highest under the dark paper. The pineapple plants grew better under the mulch culture, but the effects of soil temperatures were not clearly indicated. In connection with a study of the effect of mulches on runoff, erosion, and evaporation, Lamb and Chapman (1943) observed at the Arnot Station in New York that soil temperatures under a stone mulch (65 percent flagstone cover) were higher than in the normal fallow soil, and that under a straw mulch temperatures were lower than in fallow soil.

The use of a mulching material for changing the absorptivity or color of the soil surface has been reported in several publications. Bouyoucos (1913) measured differences in the soil temperatures at 3- and 5-inch depths where the surface was covered with a white sand and compared these with temperatures at the same depths where the soil was covered with the same sand dyed black. He also refers to earlier work by Lang and Ahr. Dravid (1940), in India where daily insolation values were high, showed the marked effect of covering Poona soil with a white French chalk. Soil temperatures at a 2-inch depth were lowered by as much as 7°C. at the maximum values but were only slightly different at the early morning reading. Since the Poona soil was black, the effect was much smaller when carbon black was used as a surface cover. The temperature records seemed to indicate that long-wave radiation was not markedly increased by carbon black. Everson and Weaver (1949) used 4,000 pounds per acre of carbon black mixed with the surface 2 inches of soil. At Amherst, Mass., this treatment resulted in maximum daily temperatures about 3.4°F. higher than those of the untreated soil at a depth of 2 inches.

Moisture control

It is generally accepted that well-drained soils show faster temperature changes in response to external factors than the same soils with higher moisture content. The extensive temperature measurements by Bouyoucos (1916) exemplify this effect. Bouyoucos selected five soil types and placed them side by side under the same climatic conditions. Temperature measurements in these blocks of soil over a period of years indicated that they all had about the same average temperature, except for short periods in the spring when rapid changes in the air temperature and other climatic factors occurred. Under these conditions the temperatures in the sand and gravel, which were faster draining, would change more rapidly than in clay, loam, or peat soils.

In contrast to the situation where it is desirable to have the soil temperature increase rapidly, there are times and locations where the soil temperatures may become too high for optimum plant growth. Under such conditions, Smith, Kinnison, and Carns (1931) reported data to show the effects of an irrigation on cooling the soil. In Arizona on the day following an irrigation measurements at 1-, 2-, and 3-inch depths indicated that temperatures had been lowered by 4 to 10, 1 to 4, and 0.5 to 2°F., respectively.

Soil moisture affects several factors, which in turn influence soil temperatures. Surface absorptivity and emissivity values are probably

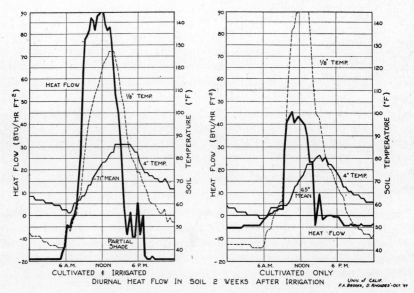

FIGURE 48.—Soil temperature and heat-flow records showing effects of an irrigation. (Records obtained near Lakeport, Calif., April, 1945, and made available through the courtesy of Prof. F. A. Brooks.)

different for wet and dry soil surfaces. Some difference in values for heat conductivity and thermal diffusivity are indicated by data given in Table 33. Evaporation rates are likely to be larger from a soil recently irrigated. In connection with a study of the relationship between air temperatures and soil properties near Lakeport, Calif., F. A. Brooks, professor of Agricultural Engineering, University of California, supplied the unpublished records shown in Figure 48. This study was made in April when spring frosts sometimes damage fruit trees. Two weeks following an irrigation the daily maximum temperature just below the soil surface was lower on the irrigated plot. The effect of the irrigation was greater, however, on the flow of heat both into and out of the soil, as indicated by the positive and negative values of the heat flow, respectively. Under the conditions of this experiment, the larger heat flow into the soil under irrigation was sufficiently effective to result in a higher mean temperature at the 4-inch depth, in spite of the fact that surface-evaporation rates were probably higher on the irrigated plot.

Soil Physical and Chemical Properties Affected by Soil Temperature

Soil temperature is important because it determines the temperature of the roots of the growing plants and, in addition, may influence other factors of the plant environment. These additional factors can best be discussed in terms of the physical and chemical properties of the soil. Microbiological factors relating to soil temperature will be covered in a later section of this chapter.

Soil moisture retention

In connection with his observations of ground water, King (1892) observed a diurnal fluctuation of the ground water level. He showed that this fluctuation in the ground water resulted because temperature changes affected the amount of moisture held in the soil above the water table. He stated:

> The amount of water which has been shown to leave the capillary spaces of the soil with an increase of temperature, and return to them again when the changes are reversed, is so great as to make it difficult to understand how a simple diminution of the surface tension of the soil water is capable of producing the whole movement.

Bouyoucos (1915) used soil samples that were close to saturation at 0°C. and measured the amounts of water released from them when the temperature was raised in increments of 10° up to 50°. He attributes some of this loss of water occurring with increased temperature, and also the observations by King (1892), to an expansion of enclosed air pockets at these relatively high moisture levels in the soil. Richards and Weaver (1944) reported the effect of temperature on the moisture retained by a group of 12 soils at ½ and 15 atmospheres of soil-moisture tension. Curves giving their data show, with but one exception, that the slopes were negative, as would be expected from the effect of temperature on surface tension. The change in moisture retention per degree of change in temperature increased from coarse to fine texture, but appeared not to be linearly related to the moisture retention of the various soils at any given temperature and tension.

In studies related to moisture retention by soils, Richards, Russell, and Neal (1937) and Moore (1940) observed that large variations in soil-moisture tension values occurred with temperature changes in a given soil having a constant moisture content. Haise and Kelley (1950) reported unusually large diurnal variations in soil-moisture tensions at shallow depths under irrigated desert conditions in the field. Using laboratory techniques, Haise and Kelley (1950) showed that the variations in soil-moisture tensions taking place with changes in temperature were partly due to the movement of soil moisture in response to thermal gradients. The thermal gradients resulted from the flow of heat along the metal parts of the tensiometers.

Moisture movement

The movement and distribution of water in soils is dealt with in Chapter 3 and will be mentioned only briefly here. The influence of temperature on moisture movement will be considered under two sets of conditions; first, where the soil temperature is uniform throughout the soil but is taken at different temperatures; and second, where thermal gradients exist. The results of experiments on water movement are usually given in terms of the Darcy equation

$$v = ki \tag{17}$$

where v is the flow velocity, i is the hydraulic gradient, and k is a permeability constant characteristic of the soil. To evaluate the effect of temperature on flow rates, the viscosity of water is introduced as a ratio of absolute viscosities, one of which is used as a reference at some given temperature

$$v = \frac{\eta_a}{\eta} ki \tag{18}$$

Experimental evaluation of k for moisture conditions near saturation has shown it to be dependent on a variety of factors such as entrapped air, Christiansen (1944); salt content of the water, Fireman and Magistad (1945); micro-organism activity, Allison (1947); and other such factors. The magnitude of such effects is large in comparison to the effect change of viscosity has on flow velocity. However, Pillsbury (1950) was able to demonstrate that the effect of temperatures on the viscosity of water gave the expected change in the flow velocities of water through a simplified soil where the effects of other variables were sufficiently minimized. Laboratory studies of the Darcy permeability constant for unsaturated flow have all been made under carefully controlled isothermal conditions. Such experiments are so tedious that as yet they have not been extended to a range of temperature values. Lewis (1937) showed experimentally that where temperature gradients do not occur within the soil, the movement of moisture in the vapor phase is insignificantly small. This result confirms the prediction made when the free energy of the soil moisture is evaluated in terms of the vapor pressure in the air voids of the soil. Over the range of soil moisture for growing plants, the relative humidity within the air voids is always greater than 98 percent; hence for isothermal conditions, the vapor-density gradients within the voids are not large enough to result in appreciable diffusion rates.

The movement of moisture in response to thermal gradients has been observed in many laboratory experiments, but the importance of this response under field conditions is yet to be evaluated. Bouyoucos (1915) and W. O. Smith (1939) showed that for each soil type studied there was an optimum moisture content that resulted in a maximum movement of water under a given thermal gradient. Haise and Kelley (1950) showed a movement through a soil sample in response to a temperature gradient when the pressure gradient was tending to move water in the opposite direction. The relative importance of liquid transfer and vapor transfer of moisture in response to temperature differences is still a matter of some uncertainty. Bouyoucos (1915) showed that the response he observed was largely in the liquid phase. However, since the equilibrium vapor pressure of water is a well known function of the temperature, the vapor-density gradients are readily obtained from temperature measurements if osmotic effects are small; and, since vapor density does vary over a wide range with temperature, it is likely that vapor transfer is significant under some conditions. Edlefsen and Anderson (1943) pointed out that one of the advantages of using free energy considerations rather than potential functions for expressing soil moisture relations is the fact that the influence of temperature is more readily evaluated.

Aeration

The rate of mass transfer of air through a soil in response to a gradient of the total gas pressure was used by Buehrer (1932) as a criterion of soil structure and by Evans and Kirkham (1949) as an index to internal drainage. The effect of soil temperature on the viscosity of air is such that this mass movement is reduced by an increase in temperature. This result was obtained experimentally by Bouyoucos (1915). It was concluded by Buckingham (1904), however, that the diffusion of gases in response to partial pressure gradients is the most important process for providing aeration for the roots of plants growing in soil. In contrast to the rate of mass transfer, the diffusion of gases increases with higher soil temperatures. Mayer and

Mayer (1940) showed that the diffusion coefficient varies directly with the absolute temperature. Since the process is similar, it is pertinent to note that Hagan (1941), working with carbon disulfide, showed that the diffusion rate increased with soil temperature.

Chemical properties

The chemistry of the soil is so complex that experimental procedures have not yet been developed for evaluating the effects of soil temperature. It is to be expected that chemical phenomena in the soil are similar to other more simple systems. Solubilities, reaction rates, equilibrium constants, and diffusion rates are all affected by temperature. The following literature is cited to illustrate the scope of the subject.

Stewart, Thomas, and Horner (1926) found a higher nitrate content in soil under paper mulches, where the temperature was observed to be higher. Robinson (1942) reported results showing that more phosphorus was fixed in a sample of Dekalb soil stored 2 months where temperatures fluctuated between 15 and 45°C. than was fixed in the same soil stored at 3°C.

Burtch, Thorne, and Wann (1948) showed that, as compared with intermediate temperatures, severity of high-lime chlorosis on bean plants was increased at low (15°C.) and high (35°C.) soil temperatures. Chapman and Kelley (1930) reported results of the determination of replaceable calcium by extractions made at both 70°C. and room temperature. Vanselow (1932) observed that the equilibrium constant relating the calcium and ammonia ions to the exchange complex varied with temperature in the range of 20 to 75°C. Jenny (1941) discussed temperature as one of the factors influencing soil formation. After pointing out that soil temperature is influenced by the same local climatic conditions which determine the air temperature, he summarized the evidence to show the relationship of temperature to such soil properties as depth, nitrogen, and organic matter content, clay content, the ratio of silica to aluminum, and aggregation. The chemistry of the soil is intimately related to the microbiological activity.

II. TEMPERATURE AND GROWTH PROCESSES
By R. M. Hagan
Nature of Growth

Growth is a very complex phenomenon, yet a commonplace process and one of the outstanding characteristics of living matter.

Growth as a process is difficult to define, and its definition is made more complex when one considers growth from various viewpoints. While growth is often considered in terms of the whole organism, it is frequently studied from the standpoint of individual parts. In the words of Weiss (1949), "Growth is a word . . . covering a variety of diverse and complex phenomena. It is not even a scientific term with defined and constant meaning, but a popular label that varies with . . . the purpose of the individual . . . using it." He recognized that growth connotes all and any of these aspects: reproduction, increase in dimensions, gain in weight, and cell multiplication, as well as others. He cautions against considering growth as an entity, which can be activated, stimulated, retarded, or suppressed. One should not be misled, he writes, by the delusion that growth is a simple process. These thoughts deserve attention as one undertakes a consideration of such a complex and confused relation as that between soil temperature and growth.

In general, growth involves the production of new protoplasm, the formation of new cells, and cellular enlargement and specialization. The formation of additional living matter is always accompanied by an increase in total weight and usually by an increase in total volume of the system. Accordingly, some authors define *growth as a permanent increase in weight, attended by a permanent change in form, induced primarily by an increase in the quantity of protoplasm* (Miller, 1938, p. 1018). While this definition is applicable to most cases, germinating seeds and sprouting tubers are exceptions. The total dry weight of the young seedling and seed combined, or of the sprout and tuber, is less for a period than the weight of the original structure because weight is lost through respiration. Since the plumule and radicle have increased in weight and have changed in form, these processes are also commonly accepted as growth processes.

Thus we must admit at the outset the lack of an entirely satisfactory definition for growth. In accepting, for practical purposes, the general definition of growth given by Miller, one must bear in mind the vagueness of the term and the cautions so well expressed by Weiss. Nevertheless, violations of Weiss' sound point of view may frequently appear in the following pages.

Growth Processes in Relation to Temperature

Physical, chemical, and physiological processes

The complex process of growth involves the interaction of an array of physical, chemical, and physiological phenomena. A general discussion of the effect of temperature upon living systems is given by Belehradek (1935). The difficulties in relating growth to temperature become apparent when it is realized that growth is a complicated summation of a number of individual processes, each of which also is influenced in varying degrees by temperature. To provide a background for the discussion to follow, the relation of temperature to some of these properties or processes will be very briefly mentioned.

The kinetic energy of molecular systems is directly proportional to temperature. The increasing kinetic activity associated with higher temperatures is responsible for such phenomena as the thermal expansion of solids, liquids, and particularly gases and for the marked changes in viscosity, solubility, diffusion rates, reaction velocities, and equilibria.

Viscosity or its reciprocal, fluidity, is an important property of liquids and biological systems. The viscosity of liquids decreases with increasing temperature. For water, the viscosity at 10°C. is approximately 73 percent of that at 0°; at 20°, 56 percent; at 30°, 45 percent; and at 40°, 36 percent. The viscosity of the cytoplasm in active cells may change rapidly in response to changes in temperature and to other stimuli.

The solubility of substances varies widely with the nature of both the solute and solvent. Solids and liquids are generally more soluble at higher than at lower temperatures, though in a few cases the reverse is true. Gases, at a given pressure, become less soluble with increasing temperature. To illustrate, the absorption coefficient[1] for oxygen is 0.0489 at 0°C., 0.0310 at 20°, and 0.0231 at 40°; and for carbon dioxide, 1.71 at 0°C., 0.878 at 20°, and 0.530 at 40° (Hodgman, 1939, p. 1014).

Many plant activities are dependent upon the process of diffusion. The rate of diffusion or, more specifically, the coefficient of diffusion is directly proportional to the absolute temperature. Diffusion in its application to biological systems has been discussed by Höber (1945).

Reaction velocities are also dependent upon temperature. Höber (1945) provided a concise review of chemical kinetics in biological systems. Although most chemical reactions proceed more rapidly at higher temperatures, the relation between the reaction velocity and temperature is seldom linear. Reference is made frequently to the *temperature coefficient* of the reaction. The temperature coefficient, which is often represented by the symbol Q_{10}, is defined as the factor by which the rate is multiplied as the result of a 10°C. increase in temperature. Many chemical reactions have Q_{10} values between 2 and 4, while physical processes, such as viscous flow or diffusion, generally have values of about 1.2 to 1.3. Q_{10} values for growth processes have frequently been calculated and used to characterize the growth and to

---

[1] The absorption coefficient represents the volume of gas, reduced to standard conditions (0°C. and 760 mm. pressure), dissolved in one volume of liquid when the pressure of the gas (without the vapor pressure of the liquid) is 760 millimeters.

determine whether chemical or physical processes were the controlling factors. The limited usefulness of Q_{10} values for characterizing the temperature relations of biological systems is becoming more widely recognized, and its use is therefore decreasing. Some values for temperature coefficients of growth for higher plants and the micro-organisms will be given in later sections, where the problem of formulating an expression to relate growth to temperature will be considered.

In addition to the purely chemical and physical reactions just referred to, plant life abounds in biochemical reactions. The enzymatic reversible oxidation-reduction systems in plants are examples. What distinguishes biochemical from chemical reactions in general is the means provided for the rapid attainment of equilibrium. Furthermore, although a very large number of reactions in a given biological system may be thermodynamically possible, the presence of enzymes greatly alters the reaction pattern by selective catalysis. Enzyme reactions are controlled in the living cell by a variety of regulating mechanisms in addition to the usual physiochemical factors governing reaction rates in solution. "These regulatory mechanisms (hormones, genes . . .) . . . by controlling the rate of enzyme reactions or by changing the orientation of these reactions . . . act as the traffic policemen in the crowded streets of a city" (Barron, 1949). In biochemical processes, the influences of temperature are conditioned by its effect on these regulating mechanisms.

Such physiological phenomena as cytoplasmic streaming, bioelectric potential, synthesis of organic materials, translocation, and respiration are all influenced by temperature. These activities are complex combinations of physical and chemical processes which, as has been pointed out, are themselves dependent on temperature.

Cytoplasmic streaming is accelerated by increases in temperature up to the temperature where injury appears and is checked by low temperatures, ceasing near the freezing point. In his review Seifriz (1943) has pointed out that the effect of temperature on streaming appears to vary with the material used and the techniques employed. For most cases, the temperature limits for streaming range between about 0 and 40 or 50°C.

Plant tissues have been shown to exhibit electrical phenomena. Apparently each living cell in a plant is electrically polarized. The summation of the potentials of individual cells may give rise to a complex distribution of electrical potentials in plant tissues. Temperature is one of the primary environmental factors that can control the magnitude and even the direction of these internal electric polarities (Lund, 1932). For a bibliography of work on bioelectric potentials, see

Rosene (1947). The importance of these potentials and the resultant electrical currents in plant growth is uncertain. While electro-osmosis may occur in many plant tissues, Kramer and Currier (1950) doubt that it is of much significance in the total water relations of plants.

Supply of organic materials

Synthesis is basic to growth. The elaboration of protoplasm from inorganic and organic building units is generally accelerated by increases in temperatures within limits. The rate of supply of organic materials, however, may be diminished at both low and high temperatures.

In the higher plants, the primary organic materials required for the formation of protoplasm are produced by photosynthesis. These

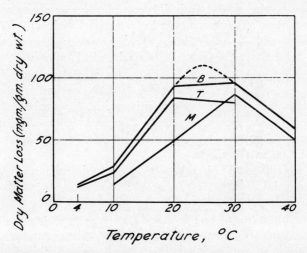

FIGURE 49.—Effect of temperature on the translocation of dry matter from the leaves of bean (B), tomato (T) and milkweed (M) plants over a 13-hour period of darkness. (Hewitt and Curtis, 1948.)

products of photosynthesis must be transported with sufficient rapidity from the photosynthesizing tissues to meet the requirements of dividing and enlarging cells in the growing portions of the plant.

Investigators disagree as to the influence of temperature on translocation. It has been generally accepted that translocation is speeded by increasing temperature, as indicated by the work of Curtis (1929) and Curtis and Herty (1936). This was questioned by Went and his associates (1944b, 1946, 1949). They believe these experiments indicated that the amount of sugar translocated in tomato plants gradually decreased as the temperature was raised from 8 to 26°C. Recently

Hewitt and Curtis (1948) have studied translocation losses from leaves of bean, milkweed, and tomato plants held in darkness overnight for 13 hours at 4, 10, 20, 30 and 40°C. (Fig. 49). Loss of dry matter caused by respiration was corrected for by comparing the total losses from attached and detached leaves, which had been previously paired. In bean and tomato plants, translocation from the leaves increased with temperature up to 20°C., remained about the same at 30°, but de-

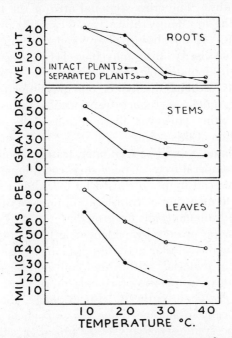

FIGURE 50.—Effect of temperature on carbohydrate (starch plus soluble sugar) contents of roots, stems, and leaves of 3-week-old bean plants maintained intact or separated into parts and held for 13 hours in darkness following exposure to a day of sunshine. (Redrawn from Hewitt and Curtis, 1948.)

clined at higher temperatures. In milkweed, translocation reached a maximum rate at 30°C.

Hewitt and Curtis also investigated the effect of temperature on the carbohydrate content of roots, stems, and leaves of bean plants maintained intact or separated into parts and held for 13 hours in darkness (Fig. 50). The higher carbohydrate content of the roots of the intact plants, together with the lower carbohydrate content of the stems and leaves of these plants, when compared with the separated plants, indicated that a considerable translocation of materials to the roots occurred at 20 and 30°C. Apparently very little material was translocated to the roots at 10°C. This supports the earlier observation by Brown (1939) that translocation to the roots seemed to be retarded noticeably when the shoot and root temperatures were held at 10°C. with Bermuda grass and at 4.4° with orchard grass and Kentucky and Canada bluegrasses.

Batjer *et al.* (1939) exposed the lower portion (approximately 12 inches) of the trunk and the roots of apple trees to a temperature of 5.6°C. for 3 months. The cross sectional area of the trunk above the portion held at the low temperature was 50 to 100 percent larger in most of these trees. In the absence of any apparent injury to the tissue, they suggested that the swelling may have been caused by a retarded translocation of food materials down through the chilled part of the trunk. From the foregoing discussion, one may infer that low soil and root temperatures might so reduce translocation through the roots as to limit their growth. However, there appears to be no direct experimental confirmation of this point.

On the other hand, as will be seen later, translocation may also limit growth at high temperatures. Under such conditions, because of the rapid carbohydrate consumption caused by increased respiratory activity, even an accelerated rate of translocation may be unable to furnish sufficient carbohydrate materials for growth.

Respiration is the process by which molecular chemical energy is made available for the cellular activities of plants. Energy is required for the transport of materials within the plant and for synthesis of the numerous substances comprising protoplasm from the simple compounds provided by photosynthesis. Furthermore, the cells of many organs—such as cells in storage tissue that do not grow—respire actively although no synthesis or any other process needing a supply of energy appears to take place within them. Thus, it seems that respiration is required for the very maintenance of life in all living cells. The rate of respiration increases as the temperature rises unless it is limited by accumulation of respiratory products, by a deficiency of oxygen or of respirable substrate, or by the inactivation of the enzyme systems involved.

Respiration as a function of temperature has been studied in many plant materials. The work of Fernandes (1923) on respiration of pea seedlings, reported by Stiles and Leach (1932), provides a concise summary (Fig. 51). Within the temperature range 0 to 30 or 35°C., the temperature coefficient of respiration appears to be about 2.0 to 2.5. At 0°C. respiration is slow. Below the freezing point the rate of respiration gradually diminishes until it becomes imperceptible, although measureable rates of respiration have been recorded in some plant tissues at temperatures as low as —20°C. (Meyer and Anderson, 1939, p. 523).

At temperatures above 35°C., although the initial rate of respiration increases, the rate soon falls off. The decreased respiratory rate at these higher temperatures is the result of a gradual inactivation or destruction of the respiratory enzymes. The higher the temperature, the faster the initial respiration rate decreases. So rapidly did respiration diminish in the pea seedlings shown in Figure 51 at temperatures above 50°C., that by the time the first measurements were made, the respiration was less than it had been at 25°. Had it been possible to measure

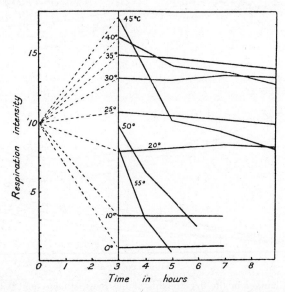

FIGURE 51.—Relation of temperature and the time factor to the respiration rate of 4-day-old garden-pea seedlings previously respiring at a constant rate at a temperature of 25°C. (Fernandes, 1923, as given by Stiles and Leach, 1932.)

directly the rate of respiration immediately after the change from 25 to 50°C., it is probable that the rate at 50° would have been about double that at 25° (Thomas, 1947, p. 282). The acceleration of respiratory activity by higher temperatures is also well illustrated by the work of Hewitt and Curtis previously referred to (Fig. 50). The separated leaves, stems, and roots all lost carbohydrates faster as the temperature was increased from 10 to 40°C.

Many workers have observed that under normal growing conditions the carbohydrate content of plants decreases as the surrounding temperature rises. The rate of photosynthesis is relatively unaffected by temperature, whereas the rate of respiration increases rapidly with temperature. Therefore, low temperatures favor accumulation of photosynthetic products, but high ones may cause a serious depletion of carbohydrate materials. Only a few examples will be cited. Bushnell (1925), working with potato plants in constant-temperature chambers, found that the yield of tubers, a storage organ, declined at temperatures above 18 or 20°C. He concluded that a reduction in carbohydrate

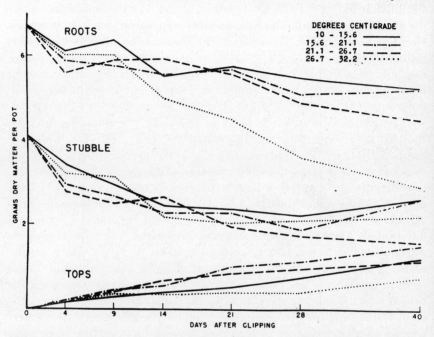

FIGURE 52.—Changes in the dry weights of the roots, stubble, and tops of perennial ryegrass at four different temperatures centigrade. (Sullivan and Sprague, 1949.)

caused by an accelerated rate of respiration accounted for the decreased tuber production at the higher temperatures.

The work of Nightingale and Blake (1934a, 1934b) and many others on fruit trees and of Decker (1944) on pine trees have shown the carbohydrate reserves to decline with increasing temperature. Brown (1939) and Sullivan and Sprague (1949) found the carbohydrates of forage grasses to fall with higher shoot and root temperatures. The latter investigators reported that high temperatures adversely affected ryegrass by causing rapid dissipation of reserve carbohydrates and re-tarded production of new leaf growth. This is illustrated in Figure 52 taken from their work, in which the influence of temperature on the consumption of reserves after defoliation was followed by determining plant weights.   At the end of a 40-day exposure to a temperature range of 26.7 to 32.2°C., the plants were stunted, the leaves spindly and dark green, and the roots discolored and near death.   Weinmann (1948) has recently reviewed the effect of environmental factors, including temperature, on the reserve substances in grasses.

Absorption of mineral nutrients

The absorption of mineral nutrients and water are also processes essential for growth.   The rate at which minerals and water pass into cells is often related to the so-called permeability of the cells.   Before considering the specific effects of temperature on the absorption of nutrients and water, a few general comments on permeability are in order.

The nature of the permeability of cell walls is quite different from that of the protoplasmic membranes of the cell.   The cell walls are composed largely of nonliving tissue.   Their permeability is believed to be relatively constant, and the passage of materials through them is considered to be controlled largely by concentration gradients.   They may be considered permeable to water and salts in the classical sense (Crafts *et al.*, 1949).   In contrast, the living membranes exhibit a differential permeability that changes under the influence of various internal and external factors (Kramer, 1949, p. 249).   Here permeability is used not with the classical meaning of a proportionality constant as in Darcy's law for fluid flow, but as a means of expressing the rate at which solutes or solvents enter the cells, regardless of the mechanism responsible for their entrance.   Thus, if a given substance enters rapidly as a consequence of a greater driving force arising from some particular mechanism, the cell is usually considered to have a high permeability for that substance under the given conditions.   Often no distinction is made between permeability in the classical sense and what might be termed an apparent permeability that is influenced by the magnitude of the driving force.   Using permeability in this broad sense, Kramer and Currier (1950) have pointed out that the permeability of the protoplasmic membranes is a variable condition related to the metabolic activity of the protoplasm itself.   They state that the protoplasmic membranes are a complex heterogeneous system containing lipoids, proteins, and water, and that the organized structure of this system, and presumably its classical as well as apparent permeability, is dependent on metabolic activity.

Let us now consider the absorption of mineral nutrients by plant roots.   As pointed out by Hoagland and Broyer (1936), the accumulation of solutes by the living cell is not merely a question of permeability. It is generally agreed that energy must be expended by the cells to bring about a transfer of solutes across cytoplasmic membranes against a concentration gradient. It is therefore to be expected that nutrient absorption will be affected by factors, such as temperature, that influence metabolic activity.

Many investigators have indicated that the absorption of solutes is reduced at low temperatures, but it is very difficult to separate the effects of low temperature on the absorption process from its effects on translocation and the utilization of the nutrients within the plant.

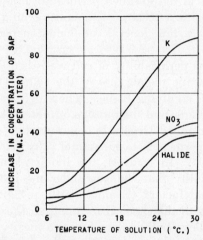

FIGURE 53.—Relation of temperature to salt accumulation by excised young barley root systems during a 10-hour period. (Redrawn from Hoagland and Broyer, 1936.)

Working under experimental conditions carefully selected to avoid complicating factors, Hoagland and Broyer found high temperature coefficients for salt accumulation within certain ranges of temperature. Some of their data on salt accumulation by excised young barley root systems for an absorption period of 10 hours are given in Figure 53. In this figure the data pertaining to nitrate refer to nitrate accumulation, as such, in the sap. Additional nitrate was also absorbed and reduced in the tissues. It will be noted that the temperature coefficients are high (2.5 to 5.0) over a considerable range of temperature (6 to 24°C.). The authors mention that similarly high temperature coefficients were obtained in comparable experiments with entire barley plants.

The absorption of ions by these excised roots continued for 24 hours, but after longer periods of time some loss of salt was observed. In a long period of time the available carbohydrates may become depleted, or other changes unfavorable to salt accumulation or retention may occur. Since these changes are accelerated by increasing temperatures, in long-time experiments the apparent paradox may arise where a lower salt content is obtained at higher temperatures.

Hoagland and Broyer also found that the power of cells to accumulate given ions is related to temperature. This they expressed in terms of accumulation ratios, which they defined as the ratio of concentration of the element in the expressed sap to that in the external solution. These data appear in Table 36. The magnitudes of these values were dependent upon the concentration of the culture solution, and in dilute cultures some exceeded 1,000.

TABLE 36.—*Accumulation ratios for potassium, nitrate, and halide in excised barley root systems (Hoagland and Broyer, 1936)*

Temperature	Accumulation ratio[a]		
°C.	K	NO_3	Halide
6	3.6	0.6	1.2
12	5.1	1.3	1.9
18	8.7	3.1	3.1
24	12.3	5.2	7.2
30	15.1	7.1	10.1

[a] Accumulation ratio is the concentration in the sap divided by the concentration in the external solution.

The temperature acceleration of salt accumulation is not necessarily of the same magnitude for all ions; therefore the degree of selective absorption of ions may be different at different temperatures (Hoagland, 1944). Some differences are apparent from the data of Figure 53 and Table 36. Further information on the influence of temperature on anion and cation absorption has been given by Wanner (1948a, 1948b). His data, given in Table 37, show (1) the temperature coefficients for anion absorption were higher than those for cation absorption and (2) these coefficients were lower at the higher external concentration. Wanner suggested that salt absorption from the higher concentration is less dependent upon temperature than absorption from the lower concentration because, as the external concentration is increased, the energy requirement for root absorption is diminished.

Hoagland and Broyer have pointed out that temperature coefficients for salt accumulation arise indirectly, inasmuch as salt absorption is dependent upon the metabolic activity of the roots. Other factors, such as reduced viscosity of the protoplasm and increased mobility of ions, may be of importance (Kramer, 1949; Hober, 1945). Surface-exchange phenomena, as reported by Overstreet and Jacobson (1946) and Jacobson and Overstreet (1947), may also be involved. These workers presented evidence that radioactive rubidium, strontium, phosphate, and iodide ions may be absorbed even at temperatures as low as 0°C. Determination of the importance of these exchange phenomena in the nutrition of the plant await further experimentation.

It is not known to what extent a reduced rate of nutrient absorption is responsible for the slow growth of plants on cold soils. Went (1944a) suggested that root temperatures will not affect shoot growth

TABLE 37.—*Temperature coefficients, Q_{10}, (15°–25°C.) for ion absorption in 0.01 N and 0.002 N solutions by the roots of 12-day-old wheat plants during a period of 8 hours (Wanner, 1948a)*

| | | Mean temperature coefficients for— | | | |
| | | Cation | | Anion | |
Experiment numbers	Salt	0.01 N	0.002 N	0.01 N	0.002 N
1 to 4	KNO_3	1.18	1.72	1.50	2.28
5 to 6	$Ca(NO_3)_2$	1.13	1.88	2.04	2.68
7 to 11	$Mg(NO_3)_2$	1.23	1.62	.92	1.56
12 to 13	KH_2PO_4	.79	1.29	1.13	2.18

of tomatoes when nutrition and other growth conditions of the roots are very favorable, but that low root temperatures under less favorable conditions may depress top growth (Riethmann, 1933). Poor growth of many plants on cold soils is commonly observed. Low temperatures may hinder growth in a number of ways. The importance of a reduced rate of mineral absorption as the limiting factor in growth at low soil temperatures has been difficult to evaluate. Only a few studies of temperature as a factor in nutrient absorption by intact plants under normal growing conditions have been reported.

Nightingale (1933, 1934, 1935) found with tomato, apple, and peach roots that nitrate was absorbed from soil at temperatures near the minimum for growth. Within a few minutes after the addition of nitrate to nutrient cultures, the fine roots of these plants showed marked nitrogen absorption at the lowest temperatures tested in each case (12.8°C. for tomatoes and 8.9°C. for apple and peach roots). Nightingale (1933) could detect no difference in the permeability of tomato roots to nitrate at 12.8, 21.1, and 35°C.; but Nightingale and Blake

(1934a) inferred that the rate of nitrogen absorption in apple roots increased with higher temperature. This view is supported by Darrow (1939) for bluegrass.

Low temperatures do not appear to retard seriously the absorption of nitrogen, but they do affect the capacity of the roots to reduce the absorbed nitrate and convert it to organic nitrogenous forms, a process commonly called assimilation. Nitrate is assimilated slowly in tomato plants at 12.8° (Nightingale, 1933) and in apple trees at 7.2° (Nightingale and Blake, 1934a) and more slowly in peach trees at 11.1°C. (Nightingale and Blake, 1934b). Translocation of assimilated nitrogen to nonabsorbing portions of the root system and aerial organs is greatly influenced by temperature. This relation was illustrated by Nightingale and Blake's (1934b) experiment with Elberta peach trees. They found that nitrate applied to nitrogen-starved trees was absorbed very quickly by the fine roots at both 11.1 and 21.1°C., although no external response in the leaves was observed for more than a week; whereas at 21.1°C. a noticeable effect on leaf color appeared within 24 hours. In this connection, closely related plants may respond quite differently. Nightingale and Blake (1934a) found that both the Stayman and Baldwin varieties of apples could assimilate nitrate in the absorbing roots at 7.2°C., but that the Stayman apple was less able to translocate the newly synthesized organic nitrogenous materials to the aerial organs.

The findings of Nightingale and Blake received support from later work by Batjer et al. (1943) on Delicious apple trees. The latter authors in greenhouse studies found that appreciable nitrogen was absorbed from both nitrate and ammonium sources and was assimilated in the roots of dormant trees at temperatures as low as 0 to 0.5°C. Analysis of the bark and wood indicated that little if any of the absorbed nitrogen was translocated during the dormant period. In field experiments where the temperature of the upper 18 inches of the soil fluctuates between 0 and 4.4°C. during winter months these workers found that winter applications of sodium nitrate resulted in an increased nitrogen content in Delicious apple roots. Similar results were reported by Aldrich (1931) and by Smith (1935). Nightingale (1948) in his review stated that the nitrogen absorbed and elaborated in apple roots during winter months apparently contributed appreciably to the nitrogen requirements of the growing tops when growth started in the spring.

Brown (1939), working with four common pasture grasses, suggested that a reduced rate of nitrogen assimilation rather than restricted nitrogen absorption was responsible for the retarded growth observed at low temperatures.   Batjer *et al.* (1943) concluded that the failure of roots to absorb nitrogen during winter was probably due to factors other than soil temperature.   They suggested that in some cases inadequate aeration accompanying excessive soil moisture may have been responsible.

Jones (1938) found that low soil temperatures caused leaf chlorosis in potted gardenia plants.   There were traces of chlorosis at soil temperatures of 22 to 20°C., distinct chlorosis at 18°, and increasingly severe chlorosis at lower temperatures.   Chemical analysis of leaves and terminal twigs from healthy and chlorotic plants failed to reveal a deficiency in nutrient elements.   As is commonly reported in unhealthy or diseased plants, some elements were found in greater concentration in the chlorotic plants.   Davidson (1941), also working with gardenias, observed foliar chlorosis at a soil temperature of approximately 20°C. and more severe chlorosis at 15°.   He observed that increases in light intensity and in length of day, as well as increases in air temperature, tended to offset the chlorosis and retarded growth induced by low soil temperatures.

Post (1949, p. 33) noted that roses, which sometimes became chlorotic during winter, often returned to normal during spring when both higher temperatures and greater light intensity prevailed.   Post stated that this chlorosis was thought to be due to lack of iron absorption resulting from poor growth and low respiratory activity in the roots. The leaves of pineapple plants in some of the Hawaiian plantations may show considerable yellowing during winter.   Much of this chlorosis can be corrected by applying nitrogen-carrying leaf sprays, which indicates that a nitrate deficiency may develop in these plants when soil temperatures are relatively low.

Absorption of water

It has been known for many years that low soil temperatures reduce the rate at which plant roots absorb water and that they may produce wilting where loss of water by transpiration is sufficiently rapid. Kramer's recent (1949) book gives a very good review of this subject. As a convenience to the reader, this important aspect of the relation of soil temperature to plant growth is summarized in the following paragraphs, portions of which have been taken from Kramer.

Sach's early experiments on water absorption indicated that plants differed in their response to low soil temperatures.   Later investigations by Döring (1935), Rouschal (1935), Kramer (1942), and others showed that soil temperature usually exerts a greater effect upon the rate of water intake by warm-weather crops and plants native to warm climates than by those plants that grow during the cooler seasons or in colder climates. Kramer's (1949) data are summarized in Table 38.

In Kramer's studies rates of transpiration were measured, and water absorption by the plant was assumed to be approximately equal to transpiration over a 24-hour period. Differences in the effect of soil temperature on transpiration losses of collards, a plant which grows

TABLE 38.—*Effects of soil temperature on transpiration rates for plants of various species (Kramer, 1949)*

Experiment number and species	Plants per experiment[a]	Final soil temperature	Transpiration of cooled plants as percent of controls at 25°C.
	Number	*°C.*	*Percent*
No. 1:			
Collards (*Brassica oleracea acephala*)	6	12.0	63.0
Cotton (*Gossypium hirsutum*)	6	12.0	7.4
No. 2:			
Collards	6	4.3	53.0
Cotton	6	4.3	4.3
No. 3:			
Collards	6	1.0	33.0
Watermelon (*Citrullus vulgaris*)	6	1.0	1.4
No. 4:			
Loblolly pine (*Pinus taeda*)	4	.5	13.7
Slash pine (*P. caribea*)	4	.5	13.9
White pine (*P. strobus*)	4	.5	37.7
Red pine (*P. resinosa*)	4	.5	25.0
No. 5:			
Elm (*Ulmus americana*)	14	.5	25.0
No. 6:			
Privet (*Ligustrum japonicum*)	12	2.5	47.0
No. 7:			
Sunflower (*Helianthus annuus*)	12	1.0	27.0

[a] The plants were divided into two groups, one of which was cooled about 5°C. per night, while the other was kept at 25°C.

well in cold soil, and of cotton and watermelons, plants that thrive only in warm soils, are further illustrated in Figure 54. Another example has been provided by the work of Brown (1939) on Bermuda grass, a native of warm regions, and on Kentucky and Canadian bluegrasses, both indigenous to cooler climates. He reported that water absorption by Bermuda grass was sufficiently retarded at 10°C. to cause wilting, but that bluegrasses were unaffected at this temperature. These data suggested, Kramer (1949) writes, that between species there exist

fundamental differences in the reaction of protoplasm to low temperature and that possibly in some species the permeability of the protoplasm is reduced by low temperatures more than in others.

Other studies of water absorption or transpiration in relation to root
temperature include: Preliminary potometric experiments on sugarcane in solution culture (Duncan and Cooke, 1932); transpiration of
sunflowers at soil temperatures from 1 to 38°C. (Clements and Martin,
1934); wilting points for sunflowers at low soil temperatures (Hendrickson and Veihmeyer, 1945); transpiration of cotton in solution cultures
and soils at temperatures from 10 to 70°C. (Arndt, 1937); potometric

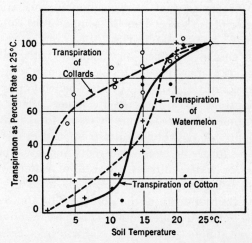

FIGURE 54.—Effects of soil temperature on transpiration of collards, a plant which
thrives in cold soil, and cotton and watermelons, plants that grow well only in
warm soils. (Kramer, 1942.)

measurements on cucumber plants at solution temperatures from 15 to
40°C. and tests on water delivered from cut root stumps under suction
(Schroeder, 1939); and observations on water absorption by hemp at
soil temperatures of 15 and 30°C. (Nelson, 1944). These studies all
showed that low root temperatures may retard water absorption and
produce water deficits in the shoots. The water relations of woody
shrubs and trees have also been observed to be affected by low soil
temperatures. Gardenia plants whose roots were cooled to soil temperatures near 10°C. wilted immediately but gradually recovered over
a period of 2 weeks (Jones, 1938). Cultivated blueberry bushes were
also observed to wilt when the roots were first cooled to about 15°C. and
to recover after several days (Bailey and Jones, 1941). With lowered
soil temperatures, the transpiration rate declined in rooted lemon and

grapefruit cuttings (Haas, 1936) and in young Valencia orange trees (Cameron, 1941). Where water absorption is retarded by cold soils, considerable winter injury to the aerial portion of the plant may arise from desiccation, especially during periods when atmospheric conditions favor high rates of transpiration.

The rate of water absorption by plants appears to increase with increasing root temperature up to a point above which absorption is depressed by a further rise in temperature. Van der Paauw (1949) wrote that Rouschal (1935) found the transpiration rate in bean plants was almost doubled by raising the root temperature from 10 to 20°C. Boonstra (1935) reported that transpiration in this same species increased by a factor of 1.3 to 1.9 over the temperature range 15 to 25°C. Data obtained by Clements and Martin (1934) indicated that the transpiration rate in sunflowers rises very rapidly with soil temperature from about 2 to 12° and appears to pass through a maximum near 24°C. Root temperatures above 27°C. in grapefruit cuttings and above 31° in lemon cuttings were observed by Haas (1936) to reduce the rate of transpiration. The reduction in water intake under high soil-temperature conditions possibly results from a decrease in absorbing surface caused by injury to some fine roots and by rapid maturation of others. Even in water cultures, the rate of water absorption may be so diminished at high root temperatures (37 to 38°C.) as to produce wilting and the eventual death of the plants (Ellis and Swaney, 1947). In this case, the retarded water uptake may be a consequence of an inadequate oxygen supply.

What reason can be advanced for the reduced rate of water absorption at low root temperatures? Undoubtedly several mechanisms are involved. These have been summarized by Kramer (1949) essentially as follows:

1. Retardation of root elongation.—In soils with moisture contents below field capacity, it is generally agreed that roots must constantly extend to obtain a continuing supply of moisture.

2. Decreased rate of movement of water from soil to roots.—The water-supplying power of soil as measured with porous ceramic pieces is only one-third to one-half as great at 0 to 25°C. (Kramer, 1934).

3. Increased viscosity of water.—The viscosity of water is twice as great at 0 as at 25°C. This condition likely slows down the movement of water not only from soil to root, but also through the root.

4. Increased viscosity of protoplasm.—In general, the viscosity of protoplasm is several times greater near 0 than at 25°C., thus retarding water movement across the mass of cells lying between the epidermis and the xylem of the root.

5. Decreased permeability of cells.—The apparent permeability of cells to water generally decreases with declining temperature. This condition is probably related to the effect of temperature on metabolic activity. Kramer (1940) has demonstrated the high resistance to water movement through roots at low temperatures. Much of this resistance could be removed by destroying the protoplasm.

Kramer (1949) concluded that the reduced intake of water by transpiring plants in cold soil is caused principally by the increased resistance to water movement across the living cells of roots. He attributed this increased resistance to the combined effects of both the higher viscosity and lower permeability of protoplasm and the greater viscosity and reduced molecular activity of water. He further pointed out that differences in the protoplasm may account for the varying effects of temperature upon water absorption by various plant species. For example, it is possible that the protoplasm of cotton or watermelon roots undergoes much greater changes in viscosity and permeability than that of collards. As a result, there is a greater reduction in water absorption by cotton and watermelon plants at low temperatures. The importance of protoplasmic changes in this connection has been suggested by experiments on elm, privet, and sunflower. Kramer found that plants cooled nearly to freezing in 4 to 5 hours, or even overnight, wilted severely; whereas those cooled over a period of 4 to 5 days wilted only slightly. Thus it seems possible that slow cooling permits protoplasmic adjustments that lessen the effects of low temperatures on the absorption of water.

It is difficult to ascertain the extent to which the retarded growth of plants in cold soils should be attributed to a reduced rate of water absorption. Concerning this matter, McDougall (1941, p. 133), wrote, "The temperature of the soil is very important to the plant largely because of its effect upon the rate of absorption of water." To cite an extreme case Lundegardh (1931, p. 87) attributed the failure of higher plants to grow in certain arctic regions, where the air temperatures are high enough to support life, to the very low soil temperatures that prevent water uptake. Cannon (1911) thought the slow rate of water absorption from cold soils during winter months limited the development of both the roots and the shoots of winter annuals. In greenhouse plants, wilting may appear during bright days following very cold nights. The air temperature in glasshouses may rise quickly, increasing transpiration loss above the rate of water absorption from the still cold soil. Under such conditions, Post (1949, p. 32) believed that the equivalent of many days of growth are lost because the plants are somewhat wilted during the sunny periods. Hubbard and Herbert (1933) observed that cotton plants in the San Joaquin Valley of California wilted on warm days following cold weather, even in the presence of ample soil moisture. Wilting disappeared as soon as the soil warmed up, and no damage resulted other than a possible temporary retardation in growth.

Insofar as the writer is aware, the importance of a reduced rate of water absorption as a factor limiting plant growth in cold soils has not been tested by direct experimentation. Under some conditions, extreme soil temperatures, particularly the low soil temperatures of winter and early spring, may cause temporary water deficits in plants and thus produce some checking of growth. It seems improbable, however, that a retarded rate of water absorption induced by unfavorable soil temperatures is commonly responsible for the slow growth of plants on cold soils.

Assimilation

Growth generally involves the division and enlargement of cells. Knowledge of the mechanisms involved in these processes is very meager. Barron (1949) wrote: "From the extensive investigations on the mechanisms of cell division it must be concluded that there is as yet no full understanding of the physical and chemical mechanisms which bring forth this process." Kramer and Currier (1950) agreed that the mechanism governing the enlargement or elongation of cells is one of the great unsolved problems in plant physiology. Thus, although little is known concerning either cell division or cell enlargement, it is certain that without metabolism there is no growth (Van Niel, 1949). This conclusion follows from thermodynamic considerations since, in the synthesis of cellular constituents, the cell must supply the required formation energies. The complexities of respiratory-energy transfers in relation to growth are under study by Bonner (1949). He has been able to trace out some of the energy transfer, but much remains to be done on this problem.

For the simplest kind of growth in isolated plant parts immersed in solution, Thimann (1949) has tentatively proposed the following steps, presented here in somewhat abbreviated form: (1) Auxin enters cells, accelerating the rate of protoplasmic streaming; (2) this acceleration causes an increased intake of water; (3) the energy for the streaming and for the accumulation of solutes is furnished by sugar breakdown (respiration); (4) the intake of solutes is at once followed by the intake of water; (5) the accelerated streaming affects wall deposition and plasticity; and (6) the increased water intake, coupled with the change in wall properties, results in cell enlargement or, in other words, growth. While Thimann stated that this scheme is still largely hypothetical, he believed that the proposed mechanism is approximately correct. In Thimann's hypothetical picture of growth, protoplasmic streaming, respiration, and (by inference) translocation of respiratory substrate, solute absorption, and water intake are all involved. It has been previously pointed out that each of these processes is influenced by temperature.

Comprehensive studies of the effect of temperature upon the quantitative aspects of growth were undertaken some years ago by Lehenbauer (1914) and Leitch (1916). Lehenbauer investigated shoot

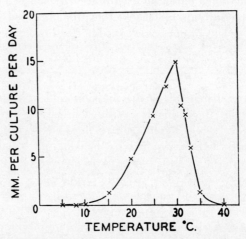

FIGURE 55.—Mean growth of excised root tips of tomato plants in nutrient solution as affected by temperature. (White, 1937.)

growth in maize seedlings in darkness under controlled temperatures. Some of his extensive data are presented in Figure 59. He found that the optimum temperature for growth decreased with an increasing period of exposure. Talma (1918) observed a similar shift in the optimum for pepperweed with increasing exposure (see Figure 58). Lehenbauer concluded that for periods of 3 hours or longer, the highest mean hourly growth rate occurred within the temperature range from 29 to 32°C. Leitch noted that the rate of elongation of pea seedlings increased consistently with rising temperature over the range from —2° to 29°C. Above 30° the growth rate diminished with increasing temperature, and growth ceased at 45°C. She found that a distinct time factor was evident in the relation between temperature and growth in the 30 to 45°C. temperature range. This factor is discussed in the section on cardinal temperatures.

White (1932, 1937) has used excised root tips of tomato and wheat plants to study the effect of temperature on growth. These root tips were grown in nutrient media containing sucrose, yeast extract, and the usual inorganic salts. His results with excised tomato roots are reproduced in Figure 55. In White's experiment 20 cultures were grown at each temperature, and the measurements were made at the end of 1 week. The optimum at 30°C. is surprisingly sharp in this study. The length of wheat root tips grown during a 2-week period increased with rising temperature up to 25° but decreased sharply at 30°C. No growth was obtained at 35 or 40°C. From a second experiment restricted to a narrower temperature range of 20 to 30°C., he concluded that under his conditions the wheat root tips grew best at 26 to 28°C.,

TABLE 39.—*Growth of wheat roots as affected by temperature* (*Burström, 1941*)

Growth	Roots of intact plants during 6 days in darkness					Excised roots during 14 days in 1/20 M glucose				
	7°C.	15°C.	20°C.	26°C.	33°C.	8°C.	15°C.	20°C.	25°C.	30°C.
Increase in—										
Length (mm.)	11.8	23.1	23.7	32.3	1.0	22.0	56.5	71.3	81.1	45.6
Fresh weight (mg.)	81	120	121	140	−1.9	63	150	193	229	233
Average length of mature cells (μ)	207	215	121	113	.....	206	177	157	147	147
Cells formed along root axis (number)	57	88	173	257	.....	152	312	413	513	321

but that the optimum was not sharply defined. More recently Burström (1941) studied cell division and elongation in both excised root tips and intact roots of wheat. His data, assembled in Table 39, indicate that growth behavior with respect to temperature was very much the same for both groups of roots. The number of cells formed during the experimental period increased with temperature within the range of 7 to 8 to 25 to 26°C. but decreased at higher temperatures. The final length of individual cells, however, declined progressively above 15°C. The increase in over-all root length became larger with temperature, reaching a maximum at 25 to 26°C. Thus, the increase in root length must have arisen from an accelerated rate of cell division.

Stuckey (1941) found evidence of cell division in the root tips of grasses at temperatures very close to 0°C. More recently, Brown and Rickless (1949) studied the process of cell division and enlargement in excised root tips of pumpkin (*Cucurbita pepo*). They employed a tissue-maceration technique for determining the total number of cells formed in the root tips cultured in nutrient media held at 5, 15, 20, and 25°C. The rate of cell division reached a maximum at 15° and declined sharply at the higher termperatures (Fig. 56). Cellular extension nearly doubled between 5 and 15° and showed a greater increase between 15 and 25° (Fig. 57). Although the greatest number of cells were produced at 15°, the over-all length of the root increased with

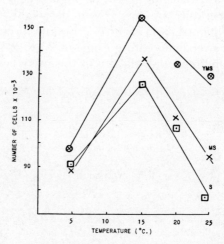

Figure 56.—Average number of cells in excised root tips of pumpkin (*Cucurbita pepo*) after 24 hours in three nutrient media as a function of temperature. *S* represents a nutrient solution containing only 2 percent sucrose; *MS*, a solution of 2 percent sucrose plus an inorganic salt mixture; and *YMS*, yeast extract added to the *MS* solution. (Redrawn from Brown and Rickless, 1949.)

temperature because of its effect on cellular elongation. These findings, particularly with reference to the final length of cells, are in contrast to Burström's data on wheat root tips. Brown and Rickless suggested that these differences were attributable to differences within species. Both studies showed, however, that the rate of cellular extension increases with rising temperature. A still more detailed study was reported by Murray (1949), who investigated the effects of temperature upon mitotic divisions of generative nuclei in pollen tubes of Solomonseal (*Polygonatum commutatum*). No divided nuclei were found at temperatures above or below a range of 5 to 30°C. While the most rapid rate of division during the first 12 hours occurred at 30°C., the maximum yield of postmetaphasic nuclei after 48 hours was obtained at 20°C.

Went (1944b) reported some interesting experiments on the effect of temperature on stem elongation in tomato plants. The growing portions of the stems were held at 15.5° in one group and at 26.5°C. in a second group; the rest of the plant in both treatments was subjected to 26.5°C. For the first 2 days, while the growing portions were still enclosed in the cooling jacket, those held at 15.5°C. grew only 14 millimeters per day, whereas those at 26.5° grew 21.5 millimeters per day.

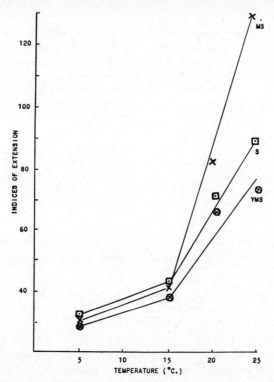

FIGURE 57.—Average indices of cellular extension in excised root tips of *Cucurbita pepo* after 36 hours in three nutrient media as a function of temperature. Symbols as in Figure 56. (Redrawn from Brown and Rickless, 1949.)

After the 2-day interval, when the growing zone of all plants had emerged above the cooling jacket, those previously at 15.5° grew 21 millimeters per day, while those at 26.5° grew 21.7 millimeters per day. In a further experiment, stem elongation on defoliated tomatoes in a dark room was observed at three temperatures. Very little growth occurred in the darkened defoliated plants. Plants defoliated except for two mature leaves, through which sucrose was supplied to the plant, showed a marked effect of temperature on growth (Table 40).

The work of Brown and Rickless (1949) further illustrates the dependence of cell division and elongation upon a supply of suitable organic substances and mineral solutes. Moreover, they found no increase in the number of cells when a carbohydrate source was omitted from the nutrient medium. Cell division was slow in the presence of sucrose only, but it was markedly increased by the addition of inorganic salts to the sucrose and was further accelerated by the addition of yeast

TABLE 40.—*Stem elongation in millimeters per day for tomatoes originally grown in the greenhouse but later transferred to dark rooms at different temperatures (Went, 1944b)*

	Temperature of dark room in which growth measurements were made (°C.)		
Plant treatment	8	18	26.5
	mm.	*mm.*	*mm.*
Plants defoliated, no sucrose	0.79 ± 0.10	0.87	1.02 ± 0.13
Plants defoliated, except for two mature leaves in 10-percent sucrose solution	1.8 ± 0.1	7.5 ± 0.4	9.4 ± 0.6

extract (see Fig. 56). Similar effects were obtained in cell elongation, except that the yeast extract was depressive under the conditions of this experiment.

Cardinal Temperatures

The many processes upon which plant life depends are influenced by the temperature to which the plant is exposed. Life is possible only within the limits of certain temperatures, and growth is confined to an even narrower range. In general, the growth of a given species in relation to temperature shows three cardinal points: The *minimum*, the lowest temperature at which growth is exhibited; the *optimum*, the temperature at which growth is the most rapid; and the *maximum*, the highest temperature at which growth will occur.

These cardinal points are not so definite as was formerly supposed but vary over a considerable range, depending upon the plant material and other factors. Pfeffer (1903, p. 79) early recognized that "the cardinal points can never be determined with more than approximate accuracy, since their positions are influenced by the external conditions, the duration of exposure, the age of the plant, and its previous treatment."

The *minimum* temperature for growth has been defined as the lowest temperature at which plants will continue to grow without injury after a specified exposure period. Near the freezing point all plant activity is extremely slow. Since even at temperatures somewhat above freezing there is little growth of many crops, Kincer (1922) has suggested a "zero of vital temperature point" and proposed that this point be taken as the temperature usually prevailing when the crop is planted. In the complicated problem of evaluating the effectiveness of temperature in crop production, differences between crops are sometimes neglected and a general zero point is arbitrarily set at 4.4°C. (Klages, 1942, p. 239). It is well known that the minimum temperature for growth varies widely with different plants. Several examples drawn from the work of Haberlandt (1874), as cited by Klages (p. 100), illustrate this point. Haberlandt reported the minimum temperature for the germination of peas, vetch, rye as 1° to 2°; for corn and sorghums, as 8° to 10°; and for tobacco, as 13° to 14°C. The minimum temperature values are difficult to determine precisely because growth rates are slow at low temperatures.

Life may continue at temperatures below the minimum, a condition sometimes referred to as *cold rigor*, but death results if the temperature falls to a lower value called the *subminimum*. The large economic losses of plants from low temperature injury or death have stimulated considerable research to determine the causes of this injury and methods for its prevention and to develop or discover plants inherently resistant to the effects of such temperatures. The problem of plant damage associated with low soil temperature will be considered in a later section.

Although the notion of an *optimum* temperature is a simple concept, its precise definition is difficult. In general, the rate of growth increases with temperature until a condition is reached where the accelerated rate of activity cannot be maintained and growth is depressed. The work of Talma (1918) cited by Klages (p. 101) showed that as the period of exposure is increased, the temperature producing the greatest growth is decreased (Fig. 58).

As Blackman (1905) had previously proposed, Leitch (1916) believed that with careful work it should be possible to determine a temperature point at which a maximum growth rate could be maintained independent of the time factor. Accordingly, Leitch defined the optimum temperature as the highest temperature at which there is no time factor operating and distinguished a *maximum-rate* temperature at which the process attains its highest rate. The maximum-rate temperature was considered as the optimum for very short exposure periods; for infinitely short periods it would coincide with the *maximum* temperature.

Considering these difficulties in precise definition of the optimum temperature and the fact that the most favorable temperatures for each of the various physiological processes—such as photosynthesis, translocation, and respiration—do not coincide and are difficult to delimit, it seems clear that the ecological optimum is never a mere point but a range of several degrees at least. Because the concept of the optimum temperature cannot be accurately defined and has frequently been misused, the writer will make but occasional use of this term. Where introduced it will be used in its popular meaning as the temperature at which, under the given conditions, the most satisfactory growth occurs in a particular stage of the plant cycle.

The *maximum* temperature is usually defined as the highest temperature at which growth occurs (Leitch, 1916; Daubenmire, 1947; and

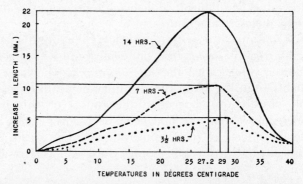

FIGURE 58.—Shift in the optimum temperature for elongation of the roots of pepperweed (*Lepidium*) with increasing periods of exposure. (Redrawn from Talma, 1918.)

others). As with the other cardinal temperatures, the maximum temperature may be defined as the highest temperature at which growth continues for a specific period of time. In maize seedlings, Lehenbauer (1914) found that at 40°C. shoot growth continued in all plants for at least 21 hours; at 41°C. growth ceased in five plants after 15 hours, and in the remaining plant after 18 hours; at 42°C. shoot growth ceased in three plants after 15 hours, and in three plants after 18 hours; and at 43°C. shoot growth ceased in three plants after 9 hours, in two after 12 hours, and in the remaining plant after 15 hours. For these seedlings, 43°C. was the maximum temperature for an exposure of 15 hours; 42° was the corresponding maximum for 18 hours and so on. For shorter periods the maximum temperature would doubtless be appreciably above 43°C. For practical purposes, the maximum temperature may be defined as the highest temperature at which plants continue to grow without injury.

Plants may survive for brief periods at temperatures above the maximum, and under these conditions they are sometimes referred to as existing in a state of *heat rigor*. They will die, however, if this temperature becomes too high or is imposed for too long a period. The data of Berkley and Berkley (1933), reproduced in Figure 59, illustrate this temperature-time relationship for cotton seedlings.

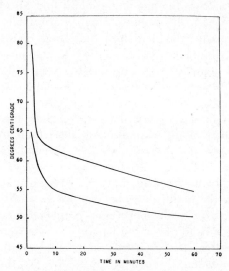

FIGURE 59.—Effect of atmospheric humidity on time required to kill cotton seedlings at various temperatures centigrade. Results at an average relative humidity of approximately 70 percent plotted on upper line; those at a relative humidity near 100 percent, on lower line. Lines in graph are not drawn through any definite set of points but are based on treatment of more than 4,000 plants. (Redrawn from Berkley and Berkley, 1933.)

They found that atmospheric humidity affected the resistance of seedlings to high temperatures and influenced the nature of the injury and the portion of the plant affected. The difficulty in defining the common term "thermal death point" is at once evident. Realizing that no really satisfactory definition of thermal death point can be given, these authors offered the following: "The thermal death point is that temperature which, at a given relative humidity, will kill the protoplasm immediately upon its assumption." They called attention to the fact that tissue temperature may lag appreciably behind surrounding temperature and that transpirational cooling may prevent the tissue from reaching the imposed temperature.

The greater sensitivity of plant tissue to heat at high humidities doubtless hinges on the effect of increased humidity in depressing the effectiveness of transpiration, but it may also arise in part from a smothering of the protoplasm resulting from an insufficient gaseous exchange. Although Berkley and Berkley wisely suggested limiting the thermal death point to the death of the protoplasm alone, they slipped into the common usage and applied the term to the entire plant. They concluded that thermal-death-point values should not be reported without stating the age of the plant and also the atmospheric conditions under which the determinations were made.

It should be pointed out that the lethal effect of high temperatures is not always attributable to a disruption of the protoplasm. Death of plants at high temperatures may result from a desiccation of the tissue or from a disturbance of the respiration-photosynthesis balance. The term "heat injury" is often used in a collective sense to include all types of plant damage induced by excessively high temperatures. Less is known about plant adaptation to heat than to cold. Despite the complications in the determination of thermal death points, one can summarize as follows: (1) The death point of protoplasm has not been accurately determined and (2) the thermal death point of plants varies with the plant, the stage of growth, and the external conditions. In spite of a wide variety of plants and methods, the apparent thermal death point for most plants lies between 45 and 55°C. (Baker, 1929; Miller, 1938, p. 481; and Lundegardh, 1931, p. 79).

From the foregoing discussion, it is obvious that the cardinal temperatures are not precise but are only approximations extending over ranges of several degrees at least. They depend upon the time of exposure, the plant species and plant organ considered, the stage of development of the plant, the physiological conditions of the plant, the atmospheric humidity, and other environmental factors. In very general terms, the temperature limits for growth lie between 0 and 50°C. A few plants may show some growth at temperatures outside these limits, but in most plants growth is confined to a much narrower range of temperature.

How do soil temperatures compare with the cardinal temperatures for plant growth? In a previous section, temperatures in cultivated soils were seen to vary between approximately 55 and −21°C. at the 1-inch depth, between approximately 35 and −17.5° at the 1-foot depth and between narrower limits with increasing depth. Thus germinating seeds and the subterranean organs of plants may at times experience soil temperatures somewhat outside the temperature limits for growth and survival.

Expressions for the Relation between Temperature and Growth

In 1889 Arrhenius empirically developed the following relationship between the rate of a chemical reaction and temperature: The rate of change of the logarithm of the velocity constant for a chemical reaction is inversely proportional to the square of the absolute temperature. More exact formulations have since been derived (see Eyring, 1935). Such relationships provide the most satisfactory method for expressing the influence of temperature on the reaction velocity of many chemical reactions (Glasstone, 1940, p. 1067). The generalization that the velocity constants in chemical reactions increase by a factor of 2 or 3 for each 10°C. rise in temperature has been referred to in the literature as the Van't Hoff or the Van't Hoff-Arrhenius rule. This rule is seldom mentioned by name in recent work, but reference is frequently made to the temperature coefficient (Q_{10}) of a reaction, defined in a previous section as the factor by which the rate is multiplied for each 10°C. increase in temperature.

The application of the relatively simple equation of Arrhenius and the usefulness of the temperature coefficient in biological systems were discussed by Wilson (1949). He pointed out that these relations are of doubtful value in predicting the influence of temperature on such complex phenomena as growth. The temperature coefficient at best provides only an approximate method for expressing the effect of temperature on growth, because the value of the coefficient for a given plant material varies with temperature. The coefficient may vary from zero around temperatures both below the minimum and above the maximum to very high values around temperatures approaching the optimum. This is illustrated in Figure 60, taken from Lehenbauer (1914), for the shoot growth of maize seedlings at different temperatures. As Lundegardh (1931) pointed out, the temperature-rate curve from Lehenbauer's study shows four principal phases that merge into each other. At low temperatures, Q_{10} exceeds 3; at intermediate temperatures below optimum, Q_{10} equals 3 to 2; near the so-called optimum, Q_{10} is very rapidly decreasing; and above the optimum, Q_{10} is less than 1. Temperature-rate data for growth in other plant materials show quite different characteristics (cf. Figs. 79, 80, 81, 82, 84, 87, 88, 90 and 91). The temperature coefficient for a given plant process varies with the age of the material and with variations in other environmental factors. Because of these limitations, and particularly because the temperature coefficient must be expressed in relation to a particular range on the temperature scale, this expression is of little use in many biological phenomena.

Under certain conditions and within a narrow range, the effects of temperature on growth may be expressed in terms of a simple formula. In the more general situation, however, growth may be determined by any one of the many temperature-dependent mechanisms involved in growth that becomes the limiting process under the given conditions. For this reason, MacDougal (1920) believed that the relation of growth to temperature cannot be expressed by any simple mathematical formulation. The recent work of Went (1944a, 1944b) has illustrated some of the difficulties in relating growth to temperature. Few data are available on growth kinetics even from the simplest systems, such as the

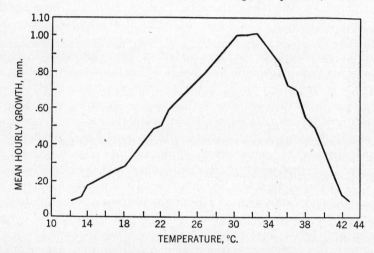

FIGURE 60.—Growth of the shoots of maize seedlings during a period of 9 hours at different temperatures. (Redrawn from Lehenbauer, 1914.)

growth of micro-organisms in single media. The use of such comparatively simple systems to give an insight into the kinetics of growth has recently been discussed by Van Niel (1949). Weiss (1949) cautioned, "The less we let our work and thoughts be misled by the delusion that 'growth' is basically but a simple elementary process, like a 'bimolecular reaction,' the faster will be our progress toward a true insight into the real mechanisms of . . . [growth]."

In undertaking a review of the effects of soil temperature on plant growth, one must bear in mind not only the fact that growth is the resultant of a complex chain of closely interrelated processes each of which is directly influenced by temperature, but also the fact that plant growth in soils under normal field conditions is influenced by numerous indirect effects of temperature. Soil temperature may influence plant growth indirectly by its effect on such factors as the availability of nutrient elements in the soil, soil moisture relations, and the occurrence and severity of plant diseases.

III. SOIL TEMPERATURE AND PLANT GROWTH

By R. M. Hagan

The ambiguity of growth as a basis for physical measurements was discussed in the previous section. Growth has come to have many meanings. It is commonly defined as *a permanent increase in weight, attended by a permanent change in form*. Growth will be used with this meaning in most of the following sections. However, in the case of seeds, bulbs, and tubers, the usual practice will be followed of considering growth to include differentiation and development of tissues, even where unaccompanied by an increase in weight or size. Such activity is of importance in the after-ripening of seeds, the internal development of bulbs, and in the early stages in germination of seeds or the sprouting of bulbs.

Although the effect of temperature on plant development has been studied by many investigators, entire plants have frequently been exposed to different temperatures in such a manner that it is difficult, if not impossible, to determine whether the growth response observed was due primarily to the effect of temperature on the shoot or on the root. In many cases, such experiments provide little help in determining the influence of soil temperature on plant growth. Not for a single plant is there available soil temperature-growth data for its various organs at different stages of development. Likewise, little is known concerning the influence of other environmental factors such as light on soil temperature-growth relations. It should be mentioned that the influence of light on growth varies with the season, according to the dependence of growth upon photosynthetic products. Summer growth is largely dependent on photosynthesis, whereas early spring growth in many plants takes place largely at the expense of stored materials in the seeds, bulbs, rhizomes, or roots. Thus, one might expect soil temperature to exert a greater influence on the early season growth of some young plants than on the summer growth of more mature plants of the same species.

Consideration will now be given to the following stages or aspects of plant development: Germination and seedling emergence; sprouting of bulbs, tubers and similar structures; root growth; shoot growth; and crop quality.

Germination and Seedling Emergence

Temperature is one of the most important factors governing the germination of all seeds. Germination, emergence, and early growth of plants are intimately related to soil temperature. The effects of weather are probably more critical during the periods of germination and early seedling development stage than during any other stage of vegetative growth. Unfavorable soil temperatures at seeding time often produce a poor stand and, consequently, a reduced yield because of the lowered plant population. A retarded growth of young seedlings may not only further reduce yield but also affect adversely the quality of the crop produced.

Fully ripened seed can germinate only when external conditions are favorable. In addition to temperature, moisture, and oxygen, other factors—as light, carbon dioxide, soil pH, mineral elements, and activities of micro-organisms—may affect the speed and completeness of germination. Each species varies in its requirements and tolerances for each of these factors.

Before the specific effects of temperature on the germination and emergence of various plant species are discussed, brief mention should be made of the problems of seed dormancy and after-ripening.

Dormancy and after-ripening

The term "dormancy" is usually applied to any condition of seed that makes it resistant to germination. Recent advances in the knowledge of seed dormancy have been reviewed by Porter (1949). The dormancy of seed and the influence of temperature upon the germination of the seed depends to a large extent on the previous after-ripening treatment. The term "after-ripening" refers to the series of chemical or physical changes within the seed which bring to a close the dormant period and make growth possible again if the environmental conditions are favorable. The ripening of seed appears to involve a sequence of phases, each phase having different optimum conditions. By exposing moistened seeds to temperatures slightly above freezing prior to sowing, the seeds of some species may be made to produce plants that flower earlier, a process referred to as vernalization. For a discussion of this highly specialized subject the reader is referred to Whyte (1939), Crocker (1948), and Murneek et al. (1949).

Properly ripened seeds usually germinate at lower temperatures and with greater rapidity than those incompletely cured. In the case of redroot (*Amaranthus retroflexus*) seeds, Crocker (1948, p. 127) reported that immediately after harvest a temperature of 35 to 40°C. was required for germination, but that as the periods in dry storage were increased lower and lower temperatures permitted germination. After several months of dry storage, seeds germinated, although slowly, at temperatures as low as 10°C. Working with two species of crabgrass (*Digitaria*), Toole and Toole (1941) also found that as the seed aged, there was a marked change in the temperature requirements for germination and in the rate of germination for a given temperature condition. Under the most favorable temperature conditions, freshly harvested seed of both species germinated extremely slowly, requiring more than 196 days for complete germination; but 1-year-old seed germinated completely in 7 to 14 days (Fig. 61). These workers observed that the two species of crabgrass showed distinct differences in response to several of the temperature treatments studied. With subterranean clover, Hills (1944a, 1944b) also found that the speed of germination and the temperature requirements depended upon the age of the seed. Many

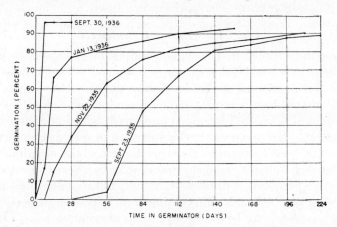

FIGURE 61.—Influence of age on the germination of seed of crabgrass (*Digitaria ischaemum*) at a 20° to 35°C. alternation temperature. Seed tested immediately after harvest September 23, 1935, and on the dates indicated. (Toole and Toole, 1941.)

other examples could be cited of the manifest influence of pretreatment or aging of seeds on their temperature relations during germination. This matter will be referred to again in later paragraphs.

Soil temperatures exceeding the maximum temperature or falling below the minimum for germination of a given species may contribute to the dormancy of seeds in soil. The germination of common weeds is often controlled by soil temperature. Crabgrass, for example, does not appear in lawns until the summer when soil temperatures have risen high enough to permit germination of its seeds. Other weeds, however, do not germinate until the fall when the surface soil temperature has fallen appreciably below that of the summer. Seeds buried in the duff under a dense forest canopy often remain dormant because the temperature is too low for germination. Upon cutting or thinning the forest, sufficient radiation may reach the forest floor to promote the production of a good stand of seedlings (Hoffman, 1920).

High soil temperatures may reduce considerably the period of viability of seeds held dormant in the soil by some factor such as lack of moisture. The more rapid deterioration of seeds at elevated temperatures is caused in part, at least, by an accelerated respiration which produces an earlier exhaustion of the carbohydrate food reserves within the seed. In seed storage, the primary objective is to preserve the seed with a minimum loss of viability and, in some cases, to facilitate the after-ripening or aging of the seeds. Temperature as a factor in seed storage has been extensively investigated. For reviews, see Baldwin (1942), Boswell *et al.* (1940), and Porter (1949).

Cardinal temperatures for germination and emergence

Alternating rather than constant temperatures appear to be more favorable to the germination of many seeds and are apparently necessary for germination of the seeds of some plants. Harrington (1923) observed that celery, parsnip, redtop, orchard grass, Kentucky bluegrass, Johnson grass, and Bermuda grass seeds germinated much better with favorable temperature alternations than at constant temperatures. On the other hand, he reported that carrot, parsley, timothy, bromegrass, perennial and Italian ryegrasses, meadow fescue, and several kinds of flower seeds germinated practically as well at favorable constant temperatures as they did under alternating ones. In some cases, a constant high temperature may be as effective as an alternating temperature for germination. Myers (1942) found germination of curly mitchellgrass (*Astrebla lappacea*) to be as satisfactory at a constant 32°C. as under temperature alternations that often have been shown favorable for grasses. Not only do species differ in their requirement for alternating temperature, but different lots of the same kind of seed somtimes vary widely in this respect. Possibly certain seeds that usually are constant temperature germinators may germinate better with an alternation of temperatures under some conditions. Incomplete after-ripening may be involved.

Alternating temperatures are often used as regular procedure in the commercial testing of many seeds. It is the common practice to maintain the upper temperature for only a small part of the day, seldom more than 8 hours and usually not more than 6 hours, and to make the change to the lower temperature quite rapidly. While an alternating temperature simulates conditions experienced by seeds in soil, no hypothesis adequate to explain its beneficial effects has appeared. It has been suggested that these temperature changes in some way stimulate respiration and catalase activity (Davis, 1939). A partial destruction of the seed coat by mechanical opening or by treatment with sulfuric acid has been found a substitute for alternating temperatures in germination of the seeds of Bermuda grass and cattail (Morinaga, 1926) and Johnson grass (Harrington, 1923), but breaking the seed coat in bluegrass and celery did not dispose of the need for alternating temperatures.

There is usually an optimum temperature range where germination is most rapid, is most complete, or results in the greatest number of healthy seedlings. The temperature producing the fastest germination may not be that at which the greatest percentage of seeds ultimately germinate nor the one producing the most vigorous seedlings. Further, the optimum constant temperature may differ from the optimum alternating temperature in each case. Thus the so-called optimum temperature may depend on the type of temperature treatment used and on the criterion selected for measurement of the growth response. As a consequence, different writers in this field have used the expression optimum temperature with markedly different meanings. In his review article, Edwards (1932) pointed out that this expression has been used with the following meanings:

1. The upper limit of a range of temperatures at which approximately the same final percentage of germination is attained when tests are continued long enough to make sure maximum germination has occurred.
2. The temperature yielding the highest germination percentage at the end of a given incubation period.
3. The temperature at which the least time is required for the appearance of the first or last of the seedlings to germinate. (This definition was popular in early work, but it is unsatisfactory since the extreme limits of variation with respect to promptness of germination are apt to vary with the number of seeds in the test sample.)
4. The temperature corresponding to the least average incubation time. (This concept is similar to that of No. 3 but has the advantage of taking into account the behavior of all individuals in the sample.)
5. The temperature giving the largest average height (or greatest degree of vigor, and so on, estimated in some suitable way) of the seedlings of a set at the end of a specified period for germination and subsequent growth. (Such an optimum must refer to a specific time period, and its use introduces a confusing combination, since seed germination and seedling growth are not related to temperature in exactly the same manner.)
6. The temperature resulting in both the highest rate of seedling production and highest final germination percentage.

Analysis of data is further impeded by lack of a standard concept of germination itself. Some writers regard a seed as germinated when the seed coat bursts; others consider a seed as germinated only after the root or shoot has emerged, or after the root or shoot, or both, have attained considerable length.

As has been previously discussed, the cardinal temperatures reported for germination are influenced by the stage of after-ripening in the seeds, the testing technique used, and the criteria employed for judging the occurrence of germination or emergence. The importance of some of these factors, unfortunately, was not generally recognized by the early workers whose investigations provide a considerable portion of the data available on this subject. Accordingly it is difficult to evaluate their findings. It should be borne in mind that the cardinal temperatures are not so definite as it is commonly believed. At best, only approximate ranges can be specified, and these depend upon other conditions discussed in a previous section. No attempt will be made here to tabulate the data to be found in the extensive writings on seed germination. Early papers on this subject are listed in the bibliography compiled by Franck (1928). A more recent index to the literature on seed germination, arranged by crops, has been drawn up by Edwards (1932). In the following paragraphs the data available for the several crop groups will be summarized briefly, and some later references will be given to supplement the index prepared by Edwards.

Grasses and forage crops.—A comprehensive survey of the work done on the germination of grasses prior to 1937 was made by Lehmann and Aichele (1937). The more recent studies on the effects of temperature on seedling emergence have been briefly summarized by Sprague (1943). He investigated the emergence and early seedling growth of seven forage grasses and Ladino clover under four ranges and daily alternating temperatures. His data are given in Table 41. Temperatures from about 30 to 38°C. favored the emergence of Sudan grass, bromegrass, and meadow fescue but severely reduced that of the other species. Low temperatures between 5 and 13°C. markedly reduced the emergence of Sudan grass and Ladino clover. Temperatures within the ranges of 12.8 to 21° and 21 to 29.4°C. were generally favorable for the germination and emergence of all species he examined.

The influence of seed maturity on the temperature requirements for germination of fescue seed was considered by Kearns and Toole (1939) and of subterranean clover by Hills (1944a, 1944b). With matured clover seed, germination was most rapid at 20°, slower at 10°, and slowest at 30°C. Recently Chippendale (1949) studied the effects of low temperature and of alternating temperatures upon the germination rate of 12 species of grasses commonly grown in Australia. He stresses the fact that the reaction of grass seeds to environmental factors during germination depends both upon the strain of the species used and upon the conditions under which the seed was grown and ripened.

Cereal crops.—The early data of Haberlandt (1874) on cardinal temperatures for germination of a number of crops are quoted in several current textbooks. Klages (1942, p. 100) gives the most complete presentation of Haberlandt's results for the common cereals as well as for several field and vegetable crops. The value of such data is limited. For example, reported optimum temperatures for germination of wheat vary from about 15 to 30°C. (Edwards). Probably much of this spread arises from differences in the maturity of the seeds tested. While a number of workers, including Dickson (1923), have found germination to be accelerated by high temperatures, Edwards reported that more

TABLE 41.—*Effects of temperature and day length on germination and emergence of eight species of forage crops[a] (Sprague, 1943)*

Species	Germi-nation[b]	Emergence at alternating soil and air temperatures[c]							
		4.4 to 12.8°C.		12.8 to 21.1°C.		21.1 to 29.4°C.		29.4 to 37.8°C.	
		16-hour day	9-hour day	16-hour day	9-hour day	16-hour day	9-hour day	16-hour day	9-hour day
	Percent	*Percent*	*Percent*	*Percent*	*Percent*	*Percent*	*Percent*	*Percent*	*Percent*
Sudan grass	92	27	32	73	60	74	78	82	80
Bromegrass	95	80	90	93	90	92	90	49	82
Meadow fescue	96	76	78	85	90	90	94	55	90
Orchard grass	96	54	53	59	71	58	65	13	33
Timothy	88	49	57	62	64	74	77	7	39
Kentucky bluegrass	88	25	23	25	31	13	17	1	1
Colonial bentgrass	97	11	24	43	36	22	21	1	5
Ladino clover	92	21	20	41	54	72	75	5	16

[a] All figures except those reporting laboratory germination tests are the average of six replicates. Laboratory tests were made in triplicate on blotters in Petri dishes under daily temperature alternations of 15 to 30°C.

[b] Laboratory tests on blotters.

[c] Lower temperature maintained for 4 hours in the middle of the dark period; higher temperature maintained for 4 hours in the middle of the light period.

uniform germination and stronger plants developed at low soil temperatures of about 8 to 10°C. This observation calls attention again to the need for care in specifying the response considered in determining optimum temperatures. Edward's index lists a number of papers on wheat, oats, barley, maize, and rice; these should be consulted for specific data. Oliveira and Vianna (1948) have recently carried out germination tests on eight forms of cultivated rice.

Other field crops.—A study of the germination and emergence of four varieties of sorghums has been reported by Martin *et al.* (1935). His data, given in Table 42, show that emergence was retarded at soil temperatures below 25°C. Depth of planting made little difference, except at 15°C., where emergence was noticeably delayed by deeper planting. The optimum temperature range for germination of Black Eyebrow soybean seed was 33 to 36.5°C., as determined by several different criteria (Edwards, 1934). Cotton has been reported to germinate best at soil temperatures of 33 to 34°C. (Camp and Walker, 1927; and Arndt, 1932). Previous work on the cardinal temperatures for germination of tobacco seed was summarized by Kincaid (1935). From his studies, he concluded that the cardinal temperatures for tobacco are approximately 10° (minimum), 24° (optimum) and 34°C. (maximum). He also considered the effects of light and of alternating temperature on germination. Leach (1947) found that the emergence of sugar beets was most rapid at soil temperatures of 25 and 30°C., with

TABLE 42.—*Time of emergence[a] of sorghum seedlings from plantings at three depths, as affected by soil temperature* (*Martin et al. 1935*)

| Depth of planting | Time of emergence at temperature of— | | | | | |
	15°C.	20°C.	25°C.	30°C.	35°C.	Average
Inches	*Days*	*Days*	*Days*	*Days*	*Days*	*Days*
0.5	6	7	5	4	4	5.2
1.5	9	8	4	4	4	5.8
2.5	11	8	5	4	5	6.6
Average	8.7	7.7	4.7	4.0	4.3	—

[a] Figures for time of emergence are averages of data from four varieties.

the highest total emergence at 25°. References to earlier work on germination of beets can be found in Edward's index.

Vegetable crops.—References to a number of papers on germination temperatures for vegetable crops were given by Edwards. The most comprehensive study was carried out by Kotowski (1926). He pointed out that at some temperatures, although the seeds had germinated, no hypocotyl growth occurred. Recognizing that the agriculturalist was primarily concerned with the temperatures required for emergence, his data were based on daily observations of emergence from quartz sand in flats held at constant temperatures from 4 to 30°C. The speed of germination for seeds of 17 species, belonging to 8 families, was found to increase with rising temperature. However, spinach, lettuce, cabbage, parsley, and beets gave a higher percentage germination at the lower temperatures. The following tabulation of minimum and optimum soil temperatures in relation to the germination and emergence of vegetable seeds has been prepared by Dr. P. A. Minges. It is based on Kotowski's emergence studies and is supplemented by field observations from California vegetable-growing areas.

Minimum temperature:	*Vegetable seed*
4°C..................	Endive,[a] lettuce, pea, radish, spinach
4 to 8°C.............	Beet, broccoli,[a] cabbage, carrot, cauliflower, celery,[a] onion, parsley, parsnip, Swiss chard,[a] turnip[a]
11 to 18°C...........	Asparagus, cucumber, lima bean, pepper, snap bean, summer squash,[a] sweet corn,[a] tomato, winter squash[a]
18°C................	Eggplant, okra,[a] watermelon[a]

Optimum temperature:	
8 to 11°C............	Cabbage, spinach
11 to 18°C...........	Beet, broccoli,[a] cauliflower, parsley, parsnip,[a] Swiss chard,[a] turnip[a]
18 to 25°C...........	Asparagus, carrot, celery,[a] endive,[a] lettuce, onion, pea, radish, tomato
25 to 30°C...........	Cucumber, eggplant, lima bean, muskmelon, okra,[a] pepper, snap bean, summer squash,[a] sweet corn,[a] tomato, watermelon,[a] winter squash[a]

[a] Emergence temperatures suggested for these crops are based entirely on Dr. Minges' field observations. Dr. Minges is Extension Truck Crops Specialist, University of California.

In the preparation of this tabulation, it has been recognized that factors other than the velocity of emergence are involved in the establishment of a stand in the field. Accordingly, the temperature ranges suggested by Dr. Minges in many cases do not coincide with those found by Kotowski (1926), Leach (1947), and Beach (1949) to produce the most rapid emergence. Inasmuch as the tabulation is based upon field observations under California conditions, many exceptions to the general temperature data may be found. However, despite uncertainties, such information on the minimum and the most favorable, or optimum, temperatures is particularly valuable to the vegetable grower who usually is eager to plant just as soon as the soil has warmed enough to produce a profitable stand. Soil temperature is involved both in the germination and emergence of the seed and, as a modifying factor, in the occurrence and severity of seedling diseases. This important indirect effect of soil temperature on the growth of young plants is discussed in a later section. With a knowledge of the temperature requirements for emergence of the seed, and by determining the prevailing soil temperatures, one may be able to time plantings so as to avoid conditions that favor severe disease infection.

Trees and ornamentals.—The germination of forest-tree seed was discussed by Baldwin (1942). He concluded that most tree seeds germinated best at temperatures between 20 and 27°C. As with other seeds, high temperatures usually induce the earliest germination in fully ripened seeds but apparently injure or inhibit germination of incompletely ripened seeds. Seeds of trees from colder climates and higher altitudes may be expected to germinate more quickly at lower temperatures than seeds from warmer regions, and vice versa. The work of Fawcett (1929) and Camp (1933) indicated that for germination and emergence of sweet orange, sour orange, rough lemon, and grapefruit seeds, the minimum is probably below 15°, the maximum a little below 40°, and the optimum about 30°C.

A brief summary of tests on germination temperature for approximately 100 flower species has been published by Heit (1946a) to serve as a guide until more complete data on 150 species under study can be obtained. In a second paper Heit (1946b) gave data on 13 species for which he believed the temperature requirements were well established. Nine of these species were found to require a temperature of only 15°C. for rapid and complete germination. The experience of Bodger Seeds, Ltd. (1935) illustrates the need for extensive testing of various strains under a number of different conditions before attempting to fix the temperature requirements for germination. They found that data from other seedsmen contradicted much of the information they had published for 43 flower species. In Heit's opinion, flower seeds are generally more sensitive to germination conditions than those of field crops and vegetables.

Influence of soil temperature on seedling morphology

Soil temperatures prevailing during the period of germination and emergence may affect appreciably the morphology of the seedling. Dickson (1923) noted that for wheat high soil temperatures greatly stimulated the elongation of the subcrown internode (the region between the seed and the first node). At 8°C. there was very little elongation of the subcrown internode, and the first node and secondary roots developed immediately above the seed; at 24°C. and above, the secondary roots developed at or near the soil surface. Similar observations were made on wheat by Taylor and McCall (1936) and on sorghum by Martin et al. (1935). Both teams of investigators reported that the length of the subcrown internode also varied directly with the depth of planting. At high soil temperatures, many of the sorghum seedlings formed their crowns above the soil surface (see Figure 62). Such high crowning, however, is seldom observed under field conditions, even at high soil temperatures, because the washing and drifting of the soil tend to fill up the planter furrows and cover the crown. The greatest number of crown roots in sorghum generally developed in shallow plantings at high soil temperatures, the largest number of subcrown rootlets in deep plantings at high soil temperatures.   Taylor and McCall (1936) have suggested that the higher crown position resulting from planting at high soil temperatures may, in part at least, contribute to the poor crops obtained from winter wheat sown early in fall.   These crowns, lying closer to the soil surface, are less protected from drought and winterkilling.

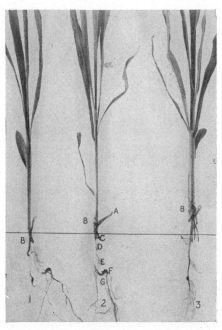

Figure 62.—Length of subcrown internode and height of crown in Feterita sorghum seedlings planted at a depth of 1 inch in soil at (1) 15°, (2) 20°, and (3) 25°C. Horizontal line shows location of soil surface. A, coleoptile; B, crown; C, crown roots; D, subcrown internode; E, subcrown rootlet; F, seed; and G, seminal root. (Martin et al., 1935.)

Dickson (1923) made the important observation that at temperatures above 20°C., the growing point of the wheat culm always broke through the coleoptile before emerging from the soil.   At temperatures below 16°C., however, the coleoptile elongated very much faster than the growing point of the culm and consequently enclosed the growing culm until after emergence.   These relationships are of considerable importance in determining the occurrence of plant diseases.   Soil temperature in relation to plant diseases will be discussed in a later section.

Sprouting of Bulbs, Tubers, and Similar Structures

As for seeds, sprouting of bulbs depends largely on the previous after-ripening treatment. A rest period is general for buds of bulbs and similar structures. When many bulbs are taken from the ground in early summer and then subjected to different constant temperatures, little vegetative growth and no flowering occur during the next year. Exposure to low temperatures is often very effective in shortening the rest periods and in inducing subsequent flowering in many bulbs. Blaauw and collaborators (1936, 1939, and earlier papers) have determined that each developmental process in these bulbs has its own optimum temperature, so that the bulbs as a whole have a decreasing optimum temperature as one stage of development is superseded by

TABLE 43.—*Effect of various soil temperatures on growth rate of disease-free potato plants during their early development (Richards, 1921)*

Age of plants	Average height of plants above soil at temperatures of—							
	9.5°C.	12°C.	15.2°C.	18°C.	21.4°C.	24°C.	27.2°C.	30.5°C.
Days	Inches	Inches	Inches	Inches	Inches	Inches	Inches	Inches
25	(a)	(a)	1.4	2.1	2.7	3.2	2.5	2.0
33	(b)	2.6	4.3	5.8	5.0	4.8	3.8	3.2

a Not up.
b Just up.

another. This aspect of temperature on the growth of bulbs, while in some cases involving soil temperature, is a highly specialized subject. The reader is referred to Crocker (1948) for a general discussion and to Post (1949) for specific information on the forcing of the bulbs of many plants.

Many plant growers believe that low soil temperatures stimulate sprouting and root growth in bulbs. The low temperature is doubtless more important through its effect on dormancy than through its stimulation of growth in fully ripened bulbs. Bulbs properly after-ripened will root and produce tops much more rapidly at higher temperatures than at the lower ones favorable for shortening dormancy. Richards (1921) studied the sprouting and early growth of potatoes in sterilized soils maintained at eight constant temperatures from 9.5 to 30.5°C. In all experiments the plants at 24°C. came up first. These appeared after a period of from 18 to 25 days, depending upon the vigor and state of dormancy of the tubers used as seed. In general, the plants in soil held at 18, 21, and 27°C. appeared from 2 to 5 days later than those at

24°, while those grown at 9 and 12° were delayed as much as 10 to 15 days.   The plants at 30° grew irregularly and in a few cases were as seriously retarded as the plants at 12°C.   Richards' data, given in Table 43, indicate a shift in the optimum temperature as the young plants develop.   The shift is from an optimum of 24° for sprouting and emergence to 18°C. for the later stages of growth (cf. Fig. 63).

In his book on potato production, Hardenburg (1949) cautioned against planting too early in cold soil.   He suggested that emergence should occur in about 2 weeks in warm soil, whereas about 4 weeks may be required in cold soils.   With such slow sprouting, seed-piece rot and sprout injury by *Rhizoctonia* may contribute to a poor stand.   Under dry farming in Nebraska Werner (1932) investigated over a 5-year

FIGURE 63.—Growth of 46-day-old Irish Cobbler potato plants on soils maintained at approximately 9, 12, 15, 18, 21, 24, 27, and 30°C.   (Richards, 1921.)

period the influence of date of planting on the rate of potato-plant emergence and on the final stand.   The early plantings emerged most slowly because of the lower temperatures.   Slightly over 3 weeks were required for half the seed pieces to emerge in the May plantings, about 2½ weeks for the early and mid-June plantings, and generally 2 weeks for the late June or early July plantings.   Over the 5-year period he found that the best final stand was obtained with the May plantings.   Stands for the May plantings averaged 93 percent, as compared with 79.5 percent for the late plantings.   The occurrence of various plant diseases complicates such studies.   The relation of soil temperature to the incidence and severity of plant diseases will be considered in a later section.

Growth of Roots and Other Underground Organs

Because of the difficulties involved in studying roots, much less is known about their growth behavior than has been learned about growth of the aerial organs of plants.   Under favorable conditions, the roots of some plants elongate rather rapidly. Potato roots may elongate at the rate of 1 inch per day for a period of 2 weeks or more. Under very favorable conditions, corn and squash roots may grow at the rate of 2 to 2.5 inches per day during periods of 3 to 4 weeks (Weaver, 1926, p. 47). The roots of many of the common grasses elongate over 0.5 inch per day. The primary root system of winter wheat has been found to maintain this rate over a period of 70 days. Such active growth soon develops a root system of remarkable extent. Dittmer (1937) reported that winter rye plants produced an average of 3.1 miles of new roots per day during a period of 4 months. Root growth of trees is considerably slower. The roots of young shortleaf and loblolly pine trees growing under field conditions were observed by Reed (1939) to elongate at a rate of nearly 0.1 inch per day during the period of maximum growth. It is not unreasonable to expect that root growth, at least during periods of rapid elongation, may be appreciably influenced by such environmental factors as soil temperature.

Requirements for root growth

To recapitulate briefly: Temperature affects the rate of the growth process *per se*. Within the limits, increasing temperature speeds cell division and elongation. Temperature also influences the supply of carbohydrates, mineral nutrients, and water, all of which are essential for growth. The carbohydrates required at the growing point must be translocated from storage tissue in the root or shoot or from the leaves where they are produced by photosynthesis. It was pointed out that high temperatures favored more rapid translocation and accelerated respiratory activity. Where soil temperatures are low, a retarded rate of translocation may restrict growth. Where soil temperatures are high—particularly if air temperatures are also high, as is usually the case—in both roots and shoots the ratio of respiration to protein synthesis may be so increased that the carbohydrate balance in the plant is depleted and the growth of roots and underground storage organs is consequently decreased. The rate at which mineral nutrients are absorbed increases with a rise in temperature. To how great an extent a reduced rate of nutrient absorption is responsible for the poor growth of plants in soils at low temperatures is not known. By retarding microbial activity, low soil temperatures may diminish the supply of mineral nutrients, but they do not appear to retard seriously the absorption of some nutrients by plant roots. Nitrogen, for example, seems to be absorbed in appreciable quantities at temperatures low enough to retard root growth, though its assimilation may be hindered. Low soil temperatures restrict the rate of water absorption by roots. When the rate of absorption is reduced below that of transpiration, wilting results. Whenever such water deficits occur within the plant, root growth is no doubt retarded or stopped. Probably low soil temperatures impede root growth as a consequence of a limited water supply only when transpiration is rapid enough to produce wilting.

In general, roots of most plants in temperate climates become relatively inactive for at least part of the winter season. This inactivity may result both directly through the retarding effect of lowered soil temperature on root activity and indirectly through a reduced supply of carbohydrate to the roots, caused by retarded translocation and limited photosynthesis. The reduced carbohydrate condition may develop in greenhouses during winter. Because of poor light, photosynthetic production is unable to balance respirational consumption, which is maintained at a normal rate by favorable air and soil temperatures. Consequently, little carbohydrate is available to the roots, and root growth is poor even though soil temperatures may be near optimum.

Reid (1933) studied the effect of shading on root production in velvet bent. She found that the plants in sunlight all day produced a dry weight of roots 3 times greater than plants in shade half a day, 7 times greater than plants in speckled shade all day, and 18 times greater than plants in shade all day. The top growth in the first three treatments showed little difference, but top growth in full shade was inferior. Plants grown at high night air temperatures develop smaller root systems in relation to the top than those grown at lower night temperatures. Thus, any set of conditions that reduces the supply of carbohydrate to the roots, either by decreasing photosynthesis or by increasing respiration, may cause poor root growth although soil temperatures may be very favorable.

The effect of alternating temperatures on root growth was studied by several investigators many years ago. A number of these papers were reviewed by Lehenbauer (1914) and Leitch (1916). There appears to be little evidence that alternating temperatures favor root growth. In fact, sudden temperature shifts may temporarily retard growth, but the growth rate characteristic of the new temperature is usually resumed soon after the change has been made.

Cardinal temperatures for root growth

Grasses and forage crops.—Several studies of forage grasses indicate that root growth is usually most active during the cooler spring and fall months of the growing season and may cease during the summer. Stuckey (1941) has examined the root systems of 10 grasses growing in the field at the Rhode Island Agricultural Experiment Station. She found in March and April a very conspicuous development of new roots and an elongation of existing roots; in May, the production of only a few new roots but continued growth at the tips of roots developed earlier; in the summer months, no growth except an occasional new tip on a mature root; but in October, the emergence of new roots in all species, with many new roots in some species. Also working under field conditions, Brown (1943) found that root growth in Kentucky bluegrass was better during the early spring months when the mean soil and air temperatures were below 15.6°C., whereas rhizomes developed most rapidly in later spring and early summer. He reported that in well-established bluegrass swards, 2 years or older, the roots and rhizomes either made no gain or actually lost weight during the summer when the temperature of the grass-covered soil 0.5 inch below the surface usually averaged near or slightly above 26.7°C.

Harrison (1934), Brown (1939), and Sprague (1943) have all found that temperatures near 15.6° were optimum for root and rhizome development in Kentucky bluegrass, and that temperatures of 26.7°C. or above were unfavorable. Since these investigators placed the entire plant in temperature cabinets, the soil temperature could not be varied without a similar change in the aerial environment. Thus, the growth responses recorded in these studies were conditioned both by the soil and the air temperature. In Brown's (1943) field study growth responses were affected also by photoperiod differences as the season advanced. These experiments do not provide a clear picture of the effect of soil temperature on the development of these underground organs. Under the conditions of these experiments, a reduced carbohydrate supply to the roots, rather than unfavorable soil temperatures, may have been the factor responsible for the lack of root growth at the higher temperatures. This possibility is suggested by Lovvorn's (1945) greenhouse study in which he found that root growth for several grasses, including Kentucky bluegrass, was approximately the same at 26.7 to 32.2° as at 15.6 to 21°C. when the tops were frequently clipped, but that the root weights at the higher temperatures significantly exceeded those at the lower temperatures when the grasses were allowed to grow undisturbed for 60 days.

A better opportunity to evaluate the importance of soil temperature for root growth in Kentucky bluegrass, Colonial bentgrass, and timothy is provided by the work of Darrow (1939) and Stuckey (1942). In Darrow's experiments, Kentucky bluegrass was grown with the the root systems in soil maintained at 15, 25 and 35°C. and the shoots exposed to the normal greenhouse conditions. The root weights at 35° were about one-half those at 25 and 15°C. At 35°C. the lowest weight of tops and the smallest number of rhizomes were produced. Many field and greenhouse experiments with bluegrass and other plants have shown the production of rhizomes to be associated with carbohydrate storage. Apparently the growth of the bluegrass at the higher temperatures was limited by carbohydrates. These reserve materials were probably being utilized in respiration faster than they were being produced. Stuckey investigated the growth of Kentucky bluegrass, Colonial bentgrass, and timothy seedlings in nutrient solutions, and Colonial bentgrass in soil cultures, all held at controlled temperatures. She found that the roots in the nutrient solutions held at 7.2°C. were healthy but only about half as long as those at 15.6°, while those at 32.2° were dark and gnarled with blackened stubby ends. Many of the plants with roots held at 32.2°C. had died, and all the others were pale yellow. Brenchley and Singh (1922), working with peas in nutrient solution, found that root temperatures above approximately 29°C. were injurious, but that the shoots could withstand high temperatures and strong insolation if root temperatures were kept below 29°C. In Stuckey's second experiment, plants of Colonial bentgrass were grown in pans filled with soil maintained at about 10, 15.6, and 26.7°C. The roots were examined 2 months later. Those at 10° were white, translucent, and relatively unbranched; they resembled roots collected outdoors in late March (Stuckey, 1941). At 15.6°C., the roots were more slender, profusely branched, and longer and were similar to those found in the field during the last of April at the time of maximum root growth. The roots at 26.7°C. were very fine and fibrous but less extensive and resembled roots found in midsummer. Lateral roots were much nearer the tips in plants grown at high temperatures. The appearance of these root systems after 5½ months is shown in Figure 64.

L. R. Jones et al. (1926) presented a photograph from the work of F. R. Jones and Tisdale (1921), showing a striking influence of soil temperature on root and shoot growth in red clover (Figure 65). These plants were grown during the months of November to January in the Wisconsin soil-temperature tanks in low-nitrate soil inoculated with Bacillus radicicola. Under these conditions, it appears that a soil temperature of about 21°C. was optimum. F. R. Jones and Tisdale (1921) noted that the marked dwarfing of the plants at 12 and 15°C. disappeared as the plants became older, especially later in the spring when light intensity became greater. The effect of soil temperature on nodule formation will be considered in a later paragraph.

For other forage crops, root growth as a function of soil temperature apparently has been investigated only by Brown (1939), Sprague (1943), and Sullivan and Sprague (1949). In these investigations both soil and air temperatures were varied.   Under conditions of equal soil and air temperatures, Brown found that the optimum temperature for root and rhizome production in Canada bluegrass was 10°; Kentucky bluegrass, 15.6°; and orchard grass, 21°C.   For Bermuda grass, growth increased with rising temperature up to 37.8°C., the highest temperature employed.   Using plants in growth chambers with controlled temperature alternations, Sprague found at the end of a 6-week period that the best root growth in Ladino clover was at 4.4 to 12.8°; in Kentucky

FIGURE 64.—Roots of Colonial bentgrass grown 5½ months at soil temperatures of 10° (marked *Low*), 15.6° (marked *Check*), and 26.7°C. (marked *High*).   (Stuckey, 1942.)

bluegrass, orchard grass, meadow fescue, bromegrass, Colonial bentgrass, and timothy, 12.8 to 21°; and Sudan grass, 21 to 29.4°C.   Sullivan and Sprague studied the effect of clipping on root growth of perennial ryegrass plants exposed in controlled-temperature growth chambers.   In all temperature treatments (10 to 15.6°, 15.6 to 21°, 21 to 26.7°, and 26.7 to 32.2°C.) the roots decreased in total dry weight throughout the 40-day period following clipping (cf. Fig. 52).   The losses were most rapid and extensive at the higher temperatures and led to the death of some roots.

The work on forage crops may be summarized as follows: Bermuda grass appears to make the most rapid root growth at high soil temperatures near 35°C.   Most other grasses, however, seem to be favored by soil temperatures in the range of 15 to 20°C.   The optimum for red clover is reported at 21°C.   Under normal field conditions, root growth in many of the grasses is best during the early spring months, diminishes to a very slow rate during summer, and again resumes in the early autumn.   Since air temperatures increase with soil temperatures in the field, the reduced root growth in the summer months may be the result of a restricted carbohydrate supply to the roots, rather than a direct effect of unfavorable soil temperatures.

FIGURE 65.—Relation of soil temperature to development of young red clover plants in low-nitrate soil inoculated with *Bacillus radicicola*.   Plants grown during the months November to January.   (Work of F. R. Jones and Tisdale, 1921, as given by L. R. Jones *et al.*, 1926.)

Cereal crops.—L. R. Jones *et al.* (1926) have summarized the studies of Dickson (1923) on the growth of spring (Marquis) and winter (Turkey) wheat carried out in the Wisconsin soil-temperature tanks.   Dickson found that both spring and winter wheat functioned best in all stages of development at relatively low soil temperatures. Though seedlings emerged most rapidly and shoots developed earliest at soil temperatures of 24 to 28°C., the largest root system was produced at about 12 to 16° (Fig. 66).   A comparison of root and plumule development in wheat seedlings at low and high soil temperatures indicated that a distinctly different growth pattern was operative at the two temperature extremes. At low temperatures (8 and 12°C.), the roots developed first and were usually several centimeters long before the plumule began to grow; whereas at higher temperatures (28 and

FIGURE 66.—Influence of soil temperatures upon development of winter wheat plants (variety Turkey). (From the work of Dickson, 1923, as given by L. R. Jones et al., 1926.)

TABLE 44.—*Growth of Marquis spring wheat after 70 days, as influenced by soil temperatures (Wort, 1940)*

Temperature[a] of soil	Average greatest length of root	Average dry weight of root
°C.	Inches	Grams
22	12.2	0.40
26	12.1	.23
30	9.9	.11
34	4.4	.03
38	3.3	.03
42[b]	2.3	.013

[a] Air temperature was same for all treatments, varying from 21° at night to at least 38°C. during most days.
[b] At this temperature only 8 of the original 15 plants survived after 70 days.

32°), the plumule was well out of the soil before the roots developed. Wort (1940) found that the length and dry weight of the roots of Marquis spring wheat decreased with increasing soil temperatures from 22 to 44°C. Unfortunately, a soil temperature of 22°C. was the lowest

Wort maintained in his experiment. His data on root growth of Marquis spring wheat after 70 days, as influenced by soil temperatures, are as shown in Table 44.

Hoagland (1944) referred to unpublished work by Broyer and Hoagland on growth of barley in nutrient solutions. Root growth at 20° was about double that at either 10 or 30°C.

The influence of soil temperature on root development in corn has been reported by Dickson (1923). The largest root system, irrespective of the age of the plant, developed at soil temperatures of about 24°C. (Fig. 67). Corn therefore appears to show its best growth at soil tem-

         12   16   20   24   28   32   36°C.

Figure 67.—Influence of soil temperature upon development of corn plants. (From the work of Dickson, 1923, as given by L. R. Jones et al., 1926.)

peratures above the optimum for any of the forage crops or small grains previously considered.

Other field crops.—The work of F. R. Jones and Tisdale (1921) on root growth in soybeans, summarized by L. R. Jones et al. (1926) (see Figure 84) suggested that soil temperatures below 18°C. retard root growth whereas those between 18 and 36°C. exerted little influence. This matter has been reexamined by Earley and Cartter (1945). They stated that although no statistically significant differences were obtained, root growth in a general way tended to increase with higher root temperature from 2 to about 27°C. Particularly interesting is their observation that the intensity of shoot illumination was the controlling factor in determining the magnitude of root-growth response to each increment of root temperature. As the radiation incident on the tops diminished, there was a tendency toward a larger proportional reduction in root growth than in shoot growth.   Accordingly, under low light conditions, root growth was less affected by soil temperature.   Earley and Cartter concluded that root temperatures from about 22 to 27°C. appeared to be most favorable for maximum dry-weight production of roots (and tops) when soybean plants were grown under a great variety of aerial environmental conditions in the greenhouse.

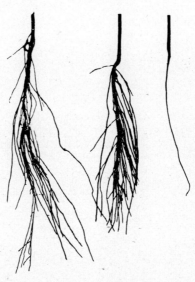

FIGURE 68.—Root development in cotton seedlings grown 18 days at a constant soil temperature of 24° (left), 21° (center), and 18°C. (right). (Arndt, 1932.)

Camp and Walker (1927) noted that roots of cotton seedlings were adversely affected by soil temperatures above 34.5°C.   At this temperature the taproots were clear white and long and well filled out, but those at 38 to 39°C. were brown, shrunken, and much shorter, with but one or two brown, stubby, and shrunken laterals.   In a brief note Arndt (1932) cited data on the growth of the taproot in cotton seedlings after 14 days.   Root growth was little affected at soil temperatures from 24 to 33°C., but at 21° it was considerably reduced, and at 18° greatly reduced.   Striking differences in growth at 18, 21, and 24°C. can be seen in Figure 68 taken from his note.   It may be inferred from his brief account that the reduced growth at the lower temperatures is due in part at least to a shorter growing period caused by the slower germination at these temperatures.   Later Arndt (1945) carried out a detailed examination of root growth in cotton seedlings grown in dark germinators. The roots were on an agar medium in test tubes, with the entire seedling exposed to the same constant temperature. Under these conditions, the minimum for growth of primary roots was clearly below 18°C.; the maximum for any growth was above 39°, though visible heat injury soon appeared at the latter temperature. A temperature range from 33 to 36°C. was optimum for elongation of the primary roots during the first few days of growth and produced the

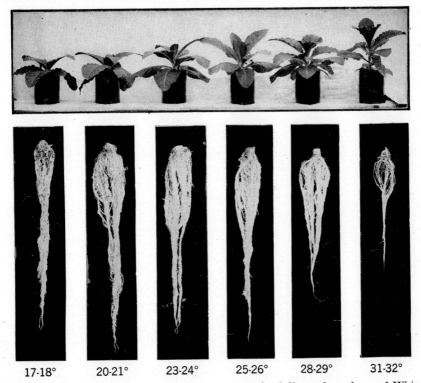

FIGURE 69.—Influence of soil temperature on growth of disease-free plants of White Burley tobacco. (L. R. Jones *et al.*, 1926, based on work of Johnson and Hartman, 1919.)

earliest emergence of secondary roots. However, after 7 days of culture, the roots had the greatest total length at 30°C. and were most numerous at 27°. This appears to be another example of an optimum shifting with the increasing age of plant material.

Johnson and Hartman (1919) studied root growth in two varieties of tobacco in relation to soil temperature. They found the best root development in White Burley tobacco at 23 to 24°C., with a marked decrease at higher temperatures (Fig. 69), and in the Connecticut

Havana variety the best root development was at 26 to 29°, with a decided falling off at 31 to 32°.   Johnson and Hartman's data on the influence of soil temperature on root growth in disease-free plants of these two varieties are presented in Table 45.

Working with sugar beets in California, Tavernetti (1944) observed that, regardless of time of planting, comparatively little increase in root weight occurred until the early part of May, when the minimum soil temperature in the root zone is above 13°C.   The roots grew most rapidly during June and July.   Tavernetti reported a close correlation between sugar beet root growth and soil temperature.

TABLE 45.—*Influence of soil temperature on root growth of disease-free plants of two varieties of tobacco (Johnson and Hartman, 1919)*

	Average dry weight of roots per plant	
Temperature of soil	White Burley	Connecticut Havana
°C.	Grams	Grams
12 to 13		0.26
17 to 18	0.32	.70
20 to 21	.66	
22 to 23		1.05
23 to 24	.86	
24 to 25	.79	
26 to 27		1.13
28 to 29	.70	1.13
31 to 32	.25	.75

Pierce and Wood (1946) related soil temperature at a depth of 8 inches to weekly growth of sugar beets in Montana (Figure 70).   They report a correlation index of 0.970, a figure considerably above the 1-percent level of significance (0.684).   Their extrapolation of the data suggests that beet growth would be expected to cease at soil temperatures near 4 or 5°C.   While as they have indicated, their data do not permit selection of the optimum soil temperature for beets, they believed the best growth would occur at soil temperatures above 21°C.

It must be recognized that these relations between beet root growth and soil temperature may be partly fortuitous.   Other factors such as air temperature, length of day, and normal maturation of the plants are likely involved in the initiation of growth in the spring and in declining growth rate towards the end of the season.   These complicating factors are very difficult to deal with in the field.   It appears that studies under controlled conditions are needed to confirm these findings.   As Tavernetti and Pierce and Wood suggested, a knowledge of the relation between soil temperature and rate of root growth may permit a more efficient timing of fertilizer applications.

Vegetable and truck crops.—Some observations on the effect of soil temperature on root growth of Canadian field peas were reported by F. R. Jones and Tisdale (1921). They gave no data but stated that peas did not flourish at a soil temperature of 30°C. and were intolerant of higher temperatures. These conclusions are supported by common field experience. The pea is well known as a low-temperature plant and is always planted in relatively cold soil during winter or very early spring. It is well to mention at this point that one must be careful in

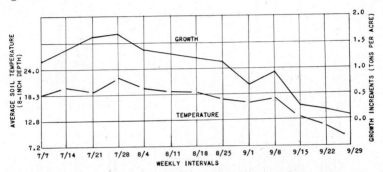

FIGURE 70.—Soil temperature at a depth of 8 inches in relation to the growth of sugar beets at Billings, Mont. Growth increments computed from measurements of beet circumference, using a constant circumference-weight ratio. Correlation index given as 0.970. (Redrawn from Pierce and Wood, 1946.)

predicting field performance of plants from data obtained during short periods under a particular set of experimental conditions. Reference was made earlier to Leitch's (1916) measurements relating temperature to the elongation of pea-seedling radicles. In observations confined to periods of less than 24 hours, she found that the optimum for growth was between 28 and 30°C. This optimum is considerably above that suggested by the work of F. R. Jones and Tisdale or by field experience. This may be another example of an optimum shifting as the plant develops.

Very little seems to have been done on beans. Reddick (1917) reported a few observations on the over-all growth of beans at soil temperatures of 15, 22, and 34°C. but gave no data for root growth. Burkholder (1920) found no noticeable difference in root growth of beans in soils at 18 and 26°C. Considering his work and the general observations of Reddick, Burkholder suggested the optimum soil temperature for beans lies between 22 and 26°C.

The only work relating temperature to root growth in tomato plants appears to be the unpublished work of Broyer and Hoagland, mentioned by Hoagland (1944). The striking differences in the root growth obtained in nutrient solutions maintained at 10, 20, and 30°C. are shown in Figure 71. No data are given. From the photograph it appears that in young plants a root temperature of 30° is superior to lower temperatures, but in older plants a root temperature of 20°C. seems to have produced better root growth.

The growth of potato plants in soils controlled at 10, 18.3, and 26.7°C. has been investigated by Fitch (1915). He published no data,

FIGURE 71.—Growth of tomato plants with roots in nutrient solutions maintained at the temperatures indicated. Plants in early stage of growth in group at left and older plants in group at right. (Unpublished work by Broyer and Hoagland, taken from Hoagland, 1944.)

but his photographs indicate that the plants growing at a soil temperature of 18.3° were the most vigorous. Unfortunately, his control of soil moisture was faulty. This point should be considered in any attempt at further analysis of his findings.

Richards (1921) reported that a soil temperature of 24°C. favored early emergence of potato shoots, but one between 15 and 18° was optimum for the later growth of the plant. L. R. Jones, McKinney, and Fellows (1922), in connection with their studies of potato scab, examined the influence of soil temperature on the development of tubers and stolons. While their data show considerable variations among the individual experiments, the average figures, given in Table 46 (computed on the basis of four experiments), suggest that soil temperatures between about 15 and 28°C. have little effect on the number of tubers formed. Temperatures beyond these limits, however, may reduce the number produced. Soil temperature seems to influence the size of the tubers considerably. The largest tubers and the greatest yield were produced at 18°C., thus checking closely with the findings of Fitch and Richards. Jones and his coworkers noted also that temperatures influenced the morphology of both the tubers and stolons, but this will be considered in a later paragraph.

Bushnell (1925) studied potato growth, using controlled temperature chambers. With this technique, of course, the growth responses observed may be influenced by both air and soil temperatures. The

TABLE 46.—*Influence of soil temperature on the development of tubers in Irish Cobbler potato (L. R. Jones, McKinney, and Fellows, 1922)*

[Figures given are averages of results from four experiments]

Temperature of soil	Average tubers per hill	Average weight tubers per hill	Average weight per tuber
°C.	Number	Grams	Grams
11 to 12	8.2	22.0	2.5
15	12.5	42.7	5.4
18	11.2	56.0	7.0
21	12.5	54.2	6.0
24 to 25	12.8	51.0	4.2
27 to 28.5	14.4	25.0	2.1
27 to 30.5	10.2	9.5	.8

average weight of tubers per plant 6 weeks after emergence was 20.9 grams at 20°, 5.0 at 23°, and 1.6 at 26°C.; no tubers appeared at 29°C. While he gives no data on root formation at these temperatures, it appears from his photograph that root growth was not appreciably reduced at 23 or 26°, though it seems to have been somewhat modified at 29°C. (Fig. 72). Bushnell reemphasized the importance of carbohydrates in relation to tuber growth and concluded that a deficiency of carbohydrate was very probably the limiting factor at the higher temperatures.

For onions the data are sketchy. Walker and Jones (1921) studied the effect of soil temperature on growth; unfortunately, however, their experiments were confined to young plants not over 30 days old. Their limited data suggest that in the Red Globe (a northern variety) the best development of roots may occur at temperatures below 20°C. and in Yellow Bermuda (a southern variety) at about 20°. Walker (1926)

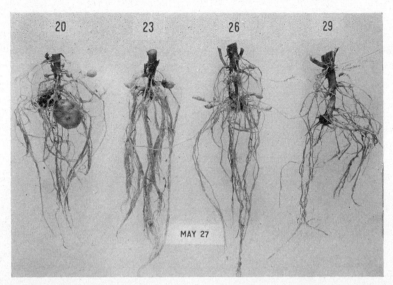

FIGURE 72.—Effect of temperature on root growth and early stages of tuber growth in Early Ohio potato plants, 6 weeks after emergence. Plants grown in controlled temperature chambers at the constant air and soil temperatures indicated. (Bushnell, 1925.)

TABLE 47.—*Influence of soil temperature on root and bulb growth in White Portugal and Crystal Wax Bermuda onions (Walker, 1926)*

Temperature of soil	White Portugal[a]		Crystal Wax Bermuda[b]	
	Average weight of roots	Average weight of bulbs	Average weight of roots	Average weight of bulbs
°C.	Grams	Grams	Grams	Grams
10	0.307	0.713	0.118	0.145
14	.250	.947	.135	.286
18	.198	1.365	.100	.615
22	.283	1.649	.066	.843
26	.099	1.527	.040	.637
30	.064	1.341	.018	.734

[a] Plants started from sets; grown April 16 to May 24.
[b] Transplanted as seedlings about 6 inches high and in fourth leaf; grown April 14 to June 5.

continued his study, using two other varieties of onions grown in soils held at intervals of 4° between 10 and 30°C. His data for the dry weights of roots and bulbs are given in Table 47. As in the previous work with young seedlings, the best root growth was at 22°C. or below, while in general the best bulb development took place at 22° or above.

To summarize, the data on most truck crops are meager.   Root formation in peas is favored by low soil temperatures, in beans by temperatures near 22 to 26°, in tomatoes at 20° or somewhat above, and in onions by intermediate temperatures in the range 14 to 22°C., depending on the variety.   The optimum range for tuber production in potato lies between 15 and 20°C., and that for bulb formation in onions is near 22°.

Trees and shrubs.—In perennials such as trees and most shrubs the beginning and end of the seasonal cycle of root growth are both controlled largely by soil temperature in temperate regions.   Crider (1928) examined root growth in a number of plants grown in observation boxes in Arizona.   He found that the roots of some deciduous and evergreen plants, both cultivated forms and native forms, usually thought to be dormant in winter, make definite growth during the coldest months. In contrast to these plants, he found that others, such as sour orange, Jerusalem-thorn (*Parkinsonia torreyana*), grape, and mesquite, made no growth in these boxes from about the first of December until the latter part of March.   Under field conditions, on the other hand, it is likely that some root growth continues in the deeper roots of this last-named group of plants.   In general, it appears that the roots of some plants grown in temperate regions make some growth as long as the soil is not frozen.   Roots in the surface soil usually cease growth at freezing or near freezing temperatures, but in the warmer subsoil elongation may continue.   Collison (1935) observed elongation of as much as 2 inches in apple roots at the 42- to 54-inch level in soil frozen to a depth of 27 to 30 inches.   He suggested that some root activity may go on at temperatures within 1 to 3°C. of the freezing point.

Root growth in apple trees has received considerable study.   Using both sand and water cultures, Nightingale (1934) found a rapid growth of roots at 9°C. in Delicious apple trees, which initially had well-developed fibrous root systems.   In a continuation of this study, Nightingale (1935) investigated the growth of apple roots from which all small roots had been previously pruned.   These roots were grown for periods of 45 to 63 days in sand cultures maintained at constant temperatures.   His data given in Figure 73 show that the greatest root growth occurred at 18.3°C.   Very little growth was evident at 7.2 or 10°C. in these pruned root systems.   This same question was studied by Batjer *et al.* (1939), who also used dormant apple roots pruned to remove all fibrous roots.   Their data are given in Table 48.   During a 60-day period (January 20 to March 20), no new roots developed on those held at 4.4°, while a number appeared on those exposed to a varying temperature of 4.4 to 18.3°C.   Indications of new root primorida were present on some of those at 4.4° on March 20, but 4.4°C. seemed to

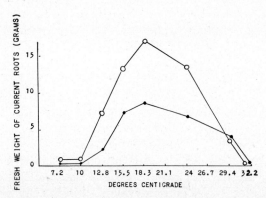

FIGURE 73.—Growth in dormant Delicious apple trees from which all small roots had been previously pruned, as influenced by temperature of sand culture. Lower curve represents growth after 45 days; upper curve, after 63 days. (Redrawn from Nightingale, 1935.)

TABLE 48.—*Effect of root temperature on root growth in dormant apple trees (Batjer et al., 1939)*

Treatment[a]	Root growth by March 20, 1939[b]		Root growth by May 16, 1939	
	New roots	Total length	New roots	Total length
	Number	*Centimeters*	*Number*	*Centimeters*
Roots held at 4.4°C.	0	0	4	4
	0		0	0
	0		0	0
	0	0	2	2
	0		4	9
	0	0	1	2
Roots exposed to greenhouse temperatures that varied from 4.4 to 18.3°C.	5	30		
	2	6		
	12	50		
	20	54	Abundant roots	
	2	6		
	15	60		
	7	16		
	25	100		

[a] Tops of trees in both treatments exposed to greenhouse temperatures that varied from 4.4 to 18.3°C.
[b] Trees remained dormant until this date.

be about the minimum for root growth in these dormant apple trees. After March 20, the trees were no longer dormant; and during the next 60 days at 4.4°C., some of these primorida developed into short new roots, though all appeared to be injured.

FIGURE 74.—Effect of root temperature on the growth of apple trees.

Tree 1: Roots held at 4.4°C. from January 19 to July 18.
Tree 2: Roots exposed to varying temperatures between 4.4 and 18.3°C. from January 19 to May 16, followed by temperature of 4.4° from May 16 to July 18.
Tree 3: Roots held at 4.4°C. from January 19 to May 16, followed by varying temperatures between 4.4 and 18.3°.
Tree 4: Roots exposed to varying temperatures between 4.4° and 18.3°C. for entire period January 19 to July 18.

Tops of all trees exposed to same varying temperatures between 4.4 and 18.3°C. Trees photographed July 18. (Batjer *et al.*, 1939.)

To determine whether the roots had been permanently injured by the 4.4°C. treatment, one of the trees (tree No. 3) was changed from the 4.4° tank to the warmer one on May 16 whereupon normal growth was resumed. The results of this experiment are shown in Figure 74.

By the use of observation trenches Rogers (1939) studied root growth of mature apple trees growing under orchard conditions.   Active root growth usually began as the mean soil temperature reached about 7°, and the rate of growth increased with rising temperature up to the maximum recorded, about 21°C. at the 8-inch depth.   Since the early root growth was initiated before the trees were in leaf, it is likely that root development was directly related to soil temperature.   Rogers noted that the response of root growth to soil temperatures was local as well as general.   In the spring most growth occurred in the upper layers of soil, which warmed up first; in the winter most of the growth

TABLE 49.—*Effect of root temperature on growth in previously pruned roots of dormant Elberta peach trees (Nightingale, 1935)*

	Fresh weight of roots			Fresh weight of roots	
Sand temperature	After 45 days (Mar. 17)	After 63 days (Apr. 4)	Sand temperature	After 45 days (Mar. 17)	After 63 days (Apr. 4)
°C.	Grams	Grams	°C.	Grams	Grams
7.2	[a]	[a]	32.2	0.4	0.2
10.0	0.3	4.5	35.0	[a]	—
12.8	7.0	7.0	15.6–7.2[b]	8.5	9.2
15.6	8.5	11.0	15.6–35.0[b]	8.5	7.0
18.3	8.0	12.0	32.2–15.6[b]	.4	2.0
23.9	5.0	7.0	7.2–15.6[b]	[a]	8.9
29.4	2.0	2.2			

[a] None.
[b] Shifted on March 17.

was in the deeper soil.   Nightingale's (1935) data (Fig. 73) showed the striking effects of comparatively small differences in root temperature.   For example, the growth at 12.8° was much greater than at 10°C., and at 18.3° was distinctly superior to that at 12.8°.   Above 18.3° growth decreased with increasing temperature.   It seems apparent that the root growth in apple trees can be greatly modified by a difference of only a very few degrees in soil temperature.

Crider (1928) reported that apricot and peach trees in large observation boxes continued root growth during the winter in Arizona.   For peach, the average daily growth in November was 5.5 millimeters, December 2.01 millimeters, January 1.65 millimeters, February 0.90 millimeters, and March 1.6 millimeters.   No temperature data are given.   Nightingale (1935) made a thorough study of growth of previously pruned peach roots in sand cultures held constant at a number of soil temperatures (Table 49).

Photographs of typical root systems at several temperatures are reproduced in Figures 75, 76, and 77. The air temperature was in all cases about 16 to 18° at night and 18 to 21°C. during the day. At 7.2° very few new roots appeared; at 10° several new roots; and at 12.8°C., many rather short, white, and typically succulent roots with few fine laterals. At 15.6 and 18.3°C. the best root systems were produced. At 24° the roots lacked succulence, and portions were dead. At 29.4° there was a limited development of nonsucculent roots, very small in

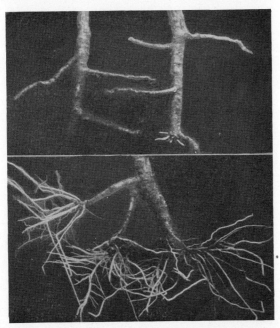

FIGURE 75.—Growth of peach roots during a 45-day period ending March 17 at the following root temperatures: Upper left, 7.2°; upper right, 10°; lower illustration, 12.8°C. (Nightingale, 1935.)

diameter, with short-lived cortex and numerous fine laterals. At 32.2°C. the roots were much like those at 29.4° but were less extensive. At 35°C. no new roots developed. When the peach trees at 15.6° with a well-developed root system of new roots were shifted to 7.2°C., there was some growth of fibrous roots. The trees shifted from 15.6 to 35°C. did not lose their fibrous roots system, although the cortex soon died. Trees that had shown little or no growth when held at 32.2 or 7.2° showed appreciable growth when shifted to 15.6°C.

Proebsting (1943) studied root growth in actively growing Lovell peach seedlings planted in loam soil and held at constant temperatures from 7.2 to 35°C. Growth curves for the extremes and for the most favorable temperatures are given in Figure 78. The best growth was obtained at 24° and the poorest at 35°C. The roots grown at the lower temperatures were thick, fleshy, and white for several centimeters back of the tip, but those at higher temperatures were fibrous and suberized close to the tips. With pear seedlings (variety Winter Nelis), Proeb-

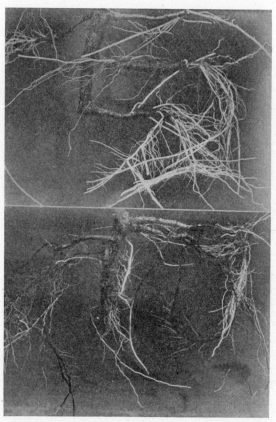

FIGURE 76.—Growth of peach roots during a 45-day period ending March 17, at the following root temperatures: Upper, 18.3°; lower, 24°C. (Nightingale, 1935.)

sting (1943) found less contrast in the appearance of roots produced at different soil temperatures than with peaches. However, the tendencies towards thicker fleshy roots at low temperatures and towards fibrous suberized roots at the higher temperatures were apparent. Four of the twelve plants exposed to the 35°C. soil temperature died, and two more showed distress by shedding their leaves.

Of the common deciduous fruit trees, apple roots seem to be the most tolerant of low soil temperatures, with about 5°C. the minimum for growth. Few roots develop in peach trees below 10°C. The best root growth in apple and peach trees seems to occur between 15 and 20°; growth is poor above 30°C.

Root growth of pecan trees was observed under orchard conditions by Woodroof and Woodroof (1934). They reported that pecan roots

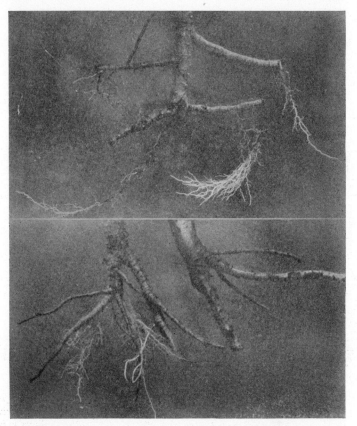

FIGURE 77.—Growth of peach roots during a 45-day period ending March 17 at the following root temperatures: Upper, 29.4°; lower left, 32.2°; lower right, 35°C. (Nightingale, 1935.)

grew very slowly at soil temperatures of 4 to 7°C. and that the growing root tips are killed at —2°. These investigators also studied, at 23 temperatures ranging from —2 to 45°C., the root growth in very young pecan seedlings placed in constant temperature chambers. After 4 days the seedlings were removed and the increase in length of the tap-roots measured. Their results are given in Table 50.

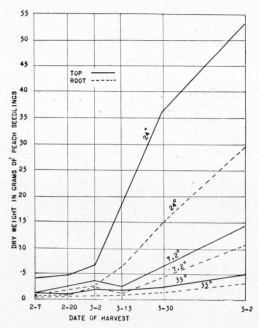

FIGURE 78.—Influence of soil temperature (centigrade) on growth of Elberta peach seedlings. Curves based on 12 trees per treatment. (Redrawn from Proebsting, 1943.)

TABLE 50.—*Growth of primary root of pecan seedlings held for 4 days in constant-temperature chambers (Woodroof and Woodroof, 1934)*[a]

Chamber temperature	Growth in length	Condition of roots at end of period[a]	Chamber temperature	Growth in length	Condition of roots at end of period[a]
°C.	Millimeters		°C.	Millimeters	
−2	−2.0	Entire roots dead	21	56.0	Roots uninjured
−1	0.2	Root tips dead	24	69.0	Roots uninjured
1	1.4	Roots uninjured	27	81.1	Roots uninjured
3	5.2	Roots uninjured	30	88.1	Roots uninjured
6	4.6	Roots uninjured	33	73.1	Roots uninjured
9	7.6	Roots uninjured	36	57.0	Roots uninjured
12	11.3	Roots uninjured	38	37.8	25 percent of tips dead
15	18.6	Roots uninjured	41.5	10.0	All root tips dead
18	41.2	Roots uninjured	43	−5.0	All roots injured

[a] Observations based on 10 roots per treatment.

Growth increased slowly as the temperature was raised from 0 to 15° and increased more rapidly from 15 to 30°C. At temperatures above 30°, growth declined sharply. At 38°C., 25 percent of the roots, and at 41.5°, all of the root tips were dead. On the basis of these data for root growth, Woodroof and Woodroof concluded that in Georgia the soil at a depth of 1 foot never reached a temperature high enough to promote maximum growth or sufficiently low to stop growth. However,

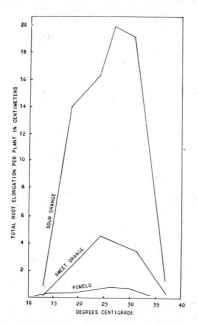

FIGURE 79.—Elongation of taproot in citrus seedlings grown in controlled-environment chambers. Growth period for Pomelo (grapefruit) and sour orange was 3 weeks; for sweet orange, 2 weeks. Seedlings 4 to 5 weeks old at beginning of experiments. Illumination on Pomelo lower than on sour orange (see text). (Redrawn from Girton, 1927.)

the feeding roots, which in pecans tend to concentrate near the surface, are often killed during freezing weather.

Root growth in grapefruit (*Citrus grandis*), sour orange (*C. aurantium*), and sweet orange (*C. sinensis*) seedlings were studied by Girton (1927). Seedlings 4 to 5 weeks old were grown in nutrient culture in controlled environment chambers, in which root- and shoot-temperatures were nearly equal and fixed at intervals of temperature from 12 to 35°C. It should be pointed out again that root growth under these experimental conditions is influenced also by corresponding changes in the aerial environment, particularly as they affect the supply of carbohydrates to the growing roots.   If the incident radiation is low, as it was in these experiments, the photosynthesis-respiration balance may become decidedly unfavorable at the higher temperatures.   Nevertheless, Girton's data are interesting and are summarized in Figures 79 and 80. Elongation of the taproots was greatest at 26°C. and consistently decreased with higher or lower temperatures.   On the other hand, the number of lateral roots showed no relation to the temperature.   The best development of root hairs occurred at 26° in grapefruit, about 31°

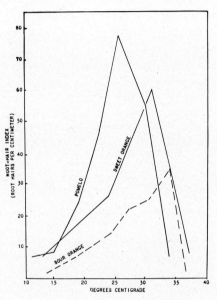

FIGURE 80.—Root-hair production in citrus seedlings grown in controlled-environment chambers.   Growth period for Pomelo (grapefruit) and sour orange was 3 weeks; for sweet orange, 2 weeks.   Seedlings 4 to 5 weeks old at beginning of experiment.   (Redrawn from Girton, 1927.)

in sweet orange, and near 34°C. in sour orange.   Growth comparisons between species cannot be made from these data, as there were some variations in the experimental conditions.   The grapefruit and sour orange plants were grown for 4 weeks, but the sweet orange for only 2 weeks.   Girton attributed the considerably greater root elongation obtained with sour orange than with the grapefruit to the increased illumination used in the sour orange experiment.

According to Marloth (1949), Cossman (1939) postulated from limited observations that the factor limiting citrus root growth during most winters in Palestine is soil temperature.   The lowest soil temperature recorded was 15°C.   This view was supported by Monselise

(1944). Marloth, however, was unable to find a specific correlation between soil temperatures above 14°C. and the periodicity of root growth in young seedlings of rough lemon and sweet orange.

Several workers have investigated root growth in forest trees. Crider (1928) observed that the roots of cypress continued to elongate in his observation boxes throughout the winter months in Arizona. Stevens (1931) reported that the lateral roots of white pine trees in the open showed no growth from November 15 to April 1; but when a 4-year-old tree was kept in the greenhouse, the roots grew approximately as fast in winter as in summer. Kaufman (1945) found that the roots of jack pine (*Pinus banksiana*) in Minnesota ceased growth in October and resumed it in April when the temperature of the upper 6 inches of soil rose above 4.4°; growth was slow, however, until the soil temperature exceeded 10°C.

A study of the effect of soil temperature on germination and on seedling root growth in white pine, under controlled soil temperature conditions, has been reported by Adams (1934). Unfortunately, his method did not give uniform soil temperature from top to bottom within his soil container. Accordingly his data on root growth are difficult to interpret. Temperatures between 7.2 and 10° appear to be near the minimum for seedling root growth, and only a small increase of about 5° greatly accelerated root growth. Over-all root growth was the greatest at 31°C., the highest temperature tested.

Barney (1947) concluded that elongation of the primary root of 2½-week-old loblolly pine (*Pinus taeda L.*) seedlings occurred most rapidly at 20 to 25°C., and that elongation at 5 and at 35° was less than 10 percent of the maximum rate. The results of two of his experiments are given in Figure 81. The root tips differed very little in general appearance when grown at soil temperatures from 5 to 30°, but they appeared to be dormant at 35°C.

From these several studies, one may conclude that, contrary to common opinion, the roots of forest trees are not necessarily dormant during winter months, but continue to grow if the soil temperature is above a minimum of approximately 5°C. The data are insufficient to warrant conclusions concerning the approximate optimum and maximum temperatures for root growth in forest trees, but it appears that temperatures near 35°C. may stop growth.

·The influence of soil temperature on root growth of some plant types indigenous to the arid areas of southwestern United States was observed by Cannon (1915) and Crider (1928). Cannon studied root growth in mesquite (*Prosopis velutina*), ocotillo (*Fouquieria splendens*), and pricklypear cactus (*Opuntia versicolor*). In mesquite, growth was best at 35°, declined rapidly below 30°, but it was still fairly active at 15°C. He thought it probable that some growth continued at 12°C. In ocotillo, growth was also best at 35°, very slow at 20°, and practically ceased at 15°C. Cactus showed a temperature response similar to ocotillo.

Crider's reports of root growth in observation boxes in Arizona during the winter months do not check very well with Cannon's work. Crider gave no soil temperature data but merely listed pricklypear cactus (*O. laevis*), creosotebush (*Covillea* [*Larrea*] *tridentata*), and Simmondsia (a common southwestern shrub) among plants that main-

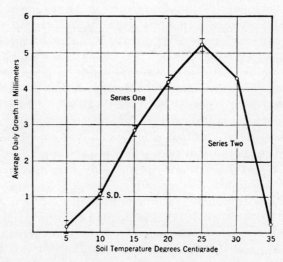

FIGURE 81.—The effect of soil temperature on the elongation of roots of loblolly pine seedlings. (Barney, 1947.)

tained root growth through the winter period, while he listed mesquite and Jerusalem-thorn (*Parkinsonia torreyana*) among those that showed no winter root growth under his conditions. The data are far too incomplete to warrant conclusions as to the soil temperature requirements for root growth in these plants native to hot arid areas.

Ornamental plants.—Although horticulturists commonly believe soil temperature is a factor of great importance in the growth of flowers and other ornamentals, apparently very little work has been done to examine its influence upon root growth. Shanks and Laurie (1949) grew Better Times roses at controlled temperatures with results as shown in Table 51.

Root growth after 80 days was determined for the eight plants used in each treatment. Their data show that the fresh weight of the roots decreased as the temperature increased, with the dry weight a maximum at 16.7°C. The roots of the plants at 11.1°C. were long, white, large in diameter, and sparsely branched. By contrast, the roots at 22.2° were brown, thin, and woody; and although well branched and fibrous in nature, they were not so extensive. Considering these data and the observation that the best top growth occurred at 19.4°, they concluded that the optimum root temperature probably lies between approximately 16 and 20°C.

Other horticultural crops.—A few observations on the effect of soil temperature on root growth in strawberries were reported by Gray

TABLE 51.—*Root growth of Better Times roses in 3-gallon containers of soil maintained at controlled temperatures (Adapted from Shanks and Laurie, 1949)*

Soil temperature[a]	Average fresh weight of roots	Average dry weight of roots
°C.	Grams	Grams
11.1	25.64	2.98
13.9	22.95	3.29
16.7	21.52	3.63
19.4	18.07	3.13
22.2	14.13	2.94

[a] Tops exposed to uniform air temperatures of 15.6° at night and 18.3 to 21°C. during the day.

(1941). He found that the majority of the small fibrous roots turned brown after exposure for 3 to 4 days to a soil temperature of about 38°C. Although root growth occurred, the new growth was practically devoid of hairs. In contrast, root development at 29.4°C. was normal with no sign of injury to the fibrous roots.

Watanabe's (1932) work on the growth of pineapple roots in tap water, as affected by root temperature, has been summarized by Nightingale (1942). Watanabe measured the elongation in roots of standard length after 48-hour periods. He found that under his experimental conditions the minimum temperature for elongation was 5 to 7°, the optimum about 29°, and the maximum 41 to 43°C. (Figure 82). Elongation was very slow below 20 to 21° and above 38°C. In a number of pineapple plantations in the Hawaiian Islands, the soil temperature during at least a part of the growing season is believed to be so low as to reduce the growth and yield of pineapple. For many years it has been the practice to cover the soil in the rows with black building paper. Presumably the increased temperature in the shallow root zone of the pineapple is responsible for the beneficial results derived from this practice. This whole question of soil temperature and the growth of pineapple is receiving much study at the present time in the Islands.

Cuttings.—The importance of the temperature of the rooting medium for good root development in cuttings is generally recognized, and propagating boxes are often provided with bottom heat. Textbooks on propagation frequently point out that proper temperature control is very important, particularly in cuttings somewhat difficult to start. It appears, however, that this aspect of propagation has not been extensively studied in comprehensive experiments. Garner (1944) in his recent review of propagation made no specific references to work on rooting temperatures.

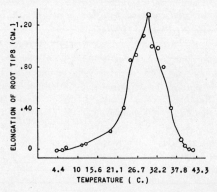

FIGURE 82.—Elongation of pineapple roots in tap water during 48-hour periods, as affected by root temperature. Variety, Smooth Cayenne. (Data from Watanabe, 1932; redrawn from Nightingale, 1942.)

The primary consideration in rooting cuttings is to induce root activity before shoot growth occurs. For this reason, it is desirable to provide bottom heat to warm the bed 2 to 5°C. above the surrounding air. The application of heat to stimulate rapid root development is more important in herbaceous cuttings than in woody cuttings. While root formation may occur over a wide range of temperatures, cuttings of some plant materials often require rather definite temperatures for best root development. A temperature of 10 to 13°C. is suitable for most kinds of coniferous hardwood cuttings (Laurie and Ries, 1942, p. 174). Hartmann (1946) found that heating sand to 24° to 27°C. gave better rooting in Mission olive cuttings than the control at 16 to 21°. Rooting of Manzanillo olive cuttings, however, was not improved by this bottom heat.

Schwartze and Myhre (1947), working where uncovered beds averaged about 14° and unheated frames 17°C., reported that root formation in blueberry cuttings (as well as shoot growth and foliage color) was improved by heating the rooting medium to 21 to 22°C. Rooting of rose cuttings was studied by Laurie and Stillings (1949). Their data (Table 52) indicate that a temperature of about 21° is generally better than 16 to 19 or 27°C. Differences in rooting observed at given temperatures varied with the period of the year during which the rooting of cuttings was undertaken.

Kains and McQuesten (1948) reported that holly cuttings rooted at temperatures from 15 to 27°C. They consider 18 to 24°C. a satisfactory range for practical purposes. In their textbook on propagation, Adriance and Brison (1939, p. 137) stated that a soil temperature of 18

TABLE 52.—*Effect of rooting-medium temperature on the rooting of rose cuttings (Laurie and Stillings, 1949)*

| | | Number of cuttings to root under— | | |
| | | High bottom heat (about 27°C.) | Medium bottom heat (about 21°C.) | Low bottom heat (about 16 to 19°C.) |
Variety	Rooting period			
Golden Rapture	Sept. to Oct.	60	58	37
Better Times	{ Sept. to Oct.	47	56	51
	{ Oct. to Nov.	13	48	45

to 24°C. gave satisfactory results with many plants. Post (1949, p. 208) suggested a wider range of about 16 to 24°C. for best rooting. From the meager data on coniferous cuttings and on olives, it appears that certain plants require temperatures outside these suggested ranges.

. . . . .

By way of summary, little can be said beyond the observation that the cardinal temperatures for root development vary with species, stage of plant development, and, to some extent, with other environmental factors. Although considerable data have been referred to in the foregoing pages, it must be admitted that they provide only a sketchy outline of the soil-temperature limits for root growth. Any attempt to tabulate the soil-temperature requirements for even the most common cultivated plants and trees is most difficult and hazardous with the limited data at present available. The investigator requiring information on the relation of soil temperature to root growth in a given species is advised to consult the text of this review and the original papers in order that he may recognize the conditions under which the data were obtained and their limitations.   It is hoped that this monograph will serve as a guide to the pertinent literature.

Soil temperature and root morphology

Soil temperature affects the rates not only of root growth but also of maturation of the roots produced.   Soil temperature, therefore, may influence markedly the characteristic of the root system developed. Relatively low soil temperatures retard root growth and slow up maturation, whereas relatively high ones accelerate both processes.   At low temperatures considerable growth may occur before the tissues mature.   Such roots typically are white, succulent, and relatively large in diameter, with few scattered laterals.   The cortex generally remains alive for some time, even at the older, or proximal, end.   At high temperature roots mature rapidly with consequent early destruction of the cortex, more complete suberization, and more frequent branching. Such roots are light brown to brown, nonsucculent, relatively small in diameter, and very finely branched, with lateral rootlets close to the growing tip.   These differences have been described by Nightingale (1935), Rogers (1939), and Proebsting (1943) for apple, peach, and apricot root (cf. Figures 75, 76, 77) and by Darrow (1939) and Stuckey (1942) for grass roots.   Nightingale has provided an extensive discussion of the effects of temperature on the anatomical structure of apple and peach roots.   He reported that the relative amount of embryonic tissue in the roots of these trees decreased as the soil temperature increased from 18 to 32°C.

In loblolly pine seedlings, according to Barney (1947), the amount of embryonic tissue, the cell size, and the number of mitotic figures appeared to be nearly equal between 5 and 30°, but the embryonic region was much smaller and the mitotic figures were absent at 35°C. Barney also noted the more rapid suberization at high temperatures and the development of a thick, apparently corky layer of cells enclosing the entire root tip at 35°C.

Nightingale reported that root hairs were more common at temperatures below 24°C. but believed that this condition may have been caused simply by the longer persistence of the cortex at the lower temperatures.   Jeffs (1925) found that root-hair growth could be altered by rapid changes in temperature but that the growth rate soon returned to the previous rate.

Nightingale observed that no callus tissue developed over the pruning wounds of apple and peach roots during a period of 2 months at temperatures of 12.8°C. or below, although it developed rapidly at the higher temperatures. It was found earliest at 29.4 and 32.2°C. At 29.4° a moderately thick layer of callus usually covered the pruning wounds completely. At 32.2° an incomplete callus covering developed that turned brown and suberized rapidly when only a few cells thick. At 24° the callus was thick and matured slowly, while at 18.3° and lower it failed to mature and broke off easily in handling. He noticed also that at the higher temperatures lenticels on living portions of the old roots became very conspicuous because of the development of callus growth that soon suberized. Lenticel callusing was much more conspicuous in peach than in apple.

An excessive lenticel development on both the underground stems and on the mother tubers of potato at a soil temperature of 30°C. was reported by Richards (1921). L. R. Jones *et al.* (1922) also observed that lenticels on potato tubers become large and protruding at high temperatures. These workers considered this excessive lenticel development to be related to the excessive respiratory activity occasioned by the high soil temperature. The shape of potato tubers also appeared to be influenced by soil temperature. At high temperatures the tubers were somewhat elongated, whereas at low temperatures they were short. This point may be of economic interest to growers who produce exhibition seed stock.

The influence of soil temperature on the morphology of the underground parts of wheat seedlings has been examined by Taylor and McCall (1936). For a given depth of seedling, the length of the subcrown internode was increased by high soil temperatures. The formation of a relatively high crown may influence the sensitivity of the plant to drought and winterkilling. The number of seminal roots in Turkey wheat was increased by germinating the seed at 25° as compared with 15°C., but seminal root formation in Hard Federation wheat was not favored by the higher temperature.

Soil temperature and development of legume nodules

The effect of soil temperature upon the development of nodules on four legumes—alfalfa, red clover, field peas, and soybeans—was studied by F. R. Jones and Tisdale (1921). The plants were grown at a series of soil temperatures over the range of 12 to 36°C. Their data, given in Table 53, do not indicate any consistent relation between the number of nodules formed and soil temperature except at the extreme upper and lower temperature limits for the host plant survival. At these extremes, the number of nodules was reduced. These data permit the conclusion that these species will form nodules in soil at any temperature at which the plant can make vigorous growth. Soil temperature,

TABLE 53.—*Effect of soil temperature on nodule formation for seeds planted in inoculated soil and grown for about 2 months (F. R. Jones and Tisdale, 1921, as reported by L. R. Jones et al., 1926)*

Soil Temperature	Average number of nodules per plant			
	Alfalfa	Red clover	Soybean	Field pea
°C.				
12	1.2	1.8	0	3.1
15	1.6	5.0	12.7	6.3
18	16.7	12.5	9.5	17.6
21	8.0	24.6	9.4	18.9
24	3.4	17.4	15.5	19.4
27	11.6	11.5	13.4	44.0
30	10.0	8.9	11.1	2.0
33	10.7	5.3	14.4	[a]
36	3.5	0	13.0	[a]

[a] Died.

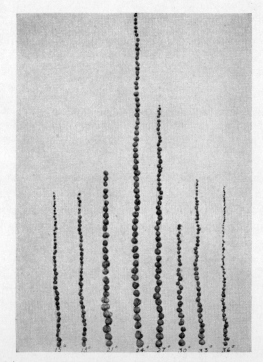

FIGURE 83.—Influence of soil temperature on size of soybean root nodules. Nodules photographed were produced on five plants at 30°C. and on six plants at the other temperatures during a 63-day period.   (F. R. Jones and Tisdale, 1921.)

however, does appear to affect appreciably the size of nodules produced.   In soybeans, the largest nodules (Fig. 83) and the maximum dry-weight production of nodules (Fig. 84) were obtained at a soil temperature of 24°C.   The sharp maximum in dry weight of nodules at 24°C. apparently arises as consequence of both the larger size and a greater number of nodules formed at this temperature.   These workers indicated that maximum nodule production on the roots of the other legumes occurred at about this same soil temperature.

The question arises whether nodule production is related to the volume of roots or shoots of the plant.   The curves of Figure 84 giving

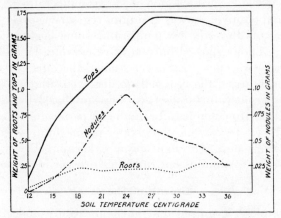

FIGURE 84.—Influence of soil temperature on relative development of nodules, roots, and shoots of soybeans.   Data plotted are combined dry weights of plants grown for 2-month periods in two successive experiments.   F. R. Jones and Tisdale, 1921, as reported by L. R. Jones *et al.*, 1926.)

the dry weight of shoots, roots, and nodules do not reveal such a relationship.   Analysis of the plant material indicated that, in general, the plants with large nodules had the higher percentage of total nitrogen in the shoots, but the data were not considered sufficient to justify definite conclusions.

Legumes may fail to develop nodules during hot dry summer months.   This is a problem of considerable importance in the establishment of alfalfa stands in the Imperial Valley of California.   Under the high soil temperatures prevalent in this area, a good stand of young plants may develop but fail to nodulate.   The work of F. R. Jones and Tisdale has indicated that nodule production should be expected in inoculated soils at all temperatures at which plants will grow.   In the Imperial Valley, the inoculum on the treated seed apparently fails to survive long enough to provide inoculation.   The influence of soil temperature on the growth and survival of micro-organisms is discussed in detail in a later section. Practices involving a post-seeding surface inoculation combined with irrigation to reduce soil temperature appear to offer some aid in securing well-nodulated stands under these high soil-temperature conditions.

Thermotropism in root growth

Root curvatures induced by exposing roots to unequal temperatures on their two sides have been studied by Eckerson (1914). Thermotropic curvatures varied with the applied temperatures and with the species. If the roots curved toward a region of higher temperatures, the response was considered positive; if away from this region, negative. Some roots gave positive curvatures at low temperatures and negative ones at high temperatures; others showed only positive curvatures; and still others gave only negative ones. Eckerson studied the effect of temperature on the permeability of the root cells to dissolved substances. She concluded that the curvatures observed were produced by differences in turgor resulting from temperature-induced permeability changes. In every case the tissue showing the greater permeability was on the concave side of the roots. Thermotropism, Eckerson believed, is not a response to heat as a stimulus but rather is a turgor movement.

Growth of Shoots

It is generally recognized that soil temperature under some conditions may affect the vegetative growth and reproductive activity of plants. Coarse soils are often preferred for early vegetable production because they warm up faster and produce a crop a few days earlier than soils that warm more slowly. Favorable soil temperatures may induce some vegetative growth of the aerial organs of plants despite unfavorable atmospheric temperature conditions (Cannon, 1917). It is a common practice among florists to supply some bottom heat to certain plants. Even with adverse atmospheric temperatures, considerable shoot growth often can be obtained by maintaining the soil temperature at a level favorable for root development.

Soil temperature may be expected to influence shoot growth to the extent that it affects the development and functioning of the root system. The primary functions of the root, besides supplying anchorage for the plant, are the absorption of water and certain inorganic salts and, in some roots, storage of food. Temperature, as has been discussed, influences not only the growth of the root system but also the absorption processes. Through its effect on respiration, temperature may also have a bearing on the efficiency of the root as a food-storage organ. It has been suggested that roots exert a stimulating action on the growth of shoots not entirely dependent upon the absorptive functions of the roots and perhaps attributable to some growth-promoting substance developed within the roots (Went, 1938; and de Ropp, 1946). This thesis is yet hypothetical. The possible influence of temperature on the formation and transfer of this growth substance, if it exists, has not been investigated.

The effect of soil temperature on shoot growth can be determined adequately only in controlled experiments where suitable arrangements are made for providing the desired variation in soil temperature while maintaining constant aerial conditions. To avoid complications caused by photoperiod, experiments should be carried out concurrently, or with proper control of the illumination if the temperature treatments are set up at different seasons of the year. Because of the scarcity of such studies, it has been necessary in the following review to use data taken from studies in which information on soil temperature and shoot growth was not the primary objective. Accordingly, many of the data are very sketchy. Field studies of the effect of soil temperature on top growth are beset with serious difficulties. Radiant energy, which is responsible for heating the soil, also affects directly the aerial environment of the plant.

Soil temperature and vegetative growth

As in previous sections, the available data on soil temperature and vegetative growth will be considered by plant groups to facilitate the use of this material by those interested in particular plant types.

Grasses and forage crops.—The growth of Kentucky bluegrass in field plots in Missouri was investigated by Brown (1943). He reported that bluegrass swards 1 year old or older made very little top growth until the average soil temperature at the ½-inch depth rose above 10°C. The rate of herbage production reached a maximum during the first half of May at an average soil temperature between 16 to 18°C. Under semimonthly mowing, top growth began to decrease in late May and reached a minimum in July, when the soil temperature averaged about 27°C. With adequate supplies of soil moisture and available nitrogen, production increased to a second but smaller peak during late August, at an average soil temperature of approximately 23°C. Top growth declined during September and remained small during October, although the mean soil temperature during October was nearly equal to that during May when production reached a maximum. It is apparent that factors other than soil temperature were affecting the growth of the bluegrass. Brown mentioned that herbage production was influenced by length of day and air temperature, as well as by soil temperature, and also by such other factors as soil moisture, fertilization, mowing practices, and age of the grass sward. These observations further illustrate the difficulty of attempting to establish the relation of soil temperature to shoot growth under field conditions.

Harrison (1934), Brown (1939), and Sprague (1943) investigated top growth of Kentucky bluegrass in controlled temperature cabinets containing the entire plant. Since the recorded growth responses were conditioned by both the soil and the air temperatures, these investigations are of little help in determining the influence of soil temperature on shoot growth.

Darrow (1939) grew Kentucky bluegrass with the root systems in soil maintained at 15, 25, and 35°C. and with the shoots exposed to normal greenhouse conditions. He reported that the character of the top growth varied considerably within the range of soil temperature used. At a soil temperature of 15°C., the plants were tall, succulent, and bushy, with many new leaves; at 35°, the tops were short, non-succulent, and erect, with few leaves. The dry weights of leaves of nitrate-fertilized plants after 11 weeks of growth were 3.59 grams at 15°, 3.13 grams at 25°, and 1.13 grams at 35°C. The increase in leaf length was almost equal at 15 and 25°, but nearly twice as many leaves formed at 15°C. These data indicate that optimum growth was obtained at a soil temperature of about 15°, with a great reduction in growth at 35°C.

A brief report on the growth during a 6-week period of Kentucky bluegrass, Colonial bentgrass, and timothy seedlings in nutrient cultures, controlled at 4.4, 15.6, and 32.2°C. has been given by Stuckey (1942). She gave no data, but her photographs, reproduced as Figure 85, indicate that the best growth occurred at 15.6°C. in all three grasses, and particularly in the Colonial bentgrass and timothy seedlings. The plants grown at 32.2°C. lacked vigor, were extremely chlorotic, and were not sufficiently rigid to stand erect; at the end of 6 weeks many were dead. She also observed the growth of Colonial bentgrass seedlings in soil cultures held at approximately 10, 15.6, and 26.7°C. Two months after germination, the dry weights of the tops were 71.3 grams at 10°, 106.0 grams at 15.6°, and 40.6 grams at 26.7°C. She commented that differences in growth were very noticeable. The seeds germinated first at 26.7°, 2 days later at 15.6°, and an additional 5 days later at 10°C. For a little over 5 weeks, the 26.7°C. plants were larger and more vigorous but had a poorer color. By the end of the seventh week, the 15.6°C. plants had surpassed the higher temperature plants in color, size, and vigor.

FIGURE 85.—Growth of Colonial bentgrass (top), Kentucky bluegrass (middle), and timothy (bottom) seedlings after 6 weeks in nutrient solutions, controlled at 4.4° (left), 15.6° (center), and 32.2°C. (right). (Stuckey, 1942.)

The data of Darrow and Stuckey indicate that a soil temperature near 15°C. favors the top growth of several common forage grasses.

Shoot growth of red clover and alfalfa as affected by soil temperature was studied by F. R. Jones and Tisdale (1921), using the Wisconsin soil tanks controlled at intervals of 3° from 12 to 36°C. Unfortunately they gave no data, but their photographs of the growth in 63-day-old alfalfa and red clover plants are reproduced in Figure 86. Alfalfa appears to have made little growth at temperatures below 18° and its best growth at 21°C. Growth seemed to decline with increasing temperatures from 24 to 30° but remained surprisingly good up to 36°C., the highest temperature tested. Red clover showed a more marked response to temperature (cf. Figure 67). This clover appears to have made its best growth at 21° also but to have shown very poor growth

FIGURE 86.—Growth of (A) alfalfa plants and (B) red clover plants after 63 days in inoculated soil at the soil temperatures indicated. (F. R. Jones and Tisdale, 1921.)

below 18 and above 33°C. There appear to be no other data on the relation of soil temperature to shoot growth in leguminous forage crops.

Cereal crops.—Dickson (1923) investigated the relation of soil temperature to the growth of spring (Marquis) and winter (Turkey) wheat. With spring wheat, the best top production during the early seedling stage was at 20 to 24°C. As the plant increased in age, the optimum temperature became lower, until in the later stages of development the best top growth was obtained at 12 to 16°C. Below 8 and above 32°C., few tillers formed. Between 8 and 32°C. temperature had little effect on tillering, although tillers appeared first at the soil temperatures producing the most rapid emergence (24 to 28°). The cardinal temperatures for shoot development in the winter wheat were, in general, about 4°C. below those for Marquis spring wheat. The responses were very similar except that Turkey wheat tillered excessively and failed to mature at soil temperatures of 24°C. and above.

Wort (1940) obtained the best top growth and tiller formation in Marquis wheat at a soil temperature of 22°C., the lowest studied. Plant height, top dry weight, and tiller number decreased as the soil temperature rose from 22 to 42°C. The leaves became lighter in color above 32°C. In unpublished work referred to by Hoagland (1944), Broyer and Hoagland studied growth of young barley plants in nutrient cultures controlled at 10, 20, and 30°C. Shoot growth, as well as root growth, at 20°C. appeared to be about double that at the other temperatures. In corn, Dickson (1923) found the heaviest and longest tops developed at a soil temperature of about 24° during the earlier stages of growth but later at temperatures near 28°C. (cf. Figure 67). Thus, corn was favored by much higher soil temperatures than wheat. Dickson concluded that the most vigorous and uniform plants were generally obtained at the following soil temperatures: spring wheat, 16 to 20°; winter wheat, 12 to 16°; and corn, 24 to 28°C.

Other field crops.—The growth of soybeans in inoculated soil held at controlled temperatures from 12 to 36°C. has been examined by F. R. Jones and Tisdale (1921). Their data, as summarized by L. R. Jones *et al.* (1926) and given in Figure 83 indicate that shoot growth in soybeans reaches a maximum rate at soil temperatures near 27°C. and declines slightly at higher ones. More recently, Earley and Cartter (1945) studied the dry weight production of soybean tops in five experiments, carried out under different light intensities and photoperiods. Unfortunately other environmental factors, particularly the day-air and night-air temperatures in the greenhouse, were not uniform in the several experiments. The amount of radiant energy to which the plants were exposed apparently influenced to a large degree the differences in yields observed at the several soil temperatures. This point is illustrated by experiments 4 and 5 (see Table 54), where all factors except light intensity were fairly uniform. In experiment 4, where the light intensity was relatively low throughout, the yield of tops showed a smaller increase from 7 to 27°C. than in experiment 5, where it was high. These findings indicate that under the variety of aerial environments they encountered in the greenhouse, soil temperatures from about 22 to 27°C. were most favorable for maximum dry-weight production of soybean tops, with the optimum temperature increasing with greater incident radiation. Root temperatures as low as 12° or as high as 37°C. distinctly reduced growth. Thus, the conclusions of F. R. Jones and Tisdale and of Earley and Cartter are in essential agreement.

A very interesting relationship was suggested by the work of Earley and Cartter. Their study indicated that as the supply of synthesized organic materials required for growth is increased by an accelerated rate of photosynthetic production (owing to greater incident radiation), root temperature may become an increasingly important limiting factor in the shoot growth of plants. This relationship between the energy

TABLE 54.—*Influence of root temperature on dry-weight production of soybean tops in five experiments carried out under different environmental conditions (Earley and Cartter, 1945)*

	Mean yield per plant for experiment—				
Root temperature	No. 1; high relative light intensity	No. 2; high relative light intensity	No. 3; medium relative light intensity	No. 4; low relative light intensity	No. 5; high relative light intensity
°C.	Grams	Grams	Grams	Grams	Grams
2	....	....	....	0.19	....
7	3.16	0.75	0.71	.56	0.69
12	....	....	....	.85	1.96
17	4.58	1.59	1.58	.89	3.02
22	....	1.99	1.60	1.09	3.34
27	8.62	2.40	1.75	1.05	3.58
32	....	1.50	1.32	....	3.95
37	5.56	1.27	.88	....	1.63

received during the photoperiod and the importance of soil temperature as a factor influencing plant growth appears to be a generalization worthy of further study.

Camp and Walker (1927) studied the growth of cotton seedlings over a period of about 2 weeks following emergence at controlled soil temperatures from 15.5 to 38°C. Daily measurements of plant heights were made. Each day's measurements are plotted as a separate curve in Figure 87, giving a family of curves which represents the daily growth of plants from each temperature group. These data indicate that the optimum soil temperature for growth of the young cotton seedlings is near 33°C. The authors called attention to the fact that actually the growth rate of the cotton shoots differed only slightly between 25 and 35°C. once the plants emerged. The peak in the succession of curves was caused largely by the initial advantage gained during germination.   They suggested that some other environmental factor such as light or carbon dioxide supply may have limited growth between 25 and 35°C.   The brief data given in Arndt's (1932) note indicate also that soil temperatures between 24 and 33°C. had little effect on the elongation of the taproot of 2-week-old cotton seedlings.

Some information relating root temperature to the growth of hemp (*Cannabis sativa*) was provided by Nelson (1944).   Four treatments

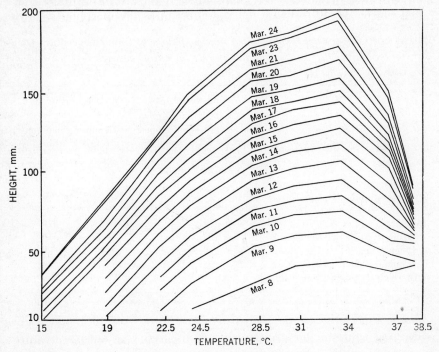

FIGURE 87.—Heights of cotton seedlings on successive days following emergence, as influenced by soil temperature.   (Redrawn from Camp and Walker, 1927.)

were established, using seedlings transplanted to gravel cultures 11 days after germination: Tops at 15° with roots at 15 and 30°, and tops at 30° with roots at 15 and 30°C.   Differences in growth began to appear after 4 weeks and became quite marked after 7 weeks.   Growth data for 14-week-old plants are given in Table 55.   At an air temperature of 15°C., the plants grown in the 30° soil produced a larger number of leaves, thicker stems, and greater total dry weight of tops than those in 15° soil.   There was little difference, however, in the size of the leaves or the height of plants grown at these two soil temperatures.   The higher air temperature of 30°C. was less favorable to the development of the hemp, and the growth differences caused by soil temperature, though smaller, reflected the same trend. These limited data again recall attention to the point that the effect of soil temperature on shoot growth is appreciably influenced by other environmental factors.

A few observations on the growth of tobacco at a series of soil temperatures have been made by Johnson and Hartman (1919). Disease-free plants grew best at soil temperatures of 29° and 31°C. Practically no growth occurred below 13°, and that at 40°C. was poor. They noted that soil temperature had a marked effect upon the morphology of the

TABLE 55.—*Growth responses of hemp plants to four temperature treatments: plants 14 weeks old at harvest; 54 plants in each series (Adapted from Nelson, 1944)*

Growth data	Air temperature 15°C.		Air temperature 30°C.	
	Soil temperature 15°C.	Soil temperature 30°C.	Soil temperature 15°C.	Soil temperature 30°C.
Leaves:				
Total number produced per plant	48	65	41	50
Number intact on plant	38	57	29	36
Mean area per leaf (cm.²)	10.7	10.4	5.7	5.5
Stems:				
Diameter at basal node (mm.)	3.1	3.4	2.7	2.7
Height (cm.)	49	47	57	60
Number of nodes produced	18	16	28	31
Dry weight of top per plant[a] (gr.)	7.34	9.30	4.10	5.10

[a] Dry weight data taken on six plants of an improved strain of hemp (Kentucky) at age 15 weeks.

plants, especially at the higher temperatures. At soil temperatures near the optimum for growth, the plants grew low and stocky, with broad but rather pointed leaves; between 36 and 40°C., they became tall and spindly with long internodes and short rounded leaves. The growth made by these plants at soil temperatures ranging from 17 or 18° to 31 or 32°C. is given in Figure 69. More recently this matter has been investigated by Kincaid and Gratz (1935). Growth measurements were made on seedlings of variety No. 301 (shown in Figure 88) and of variety Round Tip. The minimum soil temperature for growth was about 9°, and the maximum about 40°C. The optimum was not very closely defined but occurred between 24 and 32°C.

Vegetable and truck crops.—Shoot growth of vegetable and truck crops in relation to soil temperature seems to have received little study, although truck gardeners commonly seek out sandy soils to obtain more rapid growth of early vegetables. The earlier crops on such soils are generally attributed to higher soil temperatures. Other factors, such as better internal drainage and aeration, coupled with ease of management when wet may contribute to the successful production on these soils for the early market.

Using nutrient cultures, Brenchley and Singh (1922) reported that growth in young pea plants proceeded equally well whether the root temperature was fairly constant or whether it fluctuated as much as 22°C. within 7 to 29° as approximate limits. They also wrote that

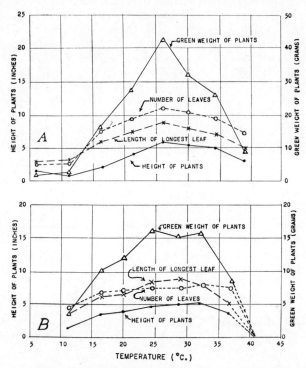

FIGURE 88.—Growth of transplanted tobacco plants of variety No. 301 at various soil temperatures. Growth period in trial *A* was 31 days; in trial *B*, 21 days. (Redrawn from Kincaid and Gratz, 1935.)

good growth could be made under high air temperatures and strong insolation if the roots were kept relatively cool. These statements suggest interesting relationships, but they require further experimental verification. The growth of disease-free bean plants at soil temperatures of 18, 26, and 33°C. is referred to briefly by Burkholder (1920). The plants at 18° were healthy but grew slowly. Those at 33°C. grew most rapidly, but those at 26° appeared to show the most normal growth. Burkholder ventured the guess that the optimum soil temperature for beans was near 22 to 26°C.

A brief report on growth of tomatoes at controlled soil temperatures was made by Clayton (1923). The development of two commercial varieties of tomato 1 month after transplanting is shown in Figure 89. Soil temperatures from about 24 to 31°C. appear to have produced the most vigorous shoot development. Riethmann (1933) studied the effect

FIGURE 89.—Influence of soil temperature upon growth of tomato plants during a 1-month period following transplanting. (Clayton, 1923.)

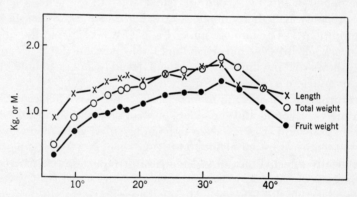

FIGURE 90.—Growth of tomato (variety Schone von Lothringen) plants after 100 days as influenced by soil temperature. Total stem length represented by crosses, total top weight by circles, and fruit weight by dots. (From the work of Riethmann, 1933, as given by Went, 1944a.)

of soil temperature on the growth and fruiting of tomato. His growth data, taken from Went (1944a), are reproduced in Figure 90. Riethmann's work indicated that stem growth and fruit production of tomatoes were influenced by root temperature, with an optimum at 33°C. under his conditions. This matter has been touched upon by Went in connection with his study of thermoperiodicity. On the basis of limited data, he stated that elongation of the stem and the green weight of the shoot were not materially influenced by soil temperatures between 15.5 and 32.5°C. Riethmann's work indicated that shoot growth and fruiting were relatively little affected by the soil temperatures over this range but were distinctly reduced by soil temperatures outside these limits.

Went offered the interesting suggestion that only when other growing conditions for the roots are suboptimal may the growth rate of tomatoes be determined by the temperature of the root system. When such environmental factors as aeration and nutrient supply of the roots are very favorable, soil temperature may have little bearing on shoot development. This point of view has received some support from the recent work of Wanner (1948b) which indicates that salt absorption by wheat roots had a lower temperature coefficient when the salt concentration external to the roots was higher. In accounting for the variances in results reported by Riethmann and himself, Went attributed the great influence of soil temperature on shoot growth noted by the former to less favorable root conditions prevailing in his study. As a further illustration of this point, he referred to Gericke's (1940) claim that heating the nutrient solution was beneficial to tomato growth in water culture and the denial of this by Arnon and Hoagland (1939), who, Went believed, probably had their tomatoes growing under more clearly optimum conditions. The photograph of Figure 71, taken from the unpublished work of Broyer and Hoagland and mentioned by Hoagland (1944), shows striking differences in shoot development of tomato plants grown in nutrient cultures maintained at 10, 20, and 30°C. A root temperature of 30°C. appears to have produced somewhat larger plants at both the very young and the older stages of growth. Thus, the findings of these several workers seem to be in essential agreement that between soil temperatures of about 16 to 32°C. shoot growth of tomatoes is not materially affected, but at soil temperatures outside this range it is appreciably reduced.

Some data on the influence of soil temperature on the growth of potato plants are given in Table 56, taken from the work of L. R. Jones, McKinney, and Fellows (1922). Sprouts emerged first in soil held from 21 to 24°C. During the early life of the plants, the height of tops was directly correlated with the time of emergence. These authors reported that as the plants developed a soil temperature of about 27°C. soon became optimum, with a marked decrease in growth rate at higher temperatures. Later, however, the plants at the higher soil temperature slackened growth and came to maturity, while the plants at the lower temperatures grew more slowly but finally surpassed those grown at the higher temperatures. By harvesttime, the optimum soil temperature for production of fresh weight of tops apparently was near 21°C.

In a previous section it was pointed out that the largest number and heaviest yield of tubers were obtained at a soil temperature near 18°C. Soil temperature was observed to affect other morphological features of the potato plants. At the higher temperatures, aerial tubers and auxiliary branches sometimes developed. Leaflets at the higher tempera-

TABLE 56.—*Influence of soil temperature upon the development of Irish Cobbler potato plants grown to maturity (L. R. Jones, McKinney, and Fellows, 1922)*

	Soil temperature in degrees centigrade						
Growth measurements	11 to 12	14.5 to 15	18	21 to 21.5	24 to 25	27 to 28.5	27 to 30.5
Fresh weight tops per hill (average of two experiments), gm.	55.1	77.0	82.2	89.0	87.0	70.0	50.0
Height of stems per hill (average of four experiments), cm.	22.0	23.0	22.6	23.5	25.0	30.2	14.0
Diameter of stems (one experiment only),[a] cm.	.71	.85	.79	.77	.67	.39	.33
Stems per hill (average of four experiments), No.	2.8	3.6	4.2	4.6	4.0	3.2	2.8
Days for emergence (average of three experiments), No.	23	17.5	14.5	12.8	12.8	16.5	24.6

[a] Measurements incorrectly reported in original paper (see Bushnell, 1925, p. 5).

tures were elongated and lanceolate in form, but at the lower temperatures they were wider in proportion to length and tended toward a round shape. The foliage became lighter in color with increasing soil temperatures.

Walker and Jones (1921) observed the growth of onion seedlings for periods up to 30 days in soils held at constant temperatures from 14 to 30°C. In Red Globe (a northern variety), the best development of tops occurred at 20° and above, while in Yellow Bermuda (a southern variety) the best top growth was at 25°C. This study was continued by Walker (1926) using older plants of two other varieties of onions. The highest dry weight of tops was found at 18 to 22°C. in both White Portugal and Crystal Wax onions. In these varieties, top growth fell off markedly at 24°C. and above.

Trees and shrubs.—The initiation of spring-season shoot growth in perennials such as trees and shrubs is often believed to be dependent upon soil temperature. This concept was not supported by Daubenmire (1949). He reported that cambial growth in fir (*Pseudotsuga taxifolia*) trees growing at different elevations on the slope of a mountain began on the same date, despite the lower soil temperatures at higher altitudes. He found, however, that the rate of growth was slower at the higher elevations. Both low soil and low air temperatures probably contributed to this retarded growth. Daubenmire concluded that the beginning of diametral growth in 17 species of angiosperms and conifers native to the temperate zones bore no close relation to soil temperature, as measured at a depth of 20 centimeters, but that growth was apparently initiated during a rather well-defined period, suggestive of photoperiodism.

Recently Marloth (1949) reported that the spring flush of top growth in citrus seedlings grown in Eastern Transvaal was not related to the occurrence of favorable soil temperatures. This flush of growth appeared when soil temperatures were still near their yearly minimum. He suggested that the stimulation of growth may arise from the influence of environmental factors on the production of growth substances.

The gain in trunk girth of apple trees grown under four systems of soil management was studied by Oskamp (1917). Although the soil temperatures differed appreciably between the tilled and the straw-mulched plots, there was no significant difference in trunk growth. He concluded that soil temperature plays a minor role in the growth of young apple trees, but one must recognize that in this type of experiment numerous other factors may have influenced the growth of the trees.

Rogers (1939) carried out extensive studies of the growth of apple trees as related to soil temperature under orchard conditions. While he found that changes in the rate of shoot growth apparently corresponded with variations in soil temperature during the first part of the growing season, one cannot evaluate the contribution of soil temperature to the observed growth.

Nightingale (1935) reported that top growth in apple and peach trees was affected by soil temperature and was closely correlated with the volume of roots produced at the different temperatures. The leaves developed on root systems previously pruned free of fibrous roots were somewhat curled at sand temperatures of 10° or below and 32.2°C. or above. At these temperature extremes there was little root growth. He attributed the leaf curl to a restricted water absorption caused by the poor growth of fibrous absorbing roots at these soil temperatures.

428   S. J. RICHARDS, R. M. HAGAN, AND T. M. MCCALLA

The investigations of Proebsting (1943) on peaches and of Batjer *et al.* (1939) on apples also illustrated the close relation between shoot growth and root development at various soil temperatures.

Preliminary work on the effect of soil temperature on the growth of rooted cuttings of lemon (*Citrus limonia*), grapefruit (*C. paradisi*), and sweet orange (*C. sinensis*) was reported by Halma (1935). In lemons, the highest dry-weight production of tops was obtained where soil temperatures varied between 16 and 27°C., the warmest range tested. In grapefruit and orange, the best top growth occurred in the 12 to 22°C. treatment. Soil temperatures varying between 3 and 20°C. greatly reduced the growth of all three species, but lemons appeared to be best adapted to a wide range of soil temperatures.

TABLE 57.—*Growth of rooted Valencia orange cuttings for a 4-month period under controlled soil temperatures (Haas, 1936)*

Soil temperature	Fresh weight of top growth	Dry weight of top growth
°C.	Grams	Grams
19 to 20	62.6	15.7
23	105.0	30.6
27	96.6	30.5
31	106.6	33.0
35	76.2	22.0

Haas (1936) studied the growth of rooted Valencia orange cuttings for a 4-month period under conditions providing better control of soil temperature. His data are presented in Table 57. They show that top growth was good at soil temperatures from 23 to 31°, with the best growth developing at 31°C. Growth was considerably poorer at 19° to 20° and at 35°C. The best root growth was found at 31°, that at 27°C. being only slightly poorer.

Cannon (1917) reported that relatively great vegetative activity could be induced in cactus (*Opuntia versicolor*) shoots exposed to low air temperatures if the soil were maintained at favorable temperatures.

Ornamental plants.—The effects of soil temperature on gardenia shoots were investigated by Jones (1938) and Davidson (1941). Jones observed that soil temperatures of 8 and 10°C. caused wilting of all leaves and a rapid senescence of the oldest. Both workers found that soil temperatures below 18 or 20°C. produced interveinal chlorosis, which increased in severity with decreasing soil temperatures and increasing periods of exposure. Jones found no measurable growth at

8°C. Although leaves formed at this temperature, they soon withered. Leaf size and stem length increased with rising soil temperature in both studies. Davidson observed that increases in length of day, as well as in air temperatures, tended to offset the chlorosis and retarded growth caused by low soil temperatures. Allen (1934) reported that stem growth in stock (*Matthiola incana*), snapdragons, and freesias was very little influenced by soil temperatures of 11, 15.6, and 22.2°C., and in calendula stem growth was reduced only at 11°.

Shoot growth of Better Times roses grown at soil temperatures from 11 to 22.2°C. was determined by Shanks and Laurie (1949). The fresh and dry weights of the shoots increased steadily with temperatures from 11.1 to 19.4° and declined at 22.2°C. (Table 58). The tops of all the plants were vigorous, but plants with roots at 11°C. grew

TABLE 58.—*Shoot growth of Better Times roses as affected by soil temperature (Adapted from Shanks and Laurie, 1949)*

Soil temperature	Average fresh weight of shoots	Average dry weight of shoots	Top: root ratio (on fresh weight basis)
°C.	Grams	Grams	Grams
11.1	32.29	8.94	1.26
13.9	46.11	12.13	2.00
16.7	53.67	15.25	2.50
19.4	62.13	18.78	3.44
22.2	57.23	15.11	4.05

much slower, with shorter internodes and darker green color. By contrast, the tops of plants at 22.2°C. were the taller and had fewer branches. Higher soil temperatures favored development of the shoot relative to the root, as indicated by the increasing top to root ratios. Pfahl *et al.* reported that irrigation of Better Times roses with warmed water did not significantly increase the growth, bottom breaks, or flowering. Little benefit from this practice would be expected in view of their observation that soils irrigated with waters at 7.8, 21, and 26.7°C. all returned to the same temperature within 8 hours after irrigation. Plants growing in haydite and irrigated twice per day with water heated to 32°C. showed some distress.

Other horticultural crops.—The top growth of 3-year-old Rubel blueberry plants in soils at controlled temperatures was studied by Bailey and Jones (1941). Measurements made after 4 months (Fig. 91) showed that the total linear growth increased with temperature from 12.8 to 32.2°C., the range studied. Plants growing at soil tem-

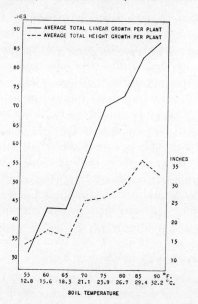

FIGURE 91.—Effect of soil temperature on the height and linear growth of Rubel blueberry plants during a 4-month period following establishment of transplants. (Redrawn from Bailey and Jones, 1941.)

peratures of 21°C. or above tended to be tall and upright, while those grown at lower temperatures tended to be short and spreading.

· · · · ·

To summarize, the influence of soil temperature on the vegetative growth of plants varies with species, stage of plant development and other environmental factors. General statements of temperature limits for shoot growth are therefore of little value. Very limited data are now available for only a few plants in certain stages of growth and under given environmental conditions. Much work remains to be done before it will be possible to evaluate the importance of soil temperature as a factor in the shoot growth of plants.

Soil temperature and reproductive activity

A number of investigators have reported that soil temperature affects the initiation of reproductive activity in a variety of plants. Dickson (1923) reported that spring wheat matured earliest at 16°C., a temperature within the range producing the best growth of shoots and roots. However, Wort (1940) stated that increasing the soil temperature from 22 to 34°C. accelerated heading in the same variety of wheat by as much as 11 days. Soil temperatures above 34°C. retarded or prevented heading. Dickson observed that maturation in winter wheat was inhibited at soil temperatures of 24°C. or above. He noted that corn developed floral parts first at soil temperatures of 28 to 32°C. and that it would not mature at soil temperatures below 16° because of retarded vegetative development. Relatively high soil temperatures favored early flowering and the production of staminate flowers in hemp (Nelson, 1944). Soil temperature had been reported previously to affect the balance between staminate and pistillate flowers in cucumber (Hedrick, 1905). The life cycle of potato plants was short at high and long at low soil temperatures (L. R. Jones et al., 1922). Allen's (1934) study of flower production in ornamentals indicated that species and even varieties differed in their response to soil temperatures of 11, 15.6, and 22.2°C. Davidson (1941) reported that the number of buds formed and the quality of the flowers produced in gardenias generally increased at higher soil temperatures.

The mechanisms leading to floral initiation are not yet well understood. It is now recognized that flowering occurs in some plants only after a suitable period of vegetative growth and of exposure in proper sequence to certain temperature and light conditions. The studies of several workers, including Hamner and Bonner (1938), have suggested that some type of growth-factor substance is manufactured in leaves exposed to suitable photoperiods and transported to other parts of the plant where it appears to be required for flower development. Knowledge of the factors responsible for flowering in photoneutral plants is also limited. Murneek et al. (1949) have recently discussed this subject. The possible role of soil temperature in the complicated pattern of events leading to the production of floral organs has apparently not been studied. Presumably, soil temperature may affect the time of flowering by influencing the time required for plants to develop vegetatively to the point where flower formation may occur when other conditions become favorable. Few of the reports claiming a definite relation between soil temperature and reproductive activity have given any consideration to the other factors involved in flowering, such as thermoperiodism and photoperiodism.

Exposure to low temperatures may shorten the vegetative period and hasten the appearance of the reproductive phase in plants. Treatment of seeds for this purpose is called vernalization and was referred to in a previous section. The term "thermoperiodism" was proposed by Arthur and Harvill (1941) for the flowering response brought about by exposing seedlings or older plants to periods of low temperature. Thompson (1933, 1944) has carried out a number of experiments of this type. He found, for example, that holding celery plants at 5 to

10°C. for as short a period as 2 days had an appreciable effect on seed-stalk formation when the plants were grown subsequently at temperatures too high for floral induction. In many cases, low temperatures during the night periods only were sufficient to produce flowering. Went (1944a) used the term "thermoperiodicity" to include all effects of a temperature differential between light and dark periods on the flowering, fruiting, or growth of plants. He reported that fruiting of tomatoes, as well as shoot growth and root growth, was significantly increased by lowering the air and, presumably to some extent, the soil temperature during the dark hours. Work with other plants led Went to suggest that thermoperiodicity is a general phenomenon in higher plants. This matter is also discussed by Murneek *et al.* (1949).

In experiments on thermoperiodicity, the whole plants have been subjected to the different temperatures. Since the earlier work of Riethmann (1933) had indicated that stem growth and fruit set in tomatoes depended largely upon root temperature, Went undertook to determine whether variations in root temperature were responsible for the better growth Riethmann had obtained with varied day and night temperatures. Went concluded from limited data that under his experimental conditions, which provided good aeration and abundant nutrient supply to the roots, shoot growth was not materially increased or decreased by root temperatures varying from 32.5 to 15.5°C. This observation suggests that root-temperature variations were not the cause of the thermoperiodic responses. Further experimentation should be carried out to ascertain more definitely the influence, if any, of soil temperature on thermoperiodicity phenomena and on the general problem of floral initiation and development.

Soil Temperature and Crop Quality

The statement is sometimes made that soil temperature may exert a qualitative as well as quantitative effect upon the development of plants. However, little is apparently known concerning this matter. LeClerc in 1907 and later other workers reported that climatic factors, including temperatures, may affect the chemical composition of plants appreciably. In his review of this problem, Beeson (1941) was also led to the conclusion that climate may modify plant composition, although he stated that evidence clearly showing this relation was not available. More recently, Brown (1939) and Sullivan and Sprague (1949) studied the chemical composition of several pasture grasses in controlled-temperature chambers where both air and soil temperatures were varied. Their data indicated that plants exposed to high temperatures were relatively high in total nitrogen, but it is difficult to evaluate the role of soil temperature in producing the observed differences.

Direct evidence relating soil temperature to the composition and quality of crops seems to be meager. Although F. R. Jones and Tisdale (1921) reported that soybean plants grown at soil temperatures near 24°C. generally had a higher percentage of total nitrogen in the shoots, their data were not considered sufficient to justify definite conclusions. The formation of large protruding lenticels on potato tubers at high soil temperatures was noted by L. R. Jones *et al.* (1922). These workers also stated that soil temperature influenced the chemical composition or enzymatic system of at least the surface tissues of the potato tubers. Mature tubers exposed to temperatures near 1 to 2°C. tended to become sweet (Heald, 1933). The mechanism responsible for the conversion of stored starch to sucrose has recently been studied by Arreguin-Lozano and Bonner (1949). The number and size of flowers on a shoot, which are considered to be important aspects of crop quality in the floral trade, may be influenced by soil temperature. This was reported by Allen (1934) in calendulas, snapdragons, and freesias, and by Davidson (1941) in gardenias.

Extreme Soil Temperatures and Plant Injury

Plant organs are not equally resistant to temperature extremes. Root tissues of many plants are more sensitive to low temperatures than the shoots (Daubenmire, 1947, p. 201, and Post, 1949, p. 44). The aerial parts of hardy plants in northern latitudes withstand temperatures of −6°C. or lower, but their roots are often injured at temperatures slightly below freezing (Post, 1949). Since the plant shoot is dependent upon the root for its supply of water, some of the top damage appearing in cold weather may be the result of frost injury to the roots. Plants in pots or other containers above ground and plants with roots in packing material are especially vulnerable to both low and high temperatures.

Temperatures in the soil near the surface fluctuate between wide limits. Iverson (1939) reported temperatures as low as −21°C. at the 2-inch depth and −19° at the 6-inch depth in bare soil at St. Paul, Minn. Patterson (1936, p. 254) reported the surprisingly low temperature of −17.5°C. at the 12-inch depth under a grassed area at Saskatoon, Canada. Soil temperatures as high as 68°C. have been measured in the top inch of soil (Bates and Roeser, 1924), and temperatures above 50° may be found in the surface 6 inches. (See Part I of this chapter for a more complete summary.)

It is evident that in some regions the entire root systems of seedlings and of mature crops, if normally shallow rooted or if grown on shallow soils, may be exposed at times to temperatures beyond the lower and upper limits for growth and survival.

Low soil temperatures

The large economic losses caused by the injury or death of plants exposed to low air and soil temperatures have stimulated much research on this problem. The occurrence of frost killing, the factors affecting the hardiness of plant tissues, and the current theories of the nature of freezing damage to plants were reviewed by Levitt (1941). The water relations of cells and the protoplasmic factors involved in frost resistance were considered in a recent review by Crafts et al. (1949). Injury from frost appears to be caused primarily by the withdrawal of water from the cells and its freezing in the intercellular spaces. With the continued removal of water, the cell contents may be coagulated, and the tissues may be damaged mechanically by the formation of the ice crystals. Ice crystals may form within the cell, especially if the temperature falls rapidly. The bark of woody roots may crack away exposing not only the cambium but also the phloem and xylem to desiccation. The severity of the damage to plants depends on the temperature reached, the length of time the temperature remains low, and the rates of both cooling and thawing.

Damage to subterranean organs.—The resistance of 15 species of turf grasses to low soil temperatures was tested by Carroll (1943). Plugs of sod about 4½ inches in diameter and 3 inches deep were cut from plats, fitted into earthenware jars, and then exposed to an air temperature of $-25°C$. until thermometers placed in the centers of the cores indicated soil temperatures of -5, -10, -15, and $-20°C$. The lethal soil temperature for the majority of the species appeared to lie between -10 and $-15°C$. Nitrogen-fertilized plants were much less resistant to cold than low-nitrogen ones. The species most injured by low soil temperatures were perennial ryegrass (*Lolium perenne*), Italian ryegrass (*L. multiflorum*), crested dogtail (*Cynosurus cristatus*), sweet vernalgrass (*Anthoxanthum odoratum*), and Highland velvet bent (*Agrostis canina*). The most resistant species were Kentucky bluegrass (*Poa pratensis*), wood meadow grass (*P. nemoralis*), Cocoos bent (*Agrostis tenuis*), and Chewings fescue (*Festuca rubra fallax*). Kentucky bluegrass proved to be the most resistant of all the grasses tested. However, within the range of low soil temperatures generally encountered in the field at Wooster, Ohio, Chewings fescue and some of the bent species survived nearly as well as Kentucky bluegrass.

In areas where cold winters are common, winterkilling of alfalfa is one of the most frequent causes for loss of stands.   Smith (1948) reported that in some Nevada fields at least 95 percent of the alfalfa was winterkilled.   Much less injury is experienced where winter-hardy varieties are planted.   Injury occurs in plants of all ages but is more likely to kill young stands seeded the previous fall or spring.   When injured plants are examined in the spring, the upper part of the taproot may be dark brown or black.   The injured area usually begins in the crown and sometimes extends downward a distance of as much as 2 inches.   When injury to the root is shallow, plants recover and eventually slough off the affected tissue.

Weimar (1930) investigated the nature of the root injuries sustained by plants exposed to subfreezing soil temperatures.   Many of the plants frozen in his experiment either died or recovered without showing any very striking external evidence of injury to the roots.   Within one to several weeks after freezing, however, some plants developed lesions described as "phloem injury," where tissues external to the cambium were damaged, and "heart rot," where tissues inside the cambium were involved.   In one experiment both phloem injury and heart rot appeared in the roots of potted Kansas common and Grimm alfalfa plants frozen in soil at an average temperature of $-6.6°C$. for 5 hours; in another test, phloem injury alone appeared where plants were exposed to lower average temperatures for similar periods of time.   It was evident that given types of injury might be produced by a considerable variety of conditions.   Histological studies of some of the frozen roots showed that the cells, particularly along the root rays, were usually split apart.   These damaged cells died and collapsed, permitting saprophytic or parasitic organisms to gain entrance.   If the injury was not too severe, the cracks formed were practically all closed during the following growing season.

Extensive winterkilling of Ladino clover frequently occurs when a protective snow cover is absent.   Losses due to winter injury are usually heavier in older stands than in younger ones (Ahlgren and Burcalow, 1949).   Winter injury to Ladino can be reduced by seeding with grasses and by allowing a good top growth to remain at the end of the growing period.

Potato tubers close to the soil surface are sometimes caught by early fall freezes.   The freezing injury may assume any one of several forms. If the tuber is completely frozen, the cells rupture and break down into a watery fluid.   In the case of partial freezing, a dark line may separate the frozen tissue from the normal.   In many cases, microbial decay further injures the partially frozen tubers; under other conditions the frozen tissues dry out, shrink without decay, and later appear dry, whiter, and more powdery than normal (Heald, 1933, p. 171).

In northern areas, strawberry plants are usually protected by a mulch during the winter. Where inadequately protected, the roots and lower portion of the crown are often winterkilled. Angelo (1939) reported that most of the large roots and the pith of the crown clear to the apex were badly browned in plants which failed to recover after freezing. Less severely injured plants showed pith browning only at the base of the crown. He found that the killing temperature for strawberry plants growing in pots was about −10°C. after hardening 10 days at 0°C. The terminal bud sometimes remained alive, although a considerable portion of the crown and roots were killed. These terminal buds may begin growth in the spring, but the plants will die if insufficient crown has survived to send out new roots.

Carrick (1920) studied the cold resistance of the roots of apple, pear, peach, cherry, and plum trees, six varieties of grapes, three varieties of vine berries, gooseberries, and currants. Soil-free roots were used in his tests, but he stated that surrounding the roots with soils at several moisture contents caused no appreciable differences in the amount of injury. This work has been questioned by Patterson (1936) and by Brierly and Landon (1946). Though Patterson agreed that many small roots of some of the species studied by Carrick were usually either seriously injured or killed by low soil temperatures at some time during winter in the prairie region of Canada, he commented that a number of these plants commonly survive at soil temperatures below those reported as lethal by Carrick. However, as he pointed out, definite information on the hardiness of the roots of some varieties grown successfully in this area is lacking.

Brierly and Landon reported that the roots of Latham red raspberry when undisturbed in soil were able to withstand much lower temperatures than those reported by Carrick. They found no severe injury until the soil temperature fell below −19°C. The killing temperature appeared to lie between −21 and −23°C. When woody plants apparently normal at the close of the growing season fail to resume growth in the spring after a cold winter, winterkilling may be indicated. The so-called "sour-sap" disease of apricot, almond, other stone fruits, and occasionally also of nonstone fruits is a form of winter injury (Heald, 1933, p. 164). In this case, the tree suddenly dies as it is leafing out in the spring, and the sap in the bark, cambium, and young wood ferments, or "sours."

Another type of plant injury occurring during cold weather is the mechanical damage caused by the heaving of the soil. The nature and causes of heaving are discussed in Part I of this chapter. Heaving occurs frequently under certain climatic conditions, and the resulting uplift may amount to as much as 60 percent of the depth frozen (Taber, 1931). Generally the most serious damage occurs among seedlings. Haasis (1923) found that pine seedlings had been raised above the surface of the soil and that a considerable portion of their root system was exposed or, in some cases, even thrown out and lying on the ground.

Lamb (1936) considered that the mechanical strength of roots may be an important factor in the resistance of given species to heaving damage. The roots of pine seedlings and young plants of clover, alfalfa, wheat, oats, and other crops are often broken off 2 to 3 inches below the surface. Plants whose root systems have been raised out of the soil or have been broken may subsequently die from desiccation. Heaving sometimes produces a nearly complete destruction of the crop. Such damage is most severe in late-seeded plantings (Janssen, 1929).

There is general agreement, according to Lamb (1936), that heaving is probably the most common cause of winter injury in the soft-wheat belt of the Northeastern United States. Klages (1942, p. 230) suggests that heaving damage may be reduced by planting winter annual crops early. This allows the development of a strong crown and the growth of sufficient basal foliage to reduce temperature fluctuations in the surface soil. Similarly, damage to perennials such as alfalfa and clover will be lessened if the plants enter the winter period with sufficient top growth to modify surface-soil temperatures.

Damage to aerial organs.—Another form of winter injury attributable to low soil temperatures is a desiccation of shoots caused by a decreased rate of water absorption from cold soil (see Part II of this chapter). This injury is aggravated by atmospheric conditions favoring rapid transpiration. Orange trees in California have been reported to wilt severely during periods of cold weather (Cameron, 1941). Cold soil may be of some ecological importance. Clements and Martin (1934) and Michaelis (1934), according to Kramer (1949, p. 230), believed that low soil temperatures occurring at high altitudes limited plant growth. Michaelis suggested that slow absorption of water at the high altitudes may affect the position of timber lines.

Winterkilling is most severe where the soil remains unprotected by a snow blanket. Root injury is more pronounced on loose sandy soils than on tight clays. The rate of temperature change may be as important as the degree of temperature change. The temperature of loose surface soils may change very rapidly, and such soils show the greatest extremes in temperature (see Part I). Heat losses from the soil surface may so modify the temperature of the air just above the ground surface as to reduce appreciably the incidence and severity of frost damage to plant shoots. As an illustration, killing frosts are less frequent on mineral soils than on organic soils similarly situated. The effectiveness of the soil in raising the above-ground air temperature depends on a number of factors, including the heat-transfer characteristics of the soil, its moisture content, and the type of cover on the soil surface. The opportunities to reduce frost damage by suitable management practices, which control heat transfers at the surface of the soil, have only recently been appreciated. This matter is discussed further in Part I and in the closing section.

High soil temperatures

In general, roots seem to be less resistant to injury by high temperatures than the aerial organs of plants. This behavior has been noted by a number of investigators, including Shirley (1936) who undertook a determination of the lethal high temperatures for conifers. He reported that for completely submerged young conifers the fibrous roots were killed before other parts of the plants. Under his conditions, an exposure of up to 5 hours at a temperature of 44.3°C. killed the roots but caused no severe damage to the tops. The various species of conifers showed little difference in their ability to withstand heat.

An interesting study of the effect of high soil temperatures on the survival of 15 species of turf grasses was reported by Carroll (1934). One group of plants had received no nitrogen fertilization; the other had been fertilized. Cores of grass sod in glass jars were heated in a water bath until a thermometer in the center of the sod plug indicated 50° in one test and 60°C. in a second. Heating required about 2 hours in each case. In a third test, the soil temperature was maintained at 50°C. for 4 hours. Merely bringing the soil temperature to 50°C. was not lethal in the low-nitrogen grasses but proved injurious to most of the high-nitrogen plants. Grass roots heated to 60° or held at 50°C. for 4 hours sustained much greater injury. Highland velvet bent (*Agrostis canina*) and Chewings fescue (*Festuca rubra fallax*) withstood the 4-hour exposure at 50°C. better than the other grasses. It is evident that the underground portions of many of these grasses cannot long endure soil temperatures between 50 and 60°C. In these experiments, injury seemed due to direct thermal effects upon the protoplasm of the exposed underground organs, inasmuch as the experiments were not continued long enough to bring about a starvation condition through increased respiration.

Julander (1945) suggested that the ability of crowns, rhizomes, and roots to withstand heat, as well as drought, may be an important factor determining the survival of range grasses in the hot and arid southwestern United States.   One should recognize that high soil temperatures are frequently accompanied by intense sunshine and extremes of drought that aggravate the resultant plant damage.   The crown and rhizomes of some plants and the roots of seedlings and shallow-rooted plants may be damaged by excessive soil temperatures; most roots of deeper rooting species develop far enough below the surface to escape injury.   However, with plants grown in containers and exposed to direct insolation, root damage may be serious.   The danger of root injury is increased by the tendency of roots to be concentrated in a layer just inside the container walls.

The distribution of roots through the upper portion of the soil profile is apparently influenced by soil temperature in some situations.   The depth distributions of the roots of cherry, almond, apricot, prune, peach, and pear trees growing in a deep well-drained soil in a clean-cultivated orchard were studied by Proebsting (1943) during the summer months at Davis, Calif.   Counts obtained in trench excavations showed very few roots in the surface foot, with most of these in the 8- to 12-inch depth, and a maximum concentration of roots between the 2- and 5-foot depths in most cases.   These root distribution patterns differ from those reported for more humid sections, particularly in the surface foot. Since cultivation was rarely deeper than 4 inches and since water loss by surface evaporation in this irrigated orchard would not dry out the soil below the 6- to 8-inch depth, Proebsting concluded that neither cultivation nor lack of moisture could be responsible for the poorer root growth in the 6- to 12-inch depth.   He suggested that the high soil temperatures prevailing in the surface foot in this clean-cultivated orchard inhibited the development of roots.   Data taken nearby (Smith, 1929) indicated that soil temperatures in Proebsting's orchard may have exceeded the temperatures shown by Nightingale (1935) and also by Proebsting [see Figure 78] to cause poor root growth.   The lack of feeder roots near the surface of the soil may be of importance not only for normal nutrition but also for the absorption of fertilizers which may be fixed in the surface soil.

Young stem tissues near the ground level may be killed by high soil temperatures at the soil surface.   This injury is generally first recognized by the formation of a discolored band of tissue a few millimeters wide around the stem.   Shrinkage of the affected tissue usually follows, and later the stem above the injured zone may swell.   Still later, the plants break over near the ground level.   This type of injury is often called "heat-canker."   It has been observed in seedlings and occasionally in young plants of flax, buckwheat, wheat, and barley (Reddy and

Brentzel, 1922); rye and cowpeas (Hartley, 1918); beans (MacMillan and Byars, 1920); parsley and carrots (Beach, 1946); cucumbers (Heald, 1933); cotton (the author[2]); ash (Tubeuf, 1914); beech (Münch, 1913); and several conifers (Hartley, 1918); Baker, 1929;

FIGURE 92A.—Four flax plants of the same age: Heat-cankered plants on left; normal plants on right. See Fig. 92B for enlarged photograph of stem and root system. (Adapted from Reddy and Brentzel, 1922.)

and others). This stem injury is often more serious on saline soils, where the damage may be caused by a combination of high temperature and excess salts (Beach, 1946). Serious loss of stand may occur. In unshaded portions of experimental flax plots at Fargo, N. Dakota (Heald, 1933, p. 151) reported that 37.2 to 46 percent of the plants were cankered. Some heat damage to cotton seedlings occurs nearly every

[2] Unpublished observations.

year in California,[2] although here it seems of little economic importance.

Heald believed that heat injury to young seedlings is probably much more common than recorded experiences indicate. Bates and Roeser (1924) suggested that high soil temperatures may determine what species of forest trees become established and in some situations may

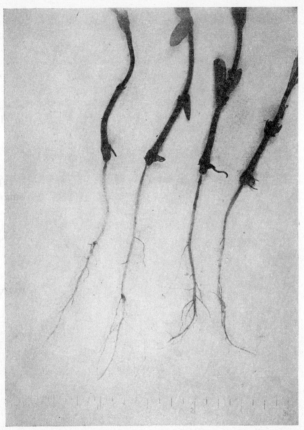

FIGURE 92B.—Enlargement of the heat-cankered plants from Fig. 92A to show the constricted portion of the stem and the enlargement of the stem above the injury. Adventitious roots, shown starting at the soil line, occur only if the surface soil is moist. (Adapted from Reddy and Brentzel, 1922.)

prevent natural reproduction. Heat injury of newly germinated seedlings was recognized by McQuilkin (1949) as an obstacle to reforestation by direct-seeding methods. He pointed out that even transplanted nursery stock may be damaged by high surface-soil temperatures.

The symptoms of heat canker so closely resemble pathogenic damping-off, which is caused by soil-inhabiting parasitic fungi, that the two are often confused. Microscopic examination of the tissue may be necessary to distinguish the nature of the injury. Such analyses are complicated by the fact that organisms often invade the tissues initially damaged by heat. Reddy and Brentzel's description of heat canker in flax may be summarized as follows:

Generally speaking, if the injury occurs when the plants are less than 3-inches high, the tissues collapse at the point of injury, and the plants wither and die. [See Figure 92.] If the injury occurs when the plants are 3- to 5-inches high, only the cortex is killed. These plants often topple over but usually remain alive for days or weeks because the vascular system has not been injured. Enlargement of the stem occurs just above and sometimes below the injury. In most cankered plants, the stem is eventually severed at the point of injury by winds or by disintegration of the remaining tissues through the action of micro-organisms. Otherwise, the plant dies when the starving roots can no longer support the increasing needs of the shoot.

Reddy and Brentzel reported that flax seedlings in a susceptible stage of growth may suffer heat-canker injury when the soil temperature at a depth of about ½ inch is near 54°C. Only in rare instances are flax plants more than 5-inches high seriously injured in this way.

Considerable attention has been given to heat injury in young coni-fers, where it frequently is called "white-spot" or "stem-girdle." Baker (1929) has carefully studied the progress of injury under strong radiant heat. While the first symptoms of injury vary, tiny white dots have indicated the onset of injury with nearly all species of conifers. The stem then darkens, followed by longitudinal wrinkling and, after several hours, by sufficient shrinkage to form a distinct constriction. The death of injured plants is often due to secondary attacks by fungi. Young conifers as much as 4 years old are reported to show heat-canker oc-casionally (Hartley, 1918). Canker seldom girdles the stem in older plants but usually develop on the south side (Korstian and Fetherolf, 1924) and are rarely fatal. Injury to the seedlings of some conifers may occur at soil temperatures of about 45°, but other species tolerate surface-soil temperatures as high as 70°C. without injury (Daubenmire, 1943).

As would be expected, heat-canker is most serious on relatively bare soils of dark color exposed to full sunlight. In some situations, a firmly crusted surface with the soil packed around the seedling is reported to increase the severity of injury (Heald, 1933, p. 151), but in others, a loose soil apparently causes more serious damage. Heat-canker may be controlled in annual crops by seeding early so that seedlings pass the susceptible stage before the advent of hot weather, or by adopting cul-tural practices that partially shade the soil surface. Using higher rates of seeding and drilling rows north and south instead of east and west have been suggested (Reddy and Brentzel, 1922). Stem-girdle in young forest tree plantings have been controlled by inclining the trees slightly to the south at the time of transplanting (Korstian and Fetherolf, 1921).

The aerial portions of plants may be injured as a result of root damage produced by high soil temperatures. These conditions, by accelerating root maturation, greatly reduce the absorbing root surface (Nightingale, 1935, and others). This reduction in root surface and the consequent retardation in water uptake were thought by Gray (1941) to account for the leaf scorch observed in strawberry plants at high soil temperatures. Although the roots of a plant may be killed by high temperatures, the plant may remain unwilted for several days under some conditions (Kramer, 1933).

Arndt (1937) heated the roots of cotton plants in solution culture to a temperature of 60°C. in 30 minutes and held them at that temperature for 75 minutes. A similar treatment was given plants with roots in soil. During the period the roots were heated, some wilting occurred in the soil-culture plants, but the leaves were turgid by the next day. A distinct retardation in the rate of transpiration from the water-culture plants was not noticeable until the third day. All plants showed conspicuous light-colored areas between the veins of the older leaves within 60 minutes after the roots reached a temperature of about 60°C. After the roots cooled, these areas disappeared, but reappeared a day or two later as conspicuous yellow or yellow-brown areas. Leaves so affected became abnormally rigid and leathery, never recovered, and eventually fell from the plant. Arndt doubted that this leaf discoloration was caused by an inadequate water supply to the leaves. He suggested that some toxic substance formed in injured roots and carried to the leaves— possibly in the transpiration stream—may have produced the leaf discoloration.

Soil Temperature and Plant Diseases

The occurrence and severity of some soil- and seed-borne diseases that often seriously impair growth are often related to soil temperatures. They may account for the geographical distribution and the relative prevalence of certain diseases at different seasons of the year and from one year to another. An excellent discussion of this subject has been given by Garrett (1944). For the convenience of the reader, a summary of some aspects of this subject is presented in the following paragraphs:

Among the diseases in which soil temperature has been shown to play a prominent role are the following, listed by Wingard (1941):

The seedling blight of cereals (*Gibberella saubinetti*); take-all disease of wheat (*Ophiobolus graminis*); wheat and barley *Helminthosporium* diseases; seedling blight of corn (*Diplodia*); flax wilt (*Fusarium lini*); tobacco black shank (*Phytophthora parastica*); root rot (*Thielaviopsis basicola*); pea blight (*Fusarium*) and root rot (*Aphanomyces*); tomato wilt (*Fusarium bulbigenum*); potato stem canker (*Rhizoctonia solani*); onion smut (*Urocystis cepulae*); and cabbage yellows (*Fusarium conglutinans*).

At favorable soil temperatures, certain diseases may produce almost complete destruction of a crop, but under different soil temperatures, they may cause very little damage or may appear to be entirely absent. Phymatotrichum root rot, which affects more than 2,000 different cultivated and wild plants and causes severe loss of cotton in Texas, Arizona, and Mexico, is limited to southwestern North America (Dickson, 1947). The northern boundary of infection is apparently determined by winter soil temperatures (Ezekiel, 1945). On the other hand, onion smut, a low-temperature disease, has become established across the Northern States where onion seed is planted in cool soil. In the Gulf States, where this disease has been regularly introduced with onion sets, it can be found only when the crop is grown during the coldest part of the growing season (Chupp, 1946). This smut was recently found in August plantings in the hot interior valley of California by Kendrick and Stevenson (1949). This outbreak had not been expected in view of the hot weather prevailing in this area at planting time. However, while the daytime air temperatures are relatively high, the night temperatures are relatively low. These workers found the average air temperature was well within the range previously reported (Walker and L. R. Jones, 1921) for abundant infection. The frequent irrigation practiced in this area also contributed to cooling the soil sufficiently to permit infection.

Bewley (1922) called attention to an interesting shift in the relative prevalence of fusarium and verticillium wilts of tomato as the growing season progressed in England. He reported that verticillium wilt appeared about the middle of April and increased in severity up to the second or third week of May. The attacks died down during the latter half of June and in July and August but reappeared at the end of September. The occurrence of this wilt on guayule in the San Joaquin Valley of California follows a very similar pattern (Schneider, 1944). Fusarium wilt, Bewley (1922) found on the other hand, occurred only during the hottest portion of the tomato growing season, usually in July and August. In California, fusarium wilt of tomato is serious only in the warm central valleys.

Soil temperature may influence the occurrence of soil-borne diseases in a number of ways. Most important is its direct influence upon the parasitic activity of the infecting organism and upon the resistance of the host. Its effect upon the survival of the causative organism between susceptible crops may also be important in some diseases. Garrett suggested the following generalization:

Soil conditions (including soil temperature) will exert the greatest direct influence upon those root-infecting fungi that spread chiefly by mycelium external to the host, and the greatest indirect influence, through the physiology of the host, upon the fungi that spread only inside the host.

It is now generally believed that soil temperature influences the incidence and severity of most plant diseases through its effect on both the host and the pathogen. In some diseases, the soil temperatures producing the most severe outbreak are also optimum for the growth of the organism. Examples are cabbage yellows (Tisdale, 1923), tomato wilt (Clayton, 1923) and flax wilt (L. R. Jones and Tisdale, 1922) caused by different species of Fusaria.

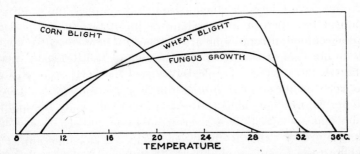

FIGURE 93.—Influence of incubator temperatures upon the growth of *Gibberella saubinetti* compared to the effect of corresponding soil temperatures upon the seedling blights in corn and wheat caused by the fungus. (From L. R. Jones, 1924, based on work of Dickson *et al.*, 1923.)

A splendid example of the importance of the temperature relations of the host is found in the classical work of Dickson (1923). He showed that a single fungus, *Gibberella saubinetti*, which produces seedling blight in corn and wheat, had widely different soil-temperature optima for development in these two hosts. Seedling blight was most serious in corn at soil temperatures of 8 to 20°, whereas wheat seedlings were affected most severely at 16 to 28°C. These relations are shown in the graph of Figure 93. In each case, the disease was most severe at temperatures unfavorable to the growth of the host seedling. In onion smut also, the rate of development of the onion seedling has a decided influence on the severity of the disease (Walker and Jones, 1921).

The importance of the effect of temperature on both the host and the pathogen has been stressed in the work of Leach (1947). In his study of eight combinations of hosts and pathogens, he reported that preemergence damping-off was most prevalent at temperatures relatively less favorable to the host than to the pathogen, as measured by their growth rates. The lower the ratio of the growth rate of the host to that of the pathogen, the more severe was the preemergence damping-off. Leach suggested that ratios below 1, which indicate the growth rate of the pathogen exceeds that of the host, represent a high probability for severe preemergence infection. As the ratios increased from 1 to 4 the probability of preemergence infection was lessened, while ratios of 4 were associated with a total absence of diseased plants. Beach (1946) has reached similar conclusions.

These studies just cited explain why, in general, high-temperature crops such as corn and cotton are more subject to seed decay and preemergence damage at low than at high soil temperatures; whereas low-temperature crops such as wheat, peas, and spinach often suffer less infection at low than at intermediate or high temperatures, provided other environmental conditions are similar. These relations also contribute to our understanding of the factors involved in the occurrence of certain diseases. For example, with sugar beets and a rapid-growing fungus such as *Pythium ultimum*, the growth-rate ratio is less than 1 at temperatures favorable to the fungus, and severe preemergence infection appears. With a slow-growing fungus, *Aphanomyces cochlioides*, the growth-ratio lies between 2.5 to 3.2 at temperatures most favorable to the fungus, and infection by this organism is limited almost entirely to the postemergence stage.

The infection susceptibility of seedlings as related to anatomical and chemical changes in the host accompanying its growth has been considered by Dickson and Holbert (1926) and by McClure and Robbins (1942). Resistance to infection is apparently related directly to the extent the cell walls of the tissues have become lignified. Any environmental conditions, including soil moisture, aeration, mineral nutrition, and light, that retard the development of the host will increase its susceptibility to infection.

Data on the cardinal soil temperatures for the incidence of diseases affecting the common crop plants may be found in numerous papers scattered through the literature. Convenient references have been prepared by Dickson (1947) for field crops and by Walker (1939) for vegetable crops.

By studying seasonal soil temperatures, one is sometimes able to plant certain crops within escape periods for specific pathogens or, at least, to avoid the period of most severe infection. If plantings of susceptible crops must be made during the period favorable for infection, then seed treatment is imperative; and one should select the specific treatment most effective against the organism or organisms most likely to be favored by the given soil temperature (Leach, 1947).

IV. SOIL TEMPERATURE AND GROWTH OF MICRO-ORGANISMS

By T. M. McCalla

Temperature is important in the reproduction, growth, and activities of soil micro-organisms. Since the micro-organisms are intimately dispersed throughout the soil, their temperature is similar to that of the soil. The soil temperature may vary over a wide range. The temperature requirements and tolerance of different micro-organisms may also vary between wide limits. Some microscopic forms will actually increase in numbers at 0°C. Some fungi may develop at —6°C. At the other temperature extreme, thermophiles will grow at 65 to 70°C. in composts. Hot-spring algae may grow at temperatures of 93°C. However, the majority of soil micro-organisms grow best at temperatures of 10 to 40°C. Growth at temperatures above the optimum for a particular organism may result in changes that are abnormal. Holding or incubating the organism at temperatures below the optimum for growth does not usually affect it adversely, except that growth may be retarded.

Temperature influences every physical or chemical process vital to microscopic plants. The processes involved are solution and diffusion of nutrients; absorption of water, gases, and nutrients; and reproduction. These processes, separate and integrated, affect the growth and activity of the microscopic plants.

The influence of temperature on the number of micro-organisms in the soil and on such microbial activities as decomposition of organic matter, ammonification and nitrification, nodule production, and soil aggregation will be presented.

Distribution, Growth, and Numbers

Temperature limits to a great extent the distribution and kinds of microscopic plants in the surface soil over the earth.

When a few micro-organisms of a single kind are placed in a favorable environment, a change in temperature toward the optimum will usually result in an increase in the number and activity of the micro-organisms. This has been shown with micro-organisms in culture media (Buchanan and Fulmer, 1930). For the majority of micro-organisms the range of temperatures favorable for most activity is between 10 and 40°C. However, conditions other than temperature soon become the limiting factors, and the growth rate decreases or may even become negative. Conditions unfavorable for growth may be reached in a shorter time at a higher temperature. The factors influencing growth may change in quantitative relationship at different temperatures; for example, nutrients may be required in different concentrations at a higher temperature.

TABLE 59.—*Effect of temperature on the number of bacteria in the soil (Russell and Hutchinson, 1929)*

Temperature in degrees centigrade	Millions bacteria per gram dry soil after incubation for—				Millions bacteria per gram dry soil treated with toluene after incubation for—			
	0 days	13 days	25 days	70 days	0 days	13 days	25 days	70 days
5 to 12	65	63	41	32	8.5	73	101	137
20	65	41	22	23	8.5	187	128	182
30	65	27	50	16	8.5	197	145	51
40	65	14	9	33	8.5	148	52	100

The growth curve for micro-organisms growing in a suitable culture medium is usually sigmoid in shape but not symmetrical. About all that can be said about the influence of temperature is that it affects the form of the growth curve (Buchanan and Fulmer, 1930). Temperature within the range 0 to 50°C. also affects such things as the time for spore formation. An increase in temperature until the optimum is reached decreases the time for spore formation, and temperatures higher than the optimum lengthen it. Furthermore, temperatures above 40°C. may cause changes in the morphology and physiology of some micro-organisms. Within the normal growth range, the rapidity, direction, and duration of movement of micro-organisms may be influenced by temperature.

The relationship of factors regulating the growth of micro-organisms in the soil is somewhat more complicated than in culture media. There is competition among the various microbial groups in the soil. Factors other than temperature may also be limiting. Russell and Hutchinson, 1912 (Table 59), found that in a soil the number of micro-organisms was not maintained at the initial level when incubation temperatures were 5 to 50°C. When the soil was partially sterilized with toluene and then incubated at different temperatures, there was an increase in number of organisms with the rising temperature until the optimum was reached. The optimum temperatures seemed to be between 20 and 30°.

Greaves and Jones (1944) incubated soils for 24 months at 10, 20, 30, and 40°C. and found that at optimum moisture conditions the most organisms developed at 10° and the fewest at 40°. Likewise, Bryan (1935) found that the total bacteria increased in soil stored at 25, 7, and —20°. The increase at the first two temperatures was due to multiplication of the bacteria, and the increase at —20° seems to have been due to a breaking up of clumps of bacteria that resulted in a higher count by the plate method of estimating numbers.

Incubation of a soil at different temperatures, as shown by Russell and Hutchinson (1912–13) did not produce significant changes in the number of organisms in the unsterile soil except in a few instances. A high soil temperature may be unfavorable for maintaining large numbers. However, the number of organisms present in the soil is not necessarily an indication of the activity of the organisms at different temperatures. A cell at 0°C. is largely in a resting state, while at 30° considerable respiration may be taking place. The response obtained by the maintenance of soil temperatures favorable for microscopic plant growth is dependent also upon the favorable regulation of other factors at that temperature level.

When the soil was partially sterilized with toluene and then incubated at different temperatures, results were obtained similar to those with culture medium. The numbers of organisms increased with higher incubation temperature up to 20 to 30°C. Temperatures of 40 to 50° were harmful (Russell and Hutchinson, 1912–13).

Soil micro-organisms in the field usually increase in number and activity in autumn and spring and drop in both during winter and summer. This difference is due to changes in soil temperature, moisture, and other factors (Bryan, 1935).

Decomposition of Organic Matter

In the decomposition of organic matter in soils, temperature and moisture are important climatic factors. Microbiological decomposition of organic matter probably accounts for a major part of the carbon losses from the soil. Since biological activity generally increases two or three times for each 10°C. rise in temperature (Van't Hoff's rule) increased decomposition of organic matter is expected in warmer soils. The rule holds up to 20 to 30° for microscopic forms. At higher temperatures the rate of change decreases and becomes zero or even negative (Fig. 94). Jenny, in 1928, studied soils from Canada to the Gulf of Mexico and found that the nitrogen content was in agreement with the concept that temperature is a principal factor in determining the nitrogen content of the soil (Figs. 95 and 96). Since microbial decomposition results in the loss of organic matter and the liberation of nitrogen, and as this loss is intensified by higher temperatures, he found

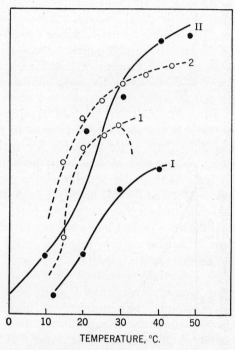

FIGURE 94.—Relation between microbiological activity in soils and temperature: I and II, CO_2 evolution, after Wollny; 1 and 2, denitrification and ammonification respectively, after Panganiban (Jenny, 1928).

that "the nitrogen content of the soil decreases exponentially when the temperature increases, provided similar humidity factors are operative." This statement also holds for humus and organic carbon content. The exceptions are for soils in swamps, river bottoms, lake borders, Southern peat and muck soils, or soils on steep slopes.

Jenny *et al.* (1948) found that a nitrogen-climate surface constructed for Colombian soils of South America had the same shape as that for soils of the Great Plains. However, the magnitude of the constants in the two equations differed. Colombian soils having annual temperature and moisture values equal to those of North American

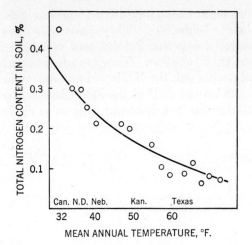

FIGURE 95.—Average total nitrogen content of the soil as related to the mean annual temperature in the semiarid region (Jenny, 1928).

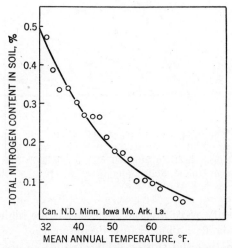

FIGURE 96.—Average total nitrogen content of the soil as related to the mean annual temperature in the semihumid region (Jenny, 1928).

soils were much higher in nitrogen and organic matter (Fig. 97). It was found that many light-colored soils from the hot, humid areas were rich in organic matter and nitrogen. The nitrogen levels of the tropical soils were similar to the nitrogen levels of soils in the Red River Valley near the Canadian border.

Waksman and Gerretsen (1931) in a study of the decomposition of fresh oat straw at different temperatures found that the higher the temperature, the more rapid was the decomposition of the plant material as a whole (Table 60). They found that loss of the ether-soluble substances, the hemicelluloses and cellulose, increased with the temperature of incubation. Temperature influenced the decomposition of lignin, although the lignin did not decompose so fast as the cellulose. At 37°C. about half of the lignin in the plant material was decomposed in 9 months, but there was little or no decomposition of the lignin at 7°. At lower temperatures the organisms bringing about

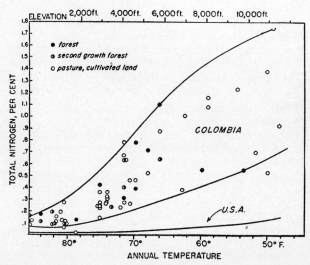

FIGURE 97.—Relationship of soil nitrogen, elevation, and corresponding annual temperature. Each point represents an individual sample. The curve *U.S.A.* represents the nitrogen latitude function of the originally timbered soils of midwestern and eastern United States (Jenny *et al.*, 1948). (Reprinted with permission of Williams and Wilkins Co.)

synthesizing activity were favored, whereas at the higher temperatures those bringing about a more rapid decomposition were more active. It was concluded that the slower decomposition of the organic matter as a whole and the high carbon content of the lignin explained the wider carbon-nitrogen ratio of the organic matter in soils of colder regions as compared with soils of warmer climates. This is in agreement with Jenny's concept.

When the decomposition of organic matter is measured by the production of carbon dioxide from plant materials incubated at different temperatures, the influence of temperature is most pronounced at the beginning of the decomposition. After 4 or 5 days, the rate of decomposition at all temperatures becomes equal. Waksman and Gerretsen (1931) showed that increases in temperature from 7°C. to 18 and from 18 to 27 resulted in sharp increases in CO_2 production. The difference between 27 and 37° was much smaller. After 21 days the rate of decomposition was similar at all temperatures. Optimum temperature for decomposition was reached at about 27°. The quantities of CO_2 produced between the 16th and 105th days at 7, 18, 27, and 37° were 400, 520, 460, and 480 milligrams, respectively. The CO_2 produced during the last period of 105 to 168 days was 188 milligrams

TABLE 60.—*Compost left after decomposition at different temperatures for various periods (Waksman and Gerretsen, 1931)*

Temperature of incubation	Moisture content	Percentage of total original material left after incubation for—			
		16 days	48 days	105 days	273 days
°C.	*Percent*				
7[a]	66	....	....	99.4	76.4
7	66	....	....	73.7	64.3
7	80	....	....	77.8	63.7
18	66	....	63.3	53.2	49.5
18	80	81.1	60.2	46.7	39.2
27[a]	66	....	72.0	56.0	36.4
27	66	66.7	51.2	44.1	35.3
27	80	67.5	46.4	37.6	29.9
37[a]	66	....	72.1	51.8	40.1
37	66	64.2	48.6	39.8	30.0
37	80	61.0	39.4	32.0	23.6

[a] Compost without nutrient salts.

at 37° and 178 milligrams at 7°, or 1.12 and 1.06 milligrams of CO_2 per day, respectively.

Waksman and Gerretsen (1931) point out that the "data bring out surprisingly the one important fact, namely, that within wide limits the rate of decomposition of organic matter is independent of temperature within a few weeks after the beginning of the process." Their data indicate that temperature effects the rate of decomposition mainly during the early stages of decomposition. In addition to affecting the rate of decomposition, temperature may influence the kind of decomposition brought about and also the quantity and quality of organic matter synthesized by the micro-organisms active in the decomposition process.

Ammonification and Nitrification

Ammonification and nitrification are two important biological processes that go on in the soil.   Nitrogen is made available to crops at critical times as a result of these processes.   Fortunately, the temperature at which nitrification occurs coincides with the temperatures at which higher plants develop.   Nitrification is virtually at a standstill in frozen soils.   As the frozen soils warm up, the nitrifying organisms begin to produce nitrates.   Higher plants begin to grow and use the nitrates.   The warming up of the soil results in an increased nitrification rate which coincides with the increased plant requirements.   This

TABLE 61.—*Production of ammonia in soils with 1 percent casein added at optimum moisture after 5 days of incubation at different temperatures (Panganiban, 1925)*

Incubation temperature	Milligrams ammonia (NH_3-N) produced per 100 grams of soil in—		
	Soil 1	Soil 2	Soil 3
°C.			
15	46	45	43
20	58	54	47
25	62	55	50
30	66	56	51
35	69	58	52
40	71	69	53

temperature control over nitrification may not only conserve soil nitrogen but also regulate its production in an available form to fit plant needs.

Greaves and Jones (1944) found that ammonia production, in peptone solution at 30°C. after 72 hours of incubation, was greatest for the soils stored for 6, 12, and 18 months at 10° and least in those stored at 40°C.   This finding would indicate that storage at lower temperatures was more beneficial than storage at higher temperatures.

Ammonification increased in three types of soil as the incubation temperature increased up to 40°C. (Table 61).   Panganiban (1925) found that maintaining a range of constant temperatures increased ammonification up to 40°.   He also found that a variation of temperature was beneficial.   Alternating the temperature with a variation of 15° between 25 and 40°C., 20 and 35°, or 15 and 30° seemed to be equally favorable.

Temperatures of 65.5°C. resulted in partial soil sterilization

(Grosby, 1911). The high temperature, resulting in partial steriliza-tion, later led to greater microbial activity and increased ammoni-fication.

Soil temperature may influence the immediate rate of ammonifica-tion by its direct effect on microbial enzymes and chemical reactions. The soil temperature may also destroy many micro-organisms that will serve as food for other organisms. This would lead to new microbial decomposition under favorable conditions and would usually result in higher ammonification.

As shown in Table 62 Tandon and Dhar (1934) found that nitrite was produced at a more rapid rate as the temperature increased in cul-ture solution. About 35°C. was the most favorable temperature. At 40° the production of nitrite was retarded.

TABLE 62.—*Amount of nitrite formed at various temperatures in culture solution (Tandon and Dhar, 1934)*[a]

	Nitrite (NO_2 as N) found at temperature of—						
Time (hours)	0°C.	15°C.	20°C.	25°C.	30°C.	35°C.	40°C.
	p.p.m.	p.p.m.	p.p.m.	p.p.m.	p.p.m.	p.p.m.	p.p.m
67	0.25	0.15	1.16	5.0	7.9	8.8	0.64
115	.28	.28	1.75	8.5	23.0	43.8	.68
187	.28	.65	2.95	26.5	67.3	143.8	.95
235	.28	2.16	4.46	57.9	102.6	271.5	1.41
259	.28	....	5.59	85.8	125.9	358.5	1.71

[a] Reprinted with permission of Williams and Wilkins Co.

The production of nitrite takes place at temperatures that corre-spond to those optimum for plant growth and ammonification. Thus it is possible for the ammonia produced during ammonification to be oxidized to nitrites at the same temperature.

The production of nitrates is also influenced by temperature condi-tions. The incubation of soil at 10 or 20°C. for 24 months resulted in a permanent change in the nitrifying flora. In part of the soils incubated at 40° the ability to produce nitrates was lost (Greaves and Jones, 1944).

Russel *et al.* (1925) showed that nitrate production was compara-tively slow at 5°C. (Table 63). At 35° nitrate production reached a maximum. Above 35° nitrification became slower and at 55°C. it ceased altogether. Fuller and Jones (1932) found 25 to 30° to be a more favorable temperature for nitrification in most instances than

35°C. Russel *et al.* (1925) estimated that if an average soil temperature of 15°C. prevailed for 8 to 10 weeks during the spring, only enough nitrate would be produced for 10 to 12 bushels of wheat in the soil at Lincoln, Nebr.; whereas under the same condition on soil at North Platte, Nebr., enough nitrate would be formed to produce 30 bushels of wheat. The higher level of nitrate production at North Platte than at Lincoln is due to the character of the soil or to the nitrifying organisms. Other results showed that summer temperatures in Nebraska were sufficiently high for nitrate production.

TABLE 63.—*Nitrate nitrogen produced at different temperatures at Lincoln, Nebr. (Russel et al., 1925)*[a]

[Soil at moisture equivalent. Initial content nitrate nitrogen, 4 parts per million]

	Quantity after—			
Temperature	1 day	8 days	15 days	29 days
°C.	p.p.m.	p.p.m.	p.p.m.	p.p.m.
6.9	0.4	2.6	2.7	2.2
15.1	.4	3.1	3.7	4.3
22.9	1.4	4.9	8.1	9.1
25.4	1.9	6.1	8.7	11.7
34.5	3.7	14.4	22.5	30.1
48.3	3.0	13.8	14.8	11.1
55.0	.2	−1.5	−2.2	

[a] Reprinted with permission of Williams and Wilkins Co.

The processes of ammonification and nitrification take place largely at soil temperatures between 5 and 40°C. and are more rapid toward the upper end of the range. Temperatures on either end of this range are unfavorable for ammonification or nitrification and for the growth of most plants.

Legume Bacteria (*Rhizobium sp.*)

In general the temperature favorable for the growth of the legume bacteria (rhizobia) coincides with the optimum temperature for the host plant. Since the organisms make very little growth at refrigeration temperatures, refrigeration is a good way to keep cultures of the organisms in a viable condition for long periods of time. Legume bacteria have survived exposures at −190°C. Freezing of the soil during winter is not believed to have much effect on legume bacteria. Soil temperature at the immediate surface of the soil in summer may reach levels detrimental to these bacteria. A temperature of 60°C.

for 2 or 3 minutes will destroy legume bacteria in a water suspension (Fred, Baldwin, and McCoy, 1932). However, below the surface inch, summer temperatures are probably not high enough to endanger their survival.

Allison and Minor (1940) observed that rhizobia made optimum growth in culture media at 29°C. At 37° no growth occurred, except with *Rhizobium meliloti*, which required a temperature of 41° to stop its growth. At 15° the growth rate of the micro-organisms in culture was about one-fourth to one-half as great as at 30°C. The generation time of some legume organisms in culture media are shown in Table 64.

TABLE 64.—*Generation time[a] of rhizobia at different temperatures (Allison and Minor, 1940)[b]*

Organism	Generation time at—							
	15.3°C.	21°C.	25°C.	30°C.	35°C.	37°C.	39°C.	41°C.
	Hours	*Hours*	*Hours*	*Hours*	*Hours*	*Hours*	*Hours*	*Hours*
Rhizobium trifolii 209	6.5	4.0	3.4	3.2	c	c	...	
R. leguminosarum 302	5.8	...	3.3	2.9	5.4	c	c	
R. phaseoli 402	7.7	...	3.3	2.9	3.3	4.4	c	c
R. op. from Dalea 900	9.0	4.7	3.0	2.5	2.6	...	...	
R. meliloti 131	8.2	3.9	2.8	2.1	2.0	2.0	2.0	c

[a] Generation time is defined as the length of time it takes a cell to grow to its full size, divide, and form two individuals.
[b] Reprinted with permission of Williams and Wilkins Co.
[c] No visible growth in 24 hours.

Soil Aggregation

Soil temperature influences the growth of micro-organisms and the amount of their decomposition products. These organisms and their decomposition products have been shown to influence the structure of the soil (McCalla, 1945; Martin and Craggs, 1946). The rate and kind of decomposition being different at low and high temperatures would be expected to affect the amount and persistence of soil aggregation.

Martin and Craggs, (1946) found that as the incubation temperature increased from 10 to 55°C., granulation and the time required for maximum aggregation decreased (Table 65). Organic materials more or less resistant to decomposition, compared with more readily decomposable types, were relatively more effective in increasing aggregation at high than at low temperatures. At the lower temperatures the readily available organic materials were more effective in improving

TABLE 65.—*Influence of temperature of incubation on soil-aggregating effect of organic residues (Martin and Craggs, 1946)*

Incubation temperature and treatment[a]	Percentage particles smaller than 50 microns after 5 days incubation	Percentage soil particles less than 50 microns bound into water-stable aggregates greater than 50 microns at incubation periods of—					Mean of treatments
		5 days	10 days	20 days	50 days	100 days	
Dispersed soil	49.0	0	0	0	0	0	
10°C. incubation temperature:							
Control	39.7	19	30	31	32	33	
Alfalfa hay	22.1	55	60	71	73	68	
Alfalfa-grass hay	25.5	48	56	67	70	66	
Sucrose	9.0	82	71	73	66	59	
Mean....................		51	54	61	60	57	57
25°C. incubation temperature:							
Control	38.5	22	31	31	32	31	
Alfalfa hay	17.5	64	69	66	66	58	
Alfalfa-grass hay	18.0	63	66	67	64	57	
Sucrose	14.1	71	70	62	58	50	
Mean....................		55	59	57	55	49	55
40°C. incubation temperature:							
Control	35.8	27	32	31	29	30	
Alfalfa hay	14.3	71	67	58	57	54	
Alfalfa-grass hay	18.4	62	59	57	56	51	
Sucrose	18.4	62	58	54	51	46	
Mean....................		56	54	50	48	45	51
55°C. incubation temperature:							
Control	34.0	31	30	32	30	31	
Alfalfa hay	24.6	50	49	50	43	41	
Alfalfa-grass hay	23.1	53	52	53	50	41	
Sucrose	24.2	51	48	47	41	34	
Mean....................		46	45	46	41	37	43

[a] Organic substances added in 2-percent concentration. Ammonium sulfate and potassium phosphate added with sucrose.

soil structure than the resistant manure. Furthermore, a longer time was required for maximum aggregation to take place and better aggregation was produced at lower than at higher temperatures. This temperature effect may be explained in two ways. At various temperature levels different microbial groups are involved in the decomposition process. A microbial population active at a low temperature may produce a greater quantity of a better aggregating substance than it would produce at a high temperature. Since high temperatures favor more rapid decomposition of organic matter, it is possible that at the higher temperatures effective organic-aggregating substances are produced that are rapidly destroyed through the activities of microorganisms. The shorter incubation period for maximum aggregation at higher temperatures, followed by a rapid decline in aggregation, supports this view. At low temperatures, the synthesizing activity of the micro-organisms may be high.

V. MANAGEMENT AND SOIL TEMPERATURE

By T. M. McCalla

Microbial Activity

Soil temperature has several important effects on the development and activity of micro-organisms. The level of organic matter and nitrogen in the soil, nitrogen fixation, production of available nitrogen, decomposition of residues, and the degree of aggregation all depend on a suitable temperature for microbial activity.

It is obvious that climate fixes the broad limits of soil temperatures and therefore the level of microbial activity. It is very difficult to maintain organic matter at levels higher than the level in equilibrium with plant production and microbial decomposition. However, within the limits fixed by climate, some things can be done to change soil temperature in order to control the various microbial activities essential to the development of higher plants and to the maintenance of soil productivity. Such a practice as tilling to let the soil dry out will change the soil temperature. Mulching of the soil with plant residues such as straw is another method of changing soil temperature. Under natural conditions mulches are composed of duff in forest and of grass litter in pastures. These mulches, through their effect on soil temperature, affect the activities of micro-organisms. Probably much of the reduction in corn yields sometimes encountered with mulching of soil with straw is due to a reduction in soil temperature and its effect on the microflora and plant nutrients. The nitrification rate is usually lower in mulched than in unmulched soil. Accompanying the lower soil temperature in mulched soil may be a slightly higher moisture content that may limit the movement of gases into and out of the soil. Thus aeration, as well as temperature, may be a basic factor in limiting the activities of the nitrifying organisms in a mulched soil.

Numerous other methods of altering soil temperature for controlling microbial activity, such as irrigating with warm or cold water, site location, or the use of a shade, are available for both greenhouse and field purposes.

Crop Production

In crop production considerable emphasis is placed upon temperature, which must constantly be taken into consideration. For example, the time of planting and harvesting of a good many crops has to be watched carefully. The plant breeder is ever searching for new varieties that will mature earlier. Temperature is important from the time of seed germination until the crop is harvested. Either too low or too high a temperature may interfere with the harvesting of superior fruit, seed, foliage, or roots.

Site selection

Site selection in regard to its effect on soil and air temperature may be of considerable importance with certain crops. For example, north or south slopes may be chosen or rejected on the basis of whether the temperature will be favorable to the plant during the growing season. North slopes are sometimes selected because plants remain dormant for a longer period of time in the spring than on south slopes and may thus avoid frost damage. Plants that start growing during warm periods in late winter or early spring on south slopes are sometimes injured by frost during late cold snaps. Citrus fruits, as well as other crops, are sometimes planted high on the slope in order to allow air drainage that may help to prevent frost damage.

Crop selection

Consideration of temperature is of primary importance in selecting a crop for a particular region. Only those crops suitable to the particular air and soil temperature prevailing in a specific region are selected. Man has attempted to grow some plants in regions where the temperature is unsuitable. Almost every year there is extensive damage to crops somewhere in the border line areas of temperature change.

After a crop and a site for a specific plant have been selected there are a number of management practices that may be used to modify air and soil temperature. Probably one of the most important decisions in management is the selection of a proper planting date. Usually this date is selected with temperature as the primary consideration. For example, corn cannot be planted until danger of frost is over or until the ground is warm enough for the seed to germinate. In many regions and with many crops the seeds must be planted as soon as possible after cold weather so that the growing season may be of sufficient length. If there is plenty of time for the plant to grow, then the part of the season with the most favorable temperature should be selected. Some crops such as winter wheat are planted in the fall while weather is still warm enough for the seed to germinate, and the plant goes through the winter before producing seed the following spring.

Mulches

Mulches are used to reduce soil temperature in the summer and to prevent freezing in the winter. Cooler soil temperatures are desirable for some crops during hot summers. During the winter, crops such as strawberries need the protection from alternate freezing and thawing that mulches afford. In addition to reducing soil temperature, mulches may have other effects.

Shading

Shading the soil for temperature and light effects is used to varying degrees with different crops over a part or whole of a growing season. Coffee, tobacco, and lettuce are a few examples of crops that may be grown under a shade. Shading of the crop is accomplished by the use of cheesecloth, lath, or other plants. Seedlings such as tomatoes or lettuce plants set out in early spring may be covered with a cap made of paper or other material to capture the heat from the sun and to protect the plant from frost. By this method it is possible to set frost-susceptible plants out 2 or 3 weeks earlier than usual.

Shelter belts

Shelter belts made up of a row of boards 18 or 20 inches high, set at 10- to 15-feet intervals, are sometimes used to protect celery from cold temperatures. Other shelter belts of trees are sometimes used to protect plants against hot or cold temperatures.

Tillage

Tillage probably affects soil temperature indirectly. When a wet soil is loosened, it dries more rapidly than an unstirred soil. A dry soil warms more rapidly than a wet one. Fall-plowed land warms up more rapidly in the spring than unplowed land, and earlier planting in the tilled soil is possible. A mulch turned under allows the soil to warm up more rapidly.

Irrigation

Irrigation is another means of changing soil temperature. The use of hot or cold irrigating water in varying amounts where possible affords a method of changing soil temperature. Cranberry bogs are sometimes flooded to prevent freezing.

Drainage

Drainage probably affects soil temperature indirectly through its influence on drying the soil. A well-drained soil warms up more rapidly in the spring. In summer, some crops such as corn may be injured if hot water is allowed to stand on them.

Fertilizer

Fertilizer such as rock phosphate or soot may be spread on snow in early spring to hasten melting. This practice may permit earlier tilling and seeding of the soil. Fertilizers also should be applied before the time when temperatures are most favorable for maximum plant growth so that they can be used more efficiently by the plants. Temperature is probably important in determining the timing of various fertilizer applications.

Use of greenhouses, hot beds and cold frames

A greenhouse with adequate heating and cooling apparatus enables one to have complete control over soil and air temperatures. Plants of all types can be grown at all seasons of the year. Hot beds are used to control soil and air temperature for plant growth. A cold frame also controls soil and air temperature to some extent. Young plants are often transplanted to cold frames for hardening and to avoid frost and cold damage during weather too cold to transplant to the field.

Modification of above ground air layer

Frost damage to specialized crops may be averted by the use of smudge pots. This use is an attempt to change the temperature of the above-ground air layer. Spraying is sometimes used to prevent frost damage during cold weather of short duration. Stirring of the air with propellers has sometimes been used to reduce damage from cold.

Literature Cited

I. Soil Temperature

Allison, L. E.   1947.   Effect of micro–organisms on permeability of soil under prolonged submergence.   *Soil Sci.* **63**: 439–450. ˙

Baver, L. D.   1948.   Soil physics.   John Wiley and Sons, Inc., New York, pp. 288–310.

Becker, J. A., Green, C. B., and Pearson, G. L.   1946.   Properties and uses of thermistors–thermally sensitive resistors.   *Trans. Am. Inst. Elec. Engrs.* **65**: 1–15.

Bliss, D. E.   1944.   Air and soil temperatures in a California citrus orchard.   *Soil Sci.* **58**: 259–274.

Bliss, D. E., Moore, D. C., and Bream, C. E.   1942.   Air and soil temperatures in a California date garden.   *Soil Sci.* **53**: 55–64.

Bodman, G. B., and Day, P. R.   1937.   Thermoelectric method of determining the freezing points of soils.   *Soil Sci. Soc. Am. Proc.* **2**: 65–71.

Boelter, L. M. K., Cherry, V. H., Johnson, H. A., and Martinelli, R. C.   1948.   Heat transfer notes.   Univ. California Press, Berkeley, Calif.

Bouyoucos, G. J.   1913.   An investigation of soil temperature and some of the most important factors influencing it.   *Mich. Agr. Expt. Sta. Tech. Bull.* **17**: 1–196.

Bouyoucos, G. J.   1915.   Effect of temperature on some of the most important physical processes in soil.   *Mich. Agr. Expt. Sta. Tech. Bull.* **22**: 1–63.

Bouyoucos, G. J.   1916.   Soil temperature.   *Mich. Agr. Expt. Sta. Tech. Bull.* **26**: 1–133.

Brooks, F. A.   1936.   Solar energy and its use for heating water in California.   *Calif. Agr. Expt. Sta. Bull.* **602**: 1–64.

Brooks, F. A., Barbee, C. E., Kepner, R. A., and Lorenzen, C., Jr.   1941.   Temperature, its measurement and control in science and industry.   American Institute of Physics.   Reinhold Publishing Corp., New York, pp. 629–633.

Brooks, F. A., and Kelly, C. F.   1951.   Instrumentation for recording microclimatological factors.   *Am. Geophys. Union Trans.*   [In press.]

Brooks, F. A., Lorenzen, C., Jr., and Boelter, L. M. K.   1939.   Observations of nocturnal winter atmospheric radiation in California.   Amer. Met. Soc. Bull. **20**: 433–439.

Brown, E. M.   1943.   Seasonal variations in the growth and chemical composition of Kentucky bluegrass.   *Mo. Agr. Expt. Sta. Research Bull.* **360**: 1–56.

Buckingham, E.   1904.   Contribution to our knowledge of the aeration of soils.   *U. S. Dept. Agr., Bur. Soils Bull.* **25**: 1–52.

Buehrer, T. F.   1932.   The movement of gases through the soil as a criterion of soil structure.   *Ariz., Agr. Expt. Sta. Tech. Bull.* **39**: 1–57.

Burtch, L. M., Thorne, D. W., and Wann, F. B.   1948.   The effect of light, soil temperature, and soil moisture on high-lime chlorosis.   *Soil Sci. Soc. Am. Proc.* **13**: 394–398.

Carslaw, H. A.   1945.   Introduction to the mathematical theory of the conduction of heat in solids.   Dover Publications, New York.

Carter, H. G.   1928.   A comparison of air and soil temperature.   *Monthly Weather Rev.* **56**: 138–139.

Chapman, H. D., and Kelley, W. P.   1930.   The determination of the replaceable bases and the base-exchange capacity of soils.   *Soil Sci.* **30**: 391–406.

CHRISTIANSEN, J. E. 1944. Effect of entrapped air upon the permeability of soils. *Soil Sci.* **58:** 355–365.

COLMAN, E. A., and HENDRIX, T. M. 1949. The Fiberglas electrical soil moisture instrument. *Soil Sci.* **67:** 425–438.

DRAVID, R. K. 1940. Studies on soil temperatures in relation to other factors controlling the disposal of solar radiation. *Indian J. Agr. Sci.* **10:** 352–389.

EDLEFSEN, N. E., and ANDERSON, A. B. C. 1943. Thermodynamics of soil moisture. *Hilgardia* **15:** 31–298.

ELSASSER, W. M. 1942. Heat transfer by infrared radiation in the atmosphere. *Harvard Univ. Ser. No.* **6:** 1–107.

EVANS, D. D., and KIRKHAM, D. 1949. Measurement of the air permeability of soils in situ. *Soil Sci. Soc. Am. Proc.* **14:** 65–73.

EVERSON, J. N., and WEAVER, J. B. 1949. Effects of carbon black on the properties of soils. I. Effects on soil temperature. *Ind. Eng. Chem.* **41:** 1798.

FIREMAN, M., and MAGISTAD, O. C. 1945. Permeability of five western soils as affected by the percentage of sodium of the irrigation water. *Am. Geophys. Union Trans.* **26:** 91–94.

FITTON, E. M., and BROOKS, C. F. 1931. Soil temperatures in the United States. *Monthly Weather Rev.* **59:** 6–16.

FORTIER, S. 1926. Use of water in irrigation. McGraw-Hill Book Co., New York.

GIER, J. T., DUNKLE, R. V., and POSSNER, L. 1949. Measurements of hemispherical radiation and net radiation exchange. Rept. No. 10, code N. R.–014–062, contract N7–ONR–295, task 1.

GUILD, W. R. 1950. Note on heat transfer at the soil surface. *J. Meteorol.* **7:** 140–144.

HAGAN, R. M. 1941. Movement of carbon disulfide vapor in soils. *Hilgardia* **14:** 83–118.

HAISE, H. R., and KELLEY, O. J. 1950. Causes of diurnal fluctuations of tensiometers. *Soil Sci.* **70:** 301–314.

HAND, I. F. 1937. Review of United States Weather Bureau solar radiation investigations. *Monthly Weather Rev.* **65:** 415–441.

HAND, I. F. 1949. Weekly mean values of daily total solar and sky radiation. *U. S. Weather Bur. Tech. Paper* **11:** 1–17.

HARRINGTON, E. L. 1928. Soil temperatures in Saskatchewan. *Soil Sci.* **25:** 183–195.

HIDE, J. E. 1942. A graphic presentation of temperatures in the surface foot of soil in comparison with air temperatures. *Soil Sci. Soc. Am. Proc.* **7:** 31–35.

HINTON, E. 1944. Soil temperature observations–Newfoundland. *Am. Geophys. Union Trans.* **25:** 755–756.

HURSH, C. R. 1948. Local climate in the copper basin of Tennessee as modified by the removal of vegetation. *U. S. Dept. Agr. Circ.* **774:** 1–38.

JANERT, H. 1934. The application of heat of wetting measurements to soil research problems. *J. Agr. Sci.* **24:** 136–150.

JENNY, H. 1941. Factors of soil formation. McGraw-Hill Book Co., New York.

JOHNSTON, C. N. 1937. Heat conductivity of soil governs heat losses from heated oil lines. *Petroleum Engr.* **9:** 41–48.

JOHNSTON, C. N. 1942. Water permeable jacketed thermal radiators as indicators of field capacity and permanent wilting percentage. *Soil Sci.* **54:** 123–125.

JULANDER, O. 1945. Drought resistance in range and pasture grasses. *Plant Physiol.* **20:** 573–599.

KEEN, B. A. 1931. The physical properties of soils. Longmans, Green, and Co., London.

KEEN, B. A., CROWTHER, E. M., and COUTTS, J. R. H. 1926. The evaporation of water from soil. III. A critical study of the technique. *J. Agr. Sci.* **16:** 105–122.

KEEN, B. A., and RUSSELL, E. J. 1921. The factors determining soil temperature. *J. Agr. Sci.* **11:** 211–239.

KERSTEN, M. S. 1949. Thermal properties of soils. *Minn. Univ. Engr. Expt. Sta. Bull.* **28:** 1–228.

KIMBALL, H. H. 1931. Solar radiation as a meterological factor. *Monthly Weather Rev.* **59:** 472–479.

KING, F. H. 1892. Fluctuations in the level and rate of movement of ground water. *U. S. Dept. Agr., Weather Bur. Bull.* **5:** 1–75.

KNOCH, K. 1929. Klimalehre und Klimaänderung. Handbuch der Bodenlehre II. Julius Springer, Berlin.

LAMB, J., JR., and CHAPMAN, J. E. 1943. Effect of surface stones on erosion, evaporation, soil temperature, and soil moisture. *J. Am. Soc. Agron.* **35:** 567–578.

LEWIS, M. R. 1937. Rate of flow of capillary moisture. *U. S. Dept. Agr. Tech. Bull.* **579:** 1–29.

LYON, T. L., and BUCKMAN, H. O. 1947. The nature and properties of soils. The Macmillan Co., New York.

McCALLA, T. M., and DULEY, F. L. 1946. Effect of crop residues on soil temperature. *J. Am. Soc. Agron.* **38:** 75–89.

McCOLLOCH, J. W., and HAYES, W. P. 1923. Soil temperature and its influence on white grub activities. *Ecology* **4:** 29–36.

MacDOUGAL, D. T. 1903. Soil temperatures and vegetation. *Monthly Weather Rev.* **31:** 375–399.

MAGISTAD, O. C., FARDEN, C. A., and BALDWIN, W. A. 1935. Bagasse and paper mulches. *J. Am. Soc. Agron.* **27:** 813–825.

MAIL, G. A. 1937. Accuracy of a soil thermograph. *Soil Sci.* **43:** 27–30.

MAYER, J. E., and MAYER, M. G. 1940. Statistical mechanics. John Wiley and Sons, New York.

MOORE, R. E. 1940. The relation of soil temperature to soil moisture, pressure potential, retention and infiltration rate. *Soil Sci. Soc. Am. Proc.* **5:** 61–64.

OSKAMP, J. 1915. Soil temperature as influenced by cultural methods. *J. Agr. Research* **5:** 173–179.

PATTEN, H. E. 1909. Heat transference in soils. *U. S. Dept. Agr., Bur. Soils Bull.* **59:** 1–54.

PENMAN, H. L. 1943. Daily and seasonal changes in the surface temperature of fallow soil at Rothamsted. *Quart. J. Meteorol. Soc.* **69:** 1–16.

PENMAN, H. L. 1948. Natural evaporation from open water, bare soil, and grass. *Proc. Roy. Soc. London* **A193:** 120–145.

PILLSBURY, A. F. 1950. Effect of particle size and temperature on the permeability of granular material to water. *Soil Sci.* **70:** 299–300.

RAMDAS, L. A., and KATTI, M. S. 1934. Agricultural meteorology: preliminary studies on soil–moisture in relation to moisture in the surface layers of the atmosphere during the clear season at Poona. *Indian J. Agr. Sci.* **4:** 923–937.

REEDER, G. 1920. Ground temperatures compared with air temperatures in a shelter. *Monthly Weather Rev.* **48:** 637–639.

RICHARDS, L. A., and CAMPBELL, R. B. 1948. Use of thermisters for measuring the freezing point of solutions and soils. *Soil Sci.* **65:** 429–436.

RICHARDS, L. A., RUSSELL, M. B., and NEAL, O. R. 1937. Further developments on apparatus for field moisture studies. *Soil Sci. Soc. Am. Proc.* **2:** 55–64.

RICHARDS, L. A., and WEAVER, L. R. 1944. Moisture retention by some irrigated soils as related to soil–moisture tension. *J. Agr. Research* **69:** 215–235.

RIGG, G. B. 1947. Soil and air temperatures in a sphagnum bog of the Pacific coast of North America. *Am. J. Botany* **34:** 462–469.

ROBINSON, R. R. 1942. Phosphorus fixation as affected by soil temperature. *J. Am. Soc. Agron.* **34:** 301–306.

RUSSELL, J. C. 1939. The effect of surface cover on soil moisture losses by evaporation. *Soil Sci. Soc. Am. Proc.* **4:** 65–70.

SCHUBERT, J. 1930. Handbuch der Bodenlehrer, VI. Julius Springer, Berlin.

SEELEY, D. A. 1901. The temperature of the soil and the surrounding surface of the ground. *Monthly Weather Rev.* **29:** 501–503.

SHAW, B., and BAVER, L. D. 1939a. An electrothermal method for following moisture changes of the soil *in situ*. *Soil Sci. Soc. Am. Proc.* **4:** 78–83.

SHAW, B., and BAVER, L. D. 1939b. Heat conductivity as an index of soil moisture. *J. Am. Soc. Agron.* **31:** 886–891.

SHAW, C. F. 1926. The effect of paper mulch on soil temperature. *Hilgardia* **1:** 341–364.

SHREVE, F. 1918. A soil temperature survey of the United States and Canada. *Carnegie Inst. Wash. Yearbook* **17:** 79–80.

SHREVE, F. 1924a. Forest soil temperatures as influenced by altitude and slope exposures. *Ecology* **5:** 128–136.

SHREVE, F. 1924b. Influence of slope exposure on soil temperature. *Carnegie Inst. Wash. Yearbook* **23:** 140–141.

SINCLAIR, J. G. 1922. Temperatures of the soil and air in a desert. *Monthly Weather Rev.* **50:** 142–144.

SMITH, A. 1926. A contribution to the study of interrelations between the temperature of the soil and of the atmosphere and a new type of thermometer for such study. *Soil Sci.* **22:** 447–458.

SMITH, A. 1927. The effect of mulches on the soil temperature during the warmest week in July, 1925. *Hilgardia* **2:** 385–397.

SMITH, A. 1929a. Daily and seasonal air and soil temperatures at Davis, California. *Hilgardia* **4:** 77–112.

SMITH, A. 1929b. Comparison of daytime and nighttime soil and air temperatures. *Hilgardia* **4:** 241–272.

SMITH, A. 1931. Effect of paper mulches on soil temperature, soil moisture, and yields of certain crops. *Hilgardia* **6:** 159–201.

SMITH, A. 1939. Value of mean and average soil and air temperature. *Soil Sci. Soc. Am. Proc.* **4:** 41–50.

SMITH, G. E. P., KINNISON, A. F., and CARNS, A. G. 1931. Irrigation investigations in young grapefruit orchards. *Ariz. Agr. Expt. Sta. Tech. Bull.* **37:** 414–591.

SMITH, W. O. 1939. Thermal conductivities in moist soils. *Soil Sci. Soc. Am. Proc.* **4:** 32–40.

SMITH, W. O. 1942. Thermal conductivity of dry soil. *Soil Sci.* **53:** 435–459.

SMITH, W. O., and BYERS, H. G. 1938. The thermal conductivity of dry soils of certain of the great soil groups. *Soil Sci. Soc. Am. Proc.* **3:** 13–19.

SPRAGUE, V. G., and WILLIAMS, E. M. 1943. A simplified integrating light recorder for field use. *Plant Physiol.* **18:** 131–133.

STEWART, G. R., THOMAS, E. C., and HORNER, J. 1926. Some effects of mulching paper on Hawaiian soils. *Soil Sci.* **26:** 35–60.

TAYLOR, E. M., and BURNS, A. C. 1924. Soil temperatures during the sharagi period and their agricultural significance. *Egypt Min. Agr. Tech. Sci. Serv. Bull.* **31:** 1–46.

THOMPSON, W. A. 1934. Soil temperatures at Winnipeg, Manitoba. *Sci. Agr.* **15:** 209–216.

TOUMEY, J. W., and STICKEL, P. W. 1925. A new device for taking maximum and minimum soil temperatures in forest investigations. *Ecology* **6:** 171–178.

VANSELOW, A. P. 1932. Equilibria of the base–exchange reactions of bentonites, permutites, soil colloids, and zeolites. *Soil Sci.* **33:** 95–113.

WHITE, R. G. 1946. Installations for noting the water and thermal relationships in soils. *Agr. Engr.* **27:** 21–25.

ZON, R. 1941. Climate and the nation's forests. *In* U. S. Dept. Agriculture Yearbook 1941. (Climate and Man): 477–498.

II. TEMPERATURE AND GROWTH PROCESSES

ALDRICH, W. W. 1931. Nitrogen intake and translocation in apple trees following fall, winter and spring sodium nitrate applications. *Proc. Am. Soc. Hort. Sci.* **28:** 532–538.

ARNDT, C. H. 1937. Water absorption in the cotton plant as affected by soil and water temperatures. *Plant Physiol.* **12:** 703–720.

BAILEY, J. S., and JONES, L. H. 1941. The effect of soil temperature on the growth of cultivated blueberry bushes. *Proc. Am. Soc. Hort. Sci.* **38:** 462–464.

BAKER, F. S. 1929. Effect of excessively high temperatures on coniferous reproduction. *J. Forestry* **27:** 949–975.

BARRON, E. S. G. 1949. Cellular metabolism and growth. *In* The Chemistry and Physiology of Growth. Ed. by A. K. Parpart, Princeton Univ. Press, Princeton, New Jersey, pp. 106–134.

BATJER, L. P., MAGNESS, J. R., and REGEIMBAL, L. O. 1939. The effect of root temperature on growth and nitrogen intake of apple trees. *Proc. Am. Soc. Hort. Sci.* **37:** 11–18.

BATJER, L. P., MAGNESS, J. R., and REGEIMBAL, L. O. 1943. Nitrogen intake of dormant apple trees at low temperatures. *Proc. Am. Soc. Hort. Sci.* **42:** 69–73.

BELEHRADEK, J. 1935. Temperature and living matter. *Protoplasma–Monographien,* **8:** 1–277. Berlin.

BERKLEY, D. M., and BERKLEY, E. E. 1933. Super optimal and thermal death temperatures of the cotton plant as affected by variations in relative humidity. *Ann. Missouri Botan. Garden* **20:** 583–604.

BLACKMAN, F. F. 1905. Optima and limiting factors. *Ann. Botany* **19:** 281–295.

BONNER, J. 1949. Relations of respiration and growth in avena coleoptile. *Am. J. Botany* **36:** 429–436.

BOONSTRA, A. E. H. R. 1935. Die bedentung des wurzeldrucks für erhöhte transpiration der erbsen bei höherer wurzeltemperatur. *Planta* **24:** 59–65.

BROWN, E. M. 1939. Some effects of temperature on the growth and chemical composition of certain pasture grasses. *Mo. Agr. Expt. Sta. Research Bull.* **299.**

BROWN, R., and RICKLESS, P. 1949. A new method for the study of cell division and cell extension with some preliminary observations on the effect of temperature and of nutrients. *Proc. Roy. Soc. London* **B136:** 110–125.

BURSTRÖM, H. 1941. Formative effects of carbohydrates on root growth. *Botan. Notiser* 3: 310–334.

BUSHNELL, J. 1925. The relation of temperature to growth and respiration in the potato plant. *Minn. Agr. Expt. Sta. Tech. Bull.* 34.

CAMERON, S. H. 1941. The influence of soil temperature on the rate of transpiration of young orange trees. *Proc. Am. Soc. Hort. Sci.* 38: 75–79.

CANNON, W. A. 1911. The root habits of desert plants. *Carnegie Inst. Wash. Pub.* 131.

CLEMENTS, F. E., and MARTIN, E. V. 1934. Effect of soil temperature on transpiration in *helianthus annuus. Plant Physiol.* 9: 619–630.

CRAFTS, A. S., CURRIER, H. B., and STOCKING, C. R. 1949. Water in the physiology of plants. Chronica Botanica Co., Waltham, Mass.

CURTIS, O. F. 1929. Studies on solute translocation in plants. Experiments indicating that translocation is dependent on the activity of living cells. *Am. J. Botany* 16: 154–168.

CURTIS, O. F., and HERTY, S. D. 1936. The effect of temperature on translocation from leaves. *Am. J. Botany* 23: 528–532.

DARROW, R. A. 1939. Effect of soil temperature, pH, and nitrogen nutrition on development of *poa pratensis. Botan. Gaz.* 101: 109–127.

DAUBENMIRE, R. F. 1947. Plants and environment. John Wiley and Sons, Inc., New York.

DAVIDSON, O. W. 1941. Effects of temperature on growth and flower production of gardenias. *Proc. Am. Soc. Hort. Sci.* 39: 387–390.

DECKER, J. P. 1944. Effect of temperature on photosynthesis and respiration in red and loblolly pines. *Plant Physiol.* 19: 679–688.

DÖRING, B. 1935. Die temperatur abhängigkeit der wasseraufnahme und ihre ökologische bedeutung. *Z. Botan.* 28: 305–383.

DUNCAN, H. F., and COOKE, D. A. 1932. A preliminary investigation of the effect of temperature on root absorption of the sugar cane. *Hawaiian Planter's Record* 36: 31–40.

ELLIS, C., and SWANEY, M. W. 1947. Soilless growth of plants. Revised by T. Eastwood. Ed. 2. Reinhold Publishing Co., New York.

EYRING, H. 1935. The activated complex and absolute rate of chemical reactions. *Chem. Revs.* 17: 65–77.

FERNANDES, D. S. 1923. Aerobe und anaerobe atmung bei keimlingen von *pisum sativum. Rec. trav. botan. néerland.* 20: 107–256.

GLASSTONE, S. 1940. Textbook of physical chemistry. D. Van Nostrand Co., Inc., New York.

HAAS, A. R. C. 1936. Growth and water losses in citrus as affected by soil temperature. *Calif. Citrograph* 21: 467, 479.

HABERLANDT, F. 1874. Die oberen und unteren temperaturgrenzen für die keimung der wichtigeren landwirtschaftlichen sämereien. *Landw. Vers. Sta.* 17: 104–116.

HEDRICK, V. P. 1905. Effects of super-heated soils on plants. *Proc. Am. Soc. Hort. Sci.* 3: 51–55.

HENDRICKSON, A. H., and VEIHMEYER, F. J. 1945. Permanent wilting percentages of soils obtained from field and laboratory studies. *Plant Physiol.* 20: 517–539.

HEWITT, S. P., and CURTIS, O. F. 1948. The effect of temperature on loss of dry matter and carbohydrate from leaves by respiration and translocation. *Am. J. Botany* 35: 746–755.

HOAGLAND, D. R., and BROYER, T. C. 1936. General nature of the process of salt accumulation by roots with description of experimental methods. *Plant Physiol.* 11: 471–507.

HOAGLAND, D. R. 1944. Lectures on the inorganic nutrition of plants. Chronica Botanica Co., Waltham, Mass.

HÖBER, R. 1945. Physical chemistry of cells and tissues. The Blakiston Co., Philadelphia.

HODGMAN, C. D. 1939. Handbook of chemistry and physics. Ed. 23. Chemical Rubber Publishing Co., Cleveland, Ohio.

HUBBARD, J. W., and HERBERT, F. W. 1933. Root development of cotton plants in the San Joaquin Valley of California. *U. S. Dept. Agr. Circ.* 262.

JACOBSON, L., and OVERSTREET, R. 1947. A study of the mechanism of ion absorption by plant roots using radioactive elements. *Am. J. Botany* 34: 415–420.

JONES, L. H. 1938. Relation of soil temperature to chlorosis of gardenia. J. Agr. Res. 57: 611–621.

KINCER, J. B. 1922. The relation of climate to the geographical distribution of crops in the United States. *Ecology* 3: 127–133.

KLAGES, K. H. W. 1942. Ecological crop geography. The Macmillan Co., New York.

KRAMER, P. J. 1934. Effects of soil temperature on the absorption of water by plants. *Science* 79: 371–372.

KRAMER, P. J. 1940. Root resistance as a cause of decreased water absorption by plants at low temperatures. *Plant Physiol.* 15: 63–79.

KRAMER, P. J. 1942. Species differences with respect to water absorption at low soil temperatures. *Am. J. Botany* 29: 828–832.

KRAMER, P. J. 1949. Plant and soil water relationships. McGraw-Hill Book Co., New York.

KRAMER, P. J., and CURRIER, H. B. 1950. Water relations of plant cells and tissues. *Ann. Rev. Plant Physiol.* 1: 265–284.

LEHENBAUER, P. A. 1914. Growth of maize seedlings in relation to temperature. *Physiol. Research* 1: 247–288.

LEITCH, I. 1916. Some experiments on the influence of temperature on the rate of growth of *pisum sativum*. *Ann. Botany* 30: 25–46.

LUND, E. J. 1932. Comparison of the effects of temperature on the radial and longitudinal electric polarities in wood and cortex of Douglas fir. *Plant Physiol.* 7: 505–516.

LUNDEGARDH, H. 1931. Environment and plant development. Edward Arnold and Co., London.

MACDOUGAL, D. T. 1920. Hydration and growth. *Carnegie Inst. Wash. Pub.* 297.

McDOUGALL, W. B. 1941. Plant ecology. Lea and Febiger, Philadelphia.

MEYER, B. S., and ANDERSON, D. B. 1939. Plant physiology. D. Van Nostrand Co., Inc., New York.

MILLER, E. C. 1938. Plant physiology. McGraw-Hill Book Co., New York.

MURRAY, G. N. 1949. Effects of temperature upon division of the generative cell in pollen tubes of *Polygonatum*. (Abstract.) *J. Tenn. Acad. Sci.* 24: 167.

NELSON, C. H. 1944. Growth responses of hemp to differential soil and air temperatures. *Plant Physiol.* 19: 294–309.

NIGHTINGALE, G. T. 1933. Effects of temperature on metabolism in tomato. *Botan. Gaz.* 95: 35–58.

NIGHTINGALE, G. T.   1934.   Ammonium and nitrate nutrition of dormant delicious apple trees at 48° F.   *Botan. Gaz.* **95**: 437–452.

NIGHTINGALE, G. T., and BLAKE, M. A.   1934a.   Effects of temperature on the growth and composition of Stayman and Baldwin apple trees.   *N. J. Agr. Expt. Sta. Bull.* **566.**

NIGHTINGALE, G. T., and BLAKE, M. A.   1934b.   Effects of temperature on the growth and metabolism of Elberta peach trees with notes on the growth responses of other varieties.   *N. J. Agr. Expt. Sta. Bull.* **567.**

NIGHTINGALE, G. T.   1935.   Effects of temperature on growth, anatomy, and metabolism of apple and peach roots.   *Botan. Gaz.* **96**: 581–639.

NIGHTINGALE, G. T.   1948.   The nitrogen nutrition of green plants. II. *Botan. Rev.* **14**: 185–221.

OVERSTREET, R., and JACOBSON, L.   1946.   The absorption by roots of rubidium and phosphate ions at extremely small concentrations as revealed by experiments with Rb^{86} and P^{32} prepared with inert carrier.   *Am. J. Botany* **33**: 107–112.

PFEFFER, W.   1903.   The physiology of plants.   (Trans. and rev. by A. J. Ewart) Vol. 2.   Clarendon Press, Oxford.

POST, K.   1949.   Florist crop production and marketing.   Orange Judd Publishing Co., Inc., New York.

RIETHMANN, O.   1933.   Der einfluss der bodentemperatur auf das wachstum und die reifezeit der tomaten.   *Ber. schweiz. botan. Ges.* **42**: 152–168.

ROSENE, H. F.   1947.   A bibliography of continuous bioelectric currents and bioelectric fields in animals and plants.   *In* Bioelectric Fields and Growth, by E. J. Lund, Univ. Texas Press, Austin, Texas, pp. 301–391.

ROUSCHAL, E.   1935.   Untersuchungen über die temperaturabhängigkeit der wasseraufnahme ganzer pflanzen (mit berücksichtingung der übergangsreaktionen). *Sitzber. Akad. Wiss. Wien, Math.–Naturw. Klasse* **144**: 313–348.

SCHROEDER, R. A.   1939.   The effect of root temperature upon the absorption of water by the cucumber.   *Mo. Agr. Expt. Sta. Research Bull.* **309.**

SEIFRIZ, W.   1943.   Protoplasmic streaming.   *Botan. Rev.* **9**: 49–123.

SMITH, G. E.   1935.   Studies of fall and spring applications of nitrogen fertilizers to apple trees.   *Proc. Am. Soc. Hort. Sci.* **33**: 120–123.

STILES, W., and LEACH, W.   1932.   Respiration in plants.   The Dial Press, New York.

STUCKEY, I. H.   1941.   Seasonal growth of grass roots.   *Am. J. Botany* **28**: 486–491.

SULLIVAN, J. T., and SPRAGUE, V. G.   1949.   The effect of temperature on the growth and composition of the stubble and roots of perennial ryegrass.   *Plant Physiol.* **24**: 706–719.

TALMA, E. G. C.   1918.   The relation between temperature and growth in the roots of *Lepidium sativum*.   *Rec. trav. botan. néerland.* **15**: 366–422.

THIMANN, K. V.   1949.   *In* The Chemistry and Physiology of Growth.   Ed. by A. K. Parpart, Princeton Univ. Press, Princeton, N. J., pp. 61–71.

THOMAS, M.   1947.   Plant physiology.   Ed. 3.   J. & A. Churchill Ltd., London.

VAN DER PAAUW, F.   1949.   Water relations of oats with special attention to the influence of periods of drought.   *Plant and Soil* **1**: 303–341.

VAN NIEL, C. B.   1949.   The kinetics of growth of microorganisms.   *In* The Chemistry and Physiology of Growth.   Ed. by A. K. Parpart, Princeton Univ. Press, Princeton, N. J., pp. 91–105.

WANNER, H.   1948a.   Untersuchungen über die temperaturabhängigkeit der salzaufnahme durch pflanzenwurzeln. I. Die relative grösse der temperaturkoeffizienten von kationen- und anionen-aufnahme. *Ber. schweiz. botan. Ges.* **58:** 123–130.

WANNER, H. 1948b. Untersuchungen über die temperaturabhängigkeit der salzaufnahme durch pflanzenwurzeln. II. Die temperaturkoeffizienten von kationen- und anionen-aufnahme in abhängigkeit von der salzkonzentration. *Ber. schweiz. Botan. Ges.* **58:** 383–390.

WEAVER, J. E., and CLEMENTS, F. E. 1929. Plant ecology. McGraw–Hill Book Co., New York.

WEINMANN, H. 1948. Underground development and reserves of grasses. A review. *J. Brit. Grassland Soc.* **3:** 115–140.

WEISS, P. 1949. Differential growth. *In* The Chemistry and Physiology of Growth. Ed. by A. K. Parpart, Princeton Univ. Press, Princeton, N. J., pp. 135–186.

WENT, F. W. 1944a. Plant growth under controlled conditions II. Thermoperiodicity in growth and fruiting of the tomato. *Am. J. Botany* **31:** 135–150.

WENT, F. W. 1944b. Plant growth under controlled conditions. III. Correlation between various physiological processes and growth in the tomato plant. *Am. J. Botany* **31:** 597–618.

WENT, F. W., and ENGLESBERG, R. 1946. Plant growth under controlled conditions. VII. Sucrose content of the tomato plant. *Arch. Biochem.* **9:** 187–199.

WENT, F. W., and HULL, H. M. 1949. The effect of temperature upon translocation of carbohydrates in the tomato plant. *Plant Physiol.* **24:** 505–526.

WHITE, P. R. 1932. Influence of some environmental conditions on the growth of excised root tips of wheat seedlings in liquid media. *Plant Physiol.* **7:** 613–628.

WHITE, P. R. 1937. Seasonal fluctuations in growth rates of excised tomato root tips. *Plant Physiol.* **12:** 183–190.

WILSON, P. W. 1949. Kinetics and mechanisms of enzyme reactions. *In* Respiratory Enzymes. Ed. by H. A. Lardy. (Revised.) Burgess Publishing Co., Minneapolis, Minn., pp. 17–57.

III. Soil Temperature and Plant Growth

ADAMS, W. R. 1934. Studies in tolerance of New England forest trees. XI. The influence of soil temperature on the germination and development of white pine seedlings. *Vt. Agr. Expt. Sta. Bull.* **379.**

ADRIANCE, G. W., and BRISON, F. R. 1939. Propagation of horticultural plants. McGraw–Hill Book Co., New York.

AHLGREN, H. L., and BURCALOW, F. V. 1949. Ladino clover is hard to beat! *Crops and Soils* **2:** 5–7.

ALLEN, R. C. 1934. The effect of soil temperature on the growth and flowering of certain greenhouse crops. *Proc. Am. Soc. Hort. Sci.* **32:** 635–637.

ANGELO, E. 1939. Studies on some factors relating to hardiness in the strawberry. I. The development of cold resistance in strawberry varieties. *Minn. Agr. Expt. Sta. Tech. Bull.* **135:** 5–18.

ARNDT, C. H. 1932. A study of the factors which may influence cotton seed germination and seedling growth. *S. Carolina Agr. Expt. Sta. Ann. Rept.* **45:** 46–48.

ARNDT, C. H. 1937. Water absorption in the cotton plant as affected by soil and water temperatures. *Plant Physiol.* **12:** 703–720.

ARNDT, C. H. 1945. Temperature–growth relations of the roots and hypocotyls of cotton seedlings. *Plant Physiol.* **20:** 200–220.

ARNON, D. I. and HOAGLAND, D. R.   1939.   A comparison of water culture and soil as media for crop production.   *Science* **89:** 512–514.

ARREGUIN-LOZANO, B., and BONNER, J.   1949.   Experiments on sucrose formation by potato tubers as influenced by temperature.   *Plant Physiol.* **24:** 720–738.

ARTHUR, J. M., and HARVILL, E. K.   1941.   Flowering in *Digitalis purpurea* initiated by low temperature and light.   *Contribs. Boyce Thompson Inst.* **12:** 111–117.

BAILEY, J. S., and JONES, L. H.   1941.   The effect of soil temperature on the growth of cultivated blueberry bushes.   *Proc. Am. Soc. Hort. Sci.* **38:** 462–464.

BAKER, F. S.   1929.   Effect of excessively high temperatures on coniferous reproduction.   *J. Forestry* **27:** 949–975.

BALDWIN, H. I.   1942.   Forest tree seed of the north temperate regions.   Chronica Botanica Co., Waltham, Mass.

BARNEY, C. W.   1947.   A study of some factors affecting root growth of loblolly pine (*Pinus taeda L.*).   Thesis, Ph. D., Duke Univ. School of Forestry.

BATES, C. G., and ROESER, J., JR.   1924.   Relative resistance of tree seedlings to excessive heat.   *U. S. Dept. Agr. Bull.* **1263.**

BATJER, L. P., MAGNESS, J. R., and REGEIMBAL, L. O.   1939.   The effect of root temperature on growth and nitrogen intake of apple trees.   *Proc. Am. Soc. Hort. Sci.* **37:** 11–18.

BEACH, W. S.   1946.   Pathogenic and physiogenic damping-off.   *Soil Sci.* **61:** 37–46.

BEACH, W. S.   1949.   The effects of excess solutes, temperature and moisture upon damping-off.   *Pa. Agr. Expt. Sta. Bull.* **509.**

BEESON, K. C.   1941.   The mineral composition of crops with particular reference to the soils in which they were grown.   *U. S. Dept. Agr. Misc. Pub.* **369.**

BEWLEY, W. F.   1922.   "Sleepy disease" of the tomato.   *Ann. Applied Biol.* **9:** 116–134.

BLAAUW, A. H., LUYTEN, I., and HARTSEMA, A. M.   1936.   Accelerated flowering of Dutch irises.   I.   Proc. *Konikl. Akad. Wetenschap. Amsterdam* **39:** 604–612.

BLAAUW, A. H., LUYTEN, I., and HARTSEMA, A. M.   1939.   Accelerated flowering of Dutch irises.   II.   Proc. *Konikl. Akad. Wetenschap. Amsterdam* **42:** 13–22.

BODGER SEEDS, LTD.   1935.   Valuable information for seedmen.   Ed. 2.   El Monte, Calif.

BONNER, J.   1949.   Relations of respiration and growth in *Avena coleoptile*.   *Am. J. Botany* **36:** 429–436.

BOSWELL, V. R., TOOLE, E. H., TOOLE, V. K., and FISHER, D. F.   1940.   A study of rapid deterioration of vegetable seeds and methods for its prevention.   *U. S. Dept. Agr. Tech. Bull.* **708.**

BRENCHLEY, W. E., and SINGH, K.   1922.   Effect of high root temperature and excessive insolation on growth.   *Ann. Applied Biol.* **9:** 197–209.

BRIERLY, W. G., and LANDON, R. H.   1946.   A study of cold resistance of the roots of Latham red raspberry.   *Proc. Am. Soc. Hort. Sci.* **47:** 215–218.

BROWN, E. M.   1939.   Some effects of temperature on the growth and chemical composition of certain pasture grasses.   *Mo. Agr. Expt. Sta. Research Bull.* **299.**

BROWN, E. M.   1943.   Seasonal variations in the growth and chemical composition of Kentucky bluegrass.   *Mo. Agr. Expt. Sta. Research Bull.* **360.**

BURKHOLDER, W. H.   1920.   The effect of two soil temperatures on the yield and water relations of healthy and diseased bean plants.   *Ecology* **1:** 113–123.

BUSHNELL, J.   1925.   The relation of temperature to growth and respiration in the potato plant.   *Minn. Agr. Expt. Sta. Tech. Bull.* **34.**

CAMERON, S. H. 1941. The influence of soil temperature on the rate of transpiration of young orange trees. *Proc. Am. Soc. Hort. Sci.* **38**: 75–79.

CAMP, A. F. 1933. Effect of soil temperature on the germination of citrus seeds. *Am. J. Botany* **20**: 348–357.

CAMP, A. F. and WALKER, M. N. 1927. Soil temperature studies with cotton. II. The relation of soil temperature to the germination and growth of cotton. *Fla. Agr. Expt. Sta. Tech. Bull.* **189**: 17–32.

CANNON, W. A. 1915. On the relation of root growth and development to the temperature and aeration of the soil. *Am. J. Botany* **2**: 211–224.

CANNON, W. A. 1917. Soil temperature and plant growth. *Plant World* **20**: 361–363.

CARRICK, D. B. 1920. Resistance of the roots of some fruit species to low temperatures. *N. Y. (Cornell) Agr. Expt. Sta. Mem.* **36**: 608–661.

CARROLL, J. C. 1943. Effects of drought, temperature and nitrogen on turf grasses. *Plant Physiol.* **18**: 19–36.

CHIPPENDALE, H. G. 1949. Environment and germination in grass seeds. *J. Brit. Grassland Soc.* **4**: 57–61.

CHUPP, C. 1946. Soil temperature, moisture, aeration and pH as factors in disease incidence. *Soil Sci.* **61**: 31–36.

CLAYTON, E. E. 1923. The relation of temperature to the *fusarium* wilt of the tomato. *Am. J. Botany* **10**: 71–88.

CLEMENTS, F. E., and MARTIN, E. V. 1934. Effect of soil temperature on transpiration in *Helianthus annuus*. *Plant Physiol.* **9**: 619–630.

COLLISON, R. C. 1935. Lysimeter investigations. IV. Water movement, soil temperatures and root activity under apple trees. *N. Y. (Geneva) Agr. Expt. Sta. Tech. Bull.* **237**.

COSSMAN, K. F. 1939. Citrus roots: their anatomy, osmotic pressure, and periodicity of growth. *Palestine J. Botany* **3**: 3–41. Rehovot, Palestine.

CRAFTS, A. S., CURRIER, H. B., and STOCKING, C. R. 1949. Water in the physiology of plants. Chronica Botanica Co., Waltham, Mass.

CRIDER, F. S. 1928. Winter root growth of plants. *Science* (n.s.) **68**: 403–404.

CROCKER, W. 1948. Growth of plants. Reinhold Publishing Co., New York.

DARROW, R. A. 1939. Effect of soil temperature, pH, and nitrogen nutrition on the development of *Poa pratensis*. *Botan. Gaz.* **101**: 109–127.

DAUBENMIRE, R. F. 1943. Soil temperature versus drought as a factor determining lower altitudinal limits of trees in the Rocky Mountains. *Botan. Gaz.* **105**: 1–13.

DAUBENMIRE, R. F. 1947. Plants and environment. John Wiley and Sons, Inc., New York.

DAUBENMIRE, R. F. 1949. Relation of temperature and daylength to the inception of tree growth in spring. *Botan. Gaz.* **110**: 464–475.

DAVIDSON, O. W. 1941. Effects of temperature on growth and flower production of gardenias. *Proc. Am. Soc. Hort. Sci.* **39**: 387–390.

DAVIS, W. E. 1939. An explanation of the advantage of alternating temperatures over constant temperatures in the germination of certain seeds. *Am. J. Botany* **26**: 175–185.

DE ROPP, R. S. 1946. Studies on the physiology of leaf growth. III. The influence of roots on the growth of leaves and stems in rye. *Ann. Botany* (n.s.) **10**: 353–359.

DICKSON, J. G. 1923. Influence of soil temperature and moisture on the development of the seedling–blight of wheat and corn caused by *Gibberella saubinetti*. *J. Agr. Research* **23**: 837–870.

DICKSON, J. G., ECKERSON, S. H., and LINK, K. P. 1923. The nature of resistance to seedling blight of cereal. *Proc. Natl. Acad. Sci., Wash.* **9**: 434–439.

DICKSON, J. G. 1947. Diseases of field crops. McGraw–Hill Book Co., New York.

DICKSON, J. G., and HOLBERT, J. R. 1926. The influence of temperature upon the metabolism and expression of disease resistance in selfed lines of corn. *J. Am. Soc. Agron.* **18**: 314–322.

DITTMER, H. S. 1937. A quantitative study of the roots and root hairs of a winter rye plant (*Secale cereale*). *Am. J. Botany* **24**: 417–420.

EARLEY, E. B., and CARTTER, J. L. 1945. Effect of the temperature of the root environment on growth of soybean plants. *J. Am. Soc. Agron.* **37**: 727–735.

ECKERSON, S. 1914. Thermotropism of roots. *Botan. Gaz.* **58**: 254–263.

EDWARDS, T. I. 1932. Temperature relations of seed germination. *Quart. Rev. Biol.* **7**: 428–443.

EDWARDS, T. I. 1934. Relations of germinating soybeans to temperature and length of incubation time. *Plant Physiol* **9**: 1–30.

EZEKIEL, W. N. 1945. Effect of low temperatures on survival of *Phymatotrichum omnivorum*. *Phytopathology* **35**: 296–301.

FAWCETT, H. S. 1929. Temperature experiments in germinating orange seeds. *Calif. Citrograph* **14**: 515.

FITCH, C. L. 1915. Studies of health in potatoes. *Colo. Agr. Expt. Sta. Bull.* **216**.

FRANCK, W. J. 1928. Bibliography of germination of seeds. Internatl. Seed Testing Assoc. Proc. Wageningen. [Mimeographed.]

GARNER, R. J. 1944. Propagation by cuttings and layers. Recent work and its application, with special reference to pome and stone fruits. *Imp. Bur. Hort. Plantation Crops, Tech. Commun. No. 14.*

GARRETT, S. D. 1944. Root disease fungi. Chronica Botanica Co., Waltham, Mass.

GERICKE, W. F. 1940. The complete guide to soilless gardening. Prentice-Hall, Inc., New York.

GIRTON, R. E. 1927. The growth of citrus seedlings as influenced by environmental factors. *Calif. Univ. (Berkeley) Agr. Sci. Pub.* **5**: 83–117.

GRAY, G. F. 1941. Transpiration in strawberries as affected by root temperature. *Proc. Am. Soc. Hort. Sci.* **39**: 269–273.

HAAS, A. R. C. 1936. Growth and water losses in citrus as affected by soil temperature. *Calif. Citrograph* **21**: 467–479.

HAASIS, F. W. 1923. Frost heaving of western yellow pine seedlings. *Ecology* **4**: 378–390.

HABERLANDT, F. 1874. Die oberen und unteren temperaturgrenzen für die Keimung der wichtigeren landwirtschaftlichen sämereien. *Landw. Vers. Sta.* **17**: 104–116.

HALMA, F. F. 1935. Effect of soil temperature on growth of citrus. *Proc. Am. Soc. Hort. Sci.* **33**: 67–69.

HAMNER, K. C., and BONNER, J. 1938. Photoperiodism in relation to hormones as factors in floral initiation and development. *Botan. Gaz.* **100**: 388–431.

HARDENBURG, E. V. 1949. Potato production. Comstock Publishing Co., Inc., Ithaca, New York.

HARRINGTON, G. T. 1923. Use of alternating temperature in the germination of seeds. *J. Agr. Research* **23**: 295–332.

HARRISON, C. M. 1934. Responses of Kentucky bluegrass to variations in temperature, light, cutting, and fertilizing. *Plant Physiol.* **9:** 83–106.

HARTLEY, C. 1918. Stem lesions caused by excessive heat. *J. Agr. Research* **14:** 595–604.

HARTMANN, H. T. 1946. The use of root-promoting substances in the propagation of olives by soft-wood cuttings. *Proc. Am. Soc. Hort. Sci.* **48:** 303–308.

HEALD, F. D. 1933. Manual of plant diseases. McGraw–Hill Book Co., New York.

HEDRICK, V. P. 1905. Effects of super-heated soils on plants. *Proc. Am. Soc. Hort. Sci.* **3:** 51–55.

HEIT, C. E. 1946a. Summarized laboratory germination data on over 100 flower seed species. *Assoc. Official Seed Analysis News Letter* **20:** 13–16.

HEIT, C. E. 1946b. Laboratory germination results with certain flower seeds. *Proc. Assoc. Official Seed Analysts* **36:** 141–149.

HILLS, K. L. 1944a. Dormancy and hardseededness in *T. subterraneum*. 2. The progress of after-harvest ripening. *J. Australian Council Sci. Ind. Research* **17:** 186–190.

HILLS, K. L. 1944b. Dormancy and hardseededness in *T. subterraneum*. 3. The effect upon dormancy of germination at three different constant temperatures. *J. Australian Council Sci. Ind. Research* **17:** 191–196.

HOAGLAND, D. R. 1944. Lectures on the inorganic nutrition of plants. Chronica Botanica Co., Waltham, Mass.

HOFFMAN, J. V. 1920. The establishment of a Douglas fir forest. *Ecology* **1:** 49–53.

HUBBARD, J. W., and HERBERT, F. W. 1933. Root development of cotton plants in the San Joaquin Valley of California. U. S. Dept. Agr. Cir. 262.

IVERSON, V. E. 1939. Studies on some factors relating to hardiness in the strawberry. II. Winter soil temperatures as a factor in the environment of the strawberry and some other herbaceous plants. *Minn. Agr. Expt. Sta. Tech. Bull.* **135:** 19–30.

JANSSEN, G. 1929. Effect of date of seeding of winter wheat on plant development and its relationship to winterhardiness. *J. Am. Soc. Agron.* **21:** 444–466.

JEFFS, R. E. 1925. The elongation of root hairs as affected by light and temperature. *Am. J. Botany* **12:** 577–606.

JOHNSON, J., and HARTMAN, R. E. 1919. Influence of soil environment on the root-rot of tobacco. *J. Agr. Research* **17:** 41–86.

JONES, F. R., and TISDALE, W. B. 1921. Effect of soil temperature upon the development of nodules on the roots of certain legumes. *J. Agr. Research* **22:** 17–32.

JONES, L. H. 1938. Relation of soil temperature to chlorosis of gardenia. *J. Agr. Research* **57:** 611–621.

JONES, L. R., MCKINNEY, H. H., and FELLOWS, H. 1922. The influence of soil temperature on potato scab. *Wis. Agr. Expt. Sta. Research Bull.* **53.**

JONES, L. R., and TISDALE, W. B. 1922. The influence of soil temperature upon the development of flax wilt. *Phytopathology* **12:** 409–413.

JONES, L. R. 1924. The relation of environment to disease in plants. *Am. J. Botany* **11:** 601–609.

JONES, L. R., JOHNSON, J., and DICKSON, J. G. 1926. Wisconsin studies upon the relation of soil temperature to plant disease. *Wis. Agr. Expt. Sta. Research Bull.* **71.**

JULANDER, O. 1945. Drought resistance in range and pasture grasses. *Plant Physiol.* **20:** 573–599.

KAINS, M. G., and McQUESTEN, L. M. 1948. Propagation of plants. Orange Judd Publishing Co., New York [Revised].

KAUFMAN, C. M. 1945. Root growth of jack pine on several sites in the Cloquet Forest, Minnesota. *Ecology* 26: 10–23.

KEARNS, V., and TOOLE, E. H. 1939. Temperature and other factors affecting the germination of fescue seed. *U. S. Dept. Agr. Tech. Bull.* 638.

KENDRICK, J. B. and STEVENSON, E. E. 1949. The occurrence of onion smut in California. *Plant Disease Rep.* 33: 451–452.

KINCAID, R. R. 1935. The effects of certain environmental factors on germination of Florida cigar–wrapper tobacco seeds. *Fla. Agr. Expt. Sta. Bull.* 277.

KINCAID, R. R., and GRATZ, L. O. 1935. Soil-temperature studies on Florida cigar–wrapper tobacco. *J. Agr. Research* 51: 441–449.

KLAGES, K. H. W. 1942. Ecological crop geography. The Macmillan Co., New York.

KORSTIAN, C. F., and FETHEROLF, N. J. 1921. Control of stem girdle of spruce transplants caused by excessive heat. *Phytopathology* 11: 485–490.

KOTOWSKI, F. 1926. Temperature relations to germination of vegetable seed. *Proc. Am. Soc. Hort. Sci.* 23: 176–184.

KRAMER, P. J. 1933. The intake of water through dead root systems and its relation to the problem of absorption by transpiring plants. *Am. J. Botany* 20: 481–492.

KRAMER, P. J. 1949. Plant and soil water relationships. McGraw-Hill Book Co., New York.

LAMB, C. A. 1936. Tensile strength, extensibility, and other characteristics of wheat roots in relation to winter injury. *Ohio Agr. Expt. Sta. Bull.* 568.

LAURIE, A., and RIES, V. H. 1942. Floriculture. McGraw-Hill Book Co., New York.

LAURIE, A., and STILLINGS, E. 1949. Studies on propagation of greenhouse roses by cuttings. *Proc. Am. Soc. Hort. Sci.* 53: 492–500.

LEACH, L. D. 1947. Growth rates of host and pathogen as factors determining the severity of preemergence damping-off. *J. Agr. Research* 75: 161–179.

LeCLERC, J. A. 1907. Effect of climatic conditions on the composition of Durum wheat. *U. S. Dept. Agr. Yearbook* 1906: 199–212.

LEHENBAUER, P. A. 1914. Growth of maize seedlings in relation to temperature. *Physiol. Research* 1: 247–288.

LEHMANN, E., and AICHELE, F. 1937. Keimungsphysiologie der gräser (Gramineen). G. Fischer.

LEITCH, I. 1916. Some experiments on the influence of temperature on the rate of growth of *Pisum sativum*. *Ann. Botany* 30: 25–46.

LEVITT, J. 1941. Frost killing and hardiness of plants. Burgess Publishing Co., Minneapolis, Minn.

LOVVORN, R. L. 1945. Effect of defoliation, soil fertility, temperature, and length of day on the growth of some perennial grasses. *J. Am. Soc. Agron.* 37: 570–582.

MacMILLAN, H. G., and BYARS, L. P. 1920. Heat injury to beans in Colorado. *Phytopathology* 10: 365–367.

MARLOTH, R. H. 1949. Citrus growth studies. I. Periodicity of root-growth and top-growth in nursery seedlings and budlings. *J. Hort. Sci.* 25: 50–59.

MARTIN, J. H., TAYLOR, J. W., and LEUKEL, R. W. 1935. Effect of soil temperature and depth of planting on the emergence and development of sorghum seedlings in the greenhouse. *J. Am. Soc. Agron.* 27: 660–665.

McClure, T. T., and Robbins, W. R. 1942. Resistance of cucumber seedlings to damping-off as related to age, season of the year and level of nitrogen nutrition. *Botan. Gaz.* **103**: 684–697.

McQuilkin, W. E. 1949. Direct seeding of trees. *U. S. Dept. Agr. Yearbook* 1949: 136–146.

Michaelis, P. 1934. Okologische studien an der alpinen baumgrenze. IV. Zur kenntnis des winterlichen wasserhaushaltes. *Jahrb. wiss. Botan.* **80**: 169–247.

Monselise, S. P. 1944. On the growth of citrus roots and shoots. J. A. P. Agr. Research Sta. Rehovoth, Palestine. (Unpublished thesis.)

Morinaga, T. 1926. The effect of alternating temperatures upon the germination of seeds. *Am. J. Botany* **13**: 141–158.

Münch, E. 1913. Hitzeschäden an waldpflanzen. Vorläufige mitteilungen. *Naturw. Z. Forst-u. Landw.* **11**: 557–562.

Murneek, A. E., Whyte, R. O., et al. 1949. Vernalization and photoperiodism, a symposium. Chronica Botanica Co., Waltham, Mass.

Myers, A. 1942. Germination of curley mitchell grass (*Astrebla lappacea*). (Domin.) *J. Australian Inst. Agr. Sci.* **8**: 31–32.

Nelson, C. H. 1944. Growth responses of hemp to differential soil and air temperatures. *Plant Physiol.* **19**: 294–309.

Nightingale, G. T. 1934. Ammonium and nitrate nutrition of dormant delicious apple trees at 48°F. *Botan. Gaz.* **95**: 437–452.

Nightingale, G. T. 1935. Effects of temperature on growth, anatomy, and metabolism of apple and peach roots. *Botan. Gaz.* **96**: 581–639.

Nightingale, G. T. 1942. Nitrate and carbohydrate reserves in relation to nitrogen nutrition of pineapple. *Botan. Gaz.* **103**: 409–456.

Oliveira e. Sousa, E., and Vianna e Silva, M. 1948. A influencia da temperatura na germinacas de algumas formas cultivadas de arroz. *Agronomia Lusitana* **4**: 323–338.

Oskamp, J. 1917. The role of soil temperature in tree growth. *Proc. Am. Soc. Hort. Sci.* **14**: 118–126.

Patterson, C. F. 1936. Hardy fruits. R. R. Clark, Ltd., Edinburgh.

Pfahl, P. B., Orr, H. P., and Laurie, A. 1949. The effect of warm water applications to greenhouse roses. *Proc. Am. Soc. Hort. Sci.* **53**: 489–491.

Pierce, L. T., and Wood, R. R. 1946. Effect of temperature upon the growth rate of sugar beets. *Proc. Am. Soc. Sugar Beet Technol.* **4**: 129–134.

Porter, R. H. 1949. Recent developments in seed technology. *Bot. Rev.* **15**: 221–344.

Post, K. 1949. Florist crop production and marketing. Orange Judd Publishing Co., Inc., New York.

Proebsting, E. L. 1943. Root distribution of some deciduous fruit trees in a California orchard. *Proc. Am. Soc. Hort. Sci.* **43**: 1–4.

Reddick, D. 1917. Effect of soil temperature on the growth of bean plants and on their susceptibility to a root parasite. *Am. J. Botany* **4**: 513–519.

Reddy, C. S. and Brentzel, W. E. 1922. Investigations of heat canker of flax. *U. S. Dept. Agr. Bull.* **1120**: 1–18.

Reed, J. F. 1939. Root and shoot growth of shortleaf and loblolly pines in relation to certain environmental conditions. *Duke Univ. Forestry Bull.* **4**.

Reid, M. E. 1933. Effects of shade on the growth of velvet bent and metropolitan creeping bent. *U. S. Golf Assoc., Green Sect. Bull.* **13**: 131–135.

RICHARDS, B. L. 1921. Pathogenicity of *Corticium vagum* on the potato as affected by soil temperature. *J. Agr. Research* **21**: 459–482.

RIETHMANN, O. 1933. Der einfluss der bodentemperatur auf das wachstum und die reifezeit der tomaten. *Ber. schweiz. botan. Ges.* **42**: 152–168.

ROGERS, W. S. 1939. Root studies. VIII. Apple root growth in relation to rootstock, soil, seasonal and climatic factors. *J. Pomol. Hort. Sci.* **17**: 99–130.

SCHNEIDER, H. 1944. *Verticillium* wilt of guayule. *Phytopathology* **34**: 936.

SCHWARTZE, C. D., and MYHRE, A. S. 1947. Rooting blueberry cuttings. *Wash. Agr. Expt. Sta. Bull.* **488**.

SHANKS, J. B., and LAURIE, A. 1949. A progress report of some rose root studies. *Proc. Am. Soc. Hort. Sci.* **53**: 473–488.

SHIRLEY, H. L. 1936. Lethal high temperatures for conifers, and the cooling effect of transpiration. *J. Agr. Research* **53**: 239–258.

SMITH, A. 1929. Daily seasonal air and soil temperatures at Davis, Calif. *Hilgardia* **4**: 77–112.

SMITH, O. F. 1948. Diseases of alfalfa in Nevada and their influence on choice of varieties. *Nev. Agr. Expt. Sta. Bull.* **182**.

SPRAGUE, V. G. 1943. The effects of temperature and day length on seedling emergence and early growth of several pasture species. *Soil Sci. Soc. Am. Proc.* **8**: 287–294.

STEVENS, C. L. 1931. Root growth of white pine (*Pinus strobus* L.). *Yale Univ. School Forestry Bull.* **32**.

STUCKEY, I. H. 1941. Seasonal growth of grass roots. *Am. J. Botany* **28**: 486–491.

STUCKEY, I. H. 1942. Influence of soil temperature on the development of Colonial bentgrass. *Plant Physiol.* **17**: 116–122.

SULLIVAN, J. T., and SPRAGUE, V. G. 1949. The effect of temperature on the growth and composition of the stubble and roots of perennial ryegrass. *Plant Physiol.* **24**: 706–719.

TABER, S. 1931. Frost heaving, mechanics of frost heaving, freezing and thawing of soils as factors in the destruction of road pavements. *J. Forestry* **29**: 403–405.

TAVERNETTI, A. A. 1944. Beet growth controlled by soil temperature and fertility. *Spreckles Sugar Beet Bull.* **8**: 23–24.

TAYLOR, J. W., and MCCALL, M. A. 1936. Influence of temperature and other factors on the morphology of the wheat seedling. *J. Agr. Research* **52**: 557–568.

THOMPSON, H. C. 1933. Temperature as a factor affecting flowering of plants. *Proc. Am. Soc. Hort. Sci.* **30**: 440–446.

THOMPSON, H. C. 1944. Further studies on effect of temperature on initiation of flowering in celery. *Proc. Am. Soc. Hort. Sci.* **45**: 425–430.

TISDALE, W. B. 1923. Influence of soil temperature and soil moisture upon the *Fusarium* disease in cabbage seedlings. *J. Agr. Research* **24**: 55–86.

TOOLE, E. H., and TOOLE, V. K. 1941. Progress of germination of seed of *Digitaria* as influenced by germination temperature and other factors. *J. Agr. Research* **63**: 65–90.

TUBEUF, C. VON. 1914. Erkrankungen durch luftabschluss und uberhitzung. *Naturw. Z. Forst-u. Landw.* **12**: 67–88; 161–169.

WALKER, J. C., and JONES, L. R. 1921. Relation of soil temperature and other factors to onion smut infection. *J. Agr. Research* **22**: 235–262.

WALKER, J. C. 1926. The influence of soil temperature and soil moisture upon white rot of *Allium*. *Phytopathology* **16**: 697–710.

WALKER, J. C. 1939. Diseases of vegetable crops. Edwards Brothers, Inc., Ann Arbor, Mich.

WANNER, H. 1948b. Untersuchungen über die temperaturabängigkeit der salzaufnahme durch pflanzenwurzeln. II. Die temperaturkoeffizienten von kationen- und anionen–aufnahme in abhängigkeit von der salzkonzentration. *Ber. schweiz. Botan. Ges.* **58**: 383–390.

WATANABE, S. 1932. Effect of temperatures upon the root development of pineapples. I. The maximum, minimum, and optimum temperatures for the elongation of main roots. *Taihoku Imp. Univ. Hort. Inst. Commun. No.* **24**. [In Japanese.]

WEAVER, J. E. 1925. Root development of field crops. McGraw-Hill Book Co., New York.

WEIMER, J. L. 1930. Alfalfa root injuries resulting from freezing. *J. Agr. Research* **40**: 121–143.

WENT, F. W. 1938. Specific factors other than auxin affecting growth and root formation. *Plant Physiol.* **13**: 55–80.

WENT, F. W. 1944a. Plant growth under controlled conditions. II. Thermoperiodicity in growth and fruiting of the tomato. *Am. J. Botany* **31**: 135–150.

WERNER, H. O. 1932. Tuber development in Triumph potatoes as influenced by time of planting on dry land in northwestern Nebraska. *Nebr. Agr. Expt. Sta. Research Bull.* **61**.

WHYTE, R. O. 1939. Phasic development of plants. *Biol. Revs.* **14**: 51–87.

WINGARD, S. A. 1941. The nature of disease resistance in plants. *Bot. Rev.* **7**: 59–109.

WOODROOF, J. G., and WOODROOF, N. C. 1934. Pecan root growth and development. *J. Agr. Research* **49**: 511–530.

WORT, D. J. 1940. Soil temperature and growth of Marquis wheat. *Plant Physiol.* **15**: 335–342.

IV. SOIL TEMPERATURE AND GROWTH OF MICRO-ORGANISMS

ALLISON, F. E., and MINOR, F. W. 1940. The effect of temperature on the growth rates of rhizobia. *J. Bact.* **39**: 365–371.

BRYAN, C. S. 1935. The influence of controlled temperature and soil treatment on some soil bacteria. *Mich. Agr. Expt. Sta. Quart. Bull.* **18**: 1–8.

BUCHANAN, R. E., and FULMER, E. I. 1930. Effects of environment upon microorganisms. Physiology and biochemistry of bacteria. V. II. Williams and Wilkins Co., Baltimore, Md.

FRED, E. B., BALDWIN, I. L., and McCOY, E. 1932. Root nodule bacteria and leguminous plants. Wis. Univ. Studies No. 5.

FULLER, J. E., and JONES, L. H. 1932. The influence of temperature on the nitrate content of soil in the presence of decomposing cellulose. *Soil Sci.* **34**: 337–350.

GREAVES, J. E., and JONES, L. W. 1944. The influence of temperature on the microflora of the soil. *Soil Sci.* **58**: 377–387.

GROSBY, W. C. 1911. Summer temperature of the soil in relation to the supply of available nitrogen in the wheat areas. *J. Nat. Hist. Soil Soc. West. Austral.* **4**: 9–11. Chem. Abstracts **8**, 193.

JENNY, H. 1928. Relation of climatic factors to the amount of nitrogen in soils. *J. Am. Soc. Agron.* **20**: 900–912.

JENNY, H., BINGHAM, F., and PADILLA–SARAVIA, B. 1948. Nitrogen and organic matter contents of equatorial soils of Colombia, South America. *Soil Sci.* **66:** 173–186.

McCALLA, T. M. 1945. Influence of microorganisms and some organic substances on soil structure. *Soil Sci.* **59:** 287–297.

MARTIN, J. P., and CRAGGS, B. A. 1946. Influence of temperature and moisture on the soil-aggregating effect of organic residues. *J. Am. Soc. Agron.* **38:** 332–339.

PANGANIBAN, E. H. 1925. Temperature as a factor in nitrogen changes in the soil. *J. Am. Soc. Agron.* **17:** 1–31.

RUSSEL, J. C., JONES, E. G., and BAHRT, G. M. 1925. The temperature and moisture factors in nitrate production. *Soil Sci.* **19:** 381–398.

RUSSELL, E. J., and HUTCHINSON, H. B. 1912–13. The effect of partial sterilization of soil on the production of plant food. *J. Agr. Sci.* **5:** 152–221.

TANDON, S. P., and DHAR, M. R. 1934. Influence of temperature on bacterial nitrification in tropical countries. *Soil Sci.* **38:** 183–189.

WAKSMAN, S. A., and GERRETSEN, F. C. 1931. Influence of temperature and moisture upon the nature and extent of decomposition of plant residues by microorganisms. *Ecology* **12:** 33–60.

EPILOGUE

By Byron T. Shaw

Having read this far, the thoughtful reader may well be amazed that a plant is able to grow in such a complex environment. He doubtless has arrived at the conclusion of the authors; namely, that although we have some understanding and limited techniques for control of single factors affecting plant growth, we understand very little of the complex interrelationships among these factors, and hence are not in good position to modify them intelligently.

The division of the present monograph into separate considerations of soil air, soil moisture, and so on, was adopted in an attempt to clarify the status of our knowledge of these individual factors. Such a division has also served to emphasize the inseparability of factors in their effects on plant growth.

Soil temperature may be varied experimentally by heating, by angle of exposure, and by mulching, as well as by season and location. Regardless of how temperature is varied, changes in evaporation or soil-moisture distribution are unavoidable. Further, soil temperature changes in a critical range may have large effects on the air or water requirement and utilization by plants.

When the moisture content of a soil is increased, there is an immediate and closely corresponding reduction in volume of soil air. Consequently, since wet soil is a better conductor of heat than a dry soil, soil temperature relations are changed at the same time, along with soil air and soil moisture.

Simultaneous change in the physical plant-growth factors is but one of the complications with which we must deal. During a given season, first one and then another of the physical factors may limit plant growth. For example, a soil with a claypan may be slowly drained in the spring. Because the soil is nearly saturated with water, it warms up slowly. In addition to the unfavorable soil temperature, root growth may be limited also by lack of adequate quantities of soil air, because a large proportion of the soil pores are filled with water. As the season progresses, a shallow pattern of root growth is formed, whether root penetration is inhibited by mechanical impedance or by lack of aeration in the claypan. Still later in the season, lack of adequately distributed rainfall may result in soil moisture being limiting to the shallow rooted crop. Then, conceivably, saturation of the soil by a heavy rain still

481

later on would bring soil aeration back into play as the factor most seriously limiting plant growth at that time.

The almost complete interdependence among the soil physical factors in their effects on plant growth makes exceedingly difficult the study and understanding of their separate effects.

But even this is not the whole story, by far. Soil fertility levels and the nutrient status of the plant are inseparably related to the soil physical factors in their effects on plant growth. Recent work under irrigation has shown that the uptake of phosphorus by sugarbeets may depend more on the soil-moisture regimen than on the level of phosphorus fertilization. Low oxygen tensions in the root zone appear to repress the uptake of certain nutrients, such as potassium, more than other nutrients. Conversely, the benefits of improved aeration, temperature, or soil-moisture supply are reflected not at all in the growth of a plant that is deficient in nitrogen or boron, or any of the other plant nutrients.

This interplay of physical and chemical factors is illustrated in a general way by a recent fertility-moisture experiment with potatoes on Ephrata loamy sand in the Columbia River Basin. Three rates of irrigation and three levels of nitrogen fertilization were studied in all combinations. At the lower rate of nitrogen fertilization, increasing the moisture supply reduced yields from 392 down to 346 bushels per acre, while the same moisture treatment increased yields at the higher level of fertilization from 414 to 552 bushels per acre. In other words, high levels of both water and nitrogen were required for efficient utilization of either.

Accelerated progress in soil-management research has been made in recent years by this very technique of attempting to determine optimum combinations of crop varieties, disease and insect control measures, cultural practices, and soil and water management variables. In many cases the relationships produced among the physical and chemical plant growth factors are so imperfectly understood that the results of the experiment have little prediction value in terms of other soils and other seasons.

Despite all these difficulties, we are making progress. The outlook for developing a better understanding of soil properties and their relationships to plant growth is brighter than ever before. The lines of investigation that seem to be required are threefold, and might be summarized briefly as follows:

1. Determination under very highly controlled conditions of the effects of temperature, aeration, moisture, and mechanical impedance on rate and nature of growth of various plant species at different stages of development. Control should be of such type that the techniques

would approach single-variable experimentation to as great an extent as possible. Although levels of all other plant-growth factors should be constant in a given experiment, the effect of temperature, for example, on plant growth must be determined at several levels of moisture, aeration, light, and nutrient supply.

2. The effects of soil physical properties and environmental factors on soil temperature, aeration, and moisture relationships must be clarified. These studies will also require better control and possibly different techniques than those that have been brought to bear this far. Much but not all of this work can be carried out under laboratory conditions. Techniques for obtaining undisturbed sample of soil to considerable depths have been greatly improved of late, but simulation of all profile characteristics and study of the combined effects of soil horizons of differing structure will certainly require some work under field conditions.

3. A fundamental approach—a study of the basic or underlying processes—must be applied to the extremely practical problem of understanding and controlling the relationships among soil physical properties, soil processes, and plant growth.

A good part of this brief discussion has been devoted to pointing out the interplay of soil physical, biological, and chemical processes, as they simultaneously influence plant growth directly, and as they modify the influence of the other factors on plant growth. Perhaps the new electronic calculating machines offer us hope on this score. If the effects of all individual plant-growth factors could be determined at several levels of each of the other factors, perhaps a series of relationships, or even a single plant-growth equation, could be developed which would present in organized and usable form our knowledge of the interactions among plant-grown factors.

This may be a possibility some day, but currently we certainly do not have the basic data on plant-growth factors and their interactions to feed into such a machine. As a matter of fact, there is no record of a single experiment in which each of the physical and chemical plant-growth factors was even characterized—much less controlled. That could be done—we have some type of measurement of each one of the factors known to affect plant growth. Some are crude, some are cumbersome, and some are only indirect measures. To date, no one has felt that the simultaneous characterization of all plant-growth factors throughout the course of an experiment was desirable or feasible with the facilities at hand. In a field experiment where only a few plant-growth factors are varied, measurement of additional factors has the disadvantage that the maximum or even the critical range of all factors may not be covered. We do feel safe in pointing out, however, that equipment for the control of the total plant environment over a range comparable to field conditions would seem to be far in the future. There would seem to be considerable basis at this time for stressing a more fundamental approach to the characterization of plant growth factors as they interact in expressing the effect of the total environment on plant growth. Such a fundamental approach to field problems is involved and difficult, but it might prove to be the most direct path to our ultimate goal.

INDEX

A

Absorption, nitrate, 348–349
  nutrient, 345, 346–348, 350, 380
  water, by plants, 215, 349, 350–355, 380–381, 437, 443
Absorptivity, soil surface, 319, 332
Adsorbed film, 83
Aeration, soil, 192, 257–259, 261–273, 335
Aggregation of soil, effect of soil temperature on, 457
Albedo, 319
Alfalfa, 131, 140, 203, 411–414, 417–418, 435, 437
Alkali soil, 194
Alternating temperatures, 370–371
Amendments, effect on soil structure, 24, 31, 32
Ammonification and nitrification, effect of soil temperature on, 454
Anaerobes, 197
Anaerobic conditions in soil, 195
Animals, importance in altering soils, 3
Apparent density, critical, 53
Apples, 105, 116, 139, 194, 342, 348–349, 395–398, 400–401, 410–411, 427–428, 436
Apricots, 105, 398, 410
Arctic plants, 354
Assimilation, effect of soil temperature on, 350, 355–360
Auxanometer, 109
Auxin, 173
Available moisture, 86, 106, 118, 144
Available water, range of, 86
  ratio, 106

B

Barley, 346–348, 419, 439, 440
Beans, 119, 141, 340–341, 353, 375, 391, 423, 440
Bedrock, 43, 65–66
Bermuda grass, 351, 370, 384

Bicarbonate, irrigation water, 194
Bio-electric potentials, 261, 287, 339
Bluegrass, 183, 349, 370, 382–384, 415–417
Boron, 200
Bulbs and tubers, 344, 378–379, 392–393, 394, 411, 426, 433, 435–436
Bulk density, 320, 322

C

Canada, 88
Capillary potential, 91
Capillary water, 86
Carbohydrate content, plants, effect of soil temperature on, 341, 343–345, 380, 381, 383, 385, 393, 403–404
Carbon dioxide, effect on oxygen tolerances of roots, 269–271
  effects on solubility of soil constituents, 263–264
  in soil atmosphere, 192, 195
  rate of evolution from soil, 259
Cardinal temperatures, 370–376
Cells, plant, effect of temperature on, 337, 345, 355, 357–360
Ceramic plates, 95
Cereal crops, 372–373, 385–387, 418–419, 437, 444
Characteristic curves, 94
Chlorosis, 196, 350
Citrus, 352–353, 376, 403–405, 427–428, 437
Clay, 14, 48
Claypans, 43, 57–59
  and crusts, in soils, 22, 23
  treatment of, 61–65
Climatic zones, schematic, 6
Clods and granules, 43, 44, 49–51
Clover, 198, 383–384, 411–413, 417–418, 435, 437
Cohesive action, water in plants, 176
Compact soils, 49, 52–56
Condensation, 317, 318
Consistency, 57, 67

Contour furrowing, 37
Convection, 319
Corn, 84, 120, 193, 356–357, 361–362, 366, 387, 419, 431, 444–445
Cotton, 109, 110, 121, 150, 180, 198, 219, 228, 351–352, 355, 363, 374, 388–389, 420–421, 441, 443, 444
Crop quality, effect of soil temperature on, 432–433, 460
Crusts, surface, 43, 49, 51–52
Cultural practices, 328–333
Cuttings, effect of soil temperature on, 408–409, 428
Cytochrome-Cytochrome oxidase, 284–285, 289
Cytoplasmic streaming, 339, 355

D

Darcy flow law, 77
Density, bulk of soil, 74, 320, 322
Desert shrubs, 395, 405, 406, 428
Diffusion, entry of ions into plants by, 280, 285
  importance in soil aeration, 258–259
  -pressure deficit, 104, 159, 175, 177
  water vapor, 82
Drainage, 34, 88, 89, 188
Drought, 180, 201, 222

E

Earthworms, effect on soil structure, 31
Electrothermal method for measuring soil moisture, 101
Emissivity, soil surface, 319, 332
Entry of water into plants, 157
Erosion, effects of, 32
Evaporation, 176, 177, 317–319
Excess moisture, 189
Exchangeable bases, effect on soil properties, 16
Exposure, 316, 317
Exudation, 170

F

Fiberglas-Monel resistance unit, for measuring soil moisture, 102

Field capacity, 82, 86, 87, 88, 95, 98
Field crops, effect of soil temperature on, 373–374, 387–391, 419–423, 440, 444–446
Field experiments, response of crops to soil moisture, 119
  with fruits, response of plants to soil moisture, 112
Field moisture, 87
Fifteen-atmosphere percentage, 96
  in relation to wilting, 156
Film, adsorbed, 83
  flow, 83
First permanent-wilting percentage, 86
Flow patterns, 78
  unsaturated, soil moisture, 78
Flowers, effect of soil temperature on, 370, 376, 429, 431, 433
Forest trees, effect of soil temperature on, 375, 380, 405–406, 408, 410, 427–428, 437–438, 440–442
Free energy, 91, 93, 103
Freezing point, soil, 93, 153
Fruit crops, 105, 344, 352, 376, 395–405, 409, 429–430, 436, 439, 443
Funicular stage, soil water, 86

G

Gardenia, effect of soil temperature on, 350, 352, 428–429, 431, 433
Gaseous interchange, mechanisms involved in soil aeration, 257–259
Gases, solubility in water, 338
Germination, seed, 272–273, 367–376
Granules and clods, 43, 44, 49–51
Grape, 105, 109, 198
Grasses and forage crops, 344–345, 349–350, 370–372, 380–385, 410, 415–418, 432–434, 438–439
Gravitational head, 80
Gravity water, 86
Ground water, 78
Growth, criteria for, 218
Guayule, 111, 129, 184, 199
Guttation, 170
Gypsum blocks, for measuring soil moisture, 101

H

Hardpans, 23, 43, 59–65
"Heat canker" of stems, 439, 440
Heat capacity, 320, 321, 322
Heat flow, 332
Heat injury, 363, 438–439, 440–442, 443
Heat of wetting, 321
Heaving injury, 437
Hemp, 352, 421–422, 431
Horizon, designation of, 11
Hydraulic gradient, 77, 80
Hydraulic head, 78, 80
Hydrophilic colloids, 166
Hygroscopic water, 86
Hysteresis, soil moisture, 94, 99

I

Inbibition, 166
Infiltration rate, 76
Insolation, 312, 314
Instrumentation, soil temperature, 310–312
Insulation, 317
Ion transport, principles governing, 288–289
Irrigation, 32, 35, 36, 88, 89, 105, 150, 194, 414, 429, 444

K

Koroseal, 100

L

Leaching, 189
Lemon, 110, 118
Lento-capillary moisture, 86
Lettuce, 134
Lime-induced chlorosis, 196
Low countries, water tables, 90
Lysimeters, 189

M

Management, influence on soil temperature, 459
Manganese, 197
Maturation, 220

Mechanical impedance and plant growth, summary, 67
Mechanized farming, effect on soil structure, 28
Membrane, permeable, 93
  semi-permeable, 92
Mercury-manometer, 99
Metabolism, 172, 281–284, 286–287
Microbial activity, effect of soil moisture on, 206
Microorganisms, aerobic, 264–265
  anaerobic, 264–265
  distribution, growth and number as influenced by temperature, 447
  effect of soil temperature, 447, 459
Mineral nutrition, 198
Moisture, available, 86, 106, 118, 144
  effect on microbial activity, 206
  excess, 189
  measurement, 94, 99, 101, 102
Moisture absorption unit, 102
Moisture characteristic, 94
Moisture equivalent, 86, 87, 98
Moisture extraction, from soil, 85
Moisture-holding capacity, 86
Moisture percentage, of soil, 75
Moisture potential, 91
Moisture-retention curve, 90, 97
Mulching, 37, 329
Mustard, 183

N

Negative pressure, 79
Neoprene, 100
Nitrate absorption by plants, 269, 348–349
Nodulation, 411–414
Nomograph, 88
Nutrient absorption by plants, 199, 203, 278–289, 345, 346–348, 350, 380
Nutrient ions, concentration against gradients, 280
Nylon-nickel resistance unit, for measuring soil moisture, 102

O

Oats, 183, 187, 209
One-third-atmosphere percentage, 98

Onion, effect of soil temperature on, 393–394, 426, 444–446

Oranges, 209

Organic matter, contribution to soil properties, 17
decomposition, 264, 449
effect on physical properties, 30

Ornamentals, effect of soil temperature on, 406–407, 409

Osmotic pressure, 92, 104, 145, 158, 164, 168, 179

Oxidation-reduction potential, 196, 260

Oxidation-reduction reactions, effects of soil aeration on, 262–263

Oxygen diffusion, 260

Oxygen supplying rate, 260, 267, 268

P

Parent material, effect on soil, 7

Pea, effect of soil temperature on, 342–343, 356, 361, 375, 383, 391, 411–413, 423, 444

Peaches, 105, 110, 112, 113, 199, 348, 398–402, 410–411, 427–428, 436

Pears, 105, 114, 116, 117, 194, 400, 436

Pendular stage, soil water, 86

Permanent-wilting percentage, 85, 86, 105

Permeability, roots, 185
soil, 76, 77

pF, 91

Photosynthesis, 210

Physical condition, water in soil, 91

Physical properties of soil, 25, 26, 86

Physiological processes, influence of soil moisture on, 207

Piezometers, 78

Pineapple, 205, 350, 407–408

Plant cells, effect of temperature on, 337, 345, 355, 357–360

Plant composition, effects of aeration on, 271–272

Plant diseases, 289–291, 443–446

Plant factors, response of plants to soil moisture, 108

Plant growth, effect of soil temperature on, 336–338, 348, 354, 355–356, 365–367, 378–430
effect of stones on, 44, 45

Plant injury, by soil temperature, 433–443

Plant lenticels, 411, 433

Plant osmometer, 158

Plant tissues, air-conducting, 274–275

Plants, Arctic, 354
carbohydrate content, effect of soil temperature on, 341, 343–345, 380–381, 383, 385, 393, 403–404
cohesive action of water in, 176
entry of ions by diffusion, 280, 285
entry of water into, 157
nitrate absorption by, 348–349
nutrient absorption by, 345, 346–348, 350, 380
water absorption by, 215, 349, 350–355, 380–381, 437, 443

Plasmolysis, 159

Plow, subsoil, 28

Pore-size distribution, soil, 95

Pore space, of soils, 22

Porosity, total, 44, 75
unfilled, 75

Porous cups, 78, 100

Porous plates, 93

Potatoes, 141, 198, 229, 344, 378–380, 392–394, 411, 425–426, 433, 435–436, 444

Potentiometric titrations, 260

Potometers, 104

Pressure deficiency, soil water, 78

Pressure-membrane apparatus, 95

Pressure-plate apparatus, 95

Protein, 214

Protein synthesis, relation to respiration, 282–283

Protoplasm, viscosity of, 338, 347, 353

Protoplasmic colloids, 167

Prunes, 105, 137, 228

Pulverization modulous, 50

Pumpkins, 119

Pyrheliometer, 315, 316

R

Radiation, long-wave, 314

Radiation measurements, 315, 316

Radiometer, 316

Relief, as a factor in soil formation, 7

Respiration, 173, 212, 342–344, 355–356, 380

Retention curve, soil moisture, 94

Root distribution, 84, 85

Root growth, 266–268, 380–391, 393–395, 398–408, 410–411, 434, 437, 439

Root injury, 410–411, 434, 438–439

Root morphology, effects of aeration on, 273–275

Root permeability, 185, 278

Root respiration, 276, 281, 283, 286

Root rots, effects of soil aeration on, 290–291

Roots, cold resistance of, 436
  effect of carbon dioxide on oxygen tolerances, 269–271
  effect on physical characteristics of soils, 3

Rose, 144, 350, 409, 429

Rye, 183

S

Salt, 102, 146, 281, 283

Sands, 43, 47–48, 57

Saturated flow, 77

Saturation percentage, 75

Seed dormancy, 368–370

Seed germination, 272–273, 361, 367–376, 405

Seedling emergence, 44, 49–51

Seedlings, effect of soil temperature on, 367–368, 370–377, 385–386, 411, 443–446

Seeds, effect of temperature on, 367–376

Shade, 317, 328

Shoot growth, 356–359, 362, 383, 385–387, 392, 414–415, 417–423, 426–433, 437, 443

Sod mats, 43, 49, 56

Soil, aeration of, 192, 257–259, 261–273, 335
  alkali, 194
  anaerobes in, 195, 197
  clay, 14, 48
  claypans and crusts, 22, 23, 43, 57–59, 61–65
  clods and granules, 43, 44, 49–51
  color of, 331
  compact, 49, 52–56

conditioning of, for crop production, 24
  effect of stones on, 43–46, 49
  freezing point of, 93, 153
  hardpans, 23, 43, 59–65
  permeability of, 76, 77
  physical properties of, 25, 26, 86
  pores in, 22, 44, 75, 78, 93, 95, 100
  respiration of, 257, 259
  saline, 90, 146
  structure of, 18, 19, 24, 26, 29, 31, 32, 48–56, 57
  surface absorptivity of, 319, 332
  surface emissivity of, 319, 332
  temperature of, 305–312, 333–336, 350, 355–360, 367–447, 449, 454, 456–457, 459–462
  texture of, 12–14
  water logged, 197

Soil aggregation, effect of soil temperature on, 457

Soil atmosphere, 192, 195, 254–261

Soil conservation practices, 37

Soil crusts, surface, 43, 49, 51–52

Soil factors, plant growth in relation to water, 106

Soil moisture, available, 86, 106, 118, 144
  effect on microbial activity, 206
  excess, 189
  hysteresis, 94, 99
  measurement, 101–102
  unsaturated flow, 78

Soil moisture stress, 91, 92, 102, 104, 105, 145, 146, 158

Soil moisture tension, 78, 79, 92, 93, 158
  profile of, development, 10

Soil water, pendular stage, 86

Soil water suction, 95

Sorghums, effect of soil temperature on, 361, 373–374, 376–377

Sorption blocks, 101

Sorption curve, 94

Soybean, effect of soil temperature on, 374, 387–388, 411–413, 419–420, 433

Specific free energy, 158

Specific surface, soils, 102

Starch, 213

Stefan's law, 314

Stones, effect on soil and plant growth, 43, 44–46, 49
Storage, water in soil, 86
Stress, soil moisture, 92
  total, 93
Subsidence, of organic soils, 35
Subsoil or substrata characteristics, 43, 57–67
Subsoil plow, 28
Subsoiling, 43, 63–65
Suction, soil water, 95
Sugar beets, 129, 203, 218, 374, 390–391
Sugar cane, 109, 133
Summer fallow, 88, 89
Sunflowers, 105, 142, 152, 209
Surface erosion, 189
Surface force action, 153
Surface soil characteristics, 43, 44–57

T

Take-all disease, 290
Temperature, alternating, 370–371
  cardinal, 370–376
  coefficient of reactions, 338–339, 365
  effects on growth processes, 266, 267, 337–366
Temperature gradient, 83
Tensiometers, 78, 79, 92, 98, 99
Tension head, 80
Tension, water in plants, 177
Terracing, 37
Texture, 44–49, 57
Thermal conductivity, 321, 323
Thermal diffusivity, 323, 326–328
Thermal properties of soils, 319–328
Thermodynamic potential, 91
Thermoperiodism, 431–432
Tillage implements, effect on soil structure, 26
Time, as a factor in soil formation, 8
Tissues, air-conducting, 274–275
Tobacco, 361, 374, 389–390, 422–423, 444
Tomato, 165, 340, 348, 356–359, 375, 392, 423–425, 432, 444
Topsoil, depth of, 56–57
Total porosity, of soil, 75
Total potential, 91

Translocation, 340–342, 349, 380
Transmission velocity, 77
Transpiration, 178, 210, 276–277, 350–355
Tubers and bulbs, 344, 378–379, 392–393, 394, 411, 426, 433, 435–436
Turgor, of plants, 145, 159, 163, 211

U

Ultimate, wilting percentage, 86
Unsaturated flow, soil moisture, 78
Unsaturated permeability, 80

V

Vapor-pressure, 83, 93, 318
Vegetable crops, 370, 374–375, 391–395, 431–432, 440, 444–445
Vegetation, effect of on soils, 1
Vegetative growth, 217
Vernalization of seeds, 368
Viscosity, 338, 347, 353
Visking sausage casing, 96

W

Wall pressure, 159
Water absorption by plants, 166, 215, 225, 275–278, 349, 350–355, 380–381, 437, 443
Water, available, 75, 86, 90, 108, 188, 192
  bound, 167
Water deficit, in plants, 115, 169, 180
Water-depth ratio, 75
Water entry into plants, osmosis, 168
  tension, 173
Water entry into roots, 186, 187
Water, evaporation, 176, 177, 317–319
  gravity, 86
  ground, 78
  hygroscopic, 86
  irrigation, 32, 35, 36, 88, 89, 105, 150, 194, 414, 429, 444
  low countries, 90
Water flow, in soil, saturated, 77
Water in plants, cohesive action, 176

Water movement, 80, 91
Water requirement, 106, 111, 225
Water vapor diffusion, 82
Watermelon, 351–352, 375
Weather factors, response of plants to soil moisture, 111
Wetting front, soil water, 85
Wheat, 183, 187, 356–358, 376–377, 385–387, 411, 418–419, 430–431, 437, 439, 444–445
Wien's law, 315

Wilting, 84–86, 87, 88, 105, 151, 153, 156, 200, 352, 428
Winterkilling, 435, 436

X

Xylem sap, 177

Y

Yield, crop, 88